The Ecology of Malnutrition In the Far and Near East

(Food Resources, Habits, and Deficiencies)

by JACQUES M. MAY, M.D

with the collaboration of Irma S. Jarcho, M.P.H.

220 tables

30 illustrations

HAFNER PUBLISHING COMPANY, INC.

New York 1961

This study has
been made under the
auspices of the
American
Geographical
Society
and constitutes its

STUDIES IN MEDICAL GEOGRAPHY, Vol. III

7/64

CONTENTS

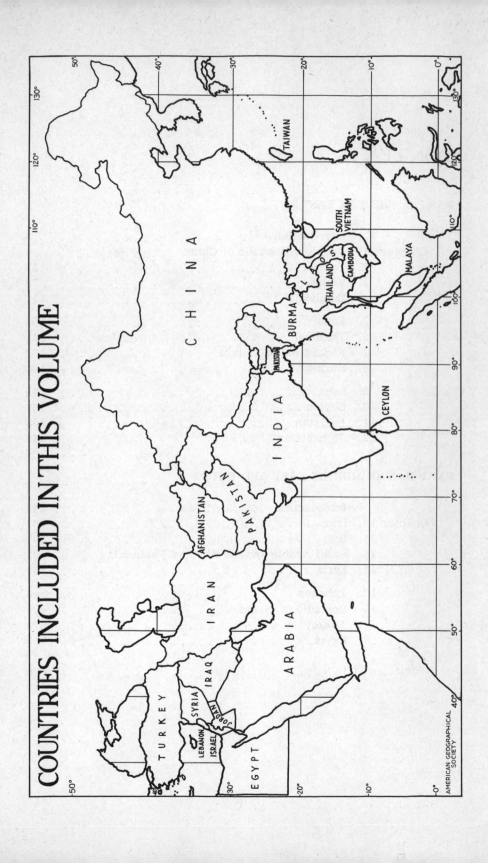

COUNTRIES INCLUDED IN THIS VOLUME

50°

130°

120°

110°

CHINA

TAIWAN

40°

30°

20°

10°

0°

120°

110°

100°

SOUTH
VIETNAM

THAILAND

CAMBODIA

MALAYA

BURMA

PAKISTAN

90°

CEYLON

80°

INDIA

70°

AFGHANISTAN

PAKISTAN

60°

IRAN

50°

ARABIA

TURKEY

SYRIA

IRAQ

LEBANON

ISRAEL

JORDAN

EGYPT

40°

30°

20°

10°

0°

AMERICAN GEOGRAPHICAL
SOCIETY

LIST OF
MAPS AND FIGURES

LIST OF
TABLES

CEYLON

PAKISTAN

AFGHANISTAN

PART II INTRODUCTION

SAUDI ARABIA AND THE ARABIAN PENINSULA

SYRIA

LEBANON

REPUBLIC OF ISRAEL

ACKNOWLEDGMENT

The work which is encompassed in the present volume was accomplished under contract with the Quartermaster Research and Engineering Command, United States Army, to whom the authors make grateful acknowledgment.

Many individuals and agencies have kindly supplied published and unpublished reports which provided valuable data for the study. Special thanks are due the Human Relations Area Files at Yale University, the United State Government's Interdepartmental Committee on Nutrition for National Defense, the Foreign Agricultural Service of the United States Department of Agriculture, and the Food and Agriculture Organization of the United Nations, through its regional office in Washington, D.C.

The authors also wish to express gratitude and deep appreciation to Mrs. Marie-Anne May and Miss Frances Lanzisera, who helped in the preparation and typing of the manuscript, and to the several members of the American Geographical Society's staff who assisted in the cartographic and editorial phases of the work.

Jacques M. May, M.D.
Irma S. Jarcho, M.P.H.

Errata

We regret that after a final reading of the finished text, the following errors have been noted:

p. 79, line 5: change "10,500" to "10,500,000"

p. 84, line 18: change "this" to "the"

p. 92, line 1: change "03.67" to "103.67"
        line 2: omit (see Table 10)

p. 147, line 10: change "tuber" to "rubber"

p. 177: VII NUTRITIONAL (misspelling)

p. 189, line 11: omit period before "Although"; use lc for "although"

p. 193, line 37: change "maxillary" to "maxilla"

p. 367, line 8: add "rice-threshers" before "of"

p. 371, line 27: change "meat" to "milk"

p. 401, line 1: add "1000" before "Iraqi dinars"

p. 404, Table: substitute "(000 head)" for "(000 deleted)"

p. 413, line 9: add (IV) after worker
        line 13: add (V) after fellaheen

p. 456, line 36: omit generally; put comma after small

p. 599, line 29: inadequate–not adequate

Hafner Publishing Company, Inc.

PART I. THE FAR EAST

INTRODUCTION

This report concerns itself with the various factors responsible for deficiency diseases in Asia—but not with a medical discussion of the diseases themselves. The emphasis has been laid on the conditions that converge on a certain point in time and space to create the disease pattern; the report perhaps could be called "Ecology of Starvation."

These conditions, graphically represented in the diagram on the following page, include the land and water environment governing in part food production (physical geography), purchasing power and means of exchange (economic geography), and traditions and traits thought to promote survival (human geography). The combination of availability and tradition governs what a man may find on his plate, in his bowl or on his banana leaf. These diets may or may not be adequate. If they are not, the so-called deficiency diseases occur (medical geography). Yet after these factors are described, a wide gap still exists in our understanding of starvation. Although we have done our best to present a picture of the various environmental circumstances or stimuli that lead to what man finds on his table every day, we have been unable, for lack of information, to discuss what the genetic make-up of man or of ethnic groups makes of these diets. Studies designed to identify not only the role of specific nutrients, but also the factors within the body of man that make use of these nutrients, are very few.

Understanding of nutritional disorders such as goiter, beriberi, and anemia, in addition to a good knowledge of nutrients in the diet, should involve awareness of the body conditions governing absorption, utilization, or loss. How do men transform nutrients for the protection of their tissues and for the storage of their energy? Are certain ethnic groups capable of syntheses that other groups cannot make? We are ignorant of the deep mechanism of the enzymatic reactions supporting nutritional behavior. We must assume that certain species, because of their genes, have the enzymes that allow them to synthesize what other species have to obtain from their environmental food; the tissues of certain species perhaps do not require the same amino acids and contributing molecules that others do; hence certain animals feed on flesh while others are strictly vegetarians. This difference in nutritional behavior—for example, between dogs and horses—is as pregnant with research possibilities as the oft-cited fall of Newton's apple

3

from the tree, that eventually led to modern physics. So at the onset of this study, we have to confess that one major aspect of the problem of the ecology of starvation is as hidden from us as the far side of the moon.

Political units and culture groups do not conform with geographical regions, but statistics do conform to political units; therefore the report is divided into twenty chapters, each dealing with one country. A more satisfactory approach would have been to break down the subject by resources. A rice culture or a wheat culture could thus have been discussed that would have encompassed respectively South China, South India, Southeast Asia, and Ceylon on the one hand, and North China, Northern India, and the Near and Middle East on the other. However, since the economic conditions of life are not the same within each culture area, the political boundaries of the subject matter would have reappeared anyway. Moreover, economic regulations, rationing, and price support schemes, politically inspired, play an important role in the determination of the amount of food available. Thus, for several reasons, the discussion had to conform to country lines.

It has seemed logical to follow the chain of events that, in each country, starts with the land (physical geography) and ends with the disease picture (medical geography). Each chapter begins with a brief description and compilation of the agricultural potential of the country, followed by a regional breakdown reminding the reader of the basic reality of geographic boundaries as against the transitory character of political boundaries. In order to set down the problem, a few lines on the population dynamics are also given, in the first section of each chapter. Wherever possible a brief picture of daily life on a typical farm is sketched.

The second section concerns itself with production, and lists the resources from which the diet comes. It must be remembered that the statistical system varies with each country and that many possible biases exist in the computation of these figures. All studies involving populations require meticulous statistical and arithmetical attention. These requirements are sometimes ignored, or the methods used to meet them may vary from country to country. The data are as good as, but no better than, the land agent charged with collecting the figures and the sincerity of the farmer reporting his crops. Although cross checks can be made through statistics of government purchases, sampling, tax collectors, it must be borne in mind that the data are only approximate. In certain lands there are no data at all and figures are only estimates. Finally there is a gap of approximately 15 percent between availability of food and consumption due to wastage, loss, and deterioration, and, in some countries, to government purchases for foreign export.

In each country food resources are described, building a step-by-step picture of the diets and their deficiencies.

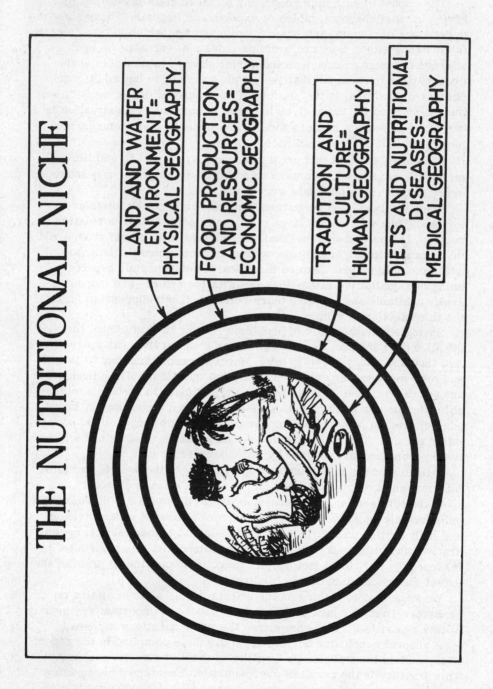

THE NUTRITIONAL NICHE

LAND AND WATER ENVIRONMENT= PHYSICAL GEOGRAPHY

FOOD PRODUCTION AND RESOURCES= ECONOMIC GEOGRAPHY

TRADITION AND CULTURE= HUMAN GEOGRAPHY

DIETS AND NUTRITIONAL DISEASES= MEDICAL GEOGRAPHY

The impact of economic geography on these diets is outlined by
giving in most chapters, tables of exports and imports. These show the
dependence of certain diets upon foreign sources which in turn, means
the need for either cash crops or for industrial exports. No such
source of foreign exchange as industrial exports is thinkable at the
present time in Asia. All that the people can sell, to buy additional
edible commodities, is the product of their land, which in many cases
they badly need for themselves in order to survive. This situation is
one of the important reasons for the low material living standard of
more than half of the human race.

The ability to store and preserve food plays a part in stabilizing
food supplies; a brief resume of this aspect of the problem is made in
every chapter for which data were found.

From the land, food resources, and economic power, diets are
formed. They vary within large countries (India, China) in relation to
regions, in small countries (Thailand, Malaya) with ethnic groups and
their local culture. In addition, within each community, diets vary
with economic status. Data on the cultural and economic aspects—
being of a qualitative rather than quantitative nature—are more generally available and are also more reliable. Their discussion forms
the third section in each chapter.

Having shown the chain of problems leading to food intake, the
question then arises: To what extent can men survive with these diets?
Are they adequate to sustain life? How vulnerable are they to natural
and man-made catastrophies? To the first question, only an inadequate
answer can be given. Diets are usually sufficient to sustain a miser-
able life for a short duration. This is measured by our scanty knowledge of disease patterns and by comparisons with longer-lived population groups. It is a relative and not an absolute value, since longer-
lived populations are plagued by different diseases.

A little more is known on the vulnerability of these diets and this
information is discussed in the fourth section of each chapter.

In the fifth section, the actual nutritional diseases are discussed;
unfortunately we know little of the indirect effects of undernutrition
and malnutrition on the resistance of people to transmissible, degen-
erative, and situational stimuli. It is assumed that this resistance is
lessened by nutritional factors, but there is no convincing proof of the
extent and mechanism of this handicap.

We know next to nothing on the effects of this state of affairs on
behavior. Thus, for lack of data, one of the most important sections
of this report is begging answers to the many questions it poses.

A general conclusion derived from the facts compiled in the report
is to confirm the well-known fragility of the diet structure in Asia.
This fragility is the result of overpopulation maintained because few
die of starvation before reproductive age. Although overpopulation
exists in other parts of the world (for example, in Britain, Belgium,

and certain urban areas of the United States), no fatal consequences accrue because of the economic resources supplied by industry. Thus a tendency to believe that the same panacea could protect the countries of Asia is only too common among policy makers in Asian governments. They overlook the fact that the industrial power of the West developed on the basis of unexploited resources, accumulated capital, a scientific culture, and a market ready to absorb their products. On the contrary, the nations of Asia have few known unexploited resources, little capital, a magnificent spiritual culture that however, does not prepare the masses to the particular aspects of science required for industrial development, and they are confronted with a saturated market wherever purchasing power exists.

Some improvement is conceivable along the lines of a better use of agricultural resources and better economic planning (providing plans are made to secure food increases, not military power), but there is no reason to believe that an abatement in the population explosion is in sight, and the prospect for a drastic change in the food geography of Asia do not seem very bright at present.

Jacques M. May

September, 1960

PEOPLE'S REPUBLIC OF CHINA

I. GENERAL REMARKS

The problem of analyzing the food situation in Communist China at the present time is difficult, since no reliable studies have been published in recent years. Statistics are often contradictory and, although official corrections are sometimes made, the accuracy of many published figures is questionable. Undoubtedly the problem of food supply in mainland China remains what it has always been—critical.

This fact is admitted by the Chinese Communists themselves. The words of Mao Tse Tung in 1956, when he wanted to prepare the people of China for the drastic communization methods soon to follow, still held true in 1959: "The situation in China is still bad. There is only half an acre of (cultivated) land per capita for the country as a whole, but in many parts of the southern provinces, the average is only one-sixth of an acre or less. There are frequent national disasters—floods, droughts, winds, frost, hail, or insects. Backward methods of farming are still being used. For all these reasons, 60-70% of the total rural population is in difficulty."

These age-old difficulties that retard agricultural production may be grouped in three categories—physical, biological, and cultural.

Physical. In spite of its vast territory, China lacks good arable land. Only 11% of the total surface is cultivated, and experts disagree on the amount of new land that could be reclaimed. Rainfall is variable so that there is either too much or too little water, and floods and droughts interfere with the attainment of production targets.

Biological. Insects, pests, and predators, especially when combined with physical calamities, play an important role in reducing crops, sometimes to famine level.

Cultural.[3,4] Lack of transportation prevents the transfer of food from surplus to deficit areas. Total railroad mileage in 1957 was expected to reach 18,000 miles for a surface area of 3,800,000 square miles (the United States has 221,098 miles of railroad and a surface area of 3,675,000 square miles). Highways in China, unevaluated as to quality, total 248,000 miles as compared to 3,418,214 in the United States. The total length of navigable waterways, which to a certain extent compensate for the lack of other means of transportation, is still only 93,600 miles. Other cultural factors responsible for the poor food situation include the inefficient agricultural habits fostered by the distribution of land ownership, the lack of fertilizers (caused in part by the absence of technical know-how to produce synthetic fertilizers and by the lack of foreign currency to purchase these from other countries), and finally the explosive growth of the population on a land that can hardly support more people.

The Chinese Communists hoped to offset most, if not all, of these causes of starvation. The total acreage of arable land was to be increased by reclamation. The government estimates that 247,000,000 acres can be reclaimed, a figure which Western experts reduce to 100,000,000 of which 26,000,000 had allegedly been reclaimed by the end of 1957.[5] Physical factors such as droughts and floods were to be controlled by gigantic dams and irrigation works. Insects, pests, and predators were to be destroyed by the import or manufacture of insecticides and by fighting the four "scourges" (flies, mosquitoes, rats and sparrows). Cultural problems were to be ameliorated by the collectivization of land, improvements in agricultural methods (including introduction of farm machinery), closer planting, plowing, and increased use of fertilizers. Other suggested means included improvement of transportation facilities, industrialization, and birth control. Although this multifaceted attack on agricultural underproduction has been successful to a limited degree, results achieved to date fall far short of the government's optimistic expectations and estimates.

In late 1958, China was still among the poorest fed nations of the world, with 1830 calories per day,[12] 75% of which came from grain foods, 9.2% from vegetable fats, and only 4.5% from animal proteins. Amended figures in August, 1959, set total production for 1958 at 250 million tons instead of the estimated 375 million, and reduced the estimated production for 1959 from a totally unrealistic 525 million tons to 275 million tons. These amended figures explain previous reports that some cities were short of food,[6] and that workers in mines and on big construction projects were not getting full rations. This situation was reported to have been caused by farm-labor shortages resulting from the priority given to the steel production program in local plants. Furthermore, according to recent reports, floods as well as administrative failures contributed to low crop yields.[2] It can also be reasonably surmised that the communization program, which took away from the farmers in 1958 the land that had been given to them between 1949 and 1954, failed to create the proper incentive for hard work.

Forced industrialization adds to the difficulty of keeping up food resources, since increases in agricultural production are earmarked for export under the policy that "one ton of pork is worth five tons of steel, one ton of oranges equals four tons of fuel, 130 million eggs would allow the government to build a power station of 25,000 kilowatts."[7] The determination of the government to carry out its industrialization plans was shown in 1954; to save the industrial centers of

Wuhan, Wuchang, and Hankow from the threat of the rising Yangtze
River, dams were destroyed upstream, which resulted in the flooding
and destroying of thousands of villages, hundreds of thousands of people, and their crops.[7]

The best hope for increasing food supplies in the future lies with
land reclamation, new irrigation projects, and birth control. Land
reclamation is to a large degree linked with industrialization, as machines are needed to do an effective job. Bulldozers, tractors, and
harvesters, however, have a low priority in industrial production because it is felt that transportation equipment should come first; 9,600
tractors and 657 combine-harvesters were known to exist in 1956 as
compared with an estimated 750,000 and 200,000, respectively, needed
by 1967. New irrigation projects made great process during the First
Five-Year Plan and work on them has been continuing. They will especially benefit rice production. An active birth-control campaign
was started in 1955, but has been almost abandoned. The reason for
this is unknown. Cressey[9] remarks that if it were possible to introduce modern sanitation, check infant mortality, eliminate famines and
reduce the death rate to Western standards, without lowering the birth
rate, a tremendous increase in population would occur within a generation. Without a corresponding increase in food supplies, large seg-
ments of the population, already at subsistence level, would be in des-
perate economic straits. There is no evidence that any significant
permanent increase in food surpluses has occurred that would nullify
Cressey's prophecy.

II. FOOD RESOURCES

A. GENERAL

The total acreage of cultivated land in China in 1947 was estimated
at 235 million acres.[11] This figure had increased to 272 million in a
report made by an Indian delegation which visited China during 1955.
Since Chinese and Indian sources do not distinguish reclamation and
irrigation of unused land from rehabilitation of land already in use
before the war, it is difficult to arrive at a reliable estimate of the
total acreage that could be reclaimed for agriculture. Chinese sources
place this total at 247 million acres but it would seem too high.[16] Buck[13]
estimated in 1936 that 35 million acres could be reclaimed in the then
provinces of China. Japanese sources quoted by Thompson[16] estimated
at 60 million acres the amount of new land that could be cultivated in
Manchuria. These two figures give a total of 100 million additional
acres on which to base increased production—a contrast with the figure of 247 million acres given by the Chinese officials to their Indian
visitors.

New irrigation added 76 million acres in 1958 to the 87 million that had been reached during the First Five-Year Plan, bringing the total of newly irrigated land to 163 million acres. The 1959 plan calls for an additional 16 million. Also, during 1959 the government reversed an earlier decision to cut down food crop planting in favor of industrial crops.

The small size of individual Chinese farms (average 4.1 acres) that gave earlier writers some misgivings is now, since communization, an obsolete consideration. However, it is too early to tell what long-term effect the communization of agriculture will have on food production and diets.

According to official statistics, 183,933,000 tons* of food were produced in 1955. Of this total, 3.5 million tons were exported. Ten per cent of the balance (18,040 millions) was set aside by the government as reserves and stored. Therefore the amount available for distribution was only about 162,400,000 tons. This total included amounts used for animal feed, for seed for oil production, and for industrial use.[3]

B. CEREALS

Grains are the most important foods in China. Non-grain carbohydrates, such as potatoes and tubers, are often converted into grain values or "rice equivalent" in Chinese statistics and computed at a ratio of 4 to 1. This is done by dividing the production figures for these non-cereal foods by four; thus four tons of potatoes equals one ton of grain, a computation which is roughly valid in terms of calories produced. Table 9 gives the annual production of basic foods since 1952. The 1958 and 1959 figures in this table represent the targets set after the crop of 1955 had been harvested. The target for 1958, which at first was thought to have been attained, was found in August, 1959, to have been too optimistic by some 75 million tons. At the same time, the target for 1959 was revised and reduced by 48% (from 525 to 275 million tons). The lack of tractors, chemical fertilizers, and effective insecticides, the occurrence of floods and droughts and the computing mistakes made when the 1958 crops were assessed were given as explanations for the disappointing results.[2]† Increases in grain and in other farm products were hoped for, and to some extent have been realized, through reclamation of new lands, improved use of fertilizers, increased irrigation, careful seed selection, closer planting, protection of plants against insects, more agricultural implements, and better field management. Yet, although these remedies

*Unless otherwise stated all tons are metric tons throughout this book.
†Identical excuses are given in 1961 to explain still more disappointing results.

seemed for a while to bear fruit, it appears that sufficient attention was not given to the ills created by the new system,[33] such as the ill-will of the farmers deprived of their incentive to work. Also the new plans were dependent on the general improvement in technology and industrialization. If this did not grow apace, then serious consequences would be felt in the agricultural field. It seems this is what happened.[32]

The Second Five-Year Plan, which started in 1958, is due to expire in 1962. In the long-term drive for higher farm production, China has been divided into zones according to natural conditions. Their respective targets are known as the "4," "5," and "8" zones, representing the average yield of grains per unit of land to be attained by 1967 (Map 2). This means 400 catties per mou in the north, 500 in the milder central region, and 800 in the moist, warm south. Translated into pounds and acres, the amounts are respectively 2,640 pounds per acre, 3,300 pounds, and 5,280 pounds.[20]

C. ANIMAL PROTEIN RESOURCES

Essentially, animal proteins come from livestock (pork and mutton), poultry, eggs, and fish (Table 7). Two major obstacles seem to stand in the way of increasing the supply of animal protein in the Chinese diet. First, it is more economical to raise grain for human consumption on an acre of land than to feed it to cows, and second, the Chinese have an ingrained distaste for milk which will be difficult to overcome. The livestock population is given in Table 9. United States experts[15] believe that, except for hogs, animal husbandry lags behind the achievements of crops. Inner Mongolia is the most important cattle-raising region and seems to be the "Texas" of China. At present there are in that province 22 centers of artificial insemination and a number of veterinary posts; 300,000 Mongolian herdsmen have been trained in animal husbandry. It is reported that the numbers of livestock have been increased by 10%, thus enabling Mongolia to supply other provinces with 7,000 tons of frozen meat and 1,200,000 head of cattle for farm work and slaughter.

Efforts to increase dairy farming are evident in some places, especially around Peking, where there is a dairy farm with 800 milch cows. Some 40,000 Peking ducks are now raised in the suburbs of Peking each year and a poultry farm near the city raises 80,000 chickens and a variety of other poultry.[19]

An increase in the production of fish is also the order of the day. In 1958, 24,000 fishing boats were employed. The amount of fish and marine products caught in 1957 was 3 million tons and increased to 8.1 million tons in 1958. No information is available on the refrigeration that is needed to preserve the catch, nor do we have precise information on fish drying. Apart from the fact that the Second Five-Year Plan aims to increase by 100% the fish harvest from fresh water reservoirs, little is known about fish farming.

D. OTHER FOODS AND CASH CROPS

Although eaten everywhere, vegetables and fruits form a very small part of the diet and of the food resources. Table 10 indicates the percentage of crop area occupied by vegetables and fruits in the various regions. Communist China aims at supplanting India as the world's biggest tea producer by 1962.[25] It now ranks third, after Ceylon, with a production of 141,000 tons in 1958. Sugar production has increased in recent years, owing to expansion of the sugar-beet acreage in northern Manchuria and on the irrigated lands of Inner Mongolia.[15] The valleys of southern and western Yunnan are suitable for many tropical plants, including citronella grass, sisal, hemp, coffee, quinine, camphor, pineapples, coconuts, and oranges.

E. REGIONAL FOOD SUPPLY

Table 11 lists the provinces and their principal crops. Table 12 gives the percentage of total grain supplies produced by each province in the corresponding year. Whatever increase or decrease may occur in the annual production, the proportional contribution of each area is likely to remain valid for a number of years. This could be changed only if further land were reclaimed. It is not likely that extensive reclamation projects will be undertaken in the coming years, though some will be carried out, especially in the former Manchurian provinces.

The diet of the Chinese people in the future is likely to contain more wheat and less rice than in the past. This is probably true for two reasons—first, because the land and climate of the areas where reclamation is possible lend themselves more to wheat production than to rice, and second, because there is a more ready market in the world for rice exports than for wheat. Since the reclamation of new land and the increase in agricultural production have as their principal aim the acquisition of foreign manufactured goods for the industrialization of the country, it is probable that, given improvements in transportation, the Chinese will in the future have to eat more wheat as a larger percentage of the rice crop is exported. Also likely is the conversion of additional area to potatoes and sugar beets, as reflected in the statistics received for 1958 and the beginning of 1959. It may be said that the diet of the Chinese people is, by force, going to be Westernized to a greater degree than it has been in past history.

F. EXPORTS AND IMPORTS

Food exports and imports are influenced by two opposing factors in China—first, the scarcity of food at home will govern imports, and, second, the industrialization policy will govern exports. Table 13, showing the balance of exports and imports of food in the past 10 years, indicates that China has gradually decreased its imports of rice and has become essentially an exporter of rice. (However, because of treaty obligations China receives 150,000 tons of rice every year from Burma, which is paid for in textiles and light industrial products.)

The principal clients for Chinese exports are naturally those countries which need rice and which have industrial products to sell. First among them is Japan,[33] which by the very nature of things is destined to tighten its trade bonds with China. Besides rice, soybeans, pulses, and livestock are on the list of commodities for export to Japan, with the unavoidable result of increasing austerity on the mainland. The export of soybeans (55-58% of all food exports; see Table 14) is somewhat detrimental to the diet at home, as it is the richest of China's vegetable products in good quality protein.

Second to Japan in general trade relation with China is Ceylon;[33] in 1957, Ceylon paid for 270,000 tons of rice with 50,000 tons of rubber. A treaty was signed the same year, assuring the continuance of this exchange until 1962. Indonesia is scheduled to supply China with rubber, copra, oil, and sugar. India will provide sugar and pepper. Syria will export some cereals to China, and Morocco will furnish fertilizers. All these goods will be paid for by products of Chinese light-industry.[22]

Relaxation of the Western economic embargo against communist block nations may cause a shift in the nature of Chinese purchases from the West. However, it is unlikely that this will basically effect the ratio of Chinese trade, 70-80% of which is with the Soviet block. In recent exchanges, China has shown interest in paying for imports only through barter.

We are thus confronted with the paradoxical situation of a vast country which is not really self-sufficient in terms of satisfactory nutrition for its population, but which is rapidly becoming one of the most active exporters of food in the world.

G. FOOD INDUSTRIES, STORAGE AND TECHNOLOGY

The food industries have grown in recent years and an effort is made to export preserves, vegetables, and fruit in addition to the rice and soybeans already discussed. However, the only important food processing industries at present are wheat- and rice-milling.

There are about 970 modern wheat mills in China, with a total capacity of 519,725 bags of flour a day, or 137,207,400 bags a year. About 20% of these mills are found in Shanghai, 9% in Wuhsi (Kiangsu), 8% in Tientsin, 6% in Hankow, 6% in Tsinan, and 5% in Peking. These cities are located near rivers which facilitate transportation.[24] Factory milling of rice, on the contrary, is not as well developed, and rice is usually milled in the villages—a circumstance which, incidentally, affords protection against beriberi because the removal of the husks is less thorough.

Further information on the location of industrial facilities concerned with food processing is found in Table 11.

Production of processed fish and meat rose from 346,000 tons in 1952 to 921,000 tons in 1957; vegetable oil from 983,000 tons to 1,794,000 tons; and sugar from 451,000 tons to 1,010,000 tons. In the past practically all of China's sugar came from sugar cane grown in the southern provinces, but as we have seen, a considerable effort is now being made to increase the planting of sugar beets under irrigation.[3]

Except for these few facts, little is known on food processing. The Chinese authorities are striving to bring about improvements and some progress is apparently evident, but is it most unlikely that more than a beginning has been made on a task that will require many years.[34]

There is also little available information concerning storage space for foods in China. This is understandable in a country where the food output just about matches the needs. However, in the large cities, and in the rural market towns, the need for storage space, where stocks of grain can be housed, must have compelled the government to consider this problem. No protection against famine can be effective if such storage facilities are not provided.

The refrigeration potential of China is not known. Shanghai is probably the best equipped city in this respect, since it exports frozen food products, especially eggs, to foreign countries. With the exception of these exports, it must be borne in mind that processed foods are intended essentially for the domestic urban segment of the population.[3]

III. DIET TYPES

A. GENERAL

The diet of the Chinese people has for thousands of years been based generally on a high consumption of cereals and a low consumption of animal protein. This is not surprising in view of the existing population pressure; it is more economical to feed people with the plants that grow in the soil rather than to depend upon animals to convert the plants into the nutrients needed by man. The Chinese are aware of the value of soybeans and rice, both rich in good vegetable proteins, yet soybeans are not as popular as they should be.

In addition to the basic grains, pulses, lentils, broad beans, and occasionally cheese and meat appear in the typical diet. Meat, when eaten, consists of pork or duck (though raising ducks in the farm-yards has recently been discouraged as uneconomical). Chicken is rarely eaten; the lacquered skin is a delicacy, but the meat is not popular. In case of famine anything is eaten, including dogs and rats. Chinese fish dishes are famous, but the people as a whole seldom have fish on their menu. Although fruit is eaten in season, nowhere is it considered real food, and the customary Chinese greeting: "Have you eaten anything good?" does not apply to fruit.

In most places, the people eat three meals a day—a breakfast of rice left over from the day before, with mustard leaves, radishes, and other vegetables; a dinner of rice and soup; and a supper of re-heated rice and vegetables left over from the noon meal (Table 8). All dishes are cooked in water or vegetable oil.

It is possible by a careful choice of different types of cereals, legumes, vegetables, tubers, and roots, to construct a reasonably well-balanced diet, containing enough of the needed protective ele-ments. Such a diet was defined in 1938.[10] Yet, this diet would not be satisfactory for the feeding of the most vulnerable group in the popu-lation, children and pregnant or nursing women. The long-term effect of this marginal diet on health and longevity is not known.

Shen[11] remarks that there is very little wastage of food in Chinese homes, and that even the viscera and blood of animals are highly val-ued. Most of the cereals are undermilled and native methods of food preservation have been developed. Moreover, as anyone who has traveled in China knows, for reasons of fuel economy most of the food eaten by the people is usually undercooked, though it is true that meats and fish (4.5% of all calories consumed) are overcooked.

Most notable of the dietary studies conducted in China is that of J. L. Buck[13] and his group in the 1930's. These workers report that in normal times the caloric intake of the adults was nearly adequate. Values ranged from 2,300 to 3,200 calories per day, which is satis-factory if one considers the lower average body weight of the Chi-nese people, and perhaps also their lower metabolic rate (though this has not been proved).

A comparison of Buck's figures with those given by the FAO food balance sheets for the 1930's and for the 1947-1948 period[11] shows that the caloric intake of the Chinese has diminished considerably since the 1930's. In 1958, the Foreign Agricultural Service of the United States published a new set of figures[12] based on more recent data which show a drastic decrease to 1830 calories per day (Table 1).

If this information is correct, it places China among the countries of
Asia in which the diet of the population is at starvation level. Yet
there are probably redeeming factors of undeterminable extent. The
Chinese eat a variety of plants and seeds whose contribution to the
caloric and protective value of the diet cannot be calculated.

United States experts believe that statistical releases include only
part of the nation's food crops and livestock and that several important food sources are left unreported. This may explain in part why
present figures based on official statistics differ so greatly from
Buck's figures based on actual sample studies of households. Lacking such sample studies, any discussion of Chinese diets must rest
on the available facts, keeping in mind that the estimates arrived at
may be too low.

Compared with the minimum nutritional requirements set forth by
the Chinese Medical Association[10] in 1938 (Table 3), the present reported diet is 76.6% of what it should be, in terms of caloric intake
and protein intake, respectively in rice and wheat areas. Compared
with the allowances recommended by the Food and Nutrition Board
of the United States National Research Council, revised in 1948, the
reported diets of present-day mainland China are especially inadequate in central and north China as opposed to the lesser requirements of people living under tropical conditions (Tables 2a and 2b).

A comparative study of the food said to be available in the early
1930's, in the late 1940's, and at the present time (Table 4) does not
show any quantitative improvement. It is difficult to compute from
production figures the amount of food actually eaten. Dividing the
total grain production for 1957 (185 million tons in round figures) by
the average estimated population for the three years 1955-1957 (630
million inhabitants) gives an availability of 815 grams per capita per
day. But from this amount 12.8% had to be deducted for agricultural
tax, 19.3% for commercial food products, and additional deductions
must be made for seeds, animal feed, and industrial use. After all
these deductions, the average food allowance drops to 664 grams a
day (including tubers in terms of rice equivalents). Allowance for
polishing of the rice brings the figure down still further—to 500
grams a day. The proportion of each food in the total cannot be easily computed, since most diets are mixed (and in different proportions in the north and the south).

Some information is available on subsidiary food stuffs. In 1956,
the output of oil was only about half of the output of a record year before the war.[36] The average distribution of edible oil for each person
amounted approximately 3 1/2 pounds per year, or between 5 and 6
grams a day. According to Chinese sources,[37] the average pork distribution was about 5,000 grams per year per person or about 16
grams a day, as compared with 24 grams in 1937. The amount of
sugar available in 1955 amounted to approximately 4 grams a day[35]

per person. Tea for domestic consumption was in greater abundance in 1955 at approximately 100 grams a year.[35] The annual consumption of vegetables for each person in 1956 was estimated according to Chinese reports at 50,000 grams a year[35] or 140 grams a day in the rural areas, and a little over 340 grams a day in the larger cities.

The qualitative character of these diets remains the same. In the 1930's, Buck found that per capita protein intake averaged between 65 and 70 grams a day; in the 1940's, according to the food balance sheets published by FAO, (see also Shen[11]) the amount was much the same. At that time, 8% of the proteins were derived from animal sources. Present protein intake seems to have dropped to 54.78 grams in rice areas and to 67.78 in wheat areas, with only 4% of animal origin. Hogs supply most of the small quantity of meat consumed. Eggs represent a cash crop and are seldom eaten at home. Soybeans, a high-quality protein food, enters to a small extent in the Chinese diet (as it did in the 1930's). Although this crop is produced in important amounts, it is chiefly an item for export, as we have seen. The government propaganda underscores the point that because soybeans are not too popular in the country, using this item for sale abroad does not seriously impair the caloric intake. This is true, but fails to take into consideration the important biologic value of soybeans.

Only 4.8% of the calories consumed are derived from fat, while in the 1930's fats produced 9% of the total amount. There is no recent evaluation of the calcium, other minerals, and vitamins, except for the information that can be derived from the figures given in Table 5, which are only approximate and are based on national averages. However, these figures confirm earlier findings[13] that calcium intake is inadequate throughout China, that phosphorus ranges from 1 to 3 grams per capita per day, and that iron intake seems to be satisfactory. The Chinese diet provides bulk with a large amount of indigestible fibers which results in an overstimulation of the muscular layers of the intestine.

Most of the diet throughout China is supplied by the produce of the local fields; even the additional rations distributed by the State, after collection of its share, come from the local area. No information is available at present on the small administrative areas. The 1937 ratio of 75% locally-supplied and 25% purchased elsewhere, quoted by Buck, probably still holds true for most of China. Areas where cash crops are produced will, of course, depend more heavily on food grown elsewhere than will areas where subsistence food is grown. Local conditions result in significant variations from area to area in a country where transportation is an important problem. Other factors also influence the difference between production and consumption. For example, foods such as peas and beans are used to manufacture starches and oils; the amount of these substances actually consumed could not be ascertained unless sample studies were carried out.

In a country such as China, where a high percentage of the national budget is used for food, variations in nutritional value of meals are also a reflection of the limited range of possible purchases; in more prosperous countries, a wider range of purchases eventually evens out occasional deficiencies due to ill-chosen menus. These variations may make the difference between marginal adequacy and marginal malnutrition.

B. DIETS IN URBAN AREAS

Food availability differs in rural and urban areas. Travelers in 1956 indicated that because of the great efforts made to win over the labor force, food was more plentiful in the industrial centers than in the rural areas. The national food rationing system seems to support this view, since it entitles some of hard workers in the urban areas to almost twice as much food as the hard working farmers. More recently, however, this situation may have been reversed. Information reaching the United States indicates that establishment of communes has created serious dislocation in the production of certain crops and has caused severe shortages of vegetables and meats.[34] Large cities, construction areas, and mines are especially hard hit. It was reported that city dwellers are being encouraged to grow their own food on plots on the outskirts of the cities as a means of relieving the food shortage.

After the November, 1953, decree on planned purchase and planned food supply, food items were provided through government organizations to the personnel of the various agencies in the cities. For ordinary residents, purchase coupons for food were issued. Food stores, restaurants, boarding houses, trains, and the like were supplied with fixed quotas. Under such a measure, food consumption in the cities showed a widespread drop.[35]

The rationing system provides for different amounts of food for the different classes of population in the towns. After 1955, daily rations, shown in the table at the top of the facing page, were allowed.[18]

At that time, the fixed average food ration for urban residents was about 410 grams per day. Subsidiary foods were also rationed, and the industrial cities received a better share. In Lanchow, for instance, the average edible oil consumption in 1954 was approximately 15 grams per capita per day; in Canton, it was 21 grams. Inhabitants of Wu-chang, a key industrial center, were especially privileged, receiving 24 grams a day. Calculated on the basis of all cities in the country, the average ration for edible oil for each urban dweller was approximately 8 grams per day. The average consumption of pork

Class of consumers	Rice areas	Wheat areas
Hard-labor worker. . . . . 833 Gm. . . . . 916 Gm.		
Medium-labor worker. . . . . . . 733 Gm. . . . . 733 Gm.		
Light-labor worker. . . . . 533 Gm. . . . . 583 Gm.		
White-collar worker. . . . . 466 Gm. . . . . 516 Gm.		
University and middle school students . . . . 533 Gm. . . . . 583 Gm.		
Residents and children over 10 . . 416 Gm. . . . . 458 Gm.		
Children 6 to 10. . . . . 333 Gm. . . . . 355 Gm.		
Children 3 to 6 . . . . 216 Gm. . . . . 233 Gm.		
Children under 3 . . . . 116 Gm. . . . . 133 Gm.		

per person in Shanghai, Peking and Tientsin dropped between 1948 and 1955. In 1955, it was only 20 grams a day in Shanghai, 22 grams in Peking, and 12 grams in Tientsin. In 1956, meat consumption per person in large and small cities was approximately 18 grams a day in rural areas only 12 grams.[35] Vegetable sales in the markets of large cities amounted to approximately 340 grams per capita per day. Tables 19 and 20 give the per capita consumption of secondary foods in Shanghai and Peking from 1953 to 1957.

These extreme shortages of subsidiary foods justify the statement that on the basis of official statistics there is very little to eat in China other than the grain foods. In certain cities, the supply of fish, vegetables, and eggs was practically cut off after 1956.[35] In addition, there was an extreme shortage of fuel.

In November, 1956,[35] it was announced that the quotas of food rations to urban residents would be reduced by 500 grams per person per month. Quotas for meat were fixed, and were to vary from month to month. After a year, it was found that the average per capita meat consumption amounted to less than 16 grams a day.

C. DIETS IN RURAL AREAS

In rural areas, the diet is governed by the amount of grain left after the state's share is paid and by the additional ration returned to the farmer by the state-owned cooperatives (usually one pound per person per day). Before complete collectivization, each household was compelled to surrender some of its harvest to the state at a price that was well below the market price. In turn, the state was supposed to supply the households with a certain amount of grain in

accordance with the rationing system. Following the disastrous 1954
harvest, serious food shortages occurred in the villages; it was officially stated then, that this shortage was artificial—a pretense to
obtain an increase in the government ration. Be that as it may, at
the end of 1955 Vice-Premier Liu Wen Huy officially complained in
Peking that the state purchase of grain was too much and the state
ration was too little, so that the peasants were short of food.[18]

Among the forced labor working on conservancy projects in rural
areas, the diet varies with the work done. At the Huai River Project,
the standard wages were two pounds of rice for every cubic meter of
earth dug at ground level and carried for 70 yards. This may correspond to a wage of approximately three pounds for a 12-hour
work day, a far cry from the 15.5 pounds earned by the average agricultural worker in 1937,[13] and less even than the 4.8-pound wage paid
to workers engaged on nonconservancy projects. These low wages
were defended on the basis that the workers would otherwise be unemployed, that the wages they got by working on these projects could
be considered a bonus, and that work on these projects was essential
to them in terms of self-preservation.

D. CLASS DIFFERENCES[18]

The party officials in general enjoy a better diet and better nutrition than the people as a whole, but there is not as yet the considerable difference that exists between the high-level functionaries and the
people in the Soviet Union. In China, the differences in salaries seldom exceed the ratio of 10 : 1, with very few exceptions (highly-skilled
technicians or highly-placed politicians). Here again, variation occur
between rural functionaries and those more fortunate who work in
the towns.

In the earlier years of the regime, wages were computed in
"points" corresponding to the prices of essential commodities (grain,
cloth, oil, salt, fuel, and so on). Recently the system has been changed
and administrative workers are paid in money, the salary being established on the basis of grade and skill. In Canton, for instance, functionaries are classified in 26 grades, and each grade is entitled to a
certain number of salary points; each point is worth 0.4284 yuan, or
approximately 10 cents. On the average, the annual earning of an administrative official is in the vicinity of United States $250 to $300.

In spite of recent reforms, there are throughout the country as
many as two to three hundred different systems for computing wages
and salaries, all of them correlated with local cost of living and
prices of basic commodities. The average annual income of each
peasant in 1955 was estimated at $30 to $40. In April, 1956, the office
and industrial workers' wage averaged $250 a year. In terms of food

and other basic commodities, these wages meant diet differences ranging from 1 pound of grain a day for the farmer to 30 pounds a day for a college professor. Excess rations, if any, could be used as barter for luxuries.

The new privileged classes in the cities can still avail themselves of the old Chinese delicacies such as "Peking duck, peanut butter pancakes, rich soups, baked fish, cured eggs, sausages, stuffed trouts, sugar-cured tongues,"[8] and many other luxury items for which there must be a market since they are still obtainable.

E. REGIONAL DIFFERENCES

Buck divided the food producing land of China into two major regions—a wheat region in the north, and a rice region in the south. Each of these in turn was subdivided, so that there are three subregions in the north (spring wheat, winter wheat-millet, and winter wheat-kaoliang) and five in the south (Yangtze rice, rice-tea, Szechwan rice, double-cropping rice and southwestern rice). (Map 1).

No information is obtainable on the quantitative differences in calories and nutrients by region. It is known, however, that the diets of the wheat regions are more varied than those of the rice regions.[13] For example, Table 6 indicates that in the rice area the percentage of calories derived from rice in the diet averages around 68.4%, while in the wheat area, wheat provides only 23.5% of the daily caloric intake and millets (25.7%), kaoliang (14.6%), and corn (11.9%) help to diversify the diet. There is no reason to believe that these values have changed greatly since Buck's surveys were made. At that time, animal products supplied 1% of the calories in the wheat region, and 4% in the rice region. Table 7 gives the origin of these animal foods and the daily calories they provide in each of the production regions.

The daily calcium intake is somewhat better in the wheat region. Also, recent changes in the diet are more marked in the wheat than in the rice region. Since the 1930's, an increase in the consumption of corn, Irish potatoes, sweet potatoes, and green beans, and a decrease in the consumption of kaoliang is noticeable in the wheat areas. Table 8 lists the foods from which daily menus are made.

Regional differences may be characterized on the basis of Buck's regions.

Spring wheat area: In this area the millets, both the proso-millet and the fox-tail type, are consumed. It is one of the few regions where Irish potatoes are eaten along with spring wheat, and a further effort is being made by the Communist government to popularize and increase the consumption of potatoes. The other characteristic foods are oats, (which is boiled into a porridge, as is kaoliang, especially in Shensi and Shansi near the southeastern border), lentils,

spring barley, and corn. There are even a few rice-eaters in the
irrigated valleys of Wuwei and Ling Shia. Near the western border of
the region milk and mutton are part of the diet, especially among
the Moslems and the Tibetans.

Winter wheat-millet area: Here, proso-millet is grown at high
altitudes where the season is too short for other forms of millet.
Corn, almost as important a crop as kaoliang, is grown mostly on
hillsides. These two grains are double-cropped in some places, corn
being chiefly a spring crop. Potatoes, tubers, and animal products
are low in the scale of calorie-producing foods.

Winter wheat-kaoliang area: The two predominant grains are
commonly converted here into vermicelli and noodles, which reduces
their nutritional value. However, corn and soybeans are also consumed, which may help to maintain the protective balance.

Yangtze-rice area: Rice is by far the most important element in
the diet in this region, providing 58% of the food supply in some
places. Winter wheat and barley supply approximately 13% of the
caloric intake but are eaten in cake and bread form, which reduces
their nutritional value. Parts of this area enjoy double cropping.
Potatoes and other tubers account for only 1.9% of the food energy
of the diet, and animal products for 2.8% (these are 1930-37 figures;
the situation has perhaps slightly improved by now).

Rice-tea area: Here the important foods are rice and vegetables;
tea is a cash crop in most sections. Two-thirds of the land is double
cropped. Rice supplies 75% of the caloric content of the diet, potatoes and tubers 2.9%, and animal products 3%.

Szechwan rice area: In this region, diet is approximately 50%
rice and 15% corn. The proportion of calories obtained from animal
products is 5.6%.[13]

Double-cropping rice area: More than 75% of this region can be
double cropped, yielding two rice harvests a year. Three-fourths of
the food energy is derived from rice. Sweet potatoes appear to be
more common in the diet here than elsewhere; the proportion of calories from these tubers is 8.9%, the highest of any area. The percentage of calories derived from animal products is about 3.1%.
Cash crops are represented by sugar cane.

Southwestern rice area: Here rice is again the chief cereal in
the diet; corn comes next, but supplies only 5% of the food energy,
whereas rice supplies 75%. Animal products provide 5.8%. In addition, people eat broad beans, soybeans, and pulses. There is a small
section in the south where rice can be harvested twice a year, with a
cash crop of opium poppies between.

IV. ADEQUACY OF FOOD RESOURCES

A. IN NORMAL TIMES

It is extremely difficult for a number of reasons to judge the adequacy of Chinese food resources. For one thing, data in Chinese sources are highly colored by propaganda, and the sources themselves do not even agree. On the other hand, non-Chinese sources also may be biased in the opposite direction. Moreover, the meaning of the term "adequacy" should be defined in relation to Chinese culture and circumstances. For example, 2,400 calories per adult per day, originating 75% from cereals, may allow work and a short life expectancy; in the Chinese environment, this may be considered "adequate." Other considerations include: the increase of population at the rate of 2% a year, resulting in a positive balance each year of 12 million new people to feed; the industrialization policy requiring that 1 to 1.5% of China's food production be exported; and the possibility that in earlier years of the regime, machinery for accurate computation and statistics may not have been available.

In any case, daily consumption of foods is controlled by a strict system of food rationing. This was established in January 1954 and was gradually applied to practically the whole of China. Grain cards are needed for the purchase of all cereal products—for instance, flour, noodles, vermicelli, bread, and cakes. Even by Chinese standards, these rations are small. Vice Premier Teng Tzu Hui declared in 1953 that every Chinese citizen should consume 935 pounds of grain a year, a target that is still far from reached. The deficiency of the grain ration is made worse by the fact that there is very little supplementary food, as we have seen. The consumption of meat, milk, eggs, and sugar is so small as to be practically negligible. In December, 1956, the pork supply in Peking was so low that people had to stand in line for several hours to obtain a small amount of meat.

Another indication of the inadequacy of Chinese food resources can be found in the recommendation by the Prime Minister that every citizen should try to economize by saving half an ounce a day of his grain ration, which at the end of the year would amount to a saving of 3 million tons for the whole nation. The idea was that this should build enough grain reserves to guard against famine. A state grain monopoly was established on November 19, 1953,[18] for the purpose of enforcing planned purchases on which official rations would be based. The price for these forced purchases from the farmers was to be decided by the central authorities. Eventually, this program was made to work by virtue of the complete communization of the farms; the total output became state property and the state, in turn, handed out rations to the people working the land.

Following the grain monopoly, an oil monopoly was established by the government. It is hinted in the Communist press that the shortage of edible oil (Table 5) is not a temporary phenomenon but a permanent condition.

The state monopolies, in general, encounter numerous difficulties owing to the large number of farmers involved, the vastness of the territory, and the cumbersomeness of the enforcing machinery. Considerable effort was made by the government, as a parallel effort with the communes, to restrict the number of private shops in rural areas and to channel all agricultural products into the cooperative state trade. The target of collectivizing the whole of China's agriculture by 1959 or 1960 has apparently now been reached.

Another factor affecting adequacy of food resources is the redistribution of the population which is now taking place, due both to the industrialization of the major cities and to the migration of disgruntled villagers who have fled their fields (which, incidentally, do not belong to them any more) with the hope of finding work in the cities. The government, with the help of the police, is trying to put a stop to this urban influx which can completely disrupt the economy of the country and result in famines in the cities. At the same time, it has attempted to distribute industrial power throughout the rural areas by creating small blast furnaces and industrial plants in the most unlikely rural places. Recent information (Aug., 1959) indicates that this effort has been abandoned, possibly because it diverted manpower from the task of growing food.

B. IN TIMES OF STRESS

Causes of stress affecting food supply in China have included floods, droughts, storms, insect pests, civil and foreign wars, and epidemics. China has had an abundance of these calamities and has unfortunately earned the appelation, "land of famine."

Droughts and floods. Many of China's worst famines have been due to drought in the northwest, far from the coast. Floods, on the other hand, have inundated the south and the southwest, and over and over again have created distress or complete famine. The wheat region has more famine than the rice region. During the first quarter of century, at least three major famines were reported in each district; these lasted an average of 13 months and resulted in migration of 14% of the population and starvation for 18%.[13] Instances of cannibalism occurred in each famine. In the rice region, famines are less frequent and less severe, although the great flood of 1931 in the

Yangtze rice-wheat area affected 25 million farm population and caused losses estimated at two billion yuan.

In 1956, according to the Communist press,[28] agricultural crops suffered from the worst natural calamities since 1949 (Table 16). Nearly a quarter (23.32%) of all arable land in China was affected. Torrential summer rains together with strong gales brought misfortune to farmers in 18 provinces—Heilungkiang, Kirin, Hopei, Shantung, Shansi, Shensi, Honan, Hupei, Anhwei, Szechwan, Hunan, Kiangsi, Fukien, Kiangsu, Chekiang, Kwantung, Kwangsi, and Yunnan. Heilungkiang suffered most; more than 1,600,000 acres of planted fields were inundated by the flooding river, with a loss of 700,000 tons of crops and 40,000 buildings. The number of people made homeless was estimated at 380,000 and an additional 4,000,000 people were affected indirectly. In Hopei, some three million people felt the blow as seven million acres of land in seven major administrative areas were flooded. In Honan, six important administrative areas were flooded, ruining seven million acres of planted fields. Two million acres were flooded in Kiangsu and more than six million acres in Anhwei. In all, more than 30 million acres of farm land suffered from overflowing rivers in that year.

Although calamities were less severe in 1957, a serious flood occurred in southern Shantung Province which inundated four million acres, caused the loss of 147,000 tons of grain and 20,000 farm animals, and affected eight million people. The government claims that evacuation was effected by inflated rubber boats, that medical assistance was available, and that considerable grain was distributed to flood refugees. This indicates a consciousness of the danger of these disasters and an effort to combat them. It has been officially declared that the government would reduce purchases and increase allotments in stricken areas.

Floods occurred again at the end of 1958 and at the beginning of 1959. While this was happening over huge sections of central China, the provinces of Kirin and Hopei were parched by drought. In Szechwan, a force of 40 million people was working desperately to keep a wheat crop, badly weakened by unseasonably warm weather in the spring, from toppling over.

Early in 1959,[29] the worst flood of the century raged over the provinces of Kiangsu, Anhwei, and Fukien into Honan and eventually threatened the south. Hundreds of thousands of people were pressed into service to keep flood waters from breaking through and inundating the city of Canton. In the surrounding province of Kwantung, 187 people were dead, 200,000 were homeless and 2 million acres of land were inundated. A little later in the year, the most damaging flood in the history of Kwantung Province struck on June 11, and it was reported that millions of peasants were forced to fight the flood waters.[2] North of the Yellow River, drought took its annual toll,

while hailstorms flattened the wheat fields in Shantung Province on the
northeast coast, damaged houses, and created a need for emergency
rations.

The government hopes to offset at least some of these calamities
by: (1) its program of irrigation and dams; (2) flexibility in the purchase program, buying more in bumper-crop areas to be distributed
to famine-strickened areas; and (3) improvements in the transportation system which will wipe out minor famines.[18]

Famine patterns by areas.   Studying the famine pattern in the
eight food regions described above, Buck has this to say: "On the
basis of duration, proportion of people emigrating and starving, and
the existence of cannibalism during the famine, the spring-wheat area
seems to be the most severely affected; in the winter wheat-millet
area, crop failures and famines are most prevalent but less severe."
In the winter wheat-kaoliang area, famines are frequent but still less
severe than in both other wheat areas. In the Yangtze rice area, their
occurrence is rarer still; however, here typhoons occur that destroy crops and level the land. In the Szechwan rice area, the most
productive food region, there were only nine calamities during the
first quarter of the century, none of which caused real famine. The
situation is just a little less favorable in the southwestern rice area.

Insects and pests.[28]   Insects and pests cause losses of approximately 10% of the grain crops and 40% of the fruit harvest every year.
Locusts, aphids, rice borers, and other plant insects were reported
in 1956 to have affected a total of 10 million acres in Shantung,
Kiangsu, Honan, Kwantung, Shensi, and other provinces.

V. NUTRITIONAL DISEASE PATTERNS

Chinese sources are silent on present-day nutritional diseases in
the country. Since the food situation has deteriorated since 1930, it
is possible to use prewar data for the evaluation of present-day deficiencies without the risk of being overly pessimistic.

The whole of China suffers sporadically from protein malnutrition,
although detailed studies on the particular nature of the missing elements are not available. Nutritional edema is known to occur, and
the low level of nutrition probably contributes to the short life expectancy (34 years in 1929-1931).[13]

Symptoms of vitamin A deficiencies are quite common; xeroph-
thalmia, keratomalacia, and night blindness are frequently encountered. Thiamine deficiency occurs in the cities, where the cereals are
more thoroughly polished than in the villages. Beriberi is known to
break out at times in epidemic form. Niacin deficiencies and pellagra
are common in areas where corn is eaten, and occur in most of the
provinces located to the northeast of the Yangtze River.

Osteomalacia, due to faulty calcium and phosphorus metabolism and to lack of vitamin D, is found in Shansi, Shensi, Kansu, and the Manchurian provinces, where its incidence may reach more than 5% of all women over puberty. Other mineral deficiencies occur in many areas; for example, goiter is found in Yunnan, Hunan, Hopei, Inner Mongolia, Kansu, and Szechwan, creating a goiter belt that extends from northeastern Manchuria to the Gulf of Siam.[11,30]

VI. CONCLUSIONS

The outlook for food production in mainland China is based on the following points:

1. The topography of China does not lend itself easily to the use of machines (with the exception of North China and Manchuria).

2. Collectivization implies considerable mechanization, which China has not yet achieved to a significant degree. The first factory to produce 15,000 tractors a year was not to be completed before the end of 1959.

3. The countries of Eastern Europe and the Soviet Union, where some degree of collectivization of agriculture has been achieved, have been transformed from food-exporting areas into food-rationing areas.

4. The Soviet Union and the countries of Eastern Europe which have carried out, with relative success, the mechanization of agriculture, had virgin land to draw upon. China has no such virgin land to use unless or until extensive irrigation and land reclamation have been carried out; this requires a large investment in capital, machinery, and labor. Yet it must not be forgotten that the Chinese government is determined, at whatever cost, to achieve forced industrialization and collectivization, even at the risk of imposing sacrifices that will dwarf those suffered by the Soviet farmers in the 1920's and 1930's.

5. The population pressure—even if checked to some degree—will tax the food production heavily for a long time.

6. Calamities can be only partially controlled.

7. Industrialization absorbs a certain percentage of the agricultural production increase.

As a result of all these considerations, China will remain for many years to come a vast area of marginal malnutrition with a most vulnerable food supply system.

SELECTED REFERENCES

1. Chao Kul-chun. Agrarian Policies of Mainland China: A Documentation Study (1949-1956). Cambridge, Harvard University Press, 1957.
2. *New York Times*, June 20, 1959.
3. Shabad, T. China's Changing Map. New York, Frederick A. Praeger Inc., 1956.
4. Statistical Yearbook of the United States, 1956. United States Department of Commerce.
5. Walker, R. L. China under Communism. New Haven, Yale University Press, 1955.
6. Red China's Food Supplies Behind Schedule This Year. *Foreign Agriculture*, Vol. 22, No. 12, December, 1958, p. 22.
7. Cartier, R. Le Farouche visage de la China rouge. *Paris-Match*, June 11, 1955, p. 15.
8. La Chine sous le masque rouge. *Realities*, Special No. 124, June, 1956.
9. Cressey, G. B. Land of the 500 Million. New York, McGraw Hill Book Co., 1955.
10. Chinese Medical Association. Minimum Nutritional Requirement for China. *Special Report Series No. 10*, Shanghai, 1958.
11. Shen, T. H. Agricultural Resources of China. Ithaca, N. Y., Cornell University Press, 1951.
12. Kirby, R. H. Communist China and the Japanese Farm Market. *Foreign Agriculture*, Vol. 22, No. 6, June, 1958, pp. 5-8.
13. Buck, J. L. Land Utilization in China. Chicago, University of Chicago Press, 1937.
14. Nicholls, L. Tropical Nutrition and Dietetics. London, Bailliere, Tindall and Cox, 1951.
15. Shabad, T. China's Year of the Great Leap Forward. *Far Eastern Survey*, Vol. 28, No. 7, July, 1959, pp. 105-109.
16. Thompson, W. S. Population and Progress in the Far East. Chicago, University of Chicago Press, 1959.
17. *New York Times*, October, 1958.
18. Gluckstein, Y. Mao's China. Boston, The Beacon Press, 1957.
19. *China Pictorial*, February 20, 1959.
20. *China Reconstructs*, October, 1958.
21. *China Reconstructs*, June, 1958.
22. Guide de Chine. (Éditions en langues étrangères.) Peking, 1958.
23. Food and Agriculture Organization. *Monthly Bulletin of Agricultural Economics and Statistics*, Vol. 7, No. 12, 1958.
24. Wu, Y. L. An Economic Survey of Communist China. New York, Bookman Associates, 1956.
25. Foreign Production News. *Foreign Agriculture*, Vol. 22, No. 7, July, 1958, p. 22.
26. The Basic Conditions of Unified Purchase and Unified Marketing of Grain in China. *Statistical Bulletin*, No. 19, October 14, 1957.
27. Adler, S. The Chinese Economy. New York, Monthly Review Press, 1957.
28. China Yearbook 1957-1958. Taipei, China Publishing Co., 1958.
29. *Times News Magazine*, June, 1959.
30. May, J. M. Atlas of Diseases, Plate 9. New York, American Geographical Society, 1953.
31. India, Ministry of Food and Agriculture. Report of the Indian Delegation to China on Agricultural and Planning Techniques. New Delhi, Government of India Press, 1956.
32. *Jen-min Jih Pao (People's Daily)*, June 11, 1959.
33. Union Research Institute. Communist China, 1957. Kowloon, Hongkong.
34. Hughes, H. S. Purlock. Far East Analysis. Br. United States Department of Agriculture. Personal communication.
35. Cheng, Chu-yuan. Income and Standard of Living in Mainland China. (2 vols.) Hongkong, Union Research Institute, 1957.
36. *Ta-Kung-Pao*, October 1, 1956.
37. *Jen-min Jih Pao (People's Daily)*, July 22, 1955.

Table 1

Calories Consumed per Capita per Day: Percentage Distribution by Food Groups for 12 Far Eastern Countries and the U. S.

Food	Burma	Ceylon	Mainland China	India	Indonesia	Japan	Malaya	Pakistan	Philippines	South Korea	Taiwan	Thailand	United States
	%	%	%	%	%	%	%	%	%	%	%	%	%
Rice	72.3	43.3	40.5	33.6	45.6	46.5	44.5	43.1	41.3	54.4	53.0	72.6	0.7
Wheat	.7	10.9	13.8	9.6	.6	14.0	7.4	18.4	3.5	6.8	9.8	.3	18.8
Millet, maize Barley etc.	2.2	3.0	20.3	20.4	11.9	9.4	1.1	6.7	15.9	17.5	.1	.3	3.5
Dry beans and peas	2.5	3.9	5.3	11.4	1.2	1.6	2.0	4.2	1.3	1.3	.9	.3	1.2
Roots, tubers & starches	.5	3.3	3.8	3.0	18.2	6.9	2.5	.8	6.4	3.8	13.0	.2	3.0
Sugar	4.7	7.6	.8	6.3	4.0	6.4	9.5	8.3	6.2	1.7	6.7	2.7	15.6
Oilseeds (incl. soybeans & peanuts)	2.0	.2	4.4	1.0	1.8	4.3	1.8	—	.5	3.6	4.6	1.1	1.0
Oils and fats (excl. oilseeds and butter)	5.8	3.8	4.8	3.5	4.3	3.4	9.8	2.0	4.1	1.0	3.5	3.9	13.7
Vegetables	1.3	1.0	.9	.8	3.2	2.3	1.7	1.5	.7	2.4	1.8	1.5	2.6
Fruit & nuts (incl. coconuts)	2.3	17.8	.9	2.3	6.2	.9	8.9	3.8	13.8	1.0	.9	11.0	4.1
Meat, fish, poultry & eggs	3.9	3.4	4.5	.6	2.5	3.4	7.3	2.5	5.1	5.8	5.0	4.7	19.2
Milk & dairy prod. (incl. butter)	1.8	1.8	—	7.5	.5	.9	3.5	8.7	1.2	.7	.7	1.4	16.6
Grand total	100.0	100.0	100.0	100.0	100.0	100.0	100.0	100.0	100.0	100.0	100.0	100.0	100.0
Number of calories	2,020	2,065	1,830	2,030	2,020	2,295	2,555	1,980	2,170	2,060	2,285	2,065	3,070

Derived from: Food Balances, Consumption Year 1955-56, for Countries in South Asia, East Asia, and Oceania, Oct. 1957
U. S. data are for the year 1954 and are derived from Food Balance sheets, second issue, FAO. 1955.

Table 2a

Daily Dietary Allowances[†]

As Recommended by Food and Nutrition Board, Nat. Res. Council, U.S.A., revised 1948

	Calories	Proteins gm.	Calcium gm.	Iron mg.	Vitamin A I.U.	Thiamine mg.	Riboflavin mg.	Niacin mg.	Ascorbic acid, mg.	Vitamin D
Man (70 Kg.):										
Sedentary	2,400	70	1.0	12	5,000	1.2	1.8	12	75	*
Physically active	3,000	70	1.0	12	5,000	1.5	1.8	15	75	*
With heavy work	4,500	70	1.0	12	5,000	1.8	1.8	18	75	*
Woman (56 Kg.):										
Sedentary	2,000	60	1.0	12	5,000	1.0	1.5	10	70	*
Active	2,400	60	1.0	12	5,000	1.2	1.5	12	70	*
Very Active	3,000	60	1.0	12	5,000	1.5	1.5	15	70	*
Pregnancy (later half)	2,400	85	1.5	15	6,000	1.5	2.5	15	100	400
Lactation	300	100	2.0	15	8,000	1.5	3.0	15	150	400
Children up to 12 years:										
Under 1 year	110/Kg.	3.5/Kg.	1.0	6	1,500	0.4	0.6	4	30	400
1-3 years	1,200	40	1.0	7	2,000	0.6	0.9	6	35	400
4-6 years	1,600	50	1.0	8	2,500	0.8	1.2	8	50	400
7-9 years	2,000	60	1.0	10	3,500	1.0	1.5	10	60	400
10-12 years	2,500	70	1.2	12	4,500	1.2	1.8	12	75	400
Children over 12 years:										
Girls 13-15 years	2,600	80	1.3	15	5,000	1.3	2.0	13	80	400
16-20 years	2,400	75	1.0	15	5,000	1.2	1.8	12	80	400
Boys 13-15 years	3,200	85	1.4	15	5,000	1.5	2.0	15	90	400
16-20 years	3,800	100	1.4	15	6,000	1.7	2.5	17	100	400

†Would apply to North China.

*Small amounts needed unless there is exposure to the sun.

Source: Nicholls, L.: Tropical Nutrition and Dietetics. London; Bailliere, Tindall and Cox, 1951.

Table 2b

Dietary Allowances Under Tropical Conditions*

	Calories	Proteins gm.	Calcium gm.	Iron mg.	Vitamin A I.U.	Thiamine mg.	Riboflavin mg.	Niacin mg.	Ascorbic acid, mg.
Man (55 Kg. (121 lb.)):									
Sedentary	2,100	60	0.5	8	2,500	1.0	1.0	12	25
Active	2,500	65	0.5	8	2,500	1.2	1.2	15	25
Very active	3,000	70	0.7	8	2,500	1.7	1.5	20	25
Woman (56 Kg. (99 lb.)):									
Sedentary	1,750	55	0.5	10	2,500	0.8	1.0	11	25
Active	2,100	60	0.5	10	2,500	0.1	1.0	12	25
Very Active	2,500	65	0.7	10	2,500	1.2	1.2	15	25
Pregnant (later half)	2,500	80	0.8	18	4,000	1.2	1.5	18	25
Lactating	2,700	85	1.0	15	4,000	1.5	2.0	20	30
Adolescents:									
Boys 15–19 years	3,000	80	1.0	12	4,000	1.5	1.5	20	30
13–14 years	2,500	70	1.0	12	3,000	1.2	1.2	15	25
11–12 years	2,000	60	0.75	10	2,500	1.0	1.0	12	25
Girls 13–17 years	2,500	70	1.0	12	3,000	1.2	1.2	15	30
11–12 years	2,200	65	0.75	10	2,500	1.0	1.2	15	25
Children:									
9–10 years	1,700	60	0.75	8	2,500	0.7	1.0	12	25
7–8 years	1,600	60	0.75	7	2,500	0.6	1.0	10	20
5–6 years	1,400	50	0.5	6	2,000	0.6	1.0	8	20
3–4 years	1,200	40	0.5	6	2,000	0.5	1.0	6	18
1–2 years	900	35	0.5	5	1,500	0.4	1.0	6	15
Under 1 year	80/Kg.	3/Kg.							

* Would apply to South China.

Source: Nicholls, L.: Tropical Nutrition and Dietetics. London: Bailliere, Tindall and Cox, 1951.

Table 3

Minimum Nutritional Requirements

	No. 1 Adult				No. 2 Child: 15 kg. (3–5 yr.)			
	Weight	Calories	Protein	Calcium	Weight	Calories	Protein	Calcium
PROTECTIVE FOODS								
Green leaf:	gm		gm	gm	gm		gm	gm
Vegetables								
Cabbage	500	75	6	0.50	300	45	4	0.30
Colza								
Spinach								
Amaranth								
Alfalfa								
Mustard								
Soybean products								
Soybean flour	60	264	24	0.06				
Tou-fu					150	100	13	0.24
Tubers								
Sweet potato	400	284	5		200	142	2	
Taro								
Meat, fish, etc.								
Pork								
Liver								
Fish								
Eggs					80 (2)	120	10	0.04
SUPPLEMENTARY FOODS								
Cereals								
Rice	500	1765	43	0.47	220	777	19	0.21
Wheat								
Maize								
Millet								
Legumes (other than soybean)								
Peas								
Cowpeas								
Oils	*				*			
Pickled vegetables and sauce	*				*			
Total		2388	78	1.03		1184	48	0.79

The estimates are based on analyses of Chinese foods. They refer to foods actually eaten and do not allow for waste. The foods listed in each group have similar dietary properties and may be used interchangeably with minor readjustment of the amounts.

* As desired.

No. 3 Child: 30 kg. (8-10 yr.)				No. 4 Pregnant women: 50 kg.				No. 5 Nursing women: 50 kg.			
Weight	Calories	Protein	Calcium	Weight	Calories	Protein	Calcium	Weight	Calories	Protein	Calcium
gm		gm	gm	gm		gm	gm	gm		gm	gm
400	60	5	0.24	500	75	6	0.50	500	75	6	0.50
300	200	26	0.48	300	200	26	0.48	300	200	26	0.48
300	213	3		400	284	5		400	284	5	
								100	250	20	
80 (2)	120	10	0.04	80 (2)	120	10	0.04	120 (3)	180	15	0.06
350	1235	30	0.33	500	1765	43	0.47	500	1765	43	0.47
								50	168	13	0.15
*				*				*			
*				*				*			
	1828	74	1.09		2444	90	1.49		2922	128	1.66

Source: Chinese Medical Association: Minimum Nutritional Requirements for China.
Special Report
Series #10. Shanghai, 1938.

Table 4

Food per Capita per Day

Period	Grains	Roots & Tubers	Sugar	Pulses	Vegetables & fruits	Meat	Eggs	Fish	Fats	Calories per day.
	Grams	Grams	Grams	Grams	Grams	Grams	Grams	Grams	Grams	
1931-1937[a]	475	84	3.5	70	157	33	4.1	7.7	17.4	2234
1949-1950[a]	415	95	2.5	60	157	12.5	2.5	15.7	17.5	2215
1955-1957[b][c]	500*		4.0	?	140 to 350**	12-16**	—	13	7-8	1830[d]

*Available for human consumption after deduction of amounts paid as taxes or devoted to non-food uses.[c]
**Rural and urban.

Source: (a) Shen, T. H.: Agricultural Resources of China. Cornell University Press, Ithaca, N.Y., 1951.
(b) Shabad, T.: China's Year of The Great Leap Forward, Far Eastern Survey, Vol. 28 #7, pp. 105-109, July, 1959.
(c) Cheng, C. Y.: Income and Standard of Living in Mainland China. Union Research Institute, Hongkong, 1957.
(d) Foreign Agriculture, Vol. 22, June, 1958.

Table 5[*]

Generalized Nutritional Values of Recent Chinese Diets

Items[a]	Amounts Eaten Gm.	Proteins[b] Gm.	Carbo-hydrates Gm.	Calcium mg.	Phosphorus mg.	Iron mg.	Vit.[e] A I.U.	Thiamin μg.	Ribo-flavin μg.	Niacin mg.	Ascorbic Acid mg.
Rice	{412	32	313	61	618	8	–	988	412	8	–
Wheat		45	288	123	1151[f]	16[f]	–	1236	412	8	–
Roots &tubers	96	1.8	25	17	42	0.7	160	79	53	0.007	14
Sugar	3	–	3	–	–	–	–	–	–	–	–
Pulses	59	15.9	21.8[c]	88	290	3.5	–	373	162	1.4	–
Veg. & fruit	153	2.7	7.6	119[d]	81	1	956	76	68	0.7	76
Meat	15.5	2.1	–	1.2	18.6	0.27	–	124	27	0.4	–
Eggs	0.2	–	–	0.18	0.4	0.005	2.0	0.28	0.6	–	–
Fish	1.5	0.28	–	0.3	3.15	–	–	1	1	0.06	–
Fats	1.8	–	–	–	–	–	–	–	–	–	–
Total — 742.0											
Total in rice areas		54.78	370.4	286.68	1053.15	13.475	1118	1641.28	723.6	10.56	90
Total in wheat areas		67.78	345.4	348.68	1586.15	21.475	,,	1889.28	723.6	10.56	,,

(a) More precise breakdown in each category is not available either for all China or even for every province.
(b) Protein content varies with each food. The average for the various foods eaten in China has been used for computation.
Figures from L. Nicholls. pp. 402–426.
(c) Average chosen between soybeans, dried peas and kidney beans.
(d) Calcium contents of vegetables and fruits vary considerably. The most favorable items have been selected.
(e) All vitamin values may vary considerably depending on the local preferences; only rough conclusions can be drawn.
(f) Phosphorus and iron content varies considerably depending on whether wheat is eaten whole, baked into bread, made into noodles, etc. An arbitrary average of 280 mg/100 Gm. of phosphorus has been chosen.
*Computed from various sources.

Table 6

Percentage of Calories Supplied by Different Important Staple Crops

17,351 persons, 2,727 families, 136 localities, 131 hsien, 21 provinces, China, 1929-1933

Regions and areas	Number of localities	Rice	Wheat	Millet	Kaoliang	Corn	Millet, proso	Potatoes sweet	Barley	Soybeans	Green beans	Oats	Potatoes Irish	Field peas	Rice glutinous	Broad beans	Soybeans black	Other grains	Other legumes
CHINA	136	35.0	14.4	10.4	7.5	7.5	2.8	2.6	2.0	2.0	1.2	1.2	0.9	0.8	0.7	0.6	0.6	0.2	1.3
Wheat Region	67	0.6	23.5	19.9	14.6	11.9	5.8	2.5	1.3	3.2	2.0	2.2	1.7	1.3	—	0.2	1.2	2.3	1.4
Rice Region	69	68.4	5.6	1.2	0.6	3.2	—	2.8	2.7	0.9	0.4	0.1	0.1	0.3	1.5	1.1	*	1.3	1.3
Wheat Region Areas:																			
Spring Wheat	13	*	15.3	20.0	4.5	*	21.7	—	1.3	0.4	0.4	10.9	7.3	3.2	—	1.0	0.7	8.6	0.8
Winter Wheat-millet	21	1.0	26.7	23.2	11.5	17.4	4.1	0.3	0.8	2.2	1.4	0.3	0.8	1.5	—	—	0.9	1.4	1.9
Winter Wheat-kaoliang	33	0.6	24.7	17.9	20.5	13.0	0.5	4.9	1.7	4.9	3.0	—	*	0.5	—	—	1.6	0.5	1.2
Rice Region Areas:																			
Yangtze Rice-wheat	22	57.8	12.8	1.2	1.6	2.1	—	1.8	7.4	0.7	1.2	—	—	0.2	1.3	1.5	—	1.9	1.1
Rice-tea	19	75.8	3.1	0.4	0.1	2.1	—	2.0	0.3	0.8	*	*	0.1	0.1	1.8	0.5	0.1	1.7	1.5
Szechwan Rice	6	56.9	5.3	—	0.1	14.0	—	3.1	0.3	1.9	0.3	1.5	0.1	2.2	0.8	1.2	—	0.7	1.2
Double Cropping Rice	11	76.9	0.5	0.1	—	—	—	8.2	1.2	0.6	0.1	—	—	*	0.6	0.1	—	0.1	1.5
Southwestern Rice	11	74.7	1.0	*	—	4.8	—	0.5	0.3	1.4	—	—	0.3	0.1	2.4	2.1	—	1.3	1.1

Source: Buck, J. L.: Land Utilization in China. University of Chicago Press, Chicago, 1937.

Table 7

Animal Food Calorie Intake

17,351 persons, 2,727 families, 136 localities, 131 hsien, 21 provinces, China, 1929–1933

Regions and areas	Number of localities	Daily intake of calories supplied by animal foods per adult-made unit	Percentage of animal calorie intake supplied by different animal foods										
			Pork	Lard	Mutton	Eggs (chicken)	Beef	Chicken	Fish	Duck	Eggs (duck)	Shrimp, dried	Meat, salted
CHINA	135	76	54	18	8	8	4	2	2	1	1	*	*
Wheat Region	67	32	59	7	17	10	6	*	1	—	*	*	—
Rice Region	69	122	51	31	*	5	3	3	4	1	1	1	*
Wheat Region Areas:													
Spring Wheat	13	35	51	5	36	2	6	*	*	—	—	—	—
Winter Wheat-millet	21	17	63	5	23	7	2	*	—	—	—	—	—
Winter Wheat-kaoliang ..	33	40	59	8	5	16	8	1	3	—	*	—	—
Rice Region Areas:													
Yangtze Rice-wheat	22	98	58	24	1	8	2	2	3	*	1	—	1
Rice-tea..	19	106	54	31	*	5	1	3	4	1	1	—	—
Szechwan Rice	6	165	48	37	2	3	7	1	1	—	1	—	—
Double Cropping Rice	11	102	42	22	*	3	7	6	8	6	2	4	—
Southwestern Rice	11	196	46	44	*	2	4	2	*	1	1	—	—

Source: Buck, J. L.: Land Utilization in China. University of Chicago Press, Chicago, 1937.

Table 8

List of Typical Foods from Which Daily Menus Are Made

	North China		Central—South China
	Winter	Summer	
Breakfast	Wheat flour cake	Millet flour cake	Rice congee
	Turnip	Millet congee	duck's egg
	Sweet potato	Soybean curd	salt
	Millet congee	Vegetables	soybeans
	Pickled bean curd		mustard leaf
Lunch	Cabbage	Wheat flour cake	Rice
	Mixed flour cake	(black and white)	Alfa Alfa
	(cornmeal—80%,	String beans	mustard
	soybean—20%)	Pork	pork soup
	mustard leaf	Tomato	fish
	rice	Egg	mungbean sprout
	pork	White gourd soup	
	sheet bean curd		
	soybean sprouts soup		
Supper	Cabbage	Rice	Rice
	oil	Eggplant	Egg
	mustard	Pork	Pork
	mixed flour cake	Seaweed soup	Cabbage soup
	salt	Pepper	Green amaranth
	noodles	Bean curd	Oil
	pork	oil	Soybean sauce
	flour paste		
	mungbean sprout		
	spinach		
	egg		

Source: Chinese Medical Association: Minimum Nutritional Requirements for China. Special Report Series, No. 10, Shanghai, 1938.

Table 9

Food Crop Production

(in million of tons)

	1952	1956	1957	1958	1959 (target)
All food crops	154.4	182.5	185	375	525
Rice*	68.4	82.5	86.8	150	
Early			19.3	43.5	
mid-season			41.5	56.5	
late			26	50	
Wheat	18.1	24.8	23.6	40	
winter			20.6	34.5	
spring			3	5.5	
Other grains	51.5	53.4	52.7	90	
corn			21.4	45	
kaoliang			7.7	9	
millet			8.6	15	
barley, oats			15	21	
Potatoes & yams†	16.3	21.9	21.9	95	
Soybeans	9.5	10.2	10.0	12.5	15
Peanuts	2.3	3.3	2.6	4	6
Rape seeds	0.9	0.9	0.9	1.1	1.6
Edible oils	0.98		1.1	1.25	1.8
Sugar cane	7.1	8.7	10.4	13.5	20
Sugar beets	0.5	1.6	1.5	2.9	5.5
Tea		0.12	0.11	0.14	
Fish & Marine products	1.7	—	—	3.1	8.2

Animal proteins

(in million heads)

	1952	1956	1957	1958	1959 (target)
Hogs	89.2	—	145.9	180	280
Goats & sheep	61.8	—	98.6	108.9	120
Cattle	56.6	— (plan)	73.6		

*The early and late rice crops are obtained from double-cropped land, semi-late rice from single-cropped land.

†For use in food-crop statistics, the output of potatoes and yams is converted into so-called grain equivalent at a ratio of 4:1. The actual tonnage of these root crops for the four years indicated was (in millions) : 65.2; 87.6; 87.6; 380.

Source: Shabad, T.: China's Year of The Great Leap Forward, Far Eastern Survey, Vol. 28 #7, pp. 105-109, July, 1959.

Table 10

Vegetables and Fruits: % of Crop Area Devoted to Them

Areas	Lychee	Orange	Arrow-head	Bamboo shoots	Brassica pekinensis	Clover	Garlic	Lentils	Mustard	Peppers	Veg.	Water-melon
Spring wheat	0	0	0	0	N.D.	0	0	3.3	0	0	0.1	1.4
Winter wheat, millet	0	0	0	0	0.1	0	N.D.	1.0	0	0.1	0	0.1
Winter wheat, kaoliang	0	0	0	0	0.1	0	0	0.1	0.1	0	N.D.	0.2
Yangtze rice, wheat	0	0	0	0	0.3	0	0	0.1	0	0	0	0.1
Rice, tea	0	0	0	0.1	0.2	0	0.2	0	0.3	N.D.	0.8	0.2
Szechwan rice	0	0	0	0	0.1	0	0	0.2	0	0	0	0
Double cropping rice	0.2	0.4	0.2	0	0	0.8	0.7	0	0.2	0	0.9	0.1
Southwestern rice	0	0	0	0	0	0	0	0	0	0.2	0	0

N.D. No data.
Source: Buck. H. L.: Land Utilization in China. University of Chicago Press, Chicago, 1937.

Table 11

Principal Cultures by Provinces: Food Centers and Relative Economic Importance

Province	Area/Sq. Mile	% of Total	Population (estimate) (in millions)	% of Total	Cultures & Animal Husbandry	Amount Produced All Grains, or Grain Equivalent (in millions of tons or heads)	Food Centers
Hopei	75,000	1.9	41	6.9	winter wheat, soy-beans, veg. oils, hogs.	1957—22.5 (hogs)—17–20	Tientsin
Honan	65,000	1.7	46	7.7	kaoliang, winter wheat, soybeans.	1958—35.1	Chengchow
Shantung	54,000	1.3	50	8.4	kaoliang, winter wheat, soybeans, peanuts, fish.	1957—16.8 (fish)—1958—0.55	Tsingtao
Kiangsu	40,000	1.0	42	7.1	winter wheat, summer rice, summer kaoliang, millet, corn, soybeans, sweet potatoes.	1955—11.2	Shanghai
Anhwei	56,000	1.4	32	5.4	winter wheat, rice (S), summer kaoliang (N), winter barley (S), soybean (N), sweet potatoes (N), tea.	1958—21	Hofei PengPu Tunki Sihsien Kimen
Hupei	72,000	1.8	29	4.9	summer rice, winter wheat, barley, rape seed, bread beans, sugar beets (recent)	1956—10.9	Hankow
Hunan	79,000	2.0	35	5.9	rice, tea, sweet potatoes	1957—11.5 (tea)—1958—0.030	Changsha Hankow Yiyang
Kiangsi	67,000	1.7	17.5	2.9	rice, tea.	1958—12	Kiukiang

Table 11 (continued)

Province	Area/Sq. Mile	Population (estimate) (in millions)	% of Total	Cultures & Animal Husbandry	Amount Produced All Grains, or Grain Equivalent	Food Centers
Chekiang	39,000	23.5 1.0	4.0	rice, winter wheat, tea fruit (peaches & oranges), fish.	All grains—N.D. (tea)—1958—0.032 (fish)—1956—0.386	Hangchow Huchow Kashing Tientai Linhai Tinghai
Fukien	46,000	13.6 1.1	2.3	rice, sweet potatoes, tea, citrus fruit, bananas, sugar cane, fish.	1958—8.85 (tea)—1958—0.008 (sugar cane)—0.8 (fish)—1956—0.327 (Plan)	Foochow Changchow Santuao Amoy
Kwantung	84,000	36 2.1	6.1	rice, sugar (refined), citrus fruit, bananas, apples, pineapples, tea, peanuts, fish.	1955—10 (sugar)—0.6 (tea)—1958—0.031 (peanuts)—0.1 (fish)—1957—0.6	Canton, Swatow Pakhoi Namoa Chuhoi Lintung
Kwangsi	84,000	20 2.1	3.4	rice, corn, barley, millet, sugar cane, fruit, veg. oil, cinnamon.	1958—11.45	Kweilin Wuchow
Kweichow	66,000	16 1.6	2.7	rice, wheat, corn (E)	1957—5.25	Kweiyang
Yunnan	162,000	18 4.0	3.0	rice, wheat, barley, corn, tea, sugar cane, salt.	1957—6.25	Kunming
Szechwan	210,000	67 5.2	11.3	summer, rice, winter wheat, kaoliang, millet, corn, sweet potatoes, veg. oil, sugar cane, citrus fruit, goats, hogs.	1958—48	Chungking Chentu
Shensi	74,000	16.5 1.8	2.8	winter wheat, summer	1955—4.5	Sian, Paoki,

				Crops	Production / Year	Cities
				winter and spring wheat, oats, veg. oil, salt.	(veg. oil)—1958—0.098 (salt)—1956—0.6	Yuncheng
Liaoning	50,000	1.2	21	3.5	kaoliang, millet, soy-beans (N), corn (SE), summer rice, fruit (apples and pears).	1958—8.5	Shenyang Darien
Kirin	70,000	1.7	12	2.0	soybeans, kaoliang & corn (N), wheat (N), rice & millet (E), sugar beets.	1958—7	Szeping
Heilungkiang	180,000	4.5	12	2.0	spring wheat, oats & barley (NW), soybeans, sugar beets, hogs.	1955—8.2 (soybeans)—1.7 (sugar beets)—2.29 (hogs)—3.3	Harbin
Inner Mongolia	450,000	11.2	7.5	1.3	spring wheat (irrigated) kaoliang, millet, corn (nonirrigated), veg. oil, soybeans, sugar beets, livestock.	1958—6.4 (livestock)—24	Huhehot Paotow Hailar
Kansu	300,000	7.5	14	2.4	winter wheat, winter millet, sugar beets, oasis agriculture, livestock	1958—9	Lanchow Linsia
Sinkiang	660,000	16.4	5	0.8	wheat, corn rice, fruit, livestock, veg. oil.	1958—3.2 (livestock)—23.124 (veg. oil)—1957—0.09	Urumchi Kashgar
Tsinghai	320,000	8.0	1.8	0.3	spring wheat, barley salt, veg. oil, livestock	1955—0.42 (salt)—1957—0.64 (veg. oil)—0.02 (livestock)—19	Sining
Tibet	580,000	14.4	1.5	0.3	N.D.		
Ninghsia	75,000	1.9	1.6	0.3	spring wheat, winter millet, livestock	1958—1.5	
	4,018,000		595.				

Sources: Shabad, T.: China's Changing Map. Frederich A. Praeger, New York, 1956.
Shabad, T.: China's Year of the Great Leap Forward, Far Eastern Survey, Vol. 28 #7, pp. 105-109, July, 1959.

Table 12

Contribution of Each Chinese Province to the Total Grain Production

Area	Provinces	% of Total Production	Year
	I. Wheat Areas		
1. Spring wheat:	Heilungkiang	4.5	1955
	Kirin	1.6	1958
	Ningshia	0.4	1958
	Tsinghai	0.3	1955
	Inner Mongolia	1.7	1958
	Shansi (north)* (Sangkan basin)	2.6	1958
	Kansu (north)*	2.4	1958
	Sinkiang (Dzungaria)*	0.8	1958
	Liaoning	2.2	1958
2. Winter wheat-millet:	Shansi	—	1958
	Shensi (parts)*	2.4	1957
	Kansu (south)*	—	
	Sinkiang (Tarim basin)*	—	
3. Winter wheat—kaoliang:	Hopei	12.	1957
	Honan (north)*	9.9	1958
	Shantung	7.1	1957
	Kiangsu (north)*	6.0	1955
	II. Rice Areas		
4. Yangtze rice-wheat:	Honan (south)*	—	1957
	Anhwei (north)*	5.6	1958
	Kiangsu (south)*	—	
	Hupei (north)*	5.9	1956
5. Rice-tea:	Hunan	6.3	1957
	Kiangsi (north)	3.2	1958
	Chekiang	(unavailable)	
	Fukien (north)	2.4	1958
	Hupei (south)	—	
6. Szechwan rice:	Szechwan	12.8	1958
	Shensi (south)	—	
7. Double crop rice:	Fukien (south)	—	
	Kwantung	5.4	1955
	Kwangsi (south)	2.7	1958
8. Southwestern rice:	Yunnan	3.3	1957
	Kwangsi (North W.)	—	
	Kweichow	2.8	1957

Note: The % are approximative since they are based on different years.

*% computed for the whole province and all types of grain.

Table 13

Mainland China: Exports and Imports of Rice (Milled Equivalent), by Destination and Origin, Prewar, 1948 and 1951-57

Thousand metric tons

Country	1934-38	1948	1951	1952	1953	1954	1955	1956	1957
EXPORTS									
Ceylon[1]	—	...	—	36.3	264.9	217,8	122.2	246.2	169.1
Japan	—	...	—	—	—	72.9	132.7	112.7	—
Hong Kong	1.5	...	49.6	5.6	3.3	—	36.9	51.9	64.5
Malaya-Singapore	1.5	...	11.5	150.4	—	—	1.1	10.9	25.8
India	—	...	66.8	—	—	—	—	46.7	14.5
Pakistan	—	...	—	—	—	—	—	68.1	—
Others[2]	13.9	...	—	—	—	2.8	11.0	8.6	6.0
Total	16.9	5.0	127.9	192.3	268.2	293.0	303.9	545.1	279.9
U.S.S.R.	—	...	...	...	...	...	293.0	458.0	181.0
Grand Total	16.9	...	...	...	...	...	596.9	1003.1	460.9
IMPORTS									
Burma	80.3	61.7	—	—	2.1	—	[3]157.2	[4]85.8	[4]79.4
Thailand	231.9	219.5	20.0	15.0	—	—	—	—	—
Indochina	299.5	3.7	—	—	—	—	—	—	—
United States	—	97.4	—	—	—	—	—	—	—
Others[5]	14.2	—	—	—	—	—	—	—	—
Grand Total	625.9	382.3	20.0	15.0	2.1	—	157.2	85.8	79.4

Note: 1951-57 figures based on shipments recorded by importing and exporting countries.
[1] Exclude rice transhipped from Burma under Ceylon-China contracts. — [2] Austria, Netherlands, Finland and Poland. — [3] Of which 51,000 tons to Ceylon. — [4] Re-exported to Ceylon. — [5] Mainly Korea and Hong Kong.
Source: Food and Agriculture Organization: Monthly Bulletin of Agricultural Economics and Statistics. Vol. 7 No. 12, 1958.

Table 14

Exports to Japan

(metric tons)

	1954	1955	1956
Soybeans	204,000	66,000	200,000
Oilseeds	26,000	18,000	6,000
Beans & peas	43,000	30,000	56,000

Source: Kirby, H. H.: Communist China and the Japanese Farm Market. For. Agr. Vol. 22, #6, pp. 5-8, 1958.

Table 15

The Stages in the Socialisation of Agriculture

Form of Production	Type of Farm	Form of Ownership
Isolated Production	(1) Individual Farm: unit, the single peasant household: purely private property.	
	(2) Individual Farms Joining in Seasonal Mutual Aid Team unit, 3 to 5 peasant households; no common property.	Individual Ownership
Mutual Aid in Production	(3) Individual Farms Joining in Year-round Mutual Aid Team: unit, 6 to 7 peasant households; little common property in animals and implements.	
	(4) Semi-socialist Producers' Co-operatives: unit, growing from 20 to 40 or 50 peasant households; more common property in land, animals and implements, but also individual ownership of all three.	Partially Collective Ownership
Co-operation in Production	(5) Socialist Producer's Co-operative or Collective Farm: unit 100 peasant households and upwards; no private property in land, animals and implements, save for small holdings.	Fully Collective Ownership

Source: Adler, S.: The Chinese Economy. Monthly Review Press, New York, 1957.

Table 16

Farm Area on Chinese Mainland Suffering from Natural Calamities in 1956

Province	Flood		Area Affected by Drought (Unit: 1,000 mou)	Area Affected by Plant insects (Unit: 1,000 mou)
	Area Flooded (Unit: 1,000 mou)*	Persons Affected (Unit: 1,000 persons)		
Heilungkiang	10,500	4,000		
Kirin	1,905	600		
Hopei	42,000	30,000		3,000
Shantung	3,500	1,000		5,000
Shansi	6,000	2,000		2,000
Shensi	1,000	400		10,000
Honan	43,000	25,000	12,000	10,000
Anhwei	40,000	20,000		3,000
Hupeh	4,000	1,200	2,000	2,000
Szechwan	5,000	5,000		
Hunan	300	100	10,000	3,000
Kiangsi	2,000	1,000	18,000	3,000
Kiangsu	21,000	10,000		15,000
Chekiang	5,000	2,000	5,000	3,000
Fukien	1,800	1,500	10,000	
Kwangtung	10,000	3,500	26,000	10,000
Kwangsi	1,500	1,500	7,500	
Yunnan	800	400		
Kansu				1,000
Chinghai				1,500
Sinkiang				1,000
Other provinces			30,000	
Total	199,355	109,200	120,500	72,500

*1 mou = 1/6 acre

Source: China Yearbook, 1957-1958. China Publishing Co. Taipei, 1958.

Map 1

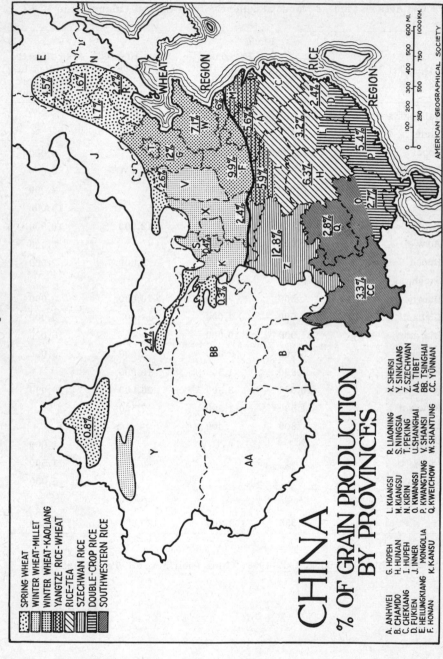

CHINA
% OF GRAIN PRODUCTION
BY PROVINCES

SPRING WHEAT
WINTER WHEAT-MILLET
WINTER WHEAT-KAOLIANG
YANGTZE RICE-WHEAT
RICE-TEA
SZECHWAN RICE
DOUBLE-CROP RICE
SOUTHWESTERN RICE

A. ANHWEI
B. CHAMDO
C. CHEKIANG
D. FUKIEN
E. HEILUNGKIANG
F. HONAN
G. HOPEH
H. HUNAN
I. HUPEH
J. INNER MONGOLIA
K. KANSU
L. KIANGSI
M. KIANGSU
N. KIRIN
O. KWANGSI
P. KWANGTUNG
Q. KWEICHOW
R. LIAONING
S. NINGSIA
T. PEKING
U. SHANGHAI
V. SHANSI
W. SHANTUNG
X. SHENSI
Y. SINKIANG
Z. SZECHWAN
AA. TIBET
BB. TSINGHAI
CC. YÜNNAN

AMERICAN GEOGRAPHICAL SOCIETY

0   100   200   300   400   500   600 MI.
0   250   500   750   1000 KM.

Map 2

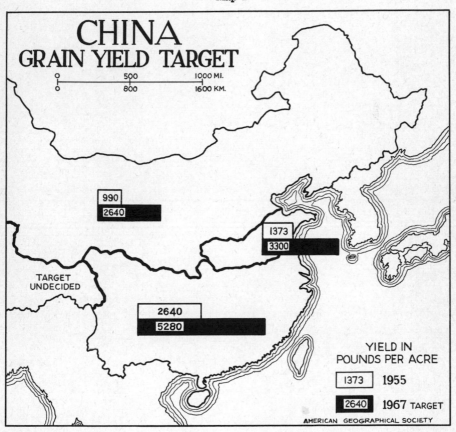

CHINA
GRAIN YIELD TARGET

| 500 | 1000 MI. |
| 800 | 1600 KM. |

990
2640

1373
3300

TARGET
UNDECIDED

2640
5280

YIELD IN
POUNDS PER ACRE

1373 1955

2640 1967 TARGET

AMERICAN GEOGRAPHICAL SOCIETY

TAIWAN

I. GENERAL REMARKS

Taiwan is a tropical island that has a total area of 3.6 million hectares (8.9 million acres), of which 0.97 million hectares (2.4 million acres) are cultivated. The estimated population of 1959 is more than 10 million.

Because of the ruggedness of the terrain there is practically no margin for further reclamation of land. And at present there are only 0.24 acres of cultivated land per capita.

Essential to a much needed increase in production are: irrigation; increase in fertilization to compensate for the poorness of the soil; better pest control; and some improvement in the quality of the rice seeds.

Taiwan is now in the middle of its second four-year plan which was inaugurated in 1957.

Basically, the problems of nutrition are similar to those of the Chinese mainland. They stem from the discrepancy between food production and population growth. However, Taiwan has benefited from circumstances that have placed it in a unique position. Because it is the seat of the Chinese Nationalist Government, and a key area in allied world strategy, it has enjoyed a privileged status in the United States foreign aid program. On the other hand, because it has to support an army, and is practically on a war footing, 30 to 50% of this aid has had to be diverted to military purposes.

The food situation in Nationalist China is well known. Rice production has risen from a prewar high of 1.4 million metric tons to 1.9 million in 1958.[13] A comparable increase has occurred in the other food crops, such as sweet potatoes, soybeans, wheat, and cash crops, essentially sugar cane and tea. Unfortunately, these not inconsiderable gains have been offset by the expansion of the population, which is increasing at the rate of 3% a year (as compared with 2% in mainland China).

Whatever increases have been achieved so far have been made possible mainly through the introduction of two reforms in the agricultural economy. The first is known as the "land to the Tiller Act of 1953," which was promoted by the Joint Commission for Rural Reconstruction (JCRR).[1] The purpose of this act was to reduce the

rents of tenants from 50% to 70% of their main crops, to a maximum
of 37.5%, and to redistribute the land so that no single owner would
possess more than 1 hectare (2.7 acres) of the best land, although he
might simultaneously possess larger tracts of poorer land.[1]

The second reform, which hinged on the first and on the technical
and financial help of the United States was modernization through
mechanization and the use of chemical fertilizers.

In spite of these advantages, the general nutritional situation is
but slightly better than on the Chinese mainland. According to the
most recent information, the total number of calories available per
day per person in Taiwan is 2,285 (See Table 2)—still slightly short
of the 2,400 deemed necessary for an average Chinese in tropical or
subtropical areas.

It is estimated that the average diet of the Taiwanese amounts to
a daily intake of approximately 800 grams, supplying the total caloric
intake mentioned above. On the mainland, cereals provide 74.6% of
the calories; in Taiwan, only 62.9%. While tubers constitute only 3.8%
of the total caloric intake on the mainland, these (including sweet
potatoes, rich in vitamin A) constitute 13% in Taiwan. Some 0.7% of
the intake is animal protein in the form of milk and butter, which is
about the same as on the mainland. The intake of animal protein in
the form of meat, fish, poultry and dairy products is also comparable
to that on the mainland. (See Table 1).

Food, as might be expected in view of the general poverty, is the
major expenditure in all social groups. It represents an average of
62% of the total budget of the inhabitants.

II. FOOD RESOURCES

A. GENERAL

Food production is affected by four paramount factors: land, climate, organization, and fertilizer.

Land. The island of Taiwan is rugged; more than half of it is
forested mountains or hills. Though there is relatively little flat
land fit for cultivation, it can be put to good use because of the subtropical climate that favors the growth of two and even three crops
a year on the same plot. This, however, results in an over-cultiva-
tion of the land which makes it imperative to replenish the soil with
natural or chemical fertilizers. (See map No. 1 for areas devoted to
important crops: rice, sugar cane and tea, as well as mixed farming
products).

Climate. Taiwan has high temperatures, heavy rainfall, and frequent strong winds, with a long, hot summer and a short, mild winter.

Throughout the island the annual mean temperatures are 22.6° to 24.9°C. The mean monthly temperatures rise from 22°-27° in April, to 28°-30° in July and August, but fall to 23°-27° in October.

The average annual rainfall ranges from 1,757 to 2,717 mms. The southwestern plain, however, which receives more than 80 per cent of the annual rainfall from April to September, has a marked dry season from October to March. This fact explains why non-irrigated fields can produce only one rice crop yearly.

As shown by field tests in various districts, the soils of the island are decidedly deficient in nitrogen, phosphoric acid, and potash.

Organization. Problems related to food supply are the concern of the Food Bureau, an office of the Department of Public Health. This bureau is headed by a commissioner appointed by the Governor General of Taiwan Province. The food policy is stated to be one of encouraging food production while discouraging food consumption. The JCRR also plays an important part in the organization of food production. Its objectives are to increase crop and livestock production, improve the living conditions of rural people, develop the potentiality of rural people for rehabilitation of their own communities support and strengthen government agencies and their services to agriculture, and encourage and develop rural leadership. Since its inception, in 1949, JCRR has carried out a total of 2,000 work projects representing an integrated program for the improvement of agriculture on the island. Between 1949 and 1957, it spent on them about $3.2 million from United States government funds and $220 million from the proceeds of United States commodity sales.[1]

Among the notable achievements of JCRR besides the land reforms mentioned above, are the development of fisheries, and rural health and economic studies. As a result of all these efforts, the production of some important agricultural products has already surpassed the peaks achieved during Japanese rule. As shown by Table 3, production of rice, sweet potatoes, wheat, peanuts, beans, and other crops has grown. However, production of some cash crops is still lagging behind.

Fertilizers.[7] Because of the lack of good soil, the shortage of fertilizers is one of the most serious problems to be overcome in Taiwan. Statistics show that the local consumption of chemical fertilizers during the period 1955-1957 exceeded 600,000 metric tons a year (690,000 in 1957). Total local production of chemical fertilizers amounted to 262,000 metric tons in 1958.

Graph 1 shows the gap between the production and consumption of fertilizers in the period 1945-1957.[8] It is hoped that near self-sufficiency will be attained in 1960 at the end of the second four-year plan, when four new plants for the manufacture of chemical fertilizers will have been completed and should be in full swing. The constant growth of the population, however, has to be kept in mind while

making prognoses for the future. It seems that for a long time to
come the earnings from exports will have to be applied to food stuffs
and fertilizers.

B. BY CATEGORIES

Rice.[2,9,12]   In 1955 rice production constituted 56.8% of the total
value of the principal farm crops. Military and civilian demands
have been met since that date and there is a surplus for export.
Yields per hectare have been steadily increasing. (In 1957, production was 2,290 kilograms per hectare, compared to 4,430 kilograms
per hectare in Japan). The area under rice has been expanded to
363,000 for the first crop and 461,000 for the second, giving a total
of 824,000 hectares. In all, 1.9 million metric tons were harvested
in 1958.

To regulate the supply and demand for rice, the government maintains a sizeable rice stock. During the 1956-57 campaign a total of
685,000 tons of paddy was collected; 300,000 came from payments of
land taxes in kind and from other sources; 223,000 from government
purchases from public lands and collections; 72,000 from the exchange
of low interest loans and commodities for paddy; 90,000 from cash
purchases of paddy produced on leased public lands and saved from
military rations and irrigation association membership fees.[1,9]

The main objective of the government's food control policy is to
assure sufficient rations for military and civilian employees as well
as an ample amount for the people and for special allocations. From
January to June 1956, 100,000 tons of brown rice were supplied to the
dependents of the armed forces and to civilian personnel, including
the poor, in Taiwan and on the surrounding islands. From July 1956
to June 1957, the total volume distributed was nearly 300,000 metric
tons, not including military rice.

To enforce its control policy, the government requires all rice
merchants, retailers, owners of warehouses and processing factories,
and brokers engaged in the food business, to obtain licenses. From
January 1956 to June 1957, 13,000 such were registered. Simultaneously, the government prohibits smuggling for export, speculation,
and illicit transactions in rice.

Wheat.   The consumption of flour from wheat has been on the increase in recent years. Wheat has been planted in paddy fields during the winter season. The planted area in 1957 was 20,000 hectares
and production was 36,000 metric tons, the average yield being 1,810
kilograms per hectare.[9]

Animal protein resources.   Although beef is not a common food,
considerable efforts are being made to improve the cattle herds.
Farm cattle are registered and an annual check is made under the regulations governing them. The butchering of farm cattle is restricted.

The hog is the main supply of meat. In 1957 there were 3.5 million animals on the island. However, hog raisers have been faced recently with a shortage of protein feeds which cuts deeply into production.[9]

The chicken and duck population is well over 10 million head.

Fish. Fish production, which reached a prewar peak of 119,521 metric tons, dropped to 16,862 metric tons in 1945, then rose, as a result of intensive efforts and American aid, to 208,000 metric tons in 1957, and 229,000 metric tons in 1958. At the end of 1957 there were 3,500 powered fishing boats totalling 50,000 tons. In addition, there were 14,500 sampans and bamboo rafts engaged in fishing in 1957. There were approximately 260,000 people occupied in the industry at the end of 1956, including 120,000 casual fishermen. In 1957, the Taiwan Fisherman's Association had a total membership of 179,578. Projects include technical and financial help, improvement in refrigeration facilities, and training.[6]

The catch consists essentially of milk fish, sardines, and sharks (see Graph 2). It is distributed among various villages as shown on map No. 2, Keelung and Kaohsiung providing the great majority of the fish-manufactured products.[10] All sales are transacted through fish markets, located in 45 landing places and 35 other localities to which the fish has to be transported.

Fish culture. Fish culture or pond fishery has long been practiced in Taiwan. In 1955, the area given over to fish culture was 39,550 hectares, and production was 45,700 metric tons, or 25% of the total fish production in that year. Most of the fish culture ponds are in the south central part of the western coastal region. Fish culture is of two types: brackish water and fresh water. The latter covers the larger area but the former produces the larger quantities. Most of the brackish water fish culture concerns milk fish, a favorite with the Taiwan people. A large variety of fish is produced by fresh water culture. These consist essentially of silver carp, and other carp species.[6]

Other foods and fruit. Sweet potatoes are one of the staple foods of Taiwan, second only to rice in importance. The volume of production has a vital bearing on the raising of farm animals. The cultivated area in 1957 was 229,000 hectares and production 2.7 million metric tons. In 1958 this rose to over 2.9 million.[5]

Peanuts provide the principal source of edible oil. Peanut cake is also used as a substitute for the soybean as hog feed. An increase in peanut production would cut down the import of soybeans. The planted area in 1957 was 104,000 hectares and production 94,000 metric tons; it rose to 98,000 in 1958.[5]

Taiwan's demand for soybeans has been rising in recent years because of the increase in population and the increase number of hogs. In 1956, production was 26,000 metric tons from 37,000 hectares of cultivated land. This was raised to 33,000 metric tons in 1957, and

37,000 in 1958. Approximately 10,000 metric tons are imported each
year. It is hoped, however, that by increasing local production of
peanuts and soybeans, it will be possible to make a mixed hog feed
that will reduce the costly import of soybeans.[5]

Fresh fruit, essentially citrus, is grown for local consumption.
Orange production has been increasing steadily in the past years.
The 1956 volume was 35,000 metric tons, which were produced on
5,800 hectares. This rose to 39,000 metric tons in 1957, and 45,000
in 1958.[5]

Cash crops.   The sugar industry is 300 years old and has known
ups and downs due to the political vicissitudes of the island as well
as to the climate. The area in sugar cane has been kept in recent
years in the neighborhood of 90,000 hectares, normally producing
15,000 - 20,000 metric tons of brown sugar. The industry is under
the management of the Taiwan Sugar Corporation, 97% of which is
owned by the government, with total assets around U. S. $100 million.
The Taiwan Sugar Corporation draws its supply of cane both from
its own plantation and from contracted farmers, 30% and 70% respectively. Sugar is the most valuable export crop, accounting for 60%
of all foreign trade receipts in 1958.[9]   But the situation is not likely
to improve in view of increasing world production. The chart hereunder indicates the ups and downs of sugar production in the seven
years between 1950 and 1956.[10]

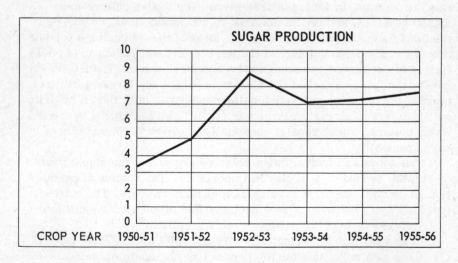

Exports of tea vary from year to year. Generally, 96% of the tea
produced is exported, though domestic consumption is on the rise. In
1956, 10.6 million kilograms were exported for a value of a little over
U. S. $5 million. In 1958 production rose to 17,000 metric tons. About
41,000 hectares are reported to be planted in tea, each hectare yielding approximately 339 kilos.[11]

Pineapples have been cultivated in Taiwan since 1654 but the canning industry began only in 1902. Although production fluctuates, it has been steadily on the increase. In 1956, over 1 million cases of canned pineapples are exported. Pineapple plantations occupy 9,000 hectares of land. In 1956, the total yield was 83,000 metric tons; in 1958 it rose to 124,000.[11]

Bananas are also a new resource in Taiwan's export trade bringing in around $4 million in 1957.[1,11]

Salt.[8]   Salt must also be mentioned, for it represents a bright possibility for export in the future. At present, not only are the domestic requirements of alimentary salt amply supplied, but there is also a large surplus available for export. The salt works are entirely owned by the central government which operates about 4,265 hectares of salt fields distributed in six groups of works, mainly in the southwest. These produce approximately 300,000 to 400,000 metric tons. Exports of salt have brought an income of $2 million a year, chiefly from Japan, where the future of Taiwan salt lies. In 1955, statistics show that the annual local consumption was 81,172 tons of which 73.2% was for use in the home, 22.7% for agricultural and industrial use, and 4% for use in the fishing industry.

Projects. A number of measures have been taken to increase the food resources of Taiwan. In 1957, there were five such measures:
1) increase in fertilizer supply;
2) production loans, made by the Food Bureau to farmers through the different farmers associations according to the size of each farm;
3) equipment loans, made to the farmers for the purpose of purchasing water pumps and constructing water conservation projects;
4) insecticides and pesticides, which the government has been importing in large amounts and allocating to the farmers free of cost;
5) subsidy for the construction of cement drying grounds and manure houses, to enable the farmers to dry their unhulled rice quickly after harvest and to avoid losses from germination.

It is yet too early to gauge the effects of these measures on food resources.

C. EXPORTS AND IMPORTS[5,1]

Food resources are also conditioned to a great degree by the import-export trade. As we have seen, Taiwan is not self-sufficient in food production, since it has to import fertilizers to produce enough cereals to supply a marginal ration to the population. Imports contributing to nutrition in the past years consisted essentially of fertilizers, beans, bean cakes, wheat and flour, peanut oil, milk and milk products, salted fish and livestock. These imports were mainly financed by United States aid and foreign exchange acquired through experts.

Fish and fish products, and agricultural products such as sugar,
some rice, bamboo shoots, salt, vegetables, dried fruits, bananas, tea,
and pineapples are exported and earn the money needed for the imports. Total exports in 1958 amounted to U. S. $164.4 million, a de-
crease of six per cent from 1957. Sugar and rice accounted for more
than two-thirds of the total earnings. Rice exports increased by
31%, to U. S. $29 million. Total imports amounted to U. S. $230.9
million in 1958, consumers' goods comprising 18% of them.[1]

D. FOOD INDUSTRIES, STORAGE AND TECHNOLOGY

There is little information on food storage, except that aid is being
given to farmers to build storage space and drying facilities. Not
much space is needed for storage since most of the food other than
cash crops is consumed locally.

The most important food processing industries are in flour, sugar,
tea, fish, and pineapples. There are around 7,000 food processing
plants. The wheat importing program has had a strong influence on
the availability of raw material for the flour milling industry. The
I. C. A., by financing importation of soybeans, likewise has provided
raw material for the food industry. A sizeable share of United States
aid has been devoted to building up the pineapple canning industry,
which is an important earner of foreign exchange. There were 56
small plants in 1955; a new plant is being establish on the east coast.
In addition, the Taiwan Sugar Corporation received assistance to
operate a yeast plant. Two small flour-mill projects and a sweet potato dehydration project also received United States assistance.[1]

There are 27 sugar mills with a total grinding capacity of 55,000
metric tons of cane. There are also six alcohol distilleries with a
daily capacity of 110,000 liters of alcohol.

Tea.   There are 315 primary tea processing plants in the producing areas.

Fish.   At the end of May 1957, there were 187 registered ice
plants with a total capacity of 1,921 metric tons per day. The annual consumption of ice in 1955 was estimated at 300,000 metric
tons, 60% of which went to the fishing industry.

Cold storage capacity at the end of May, 1955, totalled from 6,000
to 7,000 metric tons. Temperatures provided by the majority of the
storage plants are in the neighborhood of -5° centigrade. These temperatures are not suitable for the preservation of highly perishable
goods such as fish for an extended period of time.

The present freezing capacity throughout the island is about 60
metric tons per day and most of it is concentrated in the two municipalities of Keelung and Kaohsiung (see above). Most of the fisheries
products, except fish meal, fish oil, fish liver oil, canned fish, and a

small portion of the fish balls, are made in a primitive manner without the benefit of plant equipment and machinery. This industry is carried out here and there on a very small scale mostly by fishermen who catch the fish. Yet, the total output of manufactured fisheries products in 1957 had an estimated value of NT 263 millions (U. S. $65.7 million), of which boiled dried fish represented 44%; fish balls and cakes, 23%; dried shark fins, 3%; salted dried fish, 16%; fish oil and liver oil, 5%; canned fish, 3%; mullet roe, 2%; others, 4%.

Economic assistance. The United States Mutual Security Act for the fiscal year ending June 30, 1958 provided for an expenditure of U. S. $60 million. The following year it rose to U. S. $70 million, of which $31 million were earmarked for specific projects, mainly industries and communications, and $39 million essentially for agriculture.

In addition, five loans had been authorized at the end of the year by the United States government. These included $686,000 for improving the fishing fleet and $21.5 million for flood control, water supply, and hydroelectric power.

In addition, the United States was to make available $12.1 million worth of agricultural surpluses to Taiwan, the proceeds of these sales to be used locally.[1]

United States assistance to the fertilizer industry is second in magnitude to that directed towards industrial development. The purpose of the fertilizer program is to create local fertilizer plants to replace imported fertilizer and to improve existing plants. New plants such as Urea, Hualien Nitrochalk, and existing plants such as the Taiwan Fertilizer Corporation and the Kaohsiung Ammonium Sulphate Corporation were supported to the extent of U. S. $25.7 million and NT $195.4 million between 1951 and 1957.

III. DIET TYPES

Contrary to what happens on the mainland, where diets vary regionally, in Taiwan the diets are regionally rather uniform. Minor exceptions, however, are to be found among the aborigines (100,000) who eat potatoes, and a small group of northern Chinese refugees as well as "upper" class people who eat wheat and bread. It is estimated that these groups do not amount to more than 10% of the population.

On the other hand differences do exist between the mass of the agricultural population, the army, the school children, and the white collar workers in the towns, as shown by the test samples made in 1954 by Jolliffe[3] (see below). Twenty per cent of the population is urban, eighty per cent rural.

The troops stationed on the island suffer from a diet that is high enough in calories but low in protective nutrients. Multiple vitamin deficiencies among the troops range from severe to mild. The diets and the deficiencies that result vary, however, with the different units. The basic ration of cereals, soybeans, and oil is uniform for all the troops, but the system of local purchase causes significant differences in the diets of the units located in different garrisons. In general, however, the troops' diets are markedly deficient in fat, vitamin B-2, niacin, ascorbic acid, and calcium, with the result of signs of ariboflavinosis, and lack of vitamin A.[3]

School diets were inadequate in 1956 and probably still are. Some 26% of the total school population was suffering from malnutrition which the school health program was combatting with daily doses of cod liver oil.

The staple food of the population is rice of which each inhabitant has an average of 390 pounds a year. This is milled to 93% extraction and whitened with calcium carbonate. However, the custom is to wash the rice before cooking until the water is clear which leaves approximately 1 milligram of calcium for each gram of rice.

The chief subsidiary food is the sweet potato which is also used for fodder. In addition, the people enjoy a variety of tropical fruits, especially bananas, pineapples, citrus fruits, and watermelons denied to the Chinese of the mainland, although most of these are exported for cash. (Table 1 gives the list of calorie sources in the average diet; Table 2 gives the per capita consumption of nutrients.)

From these tables it is seen that to whatever group the people belong, they have sufficient energy value in their diet but lack animal protein and suffer from a number of vitamin and mineral shortages. Throughout the island, the calories come mainly from rice (53%), other grains (1%), and wheat (9.8%), giving a total of 63.8% coming from grain. Most of the animal protein of the diet comes from fish.

It was estimated in 1952 that the minimum per capita requirement of fish in a diet such as the one prevailing in Taiwan was 42 grams a day, and that the optimum should be placed as high as 84 grams. In order to provide such an intake, a total production of 300,000 metric tons would be required. In 1958, annual production reached 229,000 metric tons. This would give approximately 55 grams of fish per person per day if all the fish were consumed, which it is not. It can therefore be assumed that most of the population has approximately 40 to 45 grams of fish per day in its diet. Other animal protein comes from pork, but it is unlikely that the daily per capita consumption of this meat exceeds 10 grams. On the basis of caloric figures, as well as production figures available, it is possible to establish the average diet of the Taiwanese as shown in Tables 1, 2, and 4.

IV. ADEQUACY OF FOOD RESOURCES

From the above, it can be seen that the food resources of the island are inadequate. This inadequacy is due essentially to the everlasting Chinese problem of too many people on too little arable land, but also to factors that are proper to Taiwan. Many of the fields have been leached of plant nutrients through centuries of irrigation and heavy year-round cropping. This means that to maintain fertility, large quantities of fertilizer are needed, most of which is provided in the form of green manure crops, composts, night soil, and animal (mainly hog) manure. Most of these fertilizers do not exist on the island in adequate quantities and have to be imported and purchased with foreign currency; this, in turn, must be acquired by the sale of cash and subsistence crops.

Food resources are also jeopardized between May and November by severe typhoons. These bring strong winds and torrential downpours which can cause severe damage to crops, property, and man. Frequent earthquakes also constitute a hazard. During the 50 year period ending in 1954, for instance, the island suffered 8,000 shocks or an average of 170 a year. In 1959, torrential rains and an earthquake brought disaster to a quarter of a million people and caused as yet unevaluated damage to food resources.

V. NUTRITIONAL DISEASE PATTERNS

In 1954, Norman Jolliffe[3] made a well-sampled survey of the nutritional disease patterns in the population of Taiwan. School children, urban people, and rural people were examined. On the whole, he found no clinical and very little biochemical evidence of protein deficiency. Most of the deficiencies noted—and these were important— were in the fields of vitamins (see Tables 5 and 6).

Riboflavin deficiencies were found in an average of 70% of the population. Angular stomatitis was found to be present in 78% of the school children, in 67% of the citizens of the capital, Taipei, and in 82% of the rural population. In addition, there were other supportive findings of this deficiency, such as: magenta tongue, 5.5%; nasolabial seborrhea, 10.9%; and scleral vascularity, 11.4%. It was also found that this deficiency reaches a maximum at 15 years of age.

Niacin deficiency, although less common, was quite in evidence as shown by retinous hypertrophy, fissuring, and atrophy of the tongue. In the group of sixth-grade children, these symptoms were present in 16.8% of the cases; in the adult population of Taipei, 9%; and in the rural adult population, 18.5%. There was, however, very little evidence of skin symtoms of pellagra, but redness of the tongue and papillary lesions were the basis for an estimate that approximately 10% of the sixth-grade school children must have active niacin deficiencies.

Ascorbic acid deficiency was revealed by signs of gingivitis in approximately 30% of all people examined—school children, urban citizens and farmers. There were, however, no supporting clinical signs of these deficiencies. Thus it could be considered that the presence of the symptoms is not significant.

Vitamin A deficiency was found in 8.5% of the sixth-grade children, as shown by follicular hyperkerations, in 12.9% of the Taipei citizens, and in 7.2% of the farmers, and there was evidence that in 10% of the population, vitamin A deficiency is prevalent, mostly in school children.

Thiamine deficiency was revealed by the fact that 6% of the adults did not have normal ankle jerks, giving rise to the thought that there was neuropathy among these people strongly suggestive of beriberi. In general, it can be said that all children are underweight, under-height by American standards, and that no case of obesity was found among the adults. The above findings are summarized hereunder:

Riboflavin deficiencies 70%
Low excretion of urinary thiamine............... 60%
Anemia... 13%
Vitamin A deficiency................................. 10%
Niacin deficiency....................................... 10%
Hypoproteinemia ....   3.2% (for the
                                        whole population but 6% in the adults.)

It was suggested at the time that an increased consumption of sweet potatoes, papayas, and yellow-leaf vegetables so common in the island would considerably relieve this situation at low cost.

VI. CONCLUSIONS

From the above, it can be stated that Taiwan's future nutritional trends will be profoundly affected by the continuance or discontinuance of American aid, and by such factors as the freedom of sea communications and the availability of foreign exchange. Increased production depends upon improving yields rather than on reclaiming new lands, and the problem of keeping pace with the increase in population is serious and as yet unresolved.

SELECTED REFERENCES

1. China Yearbook 1957-1958. Taipei, China Publishing Co., 1958.
2. Food and Agriculture Organization. Yearbook of Production, Vol. 12, 1958.
3. Joliffe, Norman. Nutrition Status Survey of the Civilian Population of Taiwan. October, 1955.
4. Raper, F. A., Chuan Han-sheng, and Chen Shao-hsing. Urban and Industrial Taiwan - Crowded and Resourceful. Taipei, Foreign Operations Administration Mutual Security Mission to China and National Taiwan University, September, 1954.
5. Republic of China, Ministry of Economic Affairs. The Economy of Taiwan, Republic of China. 1958.
6. Republic of China, Ministry of Economic Affairs. Fisheries of Taiwan, Republic of China. 1958.
7. Republic of China, Ministry of Economic Affairs. The Fertilizer Industry in Taiwan, Republic of China. 1958.
8. Republic of China, Ministry of Economic Affairs. Salt Industry in Taiwan, Republic of China. 1958.
9. Republic of China. New Spirit in Agriculture in Taiwan. Taipei, June, 1958.
10. Republic of China, Ministry of Economic Affairs. The Sugar Industry in Taiwan, Republic of China. 1958.
11. Republic of China, Ministry of Economic Affairs. Tea, Banana, Pineapple. 1958.
12. Shen, T. H. Crop Improvement and Production in Taiwan. Ninth Pacific Science Congress, November 18-30, 1957. Bangkok, 1957.
13. United States Department of Commerce, World Trade Information Service. Economic Developments in Taiwan (Formosa) 1958. *Economic Reports, Part 1, No. 59-60,* 1959.

Table 1

Calories Consumed per Capita per Day: Percentage Distribution by Food Groups for 12 Far Eastern Countries and the United States

Food	Burma	Ceylon	Mainland China	India	Indonesia	Japan	Malaya	Pakistan	Philippines	South Korea	Taiwan	Thailand	United States
	%	%	%	%	%	%	%	%	%	%	%	%	%
Rice	72.3	43.3	40.5	33.6	45.6	46.5	44.5	43.1	41.3	54.4	53.0	72.6	0.7
Wheat	.7	10.9	13.8	9.6	.6	14.0	7.4	18.4	3.5	6.8	9.8	.3	18.8
Millet, maize, barley, etc.	2.2	3.0	20.3	20.4	11.9	9.4	1.1	6.7	15.9	17.5	.1	.3	3.5
Dry beans and peas	2.5	3.9	5.3	11.4	1.2	1.6	2.0	4.2	1.3	1.3	.9	.3	1.2
Roots, tubers & starches	.5	3.3	3.8	3.0	18.2	6.9	2.5	.8	6.4	3.8	13.0	.2	3.0
Sugar	4.7	7.6	.8	6.3	4.0	6.4	9.5	8.3	6.2	1.7	6.7	2.7	15.6
Oilseeds (incl. soybeans & peanuts)	2.0	.2	4.4	1.0	1.8	4.3	1.8	—	.5	3.6	4.6	1.1	1.0
Oils and fats (excl. oilseeds and butter)	5.8	3.8	4.8	3.5	4.3	3.4	9.8	2.0	4.1	1.0	3.5	3.9	13.7
Vegetables	1.3	1.0	.9	.8	3.2	2.3	1.7	1.5	.7	2.4	1.8	1.5	2.6
Fruit & nuts (incl. coconuts)	2.3	17.8	.9	2.3	6.2	.9	8.9	3.8	13.8	1.0	.9	11.0	4.1
Meat, fish, poultry & eggs	3.9	3.4	4.5	.6	2.5	3.4	7.3	2.5	5.1	5.8	5.0	4.7	19.2
Milk & dairy prod. (incl. butter)	1.8	1.8	—	7.5	.5	.9	3.5	8.7	1.2	.7	.7	1.4	16.6
Grand total	100.0	100.0	100.0	100.0	100.0	100.0	100.0	100.0	100.0	100.0	100.0	100.0	100.0
Number of calories	2,020	2,065	1,830	2,030	2,020	2,295	2,555	1,980	2,170	2,060	2,285	2,065	3,070

Source: Foreign Agriculture, June 1958. Derived from Food Balances, Consumption Year 1955-56, for Countries in South Asia, East Asia, and Oceania, Foreign Agricultural Service, U. S. Dept. of Agriculture. U. S. data are for the year 1954 and are derived from Food Balance sheets, second issue, FAO. 1955.

Table 2

Per Capita Food Consumption in Taiwan

Rice	340 grams a day providing	1,200 cal.
Wheat	66 " " "	225 "
Fish	45 " " "	70 "
Pork	10 " " "	44 "
Sweet potatoes	245 " " "	298 "
Sugar	40 " " "	150 "
Soybeans	30 " " "	105 "
Oils and vegetable fats	8 " " "	76 "
Milk, veg. peas	? " " "	77 "
Misc.	? " " "	40 "
	784 "	2,285 "

Source: Computed from data in Table 1.

Table 3

Food Production 1952-1958

Indices of Agricultural Production During the First Four-Year Plan Period as Compared with Base Year 1952

Crop	1952	1953	1954	1955	1956	1957	1958
1. Rice							
Hectares	785,729	778,384	776,660	750,739	783,629	783,000	--
Production (Metric tons)	1,570,115	1,641,557	1,695,107	1,614,953	1,789,829	1,833,500	1,890,000
Kg. per ha.	1,998	2,109	2,183	2,151	2,284	2,290	--
2. Sweet potato							
Hectares	233,502	237,788	247,551	245,513	230,236	229,000	--
Production (Metric tons)	2,090,463	2,276,942	2,556,823	2,437,443	2,568,104	2,693,000	2,930,000
Kg. per ha.	8,953	9,576	10,328	9,928	11,154	11,800	--
3. Peanut							
Hectares	80,975	82,590	94,025	96,034	98,257	104,000	--
Production (Metric tons)	60,037	60,104	65,868	66,572	81,847	94,000	98,000
Kg. per ha.	741	728	701	693	833	900	--
4. Wheat							
Hectares	14,582	13,506	11,089	12,843	15,615	20,000	--
Production (Metric tons)	16,604	14,288	15,493	19,304	27,099	36,000	39,000
Kg. per ha.	1,139	1,058	1,397	1,503	1,736	1,810	--
5. Soybean							
Hectares	24,315	28,225	30,048	34,510	37,505	41,000	--
Production (Metric tons)	14,627	17,426	20,310	24,151	26,442	33,000	37,000
Kg. per ha.	602	617	676	700	705	810	--
6. White sugar							
Hectares	95,703	108,351	93,256	76,374	87,753	--	--
Production (Metric tons)	520,453	882,141	701,155	733,160	767,328	--	894,000
Kg. per ha.	6,720	8,955	8,195	10,490	9,451	--	--

7. Brown sugar							
Hectares	3,724	4,963	3,140	2,703	3,957	--	--
Production (Metric tons)	8,007	19,022	11,828	14,832	19,536	20,000	--
Kg. per ha.	2,375	3,833	4,046	5,015	5,415	--	--
8. Tea							
Hectares	44,120	44,655	46,186	47,000	47,638	41,000	--
Production (Metric tons)	11,582	11,903	13,007	14,680	13,420	13,900	17,000
Kg. per ha.	261	267	282	312	282	339	--
9. Pineapple							
Hectares	5,849	5,670	5,489	5,671	6,441	--	9,000
Production (Metric tons)	62,760	68,471	65,567	70,537	83,065	99,060	124,000
Kg. per ha.	10,731	12,076	11,945	12,437	12,896	--	--
10. Banana							
Hectares	17,092	16,492	16,243	14,824	13,596	11,000	--
Production (Metric tons)	106,856	96,101	98,008	84,677	72,968	92,000	105,000
Kg. per ha.	6,819	5,827	6,033	5,712	5,366	8,200	--
11. Citrus							
Hectares	4,611	4,763	4,831	5,246	5,808	--	--
Production (Metric tons)	27,770	29,357	27,755	30,235	35,332	39,000	45,000
Kg. per ha.	6,022	6,164	5,742	5,763	6,083	--	--
12. Citronella oil							
Hectares	25,922	24,222	19,790	13,890	15,000	--	--
Production (Metric tons)	2,561	2,527	1,779	1,304	1,530	--	--
Kg. per ha.	99	104	90	94	102	--	--

Source: Shen, T. H.: Crop Improvement and Production in Taiwan. Ninth Pacific Science Congress, Nov. 18-30, 1957, Bangkok, Thailand.
Data for 1957 and 1958 derived from Food and Agriculture Organization Production Yearbook.

Table 4

Per Capita Consumption of Nutrients

Food Energy	1935-39 1865 Calories	1940-44 1700 Calories	1952 2130 Calories	1957 2285 Calories
Protein	45 Gm. (15 Gm. animal)	35 Gm. (8 Gm. animal)	50 Gm. (12 Gm. animal)	58.9 Gm. (12 Gm. animal)
Fat	35 "	19 "	36 "	28 "
Carbohydrate	339 "	342 "	395 "	388 "
Calcium	255 mg.	180 mg.	233 mg.	219 mg.
Phosphorus	791 "	583 "	888 "	987 "
Iron	7.98 mg.	6.37 mg.	8.64 mg.	14.6 mg.
Vitamin A	6,390 I.U.	5,025 I.U.	4,300 I.U.	12,500 I.U.
Thiamine	1.06 mg.	0.85 mg.	1.14 mg.	1.17 mg.
Riboflavin	0.53 "	0.37 "	0.48 "	0.70 "
Niacin	15.61 "	14.69 "	17.73 "	13.7 "
Ascorbic Acid	119 "	95 "	91 "	? "
Sugar Consumption	15 to 17 lbs. per capita per year			

Note: The figures for 1957 are the result of a computation from the amount of food consumption known and not from a sample study. As a result, these figures are likely to be too low since many foods such as fruit, spices, etc. are not part of the computation.
Source: Joint Commission for Rural Reconstruction – Food and Fertilizer Division – Taipei, 1958 – Mimeog. sheet.

Table 5

Clinical Findings in Sixth Grade Children in Taiwan, 1954

	Chung-San Taipei		In-Kuo Rural		Nai-Hoo Rural		Heng Zing Rural		Lu-Chow Rural		Totals M		Totals F		Grand Total	
	M	F	M	F	M	F	M	F	M	F	No.	%	No.	%	No.	%
Number	100	150	161	138	75	55	68	45	127	100	531	100	488	100	1,019	100
Obesity	0	0	0	0	0	0	0	0	0	0	0	0	0	0	0	0
Nasial Labial Seborrhoea	6	26	22	18	9	0	2	13	6	7	45	8.5	64	13.1	109	10.9
Scleral Vascularity	4	4	16	23	11	10	6	13	15	15	52	9.8	65	13.1	117	11.4
Obvious Photophobia	2	0	9	1	0	1	0	1	0	0	11	2.0	3	0.6	14	1.3
Scleral Spots	20	8	51	13	19	9	15	5	20	11	125	23.5	46	9.4	171	16.6
Angular Stomatitis	71	96	144	115	65	31	46	33	110	87	436	82.2	362	74.2	798	78.0
Angular Scars only	5	14	9	3	4	7	4	4	12	8	34	6.4	37	7.6	71	6.9
Magenta Tongue	0	3	13	23	3	2	4	0	5	3	25	4.7	31	6.3	56	5.5
Reddened Tongue	14	10	16	20	9	13	6	9	9	10	54	10.1	72	14.7	126	12.4
Papillary Lesions	15	13	44	38	10	4	9	4	12	28	83	15.6	87	17.8	170	16.8
Gums – All lesions	41	63	140	114	61	24	29	21	86	59	357	62.2	281	57.5	638	62.5
Marginal Gingivitis	14	36	74	56	28	9	21	13	38	24	175	33.1	138	28.3	313	30.7
Perifolliculosis	1	0	1	0	0	0	0	0	0	0	2	0.3			2	–
Follicular hyperkeratosis	13	20	19	12	4	6	5	3	10	5	41	7.7	46	9.4	87	8.5
Absent Ankle jerks	0	0	0	1	0	0	0	0	0	0	0	–	1	–	1	–
Xerosis Cutis	0	0	0	16	5	1	2	0	0	0	7	1.3	17	3.5	24	2.3
Trachoma	35	34	50	30	17	14	16	13	39	25	157	30.8	116	23.8	273	27.4
No. eye exam.	21	2									21		2		23	

Source: Jolliffe, N.: Nutrition Status Survey of the Civilian Population of Taiwan. October, 1955.

Table 6

Clinical Findings in Other Than Sixth Grade Children in Taiwan, 1954

	1st Grade Nai-Hoo		9th Grade In-Kuo		12th Grade High School		Normal College		Adults Wan Haw Market	
Number	No. 71	% 100	No. 50	% 100	No. 95	% 100	No. 91	% 100	No. 107	% 100
Obesity	0	0	0	0	0	0	0		9	8.4
Nasial Labial Seborrhoea	0	0	18	36	91	96	33	36.4	40	37.5
Scleral Vascularity	11	15.5	12	24	6	6.3	0		32	29.9
Obvious Photophobia	1	0	7	14	0		1		2	
Scleral Spots	4	5.6	15	30	12	12.7	16	17.6	65	60.7
Angular Stomatitis	49	69.0	43	86	37	39.0	42	46.1	62	58.1
Angular Scars	1	1.4	4	8	47	49.4	44	48.4	31	29.0
Magenta Tongue	0	0	12	24	0		1		21	19.7
Reddened Tongue	4	5.6	8	16	12	12.7	10	11.0	6	5.6
Papillary Lesions	2	2.8	30	60	6	6.3	10	11.0	42	39.2
Gums - All Lesions	25	35.1	44	88	42	44.1	55	60.5	82	76.7
Marginal Gingivitis	12	18.7	17	34	21	22.1	14	15.3	24	22.5
Peri-folliculosis	0	0	0	0	3	3.1	2	2.9	0	0
Follicular hyperkeratosis	0	0	1	2	4	4.2	2	2.9	16	15.0
Absent Ankle Jerks	0	0	0	0	0		2	2.2	6	5.6
Xerosis Cutis	1	0	0	0	0				14	13.1
Trachoma	10	14.0	15	30	26	27.4	28	30.6	not done	

Source: Jolliffe, N.: Nutrition Status Survey of the Civilian Population of Taiwan, October, 1955.

Table 7

Crops	Harvest Period	Bulk of Harvest
Wheat	Beg. Jan.-Mid May	Beg. Feb.-Beg. May
Rice:		
First crop of the double paddy crop	Mid Apr.-End Aug.	Mid May-End July
Second crop of the double paddy crop	Mid Sept.-Late Dec.	Late Oct.-Beg. Dec.
Spring planted single· paddy crop	Beg. Mar.-Late Sept.	Late Apr.-Mid Aug.
Fall planted single paddy crop	Mid Sept.-Late Dec.	Mid Sept.-Mid Dec.
Spring planted upland rice	Beg. Apr.-Late Aug.	Late Apr.-Beg. Aug.
Fall planted upland rice	Late July-Beg. Dec.	Late Aug.-Late Nov.
Intermediate rice	Beg. Sept.-Late Dec.	Mid Oct.-Mid Nov.
Sugar cane:		
Early planting	Beg. Dec.-Beg. May	Late Dec.-Mid Mar.
Late planting	Beg. Dec.-Late May	Beg. Jan.-Mid Apr.
Ratoon sugar cane	Beg. Dec.-Beg. May	Beg. Jan.-Mid Mar.
Sweet potatoes:		
Spring planted	Late Apr.-Late Dec.	Mid May-Beg. Dec.
Fall planted	Mid Sept.-Beg. July	Mid Nov.-Beg. June
Cabbage	Beg. Oct-Mid June	Beg. Nov.-Late Mar.
Radish	Beg. Aug.-Mid June	Beg. Oct.-Late Feb.
Peas	Mid Nov.-Late Apr.	Mid Dec.-Mid Mar.
Ponkan Mandarin Oranges	Beg. Sept.-Beg. Feb.	Mid Oct.-Beg. Jan.
Tonkan Mandarin Oranges	Mid Oct.-Late Mar.	Late Nov.-Late Feb.
Bananas	Mid Jan.-Late Dec.	Beg. Mar.-Mid Sept.
Pineapples	Beg. Apr.-Late Nov.	Mid June-Beg. Sept.
Groundnuts:		
Spring planted	Late Apr.-Beg. Nov.	Late May-Late Sept.
Fall planted	Beg. Oct.-Late Mar.	Late Oct.-Beg. Mar.
Soybeans:		
Spring planted	Late Apr.-Late Nov.	Mid May-Late Oct.
Fall planted	Late Dec.-Mid June	Mid Jan.-Late Mar.
Sesame seed	Mid May-Late Sept.	Beg. June-Beg. Sept.
Tea:		
First harvest	Late Feb.-Beg. June	Beg. Apr.-Beg. June
Second harvest	Beg. May-Late Aug.	Beg. June-Mid July
Third harvest	Late July-Beg. Nov.	Late Aug.-Mid Oct.
Fourth harvest	Late Sept.-Late Dec.	Beg. Oct.-Late Nov.
Tobacco	Beg. Nov.-Late Mar.	Beg. Jan.-Mid. Feb.
Jute	Beg. June-Mid Oct.	Beg. July-Mid Sept.
Kenaf	Mid June-Late Oct.	Mid July-Beg. Sept.
Citronella:		
First harvest	Beg. Feb.-Mid July	Mid Feb.-Late June
Second harvest	Beg. May-Late Oct.	Beg. June-Beg. Oct.
Third harvest	Beg. Aug.-Late Dec.	Beg. Sept.-End Nov.
Fourth harvest	Beg. Nov.-Late Dec.	Mid Nov.-Mid Dec.
Sesbania:		
Spring planted	Late May-Beg. Dec.	Mid June-Beg. Dec.
Fall - Winter planted	Mid Dec.-Late Aug.	Beg. Jan.-Beg. July

Source: Food and Agriculture Organization World Crop Harvest Calendar, Rome, 1959.

Map 1

TAIWAN (FORMOSA)   **AGRICULTURAL REGIONS**

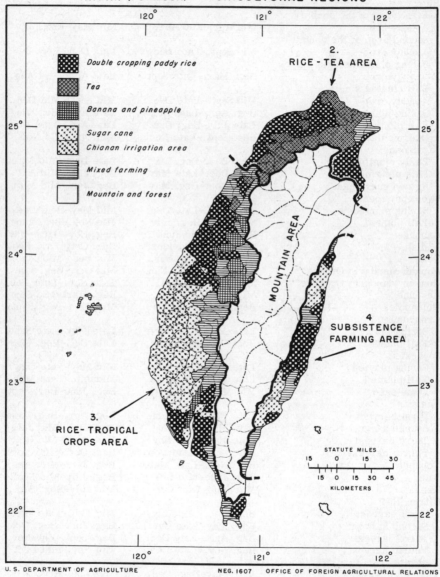

Double cropping paddy rice

Tea

Banana and pineapple

Sugar cane
Chianan irrigation area

Mixed farming

Mountain and forest

2.
RICE - TEA AREA

I. MOUNTAIN AREA

4
SUBSISTENCE
FARMING AREA

3.
RICE - TROPICAL
CROPS AREA

STATUTE MILES
15   0   15   30
15   0   15   30   45
KILOMETERS

U. S. DEPARTMENT OF AGRICULTURE   NEG. 1607   OFFICE OF FOREIGN AGRICULTURAL RELATIONS

Map 2

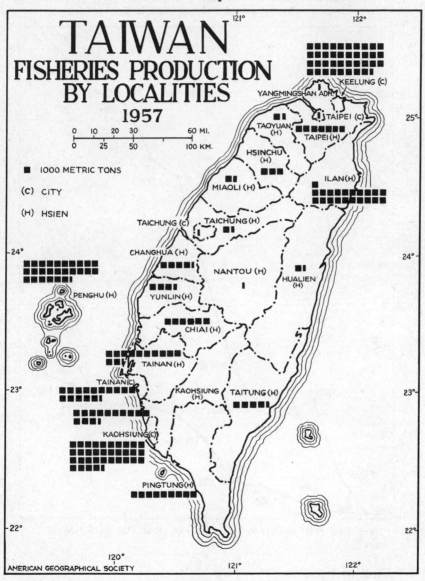

TAIWAN
FISHERIES PRODUCTION
BY LOCALITIES
1957

0   10   20   30   60 MI.

0   25   50   100 KM.

■ 1000 METRIC TONS

(C) CITY

(H) HSIEN

KEELUNG (C)

YANGMINGSHAN ADM.

TAIPEI (C)

TAOYUAN (H)

TAIPEI (H)

HSINCHU (H)

ILAN (H)

MIAOLI (H)

TAICHUNG (C)   TAICHUNG (H)

CHANGHUA (H)

NANTOU (H)

HUALIEN (H)

PENGHU (H)

YUNLIN (H)

CHIAI (H)

TAINAN (H)

TAINAN (C)

KAOHSIUNG (H)

TAITUNG (H)

KAOHSIUNG (C)

PINGTUNG (H)

AMERICAN GEOGRAPHICAL SOCIETY

Graph 1

A Comparison Between Production & Consumption of Chemical Fertilizer in Taiwan Since 1945

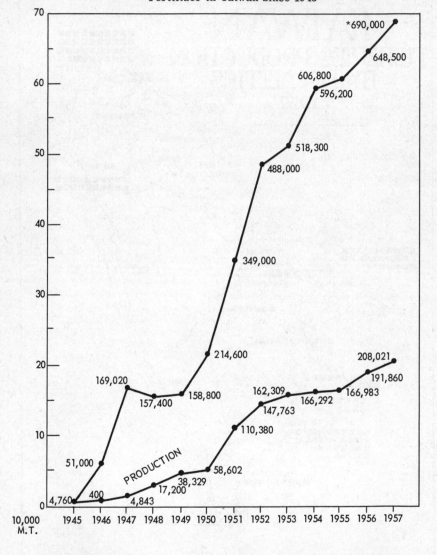

*Estimated Figure.

Source: Republic of China: <u>The Fertilizer Industry in Taiwan, Republic of China</u>. Ministry of Economic Affairs, 1958.

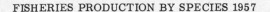

Graph 2

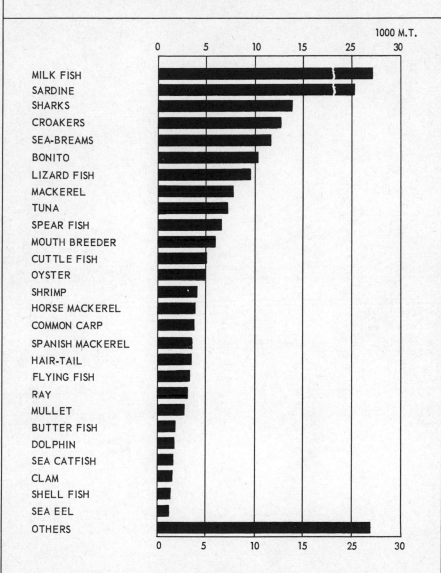

FISHERIES PRODUCTION BY SPECIES 1957

1000 M.T.

MILK FISH
SARDINE
SHARKS
CROAKERS
SEA-BREAMS
BONITO
LIZARD FISH
MACKEREL
TUNA
SPEAR FISH
MOUTH BREEDER
CUTTLE FISH
OYSTER
SHRIMP
HORSE MACKEREL
COMMON CARP
SPANISH MACKEREL
HAIR-TAIL
FLYING FISH
RAY
MULLET
BUTTER FISH
DOLPHIN
SEA CATFISH
CLAM
SHELL FISH
SEA EEL
OTHERS

Source: Republic of China: The Fisheries of Taiwan, Republic of China. Ministry of Economic Affairs, 1958.

VIETNAM

I. GENERAL REMARKS

South Vietnam, located between 8° 30' N. and 17° N. covers 170,857 square kilometers (65,968 square miles) and had a population estimated at more than 13,200,000 at the beginning of 1957. This population includes 2,754,000 urban people, of which 1,800,000 live in the teeming Saigon Cholon area, and 10,500 rural people. Discounting the 800,000 refugees from the northern zone that swelled the population in 1955, the annual growth according to local sources amounts to 750,000 a year, or 5-6% (as compared to Ceylon's 2.8% and India's 3%), a very high rate that makes it mandatory to find new food resources.*

The country is, and always has been, essentially agricultural. Among the many problems besetting the present government, the reestablishment of internal security is foremost. A state of armed truce exists between North Vietnam ruled by a Communist regime, and South Vietnam where a paternalistic dictatorship with democratic tendencies is in office. The government of South Vietnam is extensively assisted by American foreign aid, which provides 60% of the budget.

With the help of American experts a vast program of agrarian reforms designed to increase food production as well as to develop democratic institutions was started in 1957. Unfortunately, the program is constantly handicapped by the terrorist activities rampant in several provinces. It is clear that the effectiveness of the program is also jeopardized by the huge budgetary appropriations for national defense made necessary by the political situation. In a country where land tenure offered no security to the farmer, where rent was as high as 50 or 70% of the harvest, and where agricultural financing was in the hands of money lenders at rates as high as 100% a year, a good program of agrarian reform was overdue. The four basic goals of agrarian reform are: (a) To improve standards of living on the farm by guaranteeing land tenure for at least 5 consecutive years and limiting rent to 25% of the harvest; (b) To rehabilitate all the land that had been abandoned during years of civil strife and unrest;

---

*Other sources reduce this growth to 3% a year.

(c) To place a limit on rice-field ownership in order to force wealthy landowners to sell their surplus land to the government, which then parcels it out to landless peasants in 12-acre lots; and (d) To involve the former landlords in the national economy by inducing them to re-invest the amount received for their land in several state-owned or state-supported industrial enterprises.[2]

Along with the measures needed to implement this program, the official policy is to add to the traditional pillars of Vietnamese society, namely family and communal living, a third pillar - cooperative organization. It is easily understood that the scope of all food-producing programs involved in this three-pillared policy depends to a large extent on internal security.

With the exception of Taiwan, no other Asian country has received and is currently receiving more American aid than Vietnam. This factor must be kept in mind when evaluating the country's future food resources.

II. FOOD RESOURCES [*8,11,15]

A. GENERAL

The food resources in 1960 are estimated to originate on 3.2 million hectares, an increase of approximately 10% over 1957. This cultivated area is 15 to 19% of the total surface of the country and is mainly found in the south and central lowlands. In these districts, the agricultural population reaches densities of 86-89 per square kilometer (223 to 331 per square mile); 2,169 of the total 4,000 villages of the country are also located here. In the central highlands, however, the density of the population drops to 28 per square mile. Table 1 shows production and consumption figures for rice, the dominant food produced; sugar cane and tubers are poor second and third.

B. RICE

Rice is cultivated on some 3.1 million hectares distributed essentially in the south (see Map I). It is also found almost continuously in the narrow coastal strip up to the 17th parallel. Unfortunately, the rice fields are uneconomically distributed and parcels are too small for effective mechanization, as is indicated by the space (3%) taken up by the unproductive levees between properties. The average yield is about 1.5 metric tons per hectare, while certain areas of intense cultivation reach 2.1 tons with a hopeful target of 2.5 to be obtained in the

---

*Tons = Metric tons

near future. This is still low if compared to the 4 tons per hectare produced in northern Italy, for instance. It is true, however, that some progressive rice farmers using improved seed and fertilizers are growing 2 crops on the same plot of land and thus get a yield of 5 tons per hectare.[16]

The figures in Table I show a total output of 4.5 million tons in 1959-1960. This represents the product of the total harvested area including roads, dykes, and residential lots rather than the arable land used for production. The areas include double counting for double-cropping (1 hectare on which 2 crops are grown is counted as 2 hectares). Most of the land in central Vietnam is doubled-cropped. American experts have rectified downward the official Vietnamese figures for rice cultivation and production given in Table I.[15] The rectified figures give 3,010 metric tons from 2,261,000 hectares in 1956; 2,851 metric tons from 2,425,000 hectares in 1957; and 3,200 metric tons from 2,450,000 hectares in 1958.

American aid has contributed much since 1957 to the improvement of rice production. A rice station has been created at Mytho where the best of 750 strains of seeds are selected and the inferior ones discarded. Vietnamese provincial rice agents educate the farmers on the use of seeds. The objective of the program is to select and develop one or two of the good varieties of each main rice type produced in Vietnam: the long, the medium, and the short grain. About 1000 tons of seeds, enough to cultivate 20,000 hectares, will be distributed to farmers in 1960.

C. OTHER EDIBLE CROPS

Roots and tubers. Roots and tubers are not, as a rule, part of the Vietnamese diet. Yams and cassava together are not grown on more than 65,000 hectares (Table II). This area has increased in the last 3 years, from 49.9 thousand hectares in 1956 to 62.5 thousand in 1958 and 65 thousand in 1960, the yield has improved to an estimated 350,000 tons in 1959-1960 from 244 thousand tons in 1956.

Other vegetables. The consumption of vegetables, which was almost negligible up to 1954, has become more popular since refugees from the north have brought garden culture to the south. Vast tracts have been created around Dalt (altitude, 6,000 feet), where the climate favors temperate-zone agriculture, and to some extent around Saigon, to meet the increasing needs of the mushrooming population. The development of the vegetable crops has outstripped the demand and export outlets are being sought by the Commerce Department until the taste of the general public has caught up with the crops.

Fruit. Fruit resources have always been abundant in Vietnam, especially in the north. It is estimated that 33,000 hectares, an increase of 7,000 over 1957, are planted in fruit trees. The increase is

an expression of the influence of northern agriculture on the southern.
The production of the fruit trees is estimated at 210,000 tons in 1959-
1960, an increase of nearly 30,000 over 1957-1958. These figures do
not include the large amount of wild fruits, especially mangoes and
bananas, of which the population makes abundant use. The pineapple
production alone covers 6,000 hectares, an increase of 2,229 over
1957-1958, with a production of 48,000 tons.

Sugar. Sugar-cane fields covered 27,000 hectares in 1959, a reduction from 31,000 in 1957, with local production dropping from
869,890 metric tons in 1957 to 800,000 tons in 1960, possibly a result
of the insecurity prevailing in the cane-producing areas. The sugar
crop is not adequate to meet the needs of the population and Vietnam
has to import sugar. Local production includes two types: the white,
refined sugar prepared by the Hiep Hoa Company both from local and
imported raw material; and the brown sugar produced in local mills
reporting to the Department of Finance. Many small mills do not pay
taxes and their small production is unknown, though it is estimated at
10,000 tons a year. Consumption figures given in Table 2 include this
estimate.

Three-fourths of the sugar consumption in Vietnam is in the southern provinces, probably due to the higher proportion of urban population there.

Other cash crops. Vietnam is a producer of spices: mustard,
pepper, and cinnamon are cultivated in fluctuating amounts. Most of
the cinnamon production is concentrated in central Vietnam (Quang
Ngai and Quang Nam) and most of its is exported, leaving only 100
tons a year for local consumption.

Copra is also produced in Vietnam where every thousand coconuts
yield an average of 175 kilos of copra. The bulk of Vietnamese copra
is processed locally for soap production. In 1959 the total output
dropped to 16,500 tons.

Tea and coffee are also grown. The products are of high quality
but so far have conquered the taste of a limited clientele. The area
under cultivation is more or less the same from year to year, covering from 12,000 to 15,000 hectares and producing 3,500 metric tons of
tea and 2,500 tons of coffee.

In 1960, the American aid mission plans to contribute cocoa seeds
to help develop this crop in Vietnam. The planting of cocoa beans was
tried before the war and is now being resumed on a large-scale. The
prospects are particularly bright in view of the cancer-like blight that
has attacked African trees in recent years. Since 1958, the American
aid mission has introduced 480,000 disease-free seeds from Malaya;
after germination these will be distributed to land-development centers
and private planters.

D. FATS

Resources in vegetable fats come mainly from groundnuts and coconuts. Areas of production of groundnuts have grown from 24,200 hectares in 1957-1958 to 35,000 in 1959-1960, reflecting the desire of the government to bring the country to self-sufficiency. Simultaneously, production in the same crop has risen from somewhat over 16,000 tons to 23,800 tons. Animal fat comes exclusively from pork.

E. NUOC MAM AND SOYA SAUCES[9]

A description of the food resources of Vietnam should include "nuoc mam" and soya sauces. "Nuoc mam," literally "fishwater," is a national condiment that plays an important part in Vietnamese nutrition and economy. Although all countries of Southeast Asia have their favorite fish sauce, none is as important to the consumer as nuoc mam is to the Vietnamese. The product is the result of the maceration of salt and fish into a brine. It is added to all soups and dishes and is found on all tables at all times. Nuoc mam fish are carefully selected and belong mainly to the families **Carangidae decapterus** ("Ca-Huc") or Clypeidae ("Ca-Noi"). Nuoc mam is important because of its nitrogen and salt contents, as shown in Table 3. Approximately 50 grams of this substance is consumed per capita per day in Vietnam.

Soya sauces are used to a lesser degree. The sauces supply amino acids to the diet in amounts ranging from 7 to 12 grams per liter, a concentration somewhat higher than the average nuoc mam. It is also contended that these sauces contain thiamin, of which only traces are found in nuoc mam. It is estimated that 10 to 20 cubic centimeters of the soya sauces are consumed per capita per day.

F. ANIMAL PROTEIN RESOURCES[15]

Cattle and buffalo. The cattle and buffalo herds particularly have suffered during the war years, the number of head being reduced by an estimated 50 to 60%. Since 1956, however, an improvement of some magnitude is said to have taken place. The problem of maintaining animals for slaughter is a difficult one in Vietnam. In the lowlands, paddy fields have first priority in land use, while in the higher regions the climate does not favor the development of pastures, for the dry season lasts 5 months of the year and during the other 7 months, the downpours erode the land. The capital needed to create and maintain animal husbandry is not available, and there is no tradition of cattle raising for food; the Vietnamese consider cattle to be animals of burden. The land animals used in the daily fare are chiefly

pigs and fowl, as shown in Table 5. The exact number of cattle slaughtered and consumed is difficult to assess because of the large amount
of clandestine slaughtering that must take place. Thus, figures given
in Table 5 must be considered a low estimate.

The population of cattle and buffalo is concentrated in the south
and central lowlands. In recent years, 25 animal-improvement centers have been created, the most important of which are at Tan Son
Nhut, Bien Hoa, Ninh Thuan, M'Drack, and a milk farm at Bien Cat,
in Binh Duong Province. Animal husbandry is up against a lack of
knowledge of animal hygiene and the recurrence of bovine plague,
which causes regular epizootics (the last in 1956). The country has
only 35 veterinarians. An international organization destined to fight
bovine plague in Vietnam, Thailand, Cambodia, and Laos has been
created under the sponsorship of the Food and Agriculture Organization and the International Cooperation Administration. Under their
auspices, animal hygiene is making some progress. A National Institute of Microbiology has been endowed which had produced 5 million
doses of the vaccines currently needed by the end of 1958; in 1959 this
output was raised to 1.2 million doses and 324,000 animals were
inoculated.

Hogs. The main source of meat is supplied by the rather large
population of hogs, but these yield more fat than valuable animal protein. Unlike the cattle, the hogs have made good the losses of the
civil war years, the present population standing well above 2 million
head. Official sources given the number of hogs killed for meat at
929,000 in 1957, but local authors believe it to be as high as 1,250,000.

Chickens and ducks. Chickens and ducks are seen all over the
countryside. The number of chickens is estimated to be around 6 million and the number of ducks over 43 million (Table 5). The total con-
sumable egg production is estimated at 146,800,000 per year. With
the exception of the Tan Son Nhut experimental station, no modern
poultry farm exists in the country and all the chicken-egg production
results from farmers keeping a few hens scratching the ground for a
living around the house. As a result, each hen produces only 60 to
70 eggs not exceeding 45 grams in weight per year. Since 1956 an effort has been made to improve this source of protein through the
yearly import of 150,000 chickens and 50,000 chicken and duck eggs
from improved breeds. Vietnamese are fond of incubated eggs. It is
estimated that 2 million such eggs are sold annually, the chicken eggs
being incubated up to the 14th or 15th day while the duck eggs are incubated up to the 18th or 20th day. The incubation is done with locally
built incubators, heated with charcoal or paddy grist. Vietnamese
specialists test the temperature of the egg by contact with the eyelids.
Oriental medicine ascribes great nutritional value to these eggs, a
notion that was confirmed by certain Western analysts (Bunge and
Brion, quoted by Le Thuoc)[7]. Because of the relatively small number

and high price of these eggs, their consumption makes little impact
on the over-all nutritional picture.

Milk. Milk resources and consumption are low in Vietnam, because of the traditional disgust against milk originating in the Chinese
culture; the small amount produced by local herds; and the poor quality of the milk. Imported milk is available - 22,000 tons of condensed
milk were imported in 1959 - but its high price is prohibitive for extensive use. According to LeThuoc,[7] not more than 4 liters of imported milk and 35 cubic centimeters of fresh milk are available
every year to the individual Vietnamese. There are not more than a
thousand milk cows in the country and their production is estimated
at 400 tons a year. During the war, a small milk industry flourished
for a time near Saigon and Cholon, but withered after the war as a
result of the reopening of import sources. In 1960, only one milk
farm was located near Saigon at Tan Son Nut. Its Jersey cows produce 24,000 liters a year.

Fisheries.[12,15] Fish is an important item of the Vietnamese diet.
With 1,4000 miles of coast and a number of lakes and ponds available,
fisheries are a valuable section of the national economy. Fish production, which was around 180,000 tons prior to World War II, dropped to
95,000 tons in 1955, but rose again to 168,000 tons in 1959. The catch
was brought in by some 34,000 fishing craft of all kinds, some of which
are motorized. Statistics, however, are not kept in the smaller harbors where the catch is passed along to the population without going
through controlled markets. Yet, using the Saigon-Cholon area (where
almost all of the fish consumed is sold in markets and thus recorded)
as a basis for computation, there is evidence that this urban population consumes 103 pounds of fish per capita per year or approximately
94,000 tons per year. While it is likely that the rest of the population
of over 11 million people gets somewhat more fish than the balance
between urban consumption and total landings indicates, it would be
unrealistic to assume that this could amount to more than 22 pounds
per capita per year; this would place the Vietnamese third in the
amount of fish consumed compared to the Japanese (96 pounds a year)
and the Filipinos (34 pounds a year). A considerable amount of
American aid is invested in fish and shell-fish production. It is believed that in 1958 improved techniques in transportation and marketing resulted in a 10% increase in production. New landing sites are
being planned and built and 44 cooperative fishing societies with a
membership of 7,000 are now in operation. Some progress has been
made in developing fresh-water fishers. Ten fish-culture stations
were recently established and have already distributed Tilapia and
golden carp for local breeding.

COMIGAL. A special presidential committee (COMIGAL) is in
charge of an expansion program aimed at bringing more land into production by developing hitherto uncultivated areas of central and south

Vietnam. This ambitious project includes resettling families from congested areas and inducing the aborigines already living in the area to abandon their hunting and gathering cultures for a sedentary way of life. The government has spared no effort to insure the success of this enterprise, though there are many difficulties. The areas to be developed are highly malarious and it remains to be seen whether the malaria-eradication program can keep pace with the agricultural developments. Land cleared at government expense has been allotted to transplanted families in smaller amounts than is needed for survival, as an inducement to reclaim more fallow land up to a ceiling of 12 acres per family. Subsidies in rice (33 pounds per head per month) and money (5-10 cents a day) are being guaranteed to settlers for 6 to 9 months, as long as it will take to bring in a first harvest. Some working tools and household implements, such as trucks used in common and radios, have also been made available. Nurseries, experimental stations, and recreational centers have been created in new villages. By the end of 1958, approximately 75,000 settlers had been established in 44 new villages and, granting adequate preventive sanitation, the measure may have a significant influence on resources in the future.*

Fertilizers. Vietnam's agricultural production is in great need of chemical fertilizers. For centuries, the farmers have used human and animal manure as well as the by-products of nuoc mam production (but not in significant amounts) as fertilizers. As in China, the practice is fraught with dangers in terms of fecal-borne disease.
Here the environmental sanitation campaigns are at loggerheads with the need for more yield per hectare. Whether it is preferable to buy chemical fertilizers with foreign currency or to manufacture locally has not been determined. Table 4 shows the total amount of fertilizers imported and their estimated utilization. It is noteworthy that less than 3% of the total rice land in Vietnam receives application of chemical fertilizers; American aid is contributing to an extensive campaign promoting the use of chemical fertilizers among rice growers. An estimated 120,000 metric tons of commercial fertilizers are distributed to farmers every year through the American aid program.

Water control. Water-control projects are an important concern of the American aid program and receive the largest amount of American subsidies in the development of agriculture. In 1959, construction was completed on 15 joint irrigation and water control projects covering 11,000 hectares and benefiting 56,600 rural people. Thirty-nine new land-development centers were established in 1959, bringing the total up to 139,000 people in 87 centers.

---

*As of 1961, security problems created by increasing communist terrorism, severely handicap the program.

Other projects. There are rice seed testing grounds in 13 out of the 38 provinces - mainly in south and central Vietnam. Since 1954, 193 irrigation projects covering 129,500 hectares (320,000 acres) of rice land have been commissioned. Sugar production is also receiving attention. There are sugar experimental stations at Quang Ngai, Tuy Hoa and Giadinh, which distribute improve sugar-cane grafts to the producer. To facilitate the development of new land, an Agricultural Machinery Directorate was established in 1956. It is responsible for the operation and maintenance of all equipment used for clearing land, such as plows, discs, and so forth. Approximately 1,000 pieces of equipment, including tractors, trucks, and other vehicles, have been received between 1956 and 1960 through the American aid program. Preliminary results from vegetable-growing experiments indicate an annual saving of U. S. $500,000 in foreign exchange by the substitution of locally grown onions and potatoes for imported ones. New sweet potato varieties are yielding 3 times as much as local varieties. A permanent cooperative research and training institute has been established as a joint Vietnam Cooperative League of America, an American aid project. Farmer associations are organized in 77 districts with a total membership of 178,000 farm families. All credit agencies were combined into one in 1957, with American aid contributing 60% of the capital. As a result, loans to over 350,000 farmers, totaling $12 million were made during 1959 and the National Agricultural Credit Office became financially self-supporting. The initially planned physical plant of the National College of Agriculture at Bao-Loc was virtually completed in 1959 and has a student enrollment of 345.[16]

H. EXPORTS AND IMPORTS[8]

Vietnam is an importer of condensed milk, dairy products, wheat, flour, sugar, onions, garlic, potatoes, pulses, and coffee, and an exporter of rice, tea, salt, and beer. Table 6 gives the figures on agricultural export and import items. We have seen above that considerable effort is being made to try to grow the kinds of vegetables that figure high in purchases abroad, such as onions and potatoes. However, the country is not quite self-sufficient in this respect as yet.

Table 6 shows that a relatively small amount of rice, 208,874 metric tons, was exported in 1959. Yet this represents a considerable improvement over previous years. Prior to the war, Vietnam exported from 1 million to 1.5 million tons of rice annually. The substantial difference in prewar and present exportable surplus is due to geographic and political changes that have removed Cambodia as a purchaser of Vietnamese rice. Growth in population and slight increase in the per capita consumption account for the differential balance. Even taking all these factors into consideration, the present production and export is substantially inferior to the prewar figures.

As production increases and more substantial surplus become available, new channels of trade may open in Southeast Asia. In 1960, as of this writing, Indonesia has already purchased 200,000 tons of Vietnamese rice and Pakistan is scheduled to buy a sizable amount, though the quantity is as yet unknown. In addition, Ceylon and Japan recently sent commercial representatives to Vietnam to arrange the purchase of white rice. Reliable sources in the middle of 1960 announced that Ceylon intended to buy 300,000 tons of Vietnamese white rice, and Japan from 5,000 to 10,000 metric tons. All of this was subject, of course, to adequate production.

The irregularity of the country's food imports of such items as coffee, corn, tubers, areca nuts, and certain fruits reflects the variability of available foreign currency and, to a certain degree, the success of the government's efforts to limit purchases abroad.

I. STANDARDS OF LIVING

The general index of consumer prices rose from 100 in 1949 to a maximum of 250 in 1956, the year when the resettlement of 800,000 refugees from the north took place, but the index has declined since to 234 in 1958. The index-food expenditure for a working-class family is represented by 64.5%; it followed a curve parallel to the general index, rising to 248 in 1956 and dropping to 221 in 1958. Middle-class families spend approximately 51.5% of their budget on food. It must be remembered that in the huge (1.8 million people) agglomeration of Saigon-Cholon, more than 66% of the population is considered middle-class and works at white-collar jobs.

J. FOOD INDUSTRIES, STORAGE AND TECHNOLOGY

The total capacity of food storage in Vietnam at present is not known. Under the Agricultural Cooperative Program, rice-storage facilities are being expended; over 20 new storage areas were completed between 1956 and July, 1958. In 1959, 15 new rice-storage cooperatives were organized and equipped for operation, bringing the total to 41. There is no doubt that a considerable amount of storage space is available at Saigon, where 5 times as much rice as is now handled for export was handled before World War II. Rice mills and food factories exist throughout the country. In the coastal area these are found at Phan Rang, Nha Trang, Da Nayg, and Hue; in the lowlands, at Saigon, Cantho and Long Xuyen; and in the highlands, at Dalat.

Vietnam has a research program oriented toward the improved handling, storage, processing, and distribution of foods. This includes

expansion of all storage facilities, including refrigeration, expansion
of the sugar-refining industry, production of glass containers for the
canning industry, further development of the edible oils industry, and
sewage disposal and treatment. Vietnam lacks an equipped laboratory
for research in food processing, although a building is at present
available for this purpose.* A suggested inventory of required equipment for such a laboratory is now being prepared.

Cold-storage facilities exist in abundance in the Saigon area, and
in smaller amounts in the other larger towns. Hardly a small town
exists without some sort of ice-making factory, mostly in the hands of
Chinese tradesmen. In Saigon, the SEFI (Société des Entrepôts
Frigorifiques d'Indochine) has a total capacity of 2,800 cubic meters
of storage at minus 20° C. Cold-storage facilities are being built at
Choquan, which, in 1960, will have 1,400 cubic meters capacity in two
rooms of 700 cubic meters each, especially for the preservation of
fruit and fish. Another plant with a capacity of 500 cubic meters for
the preservation of frozen foods and a tunnel for quick freezing at
minus 40° C. will be completed at the end of 1960. In addition to these
resources, Saigon has approximately 800 cubic meters of rooms at
various cold temperatures belonging to 5 or 6 small firms.[13]

Food sanitation leaves much to be desired. While at Saigon and in
all other major cities, a Municipal Hygiene Service is in operation, it
is hopelessly inadequate in personnel and equipment. All food sold in
the markets or by street vendors must be considered to be heavily
polluted.

III. DIET TYPES

A. GENERAL

No adequate survey of the dietary values of food intake has been
made recently in Vietnam. The following section is based on a number of samplings made between 1950 and 1958 by the few French or
Vietnamese scientists interested in the problem. Very recently
(March, 1960) an American group studied a small number of people,
chiefly in the larger cities of Saigon, Nha Trang, and Dalat, and also
in smaller towns like Kontum and Pleku. The people in these samples were mainly military personnel with occasionally a few civilians.
While precise knowledge of dietary values among the general public
is lacking, a thorough study of the nutritive values of most Vietnamese
foods was made by Autret in 1944[1] - the present data available on
daily intakes is based on the values found in his tables.

---

*Since this writing progress is being made in establishing a nutrition
laboratory in Vietnam.

All authors agree that there is no area of famine and no genuine or local starvation. Vietnam could, under peaceful circumstances, produce a large variety of foods and should be more than able to support its present population. According to Dols (personal communication)[4] it can be safely estimated that no Vietnamese eats less than 2,100 calories a day and many, especially in the cities, eat much more. These calories are chiefly supplied by rice - the population is addicted to it, especially in the countryside, and all meals are centered around a large bowl of this cereal, filled as many times as possible - the diet is poor in meat, milk, and other valuable animal protein. On the average, every man, woman, and child could not find more than 500 grams of rice, 2 grams of beef, 13 grams of pork, and 3 grams of poultry (18 grams of meat) available a day, but this could be complemented by 30 to 100 grams depending upon place of residence and 1 egg per month. Vegetables and fruits are plentiful.

The 500 grams of rice listed above are not regularly consumed by each individual. They would be available if all of the rice produced in the country and not exported were equally distributed. This is not the case and an unknown but substantial amount, probably 10% - 15%, is wasted or lost. A more realistic estimate of the amount of rice consumed is believed to be between 400 and 450 grams a day.

In order to make a correct evaluation of the amount of food consumed every day, it must be remembered that, in common with other populations of Southeast Asia, the Vietnamese does not take into account, and does not report to an investigator, the numerous snacks taken every day. The Vietnamese considers that there are three types of meals: a filling meal, the only one that is likely to be mentioned to an investigator; a cooling meal, usually beverages, (fruit juices sold by street vendors, lemonade, orangeade, and other real or synthetic drinks); and "greed" meals, represented by sweetmeats and a number of locally prepared delicacies. These three repasts can be considered as representing respectively nutrition, refreshment, and pleasure. Street vendors appear at all times in the streets and even on the roads between the villages, selling everything from slices of pineapple to lemonade and soup. Some have their own delicacies, such as raw and green papaya, spiced with chilis and vinegar. The amount of all such foods consumed during one day is significant, but defies exact computations.

Isolated studies have been made, giving us some insight into the dietary values of certain special groups of people. Tran-vy and Nguyen Dinh Thuc[14] have established dietary values for civil servants and unskilled laborers. Their research, carried out between 1951 and 1956, is represented in tabular form in Tables No. 7, 8, 9, and 10. The tables show a daily per capita availability of 2,464 to 2,509 calories per day for the manual workers and of 2,828 to 2,972 for the civil servants. It is interesting to note that the manual worker who needs calories most gets them least. In all samples, the amount of animal protein absorbed is adequate.

This data originates in statistical offices and is based on raw supplies delivered to certain families. It would, therefore, be advisable to deduct an arbitrary 10% to 15% for losses in preparation and cooking and from waste. The middle class in Saigon represents more than 2/3 of the total population. Conditions in the countryside are not as favorable as they are in Saigon. Thus, the average consumption of 2,100 calories estimated by Dols seems a reasonable and conservative guess of the average Vietnamese diet. Such a diet is very nearly adequate for the ethnic type considered. Tran-Vy and others[14] have computed the requirements of the manual laborer of Vietnam, weight 112 pounds and height 62 inches, to be 2,491 calories. They computed the requirements of the white-collar workers to be 2,271 calories. Most of the calories are contributed by carbohydrates, essentially rice.

The working-class diet ratio is 73.8% in carbohydrate calories while the white-collar worker gets 68.9% of his calories through cereals and starchy foods. In rural areas, however, the ratio of carbohydrates to the rest of the diet stands more probably at 80%. Tran-vy and others[14] estimate the protein availability per capita at 95 grams for the white-collar worker and 90 grams for the manual laborer and believe that 50% of this amount comes from animal sources. This, if true, would seem to be adequate and even unusually satisfactory for a Southeast Asian country. In the countryside, however, this amount of protein intake is not reached. Neither is the animal-protein ratio as good. It is felt that the intake of the vitamin B complex is on the low side, while the intake of vitamin A is satisfactory in most areas but deficient in some.[14] Tran-Vy and others consider that vitamin C is supplied in large amounts and assume that the intake of this vitamin is satisfactory. These authors discount any need for intake of vitamin D in the diet because of the abundance of sunshine and the tropical climate. This, however, is debatable as conditions of squalor and neglect do exist in many city slums. At any rate, cases of rickets, whether exogenous or endogenous, are observed among the patients of childrens' hospitals in the Saigon-Cholon agglomeration. It is the view of Dols[4] that the calcium ratio in the diet, which is not mentioned in Tran-Vy's study, is generally low, a view shared by other Vietnamese nutritionists, such as Nguyeh Dinh, and supported by a study of the typical diets given to the patients of a large Saigon hospital. Other groups of population, when studied, supply similar information.

B. SPECIAL DIETS[14]

Schools. In the well-to-do schools in Saigon, rice contributes 70.6% of the total caloric intake of 2,765. Total protein intake is

03.67 grams, of which animal proteins accounts for 41.94 grams or
44.7% (see Table 10).

Hospitals.[14] In hospitals, the diet is found to be better than in the
homes and almost as good as in the schools. The total caloric intake
is 2,600 calories. The daily fare consists of:

Protein:	128 Gm.	Vitamin A:	20,239 I.U.
Carbohydrate:	345 Gm.	Thiamine:	2.37 mg.
Fat:	60.2 Gm.	Riboflavin:	3.68 mg.
Calcium:	470 mg.	Niacin:	812 mg.
Iron:	31.8 mg.	Vitamin C:	246 mg.

The actual menus vary considerably with the class considered and
they have to be discussed separately.

(1) The Well-to-do. These have the same basic Vietnamese dishes
as the lower classes but, in addition, enjoy a great variety of dishes
taken both from the local and from the Western cultures. In addition,
Chinese delicacies are frequently served, especially on festive occasions. Breakfast, not unusually will include eggs, jam, fruit, coffee,
and cream. The other meals feature meat and fish, eggs, green vegetables, and fruit. Generous helpings of hot spices and nuoc mam are
part of this menu. Rice is served at the two main meals. Northern
Vietnamese prefer the long grain ("tamthom") while Southern people
prefer shorter grains ("nanhchon"). The preferred meat is always
pork ("thit-kho"), but beef and poultry are also consumed. Meat,
especially pork, is served diced and fried, seasoned with nuoc mam
and sweetened with coconut juice. Fish is served either in a soup
("canh") or fried or stewed in nuoc mam ("Ca-kho"). Eggs are eaten
in the Western way, as are vegetables like cabbages, cauliflower,
watercress, lettuce, onions, and tomatoes. All the above vegetables
are seasoned with garlic, chili, and nuoc mam, often enriched with
sugar and vinegar. Seasoning is particularly used to "pep up" such
delicacies as noodles and lobster ("banh hoi tom"); or rice noodles
with raw pork ("banh hoi nem chua"); or minced pork, vegetables,
and crabmeat, rolled in dough and fried ("cha gio"). Often, especially
if Chinese dishes are eaten, soya sauce is used for seasoning. Such
meals are washed down with China tea, wine or beer, or all of these
beverages in succession. Fruits in season are served as dessert and
include local tropical varieties, as well as Western fruit, such as
strawberries, which are locally grown. Cooking is done with butter
or superior quality oil.

(2) The Middle Class. The diet is usually satisfactory but less
varied than that of the well-to-do, including Western dishes only occasionally and in much lesser amounts. Breakfast consists usually of
Chinese soup ("hu-tien") with rice noodles, minced pork in broth,
spiced with nuoc mam or soya sauce, while the two other meals re-

semble more the lower-class fare of rice and fish, but with more of
both, and more frequently include meat, poultry, or eggs.

(3) The Poorer Class. The poorer class eats chiefly rice. This
may be the sticky rice ("nep") or the boiled and steamed rice, usually
with some vegetables and occasionally raw or stewed fish ("ca-kho");
very seldom is pork included. The poorer classes consume more
nuoc mam than the rich but it is of a lower quality. All cooking is
done with lard or vegetable oil. Such is the daily fare of the teeming
millions of the city slums or of the rice fields, who do not eat more
than a few grams of meat a day and less than 27 grams of fish.

Children.   While in urban centers infants may receive a mixed
diet of rice and animal protein, most of the infant population of the
rural areas is fed almost exclusively on rice or rice flour by the
elderly women who take charge of them while the younger mothers
are laboring in the fields. Thus, the diet of the young children is mar-
ginally deficient in thiamine, riboflavin, vitamin C, and calcium.
Children do not receive vitamin supplements nor are they given milk
at the end of breast-feeding; 92.2% of the women breast-feed their
children up to the age of 11 months. Supplementary diets begin at a
median age of 7 months and consist of rice flour, soup, salt, or sugar.
No statistical data are available but Vietnamese pediatricians have
noted many cases of rickets, minor or even major signs of polyneuri-
tis, beriberi, diarrhea, and gross development retardation. Kwashiorkor is commonly observed.

IV. ADEQUACY OF FOOD RESOURCES

A. IN NORMAL TIMES

Under normal circumstances, south Vietnam, especially if relieved
of sending a large share of its crop to the north is a self-supporting
country as far as food is concerned. With the exception of sugar, none
of the main food imports is essential to the native population. Most of
the imports are consumed by the foreign or upper-class population.
Vietnam can and does produce a large variety of foods and can earn
some foreign exchange by exporting its surplus rice. Its supply of animal proteins can be increased as its fish resources are more adequately used. Its population problem is not yet critical.

B. IN TIMES OF EMERGENCY

The country has shown that it could survive and feed itself in case
of a world emergency. During the period 1939-1945, it managed to
find in its own resources enough food to continue supporting the ances-

tral diet of its people, a situation very different from that in Malaya and Ceylon. Yet, it is now confronted with a situation that taxes its ability to develop its resources to a significant extent. There is no internal security in the most fertile rice-producing areas. The agrarian reforms of the government and the development of American aid are threatened by the infiltration of Communist agitators from the north. The farmers are submitted to a dual system of taxation: the regular system during the day and the "Vietcong" tax during the night. It is not unusual that a representative of the terrorists will "rearrange" or "redistribute" the land according to the plan of the Communists, creating considerable discouragement and confusion. In certain areas the villagers have to be regrouped for protection, often forcing them to abandon their fields and acreages for several days when Vietcong bands roam the countryside. Because of this situation, the food production and distribution is not improving, in spite of considerable American effort and is, in the countryside, worse at present than it was during the war years.

V. NUTRITIONAL DISEASE PATTERNS

The recent American study group collected 600 blood and urine samples, resulting in over 6,000 biochemical determinations.[5] It was generally found that there was a low thiamine and riboflavin excretion. In most cases the N-methyl-nicotinamide can be considered adequate. Few groups have low serum vitamin C and vitamin A values. A small amount of anemia was found among the samples. Total serum protein values were found to be somewhat high in certain subjects. While there is no obvious starvation, a number of signs of marginal subnutrition were encountered everywhere. Angular lesions, angular scars, and cheilosis, due to riboflavin deficiencies, were found in small groups examined in the Vinh Truong fishing villages. Similar findings were recorded among 50% of the people at Kontum. Ulcers of sclerae, Bitot spots, signs of vitamin A deficiency are seen in low-class people in Saigon. No classic signs of beriberi were found among 7,428 examinations, but areflexia was noted in widely separated areas. There is no doubt, however, that beriberi exists in the country, as it is seen in hospitals. Vietnamese physicians are convinced that it is common, especially in urban and suburban areas, where the rice supply originates from mechanical milling plants. Rickets is extremely common in children, although physicians are hard put to decide whether it is due to a lack of calcium in the diet, to slum conditions depriving children of the abundant sunshine, or to a generally conditioned lack of absorption in the body.

Nutritional edema is still found in children and sometimes in adults, although much less than 50 years ago when it was described by

French authors as "Bouffissure d'Annam," Kwashiorkor is said to be commonly observed. It is, however, believed that all these nutritional deficiencies arise more as a result of ignorance and the traditionally unbalanced diets than as a result of actual scarcity. Of interest is the gleeful communiqué issued on April 15, 1960, stating that representatives of the Vegetable Cooperative Company concluded an agreement concerning the export of at least 140 tons of vegetables to the Seng Huat Company of Singapore. No doubt the surplus vegetables could usefully be kept and consumed within the country.

Goiter cases are seen in several villages in the Kontum area, 50%, and in the Cantho area, 28%. Etiology is not clear; analysis of food, water, and salt is under way. Dental caries in permanent teeth was found to be low by United States standards. Teeth loss due to marginal periodonitis was said to be frequent. Much keratoses is encountered, especially tinea versicolor and tinea corporis.

The conditions found immediately after pregnancy are worthy of note. Traditional alterations of food intake during pregnancy and postpartum were seen by American observers as a precipitating factor of nutritional diseases. The Vietnamese woman has two fears when she is pregnant: she is afraid of eating too much, lest the fetus become too heavy; she is afraid of eating products that she thinks will endanger the fetus. During pregnancy the diet is limited to a small amount of rice, soya sauce, some vegetables, and nuoc mam of inferior quality. Fish and meat are said to generate poisons in the child. However, such restrictive diets common in the countryside and followed because of tradition are not commonly found in Saigon.

VI. CONCLUSIONS

In conclusion, it can be said that Vietnam is a relatively rich country, which, given internal peace, and sufficient foreign aid, could feed not only its present population but even a larger one. It is, however, to be feared that internal insecurity will jeopardize regular progress. In addition, a thorough malaria-eradication program must be undertaken parallel to the development of the new agricultural sites. This is contemplated and could be realized with the same prerequisites as stated above, namely, adequate internal security.

SELECTED REFERENCES

1. Autret, M., and Nguyen-van Mau. Tables alimentaires indochinois. *Revue Medicale d'Extreme Orient*, Vol. 22, 1944, pp. 73-78.
2. Bilan des activités gouvernementale, *in* Government of Viet Nam. Saigon, 1958.

3. Daleas, P., Rivoalen, A., and Tran-tu-Oai, J. Le Régime des femmes enceinte au Viet Nam. *Revue Medicale d'Extreme Orient*, Vol. 22, 1942.

4. Dols, M. J. L., Food and Agriculture Organization expert. Personal communication. Saigon, 1960.

5. Follis, R., *et al*. Nutrition Mission to Viet Nam, 1960. Personal communication.

6. International Cooperation Administration. Near East and South East Asia Conference. Beirut, 1959.

7. Le-Thuoc. Contribution de l'élévage à l'alimentation humaine au Viet Nam. *Symposium Scientifique sur les Aliments et le Nutrition*. Saigon, 1957.

8. Government of Viet Nam, Ministère de la Statistique. Personal communication. Saigon, 1960.

9. Ngo-Ba-Thanh. Un Condiment-aliment azote le Nuoc-Mam. *Symposium Scientifique sur les Aliments et le Nutrition*. Saigon, 1957.

10. Richard, C. Apercu sur l'alimentation des viet namien. *Symposium Scientifique sur les Aliments et le Nutrition*. Saigon, 1957.

11. Serene, M. La Pêche et l'alimentation au Viet Nam. Symposium. *Monthly Statistical Bulletin*, January, 1960.

12. Serene, M. La Pêche et l'alimentation au Viet Nam. *Symposium Scientifique sur les Aliments et le Nutrition*. Saigon, 1957.

13. Société des Entrepôts Frigorifiques l'Indochine. Personal communication. Saigon, 1960.

14. Tran-Vy, *et al*. La Ration alimentaire du vietnamien. *Symposium Scientifique sur les Aliments et le Nutrition*. Saigon, 1957.

15. United States Operations Mission (U.S.O.M.) to Viet Nam. *Annual Statistical Bulletin - Saigon*, 1959.

16. Wireless and Cable Service, Saigon, 1960.

Table 1

Rice Paddy

Area cultivated (1,000 ha.)

	Total	South Viet-Nam	Central Viet-Nam	
			Lowlands	Highlands
1944	2,621.0	1,987.0	634.0	—
1950	...	1,237.4	...	—
1951	...	1,287.8	...	—
1952	1,439.9	1,348.9	91.0	—
1953	1,598.8	1,541.0	57.8	—
1954	1,659.8	1,572.4	87.4	—
1955	2,178.8	1,767.8	411.0	—
1956	2,540.2	2,060.0	375.2	105.0
1957	2,719.0	2,124.9	489.2	105.0
1958	2,925.9	2,337.0	514.6	74.3
1959	3,100.0			

Production (1,000 metric tons)

	Total	South Viet-Nam	Central Viet-Nam	
			Lowlands	Highlands
1944	2,840.4	2,214.1	626.3	—
1950	...	1,688.5	...	—
1951	...	1,893.0	...	—
1952	2,006.0	1,899.8	106.2	—
1953	2,069.8	1,975.8	94.0	—
1954	2,080.3	1,977.4	102.9	—
1955	2,766.7	2,335.8	430.9	—
1956	3,412.0	2,741.9	536.1	135.0
1957	3,191.6	2,541.6	587.5	62.5
1958	3,990.2*	3,232.1	680.3	77.8
1959	4,500.0			

*Preliminary Government Estimate.

Table 1 (continued)

	Yield per hectare (metric tons)		Central Viet-Nam	
	Total	South Viet-Nam	Lowlands	Highlands
1944	1.1	1.1	1.0	...
1950	1.4	1.4	...	...
1951	1.5	1.5	...	...
1952	1.4	1.4	1.2	...
1953	1.3	1.3	1.6	...
1954	1.3	1.3	1.2	...
1955	1.3	1.3	1.1	...
1956	1.3	1.3	1.4	1.3
1957	1.2	1.2	1.2	0.6
1958	1.4	1.4	1.3	1.0

	Estimated Consumption or Disappearance			
	Rice exports (in terms of paddy)	Apparent disappearance	Population (in thousands)	Paddy disappearance per capita (kilos)
1945	747.8	2,092.6	9,610	217.7
1951	413.1	...	9,655	...
1952	230.6	...	9,688	...
1953	154.0	1,852.0	9,766	189.6
1954	242.7	1,827.1	9,934	183.9
1955	104.4	1,975.9	11,534	171.3
1956	—	2,766.7	12,366	223.7
1957	275.9	3,136.1	13,217	237.2
1958	170.2	3,021.4		

Source: United States Operations Mission to Viet Nam: Annual Statistical Bulletin, Saigon, 1959.

Table 2

Sugar Production
(Metric tons)

	1950	1951	1952	1953	1954	1955	1956	1957	1958
Total	5,355	5,678	5,388	3,995	3,526	7,045	13,780	14,886	25,606
White Refined, total	1,587	1,268	1,326	326	573	1,601	1,981	1,111	4,909
Brown (artisan) total	3,768	4,410	4,062	3,669	2,953	5,444	11,799	13,775	20,697
South Vietnam	2,906	3,202	3,343	2,965	2,370	4,369	7,398	9,612	15,818
Central Vietnam	862	1,208	719	704	583	1,075	4,401	4,163	4,879

Sugar Imports
(Metric tons)

	1950	1951	1952	1953	1954	1955	1956	1957	1958
Total	28,907	33,264	45,102	45,647	49,199	53,919	52,903	55,661	44,360
Raw sugar	26,617	18,267	25,267	31,600	23,652	42,925	49,268	55,661	41,460
Refined sugar	2,290	14,997	19,835	14,047	25,547	10,994	3,635	—	2,900

(Value in thousands of U.S. dollars)

	1950	1951	1952	1953	1954	1955	1956	1957	1958
Total	5,595	6,679	10,053	9,536	9,448	6,706	5,870	7,953	4,975
Raw sugar	4,847	3,316	4,874	6,154	4,142	4,740	5,408	7,952	4,579
Refined sugar	548	3,363	5,179	3,382	5,306	1,966	462	1	396

Estimated Sugar Consumption

	1953	1954	1955	1956
Total consumption in metric tons	49,742	52,647	60,423	76,427
Population (in thousands)	9,766	9,934	11,534	2,366
Consumption per capita in kgs	5.09	5.29	5.22	6.20

Source: United States Operations Mission to Vietnam: Annual Statistical Bulletin, Saigon, 1959.

Table 3

Composition of Nuoc-Mam

NaCl	280	gr. per litter
Na (total)	12.4	''
Ammonium	3.8	''
Amino Acids*	5.7	''

*Of which: cystine, aspartic acid, glutamic acid, serine, glycocolle, threonine, alanine, valine, leucine, isoleucine, phenylalanine, lysine, arginine, histidine, proline, tryptophane, tyrosine, methionine. Also found; Ca, P, vitamin B_{12}, and PP factor.

Source: Ngo-Ba-Thanh: Un condiment-aliment azote le Nuoc-Nam. Symposium Scientifique, sur les Aliments et la Nutrition, Saigon, 1957.

Table 4

Fertilizers

A—Imports

(Metric tons)

	1951	1952	1953	1954	1955	1956	1957	1958
Total	15,869	12,950	12,381	21,090	19,957	36,768	32,150	51,678
Nitrogen	11,414	9,050	9,999	14,096	16,946	31,384	23,855	43,563
Ammonium Phosphate	10	25	70	922	41	3,114	258	2,550
Ammonium Sulphate	10,424	8,520	8,629	12,374	16,900	28,014	23,167	38,434
Urea and others	980	505	1,300	800	5	256	430	2,579
Potassium	1,900	1,787	896	1,394	1,142	2,637	4,769	5,304
Phosphate	2,506	1,196	1,256	5,339	1,614	2,477	2,098	2,597
Bicalcium phosphate	500	1,196	302	5,337	1,594	1,457	2,098	2,234
Tricalcium phosphate	2,006	0	952	0	0	720	0	363
Other phosphates	0	0	2	2	20	300	0	0
Natural	0	0	0	0	208	70	1,263	192
Mixtures and proprietary forms	49	917	230	261	47	200	165	22

B—Estimated Utilization of Chemical Fertilizers in Vietnam in 1958

(Percent)

	Rubber	Rice	Tea and Coffee	Sugar	Other Food Crops	Total
Nitrogen						
Ammonium Phosphate	100	–	–	–	–	100
Ammonium sulphate	5	40	15	20	20	100
Urea and other	80	–	10	10	–	100
Potassium	55	–	15	5	25	100
Phosphate						
Bicalcium phosphate	15	–	30	5	50	100
Tricalcium phosphate	–	94	1	5	–	100

Source: United States Operations Mission of Vietnam: Annual Statistical Bulletin, Saigon, 1959.

Table 5

Livestock and Poultry

A—Population
(Thousand heads)

	1944	1950	1952	1953	1954	1955	1956	1957	1958
Cattle, Total	860	136	141	135	149	474	595	688	659
South	230	81	90	92	100	121	119	235	184
Central (Lowlands)	{ 630	55	51	43	49	353	427	404	427
Central (Highlands)		...	...	...	...	...	49	49	48
Buffaloes, Total	600	146	161	164	222	258	379	544	381
South	280	98	115	118	150	141	182	326	183
Central (Lowlands)	{ 320	48	46	46	72	117	149	171	149
Central (Highlands)		...	—	—	—	—	48	47	49
Pigs, Total	1,750	190	662	714	961	2,297	2,565	3,384	2,362
South	750	126	600	600	750	1,802	1,800	2,497	1,597
Central (Lowlands)	{ 1,000	64	62	114	211	495	615	776	615
Central (Highlands)		...	—	—	—	—	150	111	150
Chickens, Total						5,496	5,841	7,484	5,925
South						3,881	...	4,355	3,985
Central (Lowlands)						1,615	...	2,993	1,940
Central (Highlands)						—	...	136	—
Ducks, Total						4,382	4,332	5,157	4,332
South						3,870	...	3,498	3,906
Central (Lowlands)						512	...	1,649	426
Central (Highlands)						—	...	10	—

Table 5 (continued)

B—Number Slaughtered
(Thousand heads)

	1944	1950	1951	1952	1953	1954	1955	1956	1957	1958
Cattle, Total	45	52	45	31	22	24	42	47	50	
South	...	42	34	22	15	16	27	29	31	
Central (Lowlands)	...	7	7	6	5	6	11	14	15	
Central (Highlands)	...	3	4	3	2	2	4	4	4	
Buffaloes, Total	6	11	13	10	7	12	13	16	13	
South	...	9	11	9	6	10	12	14	12	
Central (Lowlands)	...	2	2	1	1	2	1	1	—	
Central (Highlands)	...	...	...	...	...	...	...	1	1	
Pigs, Total	647	436	595	650	669	702	816	883	929	
South	...	377	522	566	564	618	717	737	787	
Central (Lowlands)	...	50	60	70	89	66	77	120	114	
Central (Highlands)	...	9	13	14	16	18	22	26	29	

Source: United States Operations Mission to Vietnam: Annual Statistical Bulletin, Saigon, 1959.

Table 6

Food Trade in Tons, Vietnam

Items	Imports			Exports		
	1957	1958	1959	1957	1958	1959
Dairy			22,000			
Sugar	55,661	44,360				
Onion, garlic	2,394	6,624	5,986			
Citrus fruit	160	92	81			
Apples, pears	180	3,520	1,989			
Dates	521	549	78			
Other fruits	59	779	622			
Coconut						
Areca Nut	1,086	926	355			
Tubers	1,821	3,207	2,541			
Pulses	8,006	7,145	157			
Coffee	257	0	17			
Tea	26	1	4	36	259	318
Spices	675	556	218	534	1,040	1,411
Rice	16,431	1,936	—	183,871	112,702	208,874
Rice flour	1	2	—	3,289	4,690	3,700
Wheat flour	42,429	38,352	45,847			
Corn	57	4,028	78			
Malt	4,777	5,400	4,689			

Source: Ministere de la Statistique, Gouvernement du Viet Nam: Personal Communication, Saigon, 1960.

Table 7

June 1951—Laboring Class
Daily Food Ration per Person

	Amount in Grams	Carbohydrates		Fats		Proteins		Vit. A	Vit. B1	Vit. B2	Vit. C
	Gm.	Gm.	Cal.*	Gm.	Cal.*	Gm.	Cal.*	I.U.	mg.	mg.	mg.
Bread	16.6	9.00	36.0	0.26	2.3	2.37	5.4		8		
Rice	533.0	403.20	1512.8	7.62	68.5	39.50	158.0		1066	400	
Beef	16.6	0.20	0.8	0.50	4.5	3.33	13.3		8		
Pork	39.9			7.99	71.9	7.99	31.9		103	369	
Poultry	6.6			0.57	2.3	1.19	4.7		2		
Lard	10.0			9.80	88.2						
Dry fish	20.0			0.60	5.4	8.00	32.0		20		
Fresh fish	56.6			0.56	5.0	6.79	27.1	56	22	42	
Eggs	6.5			0.80	7.2	1.65	6.6	248	7	28	
Nuoc Mam	50.0					2.45	9.8		10		
Chinese Cabbage	300.0	15.00	60.0	0.60	3.6	4.80	19.2	6200	90	210	120
Soya	16.6	0.08		0.93	8.3	1.89	7.5		25	16	18
Banana	64.0	14.70	58.8	0.38	3.4	1.15	4.6			16	18
Sugar	13.3	12.10	48.4								
Yams	26.6	7.47	29.8	0.07	0.6	0.26	1.0		18	47	3
Condensed milk	10.6	2.12	8.4	0.31	2.7	0.36	1.4	21	1	25	
Shell fish	10.0			0.02	0.1	1.32	5.2				
Rice alcohol	10.0	2.80	11.3								
Beer	0.0										
Total		466.67	1866.3	31.01	274.0	82.05	327.7	6525	1380	1137	141

Source: Tran-Vy et al: La Ration Alimentaire du Vietnamien. Symposium Scientifique sur les Aliments et la Nutrition, Saigon, 1957.

*calories

Table 8

July 1954—Laboring Class

Daily Food Ration per Person

	Amount in Grains	Carbohydrates		Fats		Proteins		Vit. A	Vit. B$_1$	Vit. B$_2$	Vit. C
	Gm.	Gm.	Cal.	Gm.	Cal.*	Gm.	Cal.*	I.U.	mg.	mg.	mg.
Bread	12.9	7.00	28.0	0.20	1.8	1.18	4.9		6		
Rice	516.3	390.29	1561.1	7.38	66.4	38.13	152.5		1032	387	
Beef	19.3	0.24	0.9	0.60	5.4	3.97	15.8		9		
Pork	38.7			8.19	73.7	8.11	32.4		114	360	
Poultry	52.1	0.54	2.1	4.68	42.1	9.48	37.8		20		
Lard	16.1			15.77	141.9						
Dry fish	19.2			0.56	5.0	7.64	30.5		18		
Fresh fish	64.5			0.64	5.9	7.74	30.9	64	25	47	
Egg	7.9			1.14	10.2	1.14	4.8	265	7	32	
Nuoc Mam	51.1					2.50	10.0				
Chinese cabbage	193.5	9.77	39.0	0.39	3.5	3.12	12.4	4737	60	136	78
Soya	26.8	0.12	0.4	1.62	14.5	3.21	12.6				
Banana	159.10	56.60	146.4	9.54	85.8	2.82	11.2		76	40	80
Sugar	12.9	11.73	46.9								
Yam	57.6	16.37	65.7	0.16	1.4	0.59	2.3		40	133	4
Condensed milk	18.7	5.60	14.0	0.55	5.0	6.10	24.4	30	2	42	
Shell fish	25.6			0.08	0.4	3.38	13.4				
Rice alcohol	9.6	2.69	10.7								
Beer	29.0	1.20	5.0								
Total		480.14	1820.2	51.50	463.0	99.11	396.7	5096	1409	1170	162

Source: Tran-Vy et al: La Ration Alimentaire du Vietnamien. Symposium Scientifique sur les Aliments et la Nutrition, Saigon, 1957.

*calories

Table 9

July 1956—Middle Income Class
Daily Food Ration per Person

	Amount in Grams	Carbohydrates		Fats		Proteins		Vit. A	Vit. B$_1$	Vit. B$_2$	Vit. C
	Gm.	Gm.	Cal.*	Gm.	Cal.*	Gm.	Cal.*	I.U.	mg.	mg.	mg.
Bread	55.0	29.86	119.4	0.88	7.9	4.54	18.1		57		
Rice	445.1	360.39	1441.5	6.36	52.7	33.24	132.9		890	333	
Beef	24.5	0.31	1.2	0.76	6.8	4.97	19.8		11		
Pork	35.5			7.10	63.9	7.31	29.2		100	330	
Poultry	29.6	0.32	1.2	2.82	25.3	5.16	20.6		11	25	
Fresh fish	39.1			0.38	3.4	4.70	18.8	38	15		
Dry fish	5.7			0.19	1.7	2.29	9.1		5		
Eggs	23.4			3.37	30.3	3.37	13.4	783	22	96	
Chinese Cabbage	220.0	11.00	40.0	0.44	3.9	3.52	14.0	5080	66	154	88
Potato	25.8	5.54	22.1	0.03	0.2	0.52	2.0	10	18	51	4
Soya	19.2	0.08	0.2	1.08	9.7	2.14	8.2				
Banana	147.00	33.81	133.2	0.88	7.9	2.64	10.5		58	38	
Condensed milk	25.8	5.00	20.0	0.80	7.22	8.50	34.0	50	3	60	
Sugar	14.1	13.83	54.5								
Lard	16.1			15.77	141.9						
Nuoc Mam	25.5					1.25	5.0		4		
Shell fish	19.4			0.03	0.2	2.55	10.2				
Beer	35.6	.60	6.4						3	7	
Total	461.74		1839.7	40.89	367.5	86.70	335.8	5961	1233	1094	92

Source: Tran-Vy et al: La Ration Alimentaire du Vietnamien. Symposium Scientifique sur les Aliments et la Nutrition, Saigon, 1957.
*calories

Table 10

Nutrients in Vietnamese Population Diets

	Year	Proteins		Fats	Carbohydrates	Calories	Vit. A	Vit. B$_1$	Vit. B$_2$	Vit. C
		Vegetable	Animal							
		Gm.	Gm.	Gm.	Gm.		I.U.	mg.	mg.	mg.
Working Class	1951	48.77	33.28	31.01	466.67	2464.0	6525	1380	1137	141
	1952	43.48	33.90	38.00	427.30	2359.4	5631	1289	1121	136
	1953	40.51	49.11	37.32	438.41	2437.6	5103	1312	1118	81
	1954	48.75	50.36	51.50	480.14	2776.9	5096	1409	1177	162
	Average	45.37	41.66	30.46	453.13	2509.4	5588	1347	1148	140
Middle Income Class	1951	48.68	46.08	50.98	550.60	2972.2	4770	1440	1396	125
	1952	56.69	39.61	59.60	475.30	2817.3	5598	1233	1466	203
	1953	47.76	50.13	58.41	480.98	2840.8	5164	1326	1274	169
	1954	46.99	54.47	67.80	489.76	2969.5	5148	1342	1317	188
	1956	46.60	40.10	40.89	461.74	2543.0	5961	1233	1094	92
	Average	49.34	46.25	54.90	487.63	2828.5	5326	1325	1309	155

Source: Tran-Vy, et al.: La Ration Alimentaire du Vietnamien. Symposium Scientifique sur les Aliments et la Nutrition, Saigon, 1957

Table 11

Miscellaneous Crops—Area Cultivated
(Thousands of Hectares)

	1944	1950	1951	1952	1953	1954	1955	1956	1957	1958
FOOD CROPS										
Corn, total	44.0	...	...	...	...	...	...	20.5	20.0	30.8
South	8.0	2.4	7.0	12.7	6.0	5.2	7.1	7.5	6.5	12.8
Central (Lowlands)	36.0	...	...	...	...	...	...	13.0	13.5	18.0
Sweet Potatoes and Manioc, total	...							49.9	58.6	62.5
South	...	3.7	3.5	5.0	4.4	6.8	6.6	8.5	11.6	13.8
Central (Lowlands)	...							41.4	47.0	45.7
Soya and beans, total	...							10.1	12.2	14.2
South	...	3.0	3.3	2.5	2.4	1.5	1.6	2.6	4.9	8.4
Central (Lowlands)	...							7.5	7.3	5.8
Sugar cane, total	32.6							18.3	31.0	25.3
South	14.0	7.9	6.4	7.5	8.2	9.1	11.7	10.3	15.8	16.9
Central (Lowlands)	18.6							8.0	15.2	8.4
TEXTILE CROPS										
Jute, total	4.0	0.4	0.6	0.8	0.8	0.4	0.4	0.4	...	1.5
South	3.3	0.4	0.6	0.8	0.8	0.4	0.4	0.4	0.7	1.1
Central (Lowlands)	0.7	0	0	0	0	0	0	0	...	0.4
Cotton, total	...	...						...	...	1.4
South	4.7	0.8	...	...	...	...	...	...	...	—
Central (Lowlands)	9.7							1.3	1.4	1.4
Kapok, total	1.3	0.7	0.7	0.4	0.3	0.3	0.3	0.3	0.3	0.5
South	1.1	0.7	0.7	0.4	0.3	0.3	0.3	0.3	0.3	0.5
Central (Lowlands)	0.2	0	0	0	0	0	0	0	0	—

Table 11 (continued)

	1944	1950	1951	1952	1953	1954	1955	1956	1957	1958
OLEAGINOUS CROPS										
Peanuts, total	37.8	...	...	...	...	...	...	16.5	24.2	28.4
South	17.0	2.5	3.2	3.4	3.1	4.1	4.2	4.8	10.9	13.6
Central (Lowlands)	20.8	...	...	...	...	...	...	11.7	13.3	14.8
Coconuts, total	25.3	...	...	...	...	...	...	...	31.6	31.8
South	21.3	17.8	18.0	18.0	18.2	18.5	18.9	22.1	28.6	28.8
Central (Lowlands)	4.0	...	...	...	...	...	...	...	3.0	3.0
OTHER CROPS										
Tea, total	...	...	...	...	...	...	...	...	9.5	8.5
South	0.8*	0.4	0.4	0.2	0.4	0.8	0.8	0.8	0.8	0.8
Central (Lowlands)	5.6*	...	...	...	...	...	...	...	1.0	1.3
Central (Highlands)	...	2.7	2.7	3.8	4.0	4.4	4.6	6.7	7.7	6.4
Coffee, total	7.4	3.7	3.6	3.3	2.1	3.0	3.3	3.6	4.7	5.0
South	1.1*	1.2	1.3	1.1	—	0.1	0.2	0.4	0.9	1.0
Central (Highlands)	6.3*	2.5	2.3	2.2	2.1	2.9	3.1	3.2	3.8†	4.0
Tobacco, total	6.9	...	...	...	...	...	...	7.8	8.9	8.4
South	2.1	2.7	2.8	3.3	3.4	3.0	3.9	3.5	4.7	4.7
Central (Lowlands)	4.8	...	2.7	2.2	...	...	...	4.3	4.2	3.7

*1943 figure.
†Includes 300 ha in Central Lowlands.
Source: United States Operations Mission to Vietnam: Annual Statistical Bulletin, Saigon, 1959.

Miscellaneous Crops—Production

(Metric Tons)

	1944	1950	1951	1952	1953	1954	1955	1956	1957	1958
FOOD CROPS										
Corn, total	40,000	...	...	...	...	...	...	19,337	17,561	29,267
South	7,000	2,130	6,240	11,500	4,770	4,635	6,380	6,780	5,751	13,381
Central (Lowlands)	33,000	...	...	...	...	...	...	12,557	11,810	15,886
Sweet Potatoes and Manioc, total	...	...	...	...	...	...	...	244,917	292,545	298,417
South	...	36,600	34,700	47,940	44,500	68,000	66,500	85,450	116,120	112,295
Central (Lowlands)	...	...	...	...	...	...	...	159,467	176,425	186,122
Soya and beans, total	...	...	...	...	...	...	...	5,735	6,629	7,516
South	...	1,570	1,630	1,360	870	920	930	1,542	3,167	4,973
Central (Lowlands)	...	...	...	...	...	...	...	4,193	3,462	2,543
Sugar cane, total	772,000	...	...	...	...	...	...	522,790	869,890	760,578
South	422,000	194,450	160,250	163,230	244,250	274,000	357,090	322,520	578,815	608,240
Central (Lowlands)	350,000	...	...	...	...	...	...	200,270	291,075	152,338
TEXTILE CROPS										
Jute, total	1,053	440	600	700	700	315	325	382	647	1,330
South	950	440	600	700	700	315	325	382	647	1,087
Central (Lowlands)	103	0	0	0	0	0	0	0	0	243
Cotton, total	...	...	...	...	...	...	...	...	...	544
South	550	112	...	...	...	...	...	...	...	1
Central (Lowlands)	2,012	...	...	...	...	...	...	489	446	543
Kapok, total	1,700	393	393	230	186	186	186	189	180	255
South	1,500	393	393	230	186	186	186	189	180	250
Central (Lowlands)	200	0	0	0	0	0	0			5

Table 11 (continued)

	1944	1950	1951	1952	1953	1954	1955	1956	1957	1958 Production
OLEAGINOUS CROPS										
Peanuts, total	18,846	...	...	...	...	...	...	12,319	16,059	22,352
South	8,700	1,448	1,920	2,190	1,870	2,578	2,565	3,280	6,318	12,280
Central (Lowlands)	10,146	...	...	...	...	...	...	9,039	9,741	10,072
Coconuts (copra), total	26,420								23,377	20,327
South	22,000	15,500	15,500	15,500	15,500	15,500	15,500	15,500	21,107	16,341
Central	4,420	...	...	...	...	...	...	...	2,270	3,986
OTHER CROPS										
Tea, total	...	...	...	...	...	...	...	...	4,354	3,410
South	435*	150	150	80	140	306	318	322	318	339
Central (Lowlands)	...	...	...	...	...	...	...	...	636	539
Central (Highlands)	...	...	...	1,700	2,034	1,339	2,300	3,480	3,400	2,542
Coffee, total	1,915*	...	...	1,810	...	...	2,157	2,481	3,265	2,490
South	253*	350	350	320	...	....	47	151	345	142
Central (Highlands)	1,662*	...	...	1,490	1,176	1,168	2,110	2,330	2,920†	2,348
Tobacco, total	7,128	...	...	...	...	...	...	7,007	6,769	6,721
South	2,860	2,100	2,240	2,536	2,600	2,680	3,470	3,067	4,026	4,037
Central (Lowlands)	4,268	...	...	...	...	...	...	3,940	2,743	2,684

*1943 figure.
†Includes 20 tons produced in Central Lowlands.
Source: United States Operations Mission to Vietnam: Annual Statistical Bulletin, Saigon, 1959.

Table 12

Harvest Calendar

Crops	Harvest Period	Bulk of Harvest
Rice:		
Centre	Apr.-Nov.	Apr.-May
South	Sept.-Mar.	Jan.-Feb.
Sugar cane	Oct.-May	Jan.-Apr.
Sweet potatoes	Aug.-Nov.	Oct.-Nov.
Cassava	Aug.-Dec.	Oct.-Nov.
Vegetables	Whole year round	Dec.-Feb.
Cowpeas	Nov.-Feb.	Dec.-Jan.
Citrus fruits	Aug.-Feb.	Dec.-Jan.
Bananas	Whole year round	Nov.-Jan.
Mangoes	Apr.-July	May-June
Pineapples	Whole year round	June-Aug.
Soybeans	July-Jan.	Oct.-Nov.
Coconuts	Whole year round	Dec.-Apr.
Castor beans	Oct.-Feb.	Dec.-Jan.
Tobacco	Dec.-Apr.	Feb.-Mar.
Coffee	Nov.-Mar.	Dec.-Feb.
Tea	Whole year round	Sept.-Oct.
Cotton	Feb.-May	Mar.-Apr.
Jute	July-Nov.	Oct.-Nov.
Ramie	May-Nov.	July-Aug.
Kapok	Feb.-Apr.	Mar.-Apr.
Rubber	Whole year round	Oct.-Dec.

Source: Food and Agriculture Administration: World Crop Harvest Calendar, Rome, 1959.

Map 1

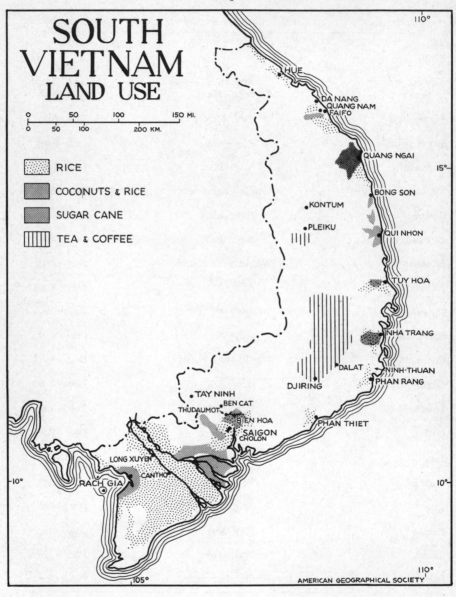

SOUTH
VIETNAM
LAND USE

0   50   100   150 MI.
0   50   100   200 KM.

RICE

COCONUTS & RICE

SUGAR CANE

TEA & COFFEE

110°

HUE

DA NANG
QUANG NAM
FAIFO

QUANG NGAI

15°

BONG SON

KONTUM

PLEIKU

QUI NHON

TUY HOA

NHA TRANG

DALAT

NINH-THUAN

DJIRING

PHAN RANG

TAY NINH

THUDAUMOT   BEN CAT

BIEN HOA

SAIGON
CHOLON

PHAN THIET

LONG XUYEN

CANTHO

10°

RACH GIA

10°

105°

110°

AMERICAN GEOGRAPHICAL SOCIETY

Map 2

LUANG PRABANG

VIENTIANE

HANOI

SAVANNAKHET

HUE

PAKSE

TONLE SAP
(GREAT LAKE)

BATTEMBANG

KOMPONG
CHAM

PNOM PENH

KOMPONG SPEU

TAKEO

KAMPOT

PREY
VENG

SUAI RIENG

SAIGON

L A O S

V I E T N A M

C A M B O D I A

MEKONG RIVER

LAOS
VIETNAM
CAMBODIA
RICE AREAS

0   50   100   150   200   250 MI.
0   100   200   300   400 KM.

AMERICAN GEOGRAPHICAL SOCIETY

CAMBODIA

I. GENERAL REMARKS

Cambodia is a country in Southeast Asia bordered on the north by Laos and Thailand, on the west by Thailand, on the south by the Gulf of Siam, and on the east by Vietnam. It has an area of 181,000 square kilometers (69,900 square miles), and an estimated population of 5 million inhabitants, of whom 400,000 live in the city of Pnom Penh.

Up to now, Cambodia has been an island of adequate food supply in a sea of food scarcity. This was due to an unusual geographical phenomenom which gives the Cambodian people an ample source of animal proteins in the form of a quasi-miraculous catch of fish every year after the floods in the inundated forests. This remarkable and possibly unique freak of nature will be discussed later.

Cambodia is heir to one of the greatest cultures and civilizations the world has ever known—the Khmer empire—which has left the Angkor monuments as a witness to its wealth and achievements. More than a million people are said to have lived in the area between the sixth and the fifteenth century A.D. Undoubtedly the food supply then was abundant, and its distribution was perhaps better than it is now. Circumstances, some of which are unknown brought about the downfall of the Khmer world at the turn of the fifteenth century. The descendents of these great ancestors have shown neither the desire nor ability to continue the tradition.

Although no vital statistics exist, except for the capital of Pnom Penh, it seems reasonably certain that Cambodia has no pressing population problem. There are no signs of unemployment, probably because employment is not ardently sought by the labor force. The low economic level is more the result of apathy and ignorance than of lack of resources. Cambodia does not even make full use of its existing commodities, and has suffered since its independence a nearly complete breakdown of its export trade, which was "in the red" by ten million dollars in 1958.

A five-year plan has been in effect since that date, aimed at increasing the gross national product by 3% a year. This goal is expected to be achieved by diversifying agriculture, which at present is tied almost exclusively to rubber and rice. Rubber culture is to be expanded from 33,000 hectares to 40,000. Cotton is to be introduced

117

with hopes of a 6,000 tons crop in 1963; sugar cane is to be developed to 60,000 tons a year by the same date. New irrigation works based on ancient Khmer irrigation systems, rehabilitated with American aid, should hopefully permit an increase in rice production, thus balancing by rice exports the imports needed for industrialization.[1] The Chinese communists are laying the foundation of industrialization by building factories for the production of cement, paper, plywood, and textiles. To this end they have placed a fund of eight million dollars at the disposal of the Cambodian government. It is said that a steel mill is also in the offing.

Because of its geographical location in one of the most strategic parts of the world, and because of its official policy of neutrality, Cambodia receives more foreign aid than any other country in Southeast Asia. No less than ten governments on both sides of the Iron and Bamboo curtains, and all the major United Nations agencies provide her with gifts and projects.

Against this favorable background, serious problems of malnutrition are known to exist, although no adequate survey has ever been conducted. These are due to traditionally ill-balanced diets and ignorance, rather than to scarcity; food is abundantly available, but the standard of living of the Cambodian people is so low that the purchasing power necessary to procure available foods is often inadequate. The average annual income amounts to approximately $44.00 per capita.

II. FOOD RESOURCES

A. CEREALS

The study of land utilization in Cambodia presents an interesting picture. Of the total surface area of 18,103,500 hectares, approximately 121,000 hectares are covered by roads, railways, and villages; 1,480,000 hectares by rivers, streams, canals, lakes, and ponds; and 12,502,500 hectares by forests, leaving some 4,000,000 hectares suitable for cultivations. These 4,000,000 useful hectares can be subdivided as follows: 2,200,000 hectares have been cleared and converted into paddy fields, only 60 per cent of which are used in any one year; 500,000 hectares of riverside lands; 500,000 hectares of "red" lands or terra rossa, fit for rice cultivation (except along the rivers. These are mostly hill lands); and 800,000 hectares of additional land available and suitable for agricultural exploitation, its utilization still undecided.

Cambodia produces three types of rice—wet rice, floating rice and dry rice. More than 80 per cent of the total acreage devoted to rice is under wet cultivation and relies on heavy rains and inundation of the rice fields by river floods. Agriculture is undertaken on a family basis with holdings not exceeding 10 acres and sometimes less, especially along the rivers.

The rice growing provinces are Battambang, Prey Veng, and Takeo. The total area under cultivation has increased by about one-half in the past eight years—from 1,027,000 hectares (exclusive of Takeo) in 1951 to 1,524,000 hectares in 1959. Production has improved in Battambang but has dropped in practically all other areas, with the result that over-all production in 1959 amounted to 1,153,000 tons, well below the 1,440,000 tons obtained in 1951. Yields also declines, from 1.22 tons per hectare in 1951 to 0.76 tons per hectare in 1959. (Table I). The reasons given for this situation are controversial and often reflect politics or propaganda biases. The lack of incentive for export due to the low prices offered by Chinese exporters on the domestic market seems to be the most important of these reasons. It has long been said that Cambodia was a Chinese colony run by the French, and it is entirely possible that harassment of the former and the withdrawal of the latter has resulted in breaking the back of the economy. Another reason for a production drop is the lack of foreign currency needed for the import of fertilizers which itself arises from the breakdown of the foreign trade. The five-year plan provides for improvement of rice production by such simple measures as raising the height of dikes in paddy fields and initiating a campaign for the use of farm manure and fertilizer, as well as by more complex measures such as the irrigation works mentioned above.

Next to rice, corn is the most extensive cereal resource although no reliable statistics exist on which to estimate surface cultivated, production, and yield. Only export figures are available, indicating a surplus of the commodity (see Table 2).

B. OTHER FOOD CROPS

Pulses are available in unknown quantities, but are adequate to provide a small export item. So also are fat producing plants such as soya, ground nuts, and sesame, and spices, especially pepper. Fruits are abundant. Pnom Penh has a special fruit market where most tropical fruits are offered for sale, including breadfruits, durians, pineapples, mangoes and mangosteens, oranges, and limes. There is no information on the supply of green vegetables.

C. SUGAR[2]

Cambodia is in an unusual situation with regard to the production of sugar. The sugar-palm tree or "Thnot" (**Borassus flabelliformis**) is characteristic of the rice fields of south and southeastern Cambodia. The tree differs in several respects from the other seventy-six species

of palm trees found in the country. Its roots are used in Cambodian
pharmacopeis. Its leaves enter into the fabrication of partitions, roofs,
sleeping mats, and bags. Its flowers when dried produce soda. But its
most valuable production is its sap which is rich in sugar and, when
allowed to ferment, produces an intoxicating wine. The sap can be collected freely for six months of the year, after the tree has reached its
twentieth birthday and for another twenty years. The collection of the
sap is rather dangerous, as it necessitates climbing to the top of the
tree. (Until recently the collectors belonged to a special group of
people who were landless and were not required to pay taxes.) The sap
is collected in a bamboo cylinder (**ampong**) placed under a wound made
on the side of the tree, allowing the juice to flow during the night. The
collection of these ampongs takes place in the early morning and the
amount of sugar that can be collected varies with the amount of sunlight that has heated the ampongs. After collection, the fluid is brought
to a boil and when the concentration of sugar reaches 85 per cent the
boiling is stopped. When allowed to cool, sugar loaves are formed; by-
products consist of wine and juices. One tree may yield up to four
hundred quarts of liquid every season, from which approximately 60
pounds of crystalline sugar is produced. An interesting sidelight is
that since the workers are not landowners, they form a migratory group,
crowding on the landed population; although the production of sugar
reached a peak of 24,000 tons, valued at $1,400,000 in 1953, the export
trade is now at a standstill. It is believed that 500,000 to 700,000 inhabitants derive a small part of their income from the sugar industry.

D. CASH CROPS

The most important cash crop of Cambodia is rubber; 36,808 hectares are devoted to this commodity in nine different areas, most of
them in the southern part of the country, north of Pnom Penh. After
suffering from the ups and downs of the rubber market around the
world, production is now stabilized at between 25,000 and 30,000 tons
a year. This gives an annual income of nine million dollars, and at
the present time seems to offer the most hopeful basis for the development of the Cambodian economy.

Other cash crops include cotton, timber, ramie, tobacco and kapok,
but these do not play any important role in the economy.[1]

E. ANIMAL PROTEIN RESOURCES[2]

Alone among South Asian countries, Cambodia has an abundance of
animal protein resources because of its fisheries. The central axis of
Cambodia is the Mekong River, which receiving on its western bank
the waters of the Tonle-Sap. During the flood season, from July

to November, the waters of the Mekong rise and flow back into the Tonle-Sap, swelling all secondary waterways and lakes (see map). The surface of the lake increases from 2700 square kilometers to 10,000 square kilometers, flooding the countryside and the neighboring forests. As a result, the stream of the Tonle Sap runs from north to south during the dry season and reverses its course during the floods.

At the time of the rising waters, the females and the young fish born in the Mekong swim back with the tide, attracted by the inundated forests which provide an enormous amount of plankton, thus offering an unusual amount of food supply. As a result certain species of fish whose length never exceeds six inches when caught in the dry season in the river, reach fourteen to sixteen inches when caught in the Tonle-Sap.

Starting with the month of November, the waters begin to recede, but the fish who start swimming with the reversed stream toward the waterways and the Mekong get caught in the trees and bushes where they can easily be taken by the fishermen. This fish migration is not continuous. It is reported to occur only during certain days of the months of December, January, and February. It begins on the sixth or seventh day of the rising moon, as soon as the moon casts a light over the landscape. If there are clouds, the pace of the migration slows down. It is then possible to place various types of fish traps in the waterways, resulting in fabulous catches. During the last days in February and March, residual pools of water are found all over the countryside where further catches can be made. The fish density of the lakes at the height of the season is estimated to be eight tons per square kilometer, or about eight times that of the North Sea, which is one of the richest fishing grounds of the world.

The fishing techniques of Cambodia vary in the rivers and in the lakes. In the wider rivers, such as the Mekong, fishing is done with seines moored to sampans, the size of the mesh varying with the size of the fish expected to be found. In the smaller streams the width is barred by bamboo screens which trap most of the fish. In larger streams a special device known as a "catching room" is built. This is a huge contraption six to eight feet high and four to six feet wide into which the fish are channeled. After the water has receded, the whole chamber is hauled and the fish collected.

In the lakes, most fishermen use nets, which are often 4570 meters (5000 yards) long and 11 meters (12 yards) high; these are carried by boats that sail around the lakes, catching entire schools of fish. Where the forest is inundated the fishermen become "hunters" and, as the waters recede, catch the fish from the treetops. In other areas, decoy bushes prepared in advance are placed where the waters are shallow. These attract the fish who usually find their food among the leaves; when the waters recede the fish are shaken from the bushes into baskets.

Since preservation facilities are lacking, the fish must be processed as soon as possible. Three main techniques are used - drying, salting, and "pasting." Drying the fish is the simplest of all operations; after removal of the head and entrails, the fish are flattened and allowed to dry in the sun for thirty-six to forty-eight hours; they are then sorted by size and put into baskets. Three kilos of fresh fish yield one kilo of dried fish. Salting is used for the smaller fish; these are pressed for twelve hours in water and brine, after which they are washed. The water is saved to produce a seasoning rich in nitrogen. The fish is then salted away in bundles for sale in the local markets.

"Pasting" is a word that covers several kinds of fish products. Fish oil is made by boiling the smaller fishes in a small amount of water; the oil collected, representing approximately 50 per cent of all the fat in the fish, can be used for lamps. Fish paste, which is considered as valuable as the actual fish, is prepared by mixing the whole fish with salt. After four to six months, the fish dissolves, and the resulting sauce is used as seasoning with rice and vegetables. The process requires several subtractions of the product, thus giving several grades of fish paste. It is believed that 95 per cent of the phosphorus and 33 per cent of the nitrogen originally present is retained. Fish meal, prepared by grinding dried fish, is said to contain 7 per cent nitrogen, 44 per cent protein, and 6 per cent phosphates. This is used as animal feed and it is hoped that a future industry of fowl and hogs might develop on this basis.

Unfortunately, the fishing industry is threatened at present by a complicated situation. Fishing grounds are leased by the government on the basis of competitive bids by Chinese fishermen, mostly Vietnamese or Chams, or they may sublet sections of the leased areas to Cambodian part-time fishermen. In most cases, these lessees depend upon the Chinese for funds with which to buy boats and equipment, and eventually find themselves in debt for life. The terms of the loans are such that in order to repay them the fishermen must turn over their catch to the Chinese at prices fixed by the Chinese themselves. Under this arrangement, the output of fish and fish products amounted to 130,000 tons in 1940. The Cambodian government, both under the French and since independence, has endeavored unsuccessfully to free the fishing industry from the Chinese yoke.

Since 1955, difficulties with Vietnam have cut off that major market. As a result, export of dried fish has stopped, and export of fresh fish has dwindled to approximately 5,000 tons a year, with a corresponding loss of valuable foreign currency.

Although Cambodia is a rich country in terms of the number of cattle per inhabitant (the ratio is 1:3), there is no scientific animal husbandry. This lack of interest is attributable to the Buddhist faith of the Cambodian, who does not feel that animals should be raised for slaughter. In certain parts of the country, even animals dead of natural causes are not eaten. However, there is no general prejudice against eating the flesh of an animal killed by someone else. This reluctance to take animal life does not extend to fish, although as we have seen most of the fishing industry is in the hands of Chinese, Vietnamese, and Chams who are not orthodox Buddhists.

There are two kinds of cattle in Cambodia: the ox, a relatively small animal weighing from six hundred to eight hundred pounds and the somewhat heavier buffalo. Oxen are used to pull the carts; buffaloes are used in the rice fields.[2]

A veterinary service created in 1920 was transformed in 1953 and its scope increased from a mere vaccination plan to a program of breeding and development. Twelve cattle farms have been established in recent years. There are no statistics on the present number of cattle but it is believed that the herds amount to more than a million head.

Hog raising is not as well developed in Cambodia as in Vietnam. The number of hogs is given as 500,000, or approximately one for every ten people. The industry is almost exclusively in the hands of the Chinese.

Meat consumption has probably fallen off in recent years, since slaughter (except for hogs, mostly consumed by the Chinese) has decreased and the population has increased (see Table 3).

The five-year plan provides for an increase in the number of head of both cattle and hogs up to 4 per cent a year. A large animal-husbandry station for cattle is scheduled to be created between Kampot and Veal Rinh. Another center, more specially for hogs, is planned for Kompong Speu. Simultaneously a modern slaughter house and a small cold storage house with a 1000 cubic meter capacity are planned.

F. EXPORTS AND IMPORTS

Cambodia is a food-surplus country, as shown in Table 2. In 1958, out of a total export trade of $25,727,628, food exports amounted to $16,448,228. The most important foodstuffs exported were rice, rice products, fish, fish products, corn, watermelon seeds, pulses, soya, ground nuts, sesame, pepper, sugar and livestock. Other exports consisted essentially of rubber.

Imports, on the other hand, included most luxury foodstuffs, such as milk and milk products, fruits, vegetables, coffee, tea, wheat flour, canned goods, refined sugar, wine, and spirits (Table 4). In 1958, these purchases amounted to $7,808,400, and total imports amounted to $38,152,971. There is no doubt that the food resources of the country are adequate for its present population and could easily be developed to meet the needs of any further population increase.

G. FOOD INDUSTRIES, STORAGE AND TECHNOLOGY

Cambodia has very little food technology. Every family husks its own rice, but some of the rice surplus is processed in the large rice-milling establishments maintained by Chinese owners in the city of Pnom-Penh. Other husking plants are in Kompong-Cham, Svairieng, and Kandal. In addition, there are some 14 distilleries, the most important of which is located at Russey Keo. No information is available on the quantity of alcohol produced from rice in the distilleries. The two largest fish-processing plants are in Kandal and Kampot.

III. DIET TYPES

Like everyone else, the Cambodian attaches great importance to his meal. This is a ritual that should not be interrupted and, as the saying goes, "Even the thunder respects the man who is eating."

Cambodians are meticulous about cleanliness and no one would partake of a meal without having previously bathed, or at least washed his hands carefully. Food is brought in serving dishes and often individual portions are placed in little squares of dry banana leaves by the owner of the house. The family sits around the table on floor mats. When bowls are used they are often covered with straw or with a cloth.

The fare varies little with the population. Khmers, Chinese and Vietnamese eat the same things. Most people eat with their fingers; only the Chinese and the Vietnamese use chop sticks.

The diet in Cambodia generally consists of rice and fish, with a variety of spices. Fish is present at every meal. Fruits are eaten in season and pulses and leafy vegetables are sometimes found in soup. Fresh fish are consumed when available at the market; as there are no refrigeration facilities. The fish are kept alive in water. The Cambodian housewife has them killed by the vendor and comes back to collect them later so as not to witness the foul deed.

The three meals of the day are similar, but every Cambodian munches food from the trays of the street vendors, which gives more variety to the menu than would otherwise be available. The diet of the Chinese population includes pork, a variety of legumes, and protein-rich soya and curds.

Small minorities such as the Khmer-loeu, who live in the less fertile lands, have a more primitive diet.[2] No study of their food habits has been made and hence no adequate basis exists to estimate the nutritive value. The Khmer-loeu live in the north in the province of Ratamakiri. They are among the most primitive people of Southeast Asia, and their culture is characterized by slash-and-burn agriculture, terrace rice,

corn, and sweet potatoes. Their rice production is inadequate. The
wealth of the village is assessed by the number of months during which
its inhabitants can live without working after harvest time. When rice
or corn are exhausted, the villagers move around, living by hunting
and gathering. The area is one of considerable undernutrition and
malnutrition. It is hoped that 56,650 hectares (140,000 acreas) in the
Khmer-loeu region can be planted in rubber, cotton and coffee. Because of its strategic value, a definite effort is being made to develop
it under the five-year plan.

Certain classes of people have a better diet than others. In Pnom-
Penh, Western customs have penetrated more widely than in the rest of
the country; soft drinks, ice cream, and other non-Cambodian delicacies are consumed. The well-to-do favor French cooking on occasion,
but the three staples remain rice, dry fish and "prahok" sauce. No
dietary studies of the food rations of the Cambodian population have
been made, but it is known that the Vietnamese laborers employed by
the French or other foreign plantation owners in Cambodia have a
standard food intake of about 3200 calories a day.

The independent laborer, however, like the rest of the nonprivileged
Cambodians gets along until his more substantial evening meal, on
what he takes with him to the fields—usually a bowl of rice and a
"tail" fish, (three little fish tied together by the tail).

Children are breast fed until they are two or three years of age,
but this is interrupted if the next child is announced. At the end of
the first month, large amounts of mashed bananas and mashed rice
are pushed into the child's mouth by the mother's tongue. The first
menstrual period of the girl is also the occasion for a change in her
diet. The girl is cloistered for a lapse of time that may vary from a
few days to a few months, depending upon the rank and social status of
the father. During that time she refrains from foods that do not have
a rice, fruit, or vegetable origin. The diet of pregnant women is limited by the desire to keep the child small, but not necessarily by taboos
as in Vietnam.

IV. ADEQUACY OF FOOD RESOURCES

A. IN NORMAL TIMES

There is no doubt that under the present circumstances, the food
supply of Cambodia is adequate. In view of the fact that no population
pressure is to be feared in the near future, the problem of food supply
is not acute. It should be noted, however, that improvement in the
food resources does not necessarily mean an improvement in the nutrition of the population. The main problems are education, better

distribution of foods, and especially the acceptance of the efforts required to procure an improved standard of living.

B. IN TIMES OF STRESS

Because the food economy is based on familial self-sufficiency, it is less vulnerable to international catastrophe than would otherwise be the case. There is no record that increased undernutrition, let alone starvation, during the second World War in Cambodia occurred when most communication with the outside world was completely severed. If the pattern of living is not too severely disrupted by the impact of the various cultures now established in Cambodia under different flags, the people generally are better protected than most against curtailment of food supplies by extraneous circumstances.

V. NUTRITIONAL DISEASE PATTERNS

There is no official information on the nutritional status of most Cambodian people. Visits to hospitals reveal many symptons of undernutrition due to ill-balanced diets and poverty rather than scarcity of food supplies. Some signs of avitaminosis are found but no cases of full-fledged beriberi are reported as, for example, in certain parts of Vietnam where mechanical milling of rice results in deprivation of thiamine. Here again the so-called backward state of the local Cambodian culture proves a protective element against disease.

VI. CONCLUSIONS

Cambodia is endowed with considerable potential in terms of food. There are a number of excellent projects designed to bring the Cambodian people to the standards of health attained by Western culture. Noteworthy among these is a home economics project in the city of Pnom-Penh, where well-to-do-Cambodian girls learn dietary principles and better cooking hygiene in an American-supported school. On the other hand, the many foreign-aid programs have a demoralizing effect on the elite and on the strata of the population which they permeate. Cambodia has through the centuries reached a status of adjustment, there is no discontent, and if the Cambodian people suffer in any way they are not aware of it. The obvious conclusion is that improvements should be balanced and gradual so as to bring about an increase in the purchasing power of the population, which in turn will provide better food supplies·and better diets.

SELECTED REFERENCES

1. Bulletins Mensuel de Statistique. Pnom Penh, 1960.
2. Cambodian Commentary, 1958-1960.
3. International Cooperation Administration. Near East and South East Asia Conference, Beirut, 1959, p. 88.
4. Steinberg, D. J. Cambodia: Its People, Its Society, Its Culture. Human Relations Area File Press, New Haven, 1959.

Table 1

Rice Production in Cambodia

Provinces		1951–52	1952–53	1953–54	1954–55	1955–56	1956–57	1957–58	1958–59
					Harvest				
				Cultivated Areas: (000 Hectares)					
Battambang		140	140	143	131	130	141	168	267
Kampot		102	90	103	102	79	91	98	106
Kandal		73	72	74	77	75	82	80	86
Kompong–Cham		110	108	113	116	115	128	125	142
Kompong–Chhnang		33	42	41	37	48	47	46	58
Kompong–Speu		85	81	81	74	62	88	95	108
Kompong–Thom		66	69	69	80	57	79	85	105
Kratié		12	12	11	9	5	9	10	12
Prey–Véng		188	169	181	200	116	207	170	201
Pursat		37	29	36	30	34	37	37	44
Siemréap		47	40	46	44	37	44	48	55
Stung–Tréng		4	2	2	6	2	8	2	10
Svay–Rieng		130	105	117	128	91	132	120	141
Takéo		—	—	—	—	—	145	143	189
				Paddy Production: (000 Tons)					
Battambang		224	238	240	57	229	260	256	319
Kampot		122	131	103	37	60	82	96	67
Kandal		80	86	80	63	70	117	100	38
Kompong–Cham		143	140	147	104	159	197	141	84

Kompong-Speu	77	89	89	62	61	116	68	50
Kompong-Thom	85	90	80	60	63	79	87	87
Kratié	13	14	15	6	8	17	11	14
Prey-Véng	226	203	208	160	131	171	143	125
Pursat	52	46	57	30	56	52	66	46
Siemréap	61	48	56	26	42	45	38	49
Stung-Tréng	3	2	2	4	2	7	2	9
Svay-Rieng	143	116	152	65	67	113	172	146
Takéo	168	154	185	62	133	161	151	73
Total	1.440	1.407	1.463	775.	1.150	1.478	1.383	1.153

Average Yield Per Hectare: (Tons)

Battambang	1,60	1,70	1,68	0,44	1,76	1,84	1,53	1,19
Kampot	1,20	1,46	1,00	0,37	0,76	0,90	0,89	0,63
Kandal	1,10	1,19	1,08	0,82	0,93	1,43	1,25	0,44
Kompong-Cham	1,30	1,30	1,30	0,90	1,38	1,54	1,13	0,59
Kompong-Chhnang	1,30	1,19	1,20	1,05	1,44	1,30	1,13	0,79
Kompong-Speu	0,91	1,10	1,10	0,84	0,98	1,32	0,72	0,46
Kompong-Thom	1,29	1,30	1,16	0,75	1,11	1,00	1,02	0,83
Kratié	1,08	1,17	1,36	0,67	1,60	1,89	1,10	1,17
Prey-Véng	1,20	1,20	1,15	0,80	1,13	0,83	0,84	0,62
Pursat	1,41	1,59	1,58	1,00	1,65	1,41	1,78	1,05
Siemréap	1,30	1,24	1,22	0,59	1,14	1,02	0,79	0,89
Stung-Tréng	0,75	1,00	1,00	0,67	1,00	0,88	1,00	0,90
Svay-Rieng	1,10	1,10	1,30	0,51	0,74	0,86	1,43	1,04
Takéo	1,10	1,10	1,17	0,41	0,89	1,01	1,06	0,39
Total	1,22	1,28	1,25	0,65	1,15	1,19	1,12	0,76

Source: <u>Bulletin Mensuel de Statistique</u>, Phnom Penh, 1960.

Table 2

Food Exports (In Tons) from Cambodia

Products	1955	1956	1957	1958	1959
White rice	5,434	14,604	64,704	83,880	60,000
Broken rice	19,296	32,604	122,484	119,616	134,064
Paddy	792	1,524	7,332	7,356	1,672
Flour (rice)	75,300	21,204	36,288	42,948	43,416
Watermelon seeds	372	312	132	240	3
Fresh fish	5,000	444	36	708	166
Dry fish	4,030	1,044	5,560	4,596	5,134
Fish oil	108	72	264	12	0
Corn	65,964	87,858	98,880	117,240	111,120
Beans (dry)	7,452	3,372	9,996	10,236	3,696
Soya	3,408	6,000	11,232	7,164	5,112
Groundnuts	192	24	444	36	840
Sesame	1,416	1,692	4,608	756	240
Pepper	696	816	984	588	1,104
Palm Sugar	3,948	852	276	—	936
Livestock (heads)	2,424	1,512	7,056	3,912	11,004

Source: Bulletin Mensuel de Statistique. Phnom Penh, 1960.

Table 3

Slaughter for Meat in Cambodia
(No. of heads)

Year	Oxen	Buffaloes	Total	Hogs
1955	38,532	1,824	40,356	304,000
1956	36,648	2,376	39,024	248,000
1957	35,952	2,244	38,196	310,942
1958	31,464	4,056	35,520	320,472
1959 (approx.)	34,871	3,464	38,335	327,996

Source: Bulletin Mensuel de Statistique, Phnom Penh, 1960.

Table 4

Food Imports (In Tons) into Cambodia

Products	1955	1956	1957	1958	1959
Milk products	2,580	2,784	3,660	8,772	3,624
Veg. & Fruit	8,676	7,368	8,028	8,608	7,032
Coffee	144	288	516	420	540
Tea	324	360	492	384	384
Wheat flour	5,232	7,488	8,500	10,668	8,568
Canned meats	588	168	432	324	264
Sugar	5,184	5,508	5,448	11,940	12,000
Canned veg. & fruit	1,116	444	1,058	804	408
Wines	456	336	408	180	240
Hard Liquors	300	312	456	840	372
Beer & other bev.	6,384	3,120	6,948	6,048	2,700

Source: Bulletin Mensuel de Statistique, Phnom Penh, 1960.

Table 5

Harvest Calendar in Cambodia

Crop	Harvest Period	Bulk of Harvest
Maize:		
main harvest	Dec.-Jan. ⎤	
secondary harvest	Feb.-Mar. ⎦	Dec.-Jan.
Rice:		
main harvest	Jan. ⎤	
secondary harvest	Feb.-Mar. ⎦	Jan.
Sweet potatoes and yams	Feb.-Mar.	. . .
Dry beans:		
Main harvest	July-Aug. ⎤	
secondary harvest	Feb. ⎦	July-Aug.
Oranges, mandarins and tangerines:		
main harvest	Oct.-Feb. ⎤	
secondary harvest	Feb. ⎦	Oct.-Feb.
Plantains	. . .	Feb.
Pineapples:		
main harvest	June-July ⎤	
secondary harvest	Feb. ⎦	June-July
Soybeans:		
main harvest	Sept.-Dec. ⎤	
secondary harvest	Mar. ⎦	Sept.-Dec.
Groundnuts:		
main harvest	July-Aug. ⎤	
secondary harvest	Mar. ⎦	July-Aug.
Sesame seed	Mar.	Mar.
Cotton	Mar.	Mar.
Tobacco:		
main harvest	May-June ⎤	
secondary harvest	Mar. ⎦	May-June
Jute:		
main harvest	Aug. ⎤	
secondary harvest	Mar. ⎦	Aug.
Kapok	Mar.-Apr.	. . .

Source: Food and Agriculture Organization: World Crop Harvest Calendar, Rome, 1959.

LAOS

I. GENERAL REMARKS

Laos is a landlocked country of Southeast Asia, bordered by Thailand on the west along a 500-mile stretch of the Mekong River, by Vietnam on the east, by Cambodia on the south, and by Burma and Communist China on the north. The total area of the country is estimated at 235,700 square kilometers (91,000 square miles). A former French protectorate, Laos acquired political independence in 1950. This status, however, has not solved the many problems faced by an underdeveloped, illiterate (80%), almost wholly agricultural (95%) country in the middle of the twentieth century.

The population is estimated by various sources at somewhere between 1 1/2 million and 3 million people, and is composed largely of primitive farmers of Thai stock (the Lao), who live on a subsistence economy in various agglomerations along the Mekong River and adjoining waterways. Minority groups comprise the mountain tribes of Indonesian and proto-Malay stocks, the traditionally commercially-inclined Chinese and Vietnamese who live mostly in the towns and larger villages, and smaller groups of Cambodians, Indians, Thais, and French. Together all these minority groups make up about 40% of the total population.

Culturally, the Lao people are related to the Thai and to the Shan of Burma. The predominant religion is Buddhism, though spirit worship of Chinese origin still prevails in some places. Every Lao male spends at least a short time as a monk in one of the country's many temples.

There are no large cities; village life dominates. In rural areas the villages are quite isolated. The two capitals—Vientiane (seat of the government) and Luang-Prabang (the royal residence)—are nothing but inflated villages, where the pattern of life is essentially rural. The country has no real economic structure. Most rural people do not use money but barter their goods; where money is occasionally involved it is used in the form of small bars of unminted silver, mostly imported, gold bars are also found now and then. However, a money economy exists in the larger towns, especially where the foreign minorities are concerned.

The present chapter is based on the scanty statistical data and

published material obtainable, on impressions personally gathered
during previous trips to the country, and on interviews held recently
with Lao residents in Vietnam and Cambodia. Nutritional studies
have not been made in Laos, nor has a medical survey been carried
out.

II. FOOD RESOURCES[1]

A. RICE AND OTHER CEREALS

There is reason to believe that the food resources of the country
are roughly adequate to meet the needs of the population, though
Laotians have always had to import a small amount of rice. Laotian
rice culture is among the most primitive in Asia. As a result, yields
are extremely poor, but it is believed that given adequate technology
and improvement in the economic structure a better yield than exists
at present could be attained. The annual harvest of rice is estimated
at slightly over 500,000 tons; requirements are said to be 550,000 tons.
The accuracy of these figures may be doubted, however, when one
knows that some domestic rice is bought by brokers at the prevailing
low price, then, after procurement of import licenses, is sold as imported rice at twice the original price.

The rice is grown on an estimated 619,700 hectares (1,531,400
acres) of land split into approximately 300,000 farms of 2 to 2.4 hectares (5 to 6 acres) each. These farms are located mainly in the lowlands and near the rivers, though tribes living in the northern mountains bordering China and Vietnam practice some terrace agriculture.
All, or almost all, of the farmers' production is for home consumption
and little more than is needed for the family is ever produced. The
Laotian of the plains knows some elements of practical agriculture; he
plows his land and uses buffalo in the fields. The mountain dweller
has no plow and bores holes in the ground with sticks to plant his rice;
he burns the hillside periodically to enrich the soil with the ashes.
Little manure is used anywhere in the country, and farm implements
are all but unknown. Most of the rice grown is of the glutinous or
sticky type. In recent years, experiment stations have been established
with foreign aid and more than 540 different varieties of glutinous rice
are being tested.[5]

Corn is also produced in certain areas, notably in the north, but the
annual yield is not known. No other cereal is worth mentioning.

B. VEGETABLES, FRUITS, AND CONDIMENTS

Leafy and other vegetables are grown in individual gardens, especially around the larger towns of Vientiane, Pakse, and Luang-Prabang,
usually by Chinese or Vietnamese gardeners who sell them to the town
dwellers. The Laotian farmer himself eats an unknown, but probably
large, amount of wild green leaves which he calls vegetables. Yams
and potatoes are also found, especially near the towns, but they are
not part of the regular diet of the masses. Tomatoes, recently introduced in certain experimental farms by UNESCO efforts, represent a
small cash crop but are scarce elsewhere.

Fruits are not abundant, with the exception of mangoes, pomegranates, tamarinds, breadfruit, durians, and bananas. Citrus fruits
are almost unknown to the bulk of the population, though they are grown
in certain areas by foreigners for sale.

Spices are abundant, especially pepper, cardamon, and chili. Palm
sugar is found here and there, as in Cambodia, but is more of a cash
product than a staple food. Laos produces about 200 tons of mined salt
every year, which forms an important part of the condiments and seasoning in the diet.

C. ANIMAL PROTEIN RESOURCES

Although cattle and other livestock are fairly numerous on a per-
capita ratio, these animals, as in most Buddhist countries, play a
small role in the diet. Occasional strips of dried or smoked meat appear on the food tray on festive occasions, especially at funerals. The
epizootic diseases that culminated during the war years have considerably reduced the herds. In recent years, however, signs of recovery
were visible (1958), and it is now possible for Laos to export annually
water buffalo, cattle, and pigs (raised mostly by Chinese). Milk is
practically unused, and eggs are considered too valuable to be eaten
except on ceremonial occasions.

The Laotians derive their animal proteins from two main sources
—fish and game.

Fish are abundant in the Mekong and subsidiary streams, and are
also found after the floods in the inundated rice fields, where women
and children catch them in baskets. In the rivers, especially in the Mekong, some gigantic species of catfish, weighing as much as 200 kilos
(450 lbs), are sometimes found.[2] No data are available regarding the
yearly amount of the fish catch, for fishing, like farming, is a family
affair. The villagers eat most of their catch and sell the rest at the
neighboring markets. Stations for fish breeding and distribution are
being established as part of the first five-year plan. Tilapia farming
has been started, following the introduction of fry from Thailand in

1954. Some fish are eaten fresh, but the greater part of the catch is processed in the form of **prajok**, fish sauces, and fish paste. These activities, known as "river-bank industries," involve only the simplest equipment. After the floods and at the beginning of the dry season, when the fish are left on the banks by the receding waters, the fishermen set up their primitive gear in well-favored spots and the farmers come to buy the fish products they need for the coming year. Ox carts on the dirt roads bring the purchases back to the villages and leave behind them a fragrance that lingers for days and weeks.

The other significant source of animal protein comes from an infinite variety of animal life which the Laotian traps, snares, clubs, spears, or just plain catches. These include representatives of every animal order—insects, worms, birds, reptiles, rodents, and the larger mammals, including dogs, cats, and tigers, and even rhinoceros and elephants. Of course the big game is not part of the everyday fare, but the smaller animals are.

D. CASH CROPS

Laos has a few cash crops, most important of which is the opium poppy. This is grown in the burned-off brushland of the hills in northern Laos and is smuggled out of the country to swell the illicit international drug traffic. Several varieties of tea are grown in the mountain areas of the north, up to 1800 meters (6,000 feet). Coffee, which use to be exported, has been blighted by disease and the crop is diminishing yearly.

E. DISTRIBUTION OF FOOD

The food resources mentioned above are as a rule not moved throughout the country. Each area has a corresponding local culture built around the most important food resources. Thus, it is possible to distinguish between the south and the north, between the rice culture and the corn culture, though farmers in each area occasionally add the other cereal to their menu. It is also true that the rice growers of the river banks eat more fish than the mountain dwellers, who in turn eat more wild game.

Whenever food has to be transported, it goes by ox cart along the trails. Other goods are moved on the Mekong, a difficult river to navigate at best. There are approximately 5600 kilometers (3,500 miles) of roads, of which only 1900 kilometers (1,200 miles) are serviceable in all kinds of weather; the rest are impassable during the rainy season. There are no railroads. This situation fosters a highly localized sort of food economy and also explains why a bag of rice which is sold

for 50 cents in the south may cost as much as $1.50 at Vientiane and
$3.00 in the north.

There is virtually no food processing and few storage facilities in
Laos.

E. EXPORTS AND IMPORTS

Laos has to import some of its rice, but the computation of exactly
how much is needed is difficult to make in view of the practice, mentioned above, of using false import licences. Available statistics of
food exports and imports are given in Tables 1 and 2.

III. DIET TYPES

Since no surveys of Laotian diets have been made, there are no reliable data on which to base either a qualitative or a quantitative estimate of the daily intake of the inhabitants. The daily intake of animal
proteins is likely to be fairly high because of the abundant fish resources and because of the omnivorous character of the Lao. Fats
from palm oil and fish are available at most meals and raw leaves of
all kinds are added to the main dish. This consists of glutinous rice
cooked with water over a charcoal fire until the water is totally absorbed in the grain—an important factor and a protection against
beriberi. Another method calls for cooking the rice in bamboo shoots
over a charcoal fire or under ashes. The poorer classes have practically nothing but the rice, to which is added salt, and some chili.
The better-off people make use of a mixture of crushed rice and fermented fish called "pa bak," or of a kind of salted fish called "badet,"
and add wild green leaves, young bamboo shoots, mushrooms, and now
and then meat, eggs, or game.

No domestic vegetables are used; sometimes farmers have small
gardens around their houses, but these are usually ill kept and produce
little. Some of the farmers cultivate the river banks, fertilized by silt
from the receding waters, during the dry season. An appreciated delicacy to season the meals is the juice extracted from the small intes-
tines of pigs or buffalo—a rather smelly sauce that only Laotians can
relish. Food is cooked once a day, for supper, and is served cold or
reheated the next day. Festive events such as marriages or funerals
offer the opportunity to add strips of smoked pork or buffalo to the
menu. Beef is not well liked, but chickens, eggs, and corn cakes may
also embellish the fare on these occasions.

Meals are taken by the family, sitting on the floor or squatting on
their heels around a tray of bamboo or, in some households, of copper.
A basketful of sticky rice is the center of the meal; if other dishes

are available, they are served in small porcelain cups surrounding the central tray. Everyone helps himself with his fingers. After the meal, the food is washed down by water taken from a big jar that is part of the household furniture. Water is drunk from one of the porcelain cups mentioned above or from a piece of coconut. Much rice alcohol is drunk, especially on festive occasions.

Salt is collected in the following way: salt-containing earth is pressed into a bamboo cylinder, one end of which contains a stopper made of straw. Water, poured through the other end, filters through the earth and then through the straw stopper. Finally, it is collected in a pan and boiled, and cakes of salt result from the evaporation of the water.

The small affluent class, consisting of upper Loatian aristocratic society and of the Chinese and Vietnamese traders, often imitate the West in their food habits or eat like the wealthy Chinese or Thai.

IV. ADEQUACY OF FOOD RESOURCES

Because of its self-contained subsistence economy, Laos is less vulnerable to outside stress than are countries like Ceylon or Malaya which depend on their trade to survive. Thus, no appreciable change was reported in the food habits of the people during the war years. Also, pests and blights are less effective in destroying food resources in a backward country.

The relatively large amount of land available for each family (5 to 6 acres) has so far been able to take care of the population pressure. Although it is true that scarcity of food may confront the country in the future, especially in view of a 2.2% growth rate, it must also be remembered that Laos is only beginning its agricultural and industrial development. It can hardly go anywhere but up.

What would happen if the country were to become a battlefield is another matter.* However, it is believed that disruption of the food economy would probably remain localized by virtue of the fact that each family supports itself. No large population group is wholly dependent for its food supply on any other group.

V. NUTRITIONAL DISEASE PATTERNS

No obvious malnutrition has been reported from Laos, though isolated cases of beriberi, expressed essentially by skin lesions and ang-

---

*In 1961 this is happening. So far, no report of food shortages has been released.

ular dermatitis, have been seen. Goiter is common in the upper valley, and in certain areas as much as 95% of the population is affected. The role of malaria in fostering wretchedness and misery in Laos is more important than that of malnutrition, and must not be overlooked.

SELECTED REFERENCES

1. Bulletin Économique du Laos. Vientiane, 1959.
2. Gosselin, C. Le Laos - protectorat français. Paris, Perrin et Cie., 1900.
3. International Cooperation Administration. Near East and South East Asia Conference, p. 106. Beirut, 1959.
4. Perazic, Elizabeth. Little Laos, Next Door to China. *National Geographic Magazine*, Vol. 117, No. 1, January, 1960, pp. 46-69.
5. Swann, Robert. Laos: Pawn in the Cold War. *Geographical Magazine*, Vol. 32, No. 8, January, 1960, pp. 365-375.
6. United States Department of Commerce, World Trade Information Service. Basic Data on the Economy of Laos. *Economic Reports, Part 1, No. 58-69*, 1958.

Table 1

Imports 1959	Weight (in Kg.)	Imports 1959	Weight (in Kg.)
Live poultry	1750	Beer	1547496
Meat and offals	2355	Wine	78801
Dried cuttle-fish	61275	Liquor and spirits (low alcohol content)	40461
Fish and shell fish	142856	Sparkling wine, champagnes etc.	16004
Milk (condensed or whole)	922636	Cordials	132996
Butter, cheese	34202	Vinegar	2678
Eggs	27221	Other alcohols	854
Onions & garlic	12412	Potatoes	1483
Sugar	66880	Dried vegetables	13152
Powdered cocoa	205	Fruit	482541
Chocolate	9175	Coffee	4371
Prepared cocoa	316	Tea	776
Chinese noodles	32769	Chillies	13526
Wheat noodles etc.	14949	Other spices	3112
Baby cereals and malt cereals	5937	Ordinary white rice	279400
Cookies	47458	Glutinous rice	4295780
Other prepared cereals	1154	Other cereals	21030
Canned vegetables	63439	Wheat flour	830630
Other preserved vegetables	31951	Other flour, tapioca	127889
Jams and canned fruits	49768	Oil producing seeds and fruit	22277
Fruit juices	8616	Other edible plants	3409
Other preserved fruit	9011	Vegetable oils	40287
Coffee extract	3774	Wax (pure and mixed)	3811
Fish sauce (nampa)	515332	Other fats	2811
Seasoning (soup)	73498	Canned meats	11498
Yeast	3175	Other preserved meats	2865
Sodium Monoglutamate	18333	Canned fish	73850
Other prepared condiments	5627	Other preserved fish	19685
Natural mineral water	40177	Beet and cane sugar	1839798
Carbonated water	89556	Glucose	8934
Ice	341270	Confectioneries and syrups	30560
Sodas and tonics	183264		

Source: Bulletin Economique de Laos, 1959. Vientiane.

Table 2a

Exports—1959

Live pigs	250	heads
" buffaloes	40,800	heads
Dried mushrooms	4,458	kilos
Fresh cabbage	460	"
Fresh fruit	100	"
Green coffee	329,480	"
Tea	1,750	"
Chillies	6,195	"
Cardamom	246,571	"
Soja seeds	135,503	"
Oil producing seeds & others	450	"
Lard	1,136	"
Refined sugar	1,100	"
Monosodium glutamate	360	"
Alcohol	7,204	"

Table 2b

Laos, Controlled Slaughter

	1958	1959
Cattle	6,759	6,953
Buffaloes	14,276	16,190
Pork	55,920	65,429

Source: Bulletin Economique de Laos, 1959. Vientiane

Table 3

Harvest Calendar in Laos

Crops	Harvest period	Bulk of Harvest
Maize	Aug.-Sept.	. . .
Rice	Nov.-Dec.	. . .
Potatoes	July-Aug. and Jan.-Feb.	. . .
Groundnuts	Aug.-Sept. and Nov.-Dec.	. . .

Source: Food and Agriculture Organization: World Crop Harvest Calendar. Rome, 1959.

THAILAND

I. GENERAL REMARKS

Thailand is a food-surplus country where people suffer from malnutrition. While in other Asian countries malnutrition is principally
due to biologic and economic causes, this Thailand paradox of hunger
in the midst of plenty has its origin in cultural conditions.

Although population has increased from a prewar total of 15 million
people to the present 23 million or more, this number is not excessive
for the carrying capacity of the 8,000,000 hectares (20-odd million
acres) of agricultural land. However, continued increase at the present
rate of 2 to 2.5 per cent a year might be of significance in two or three
decades unless a concomitant rise in the production of food, through irrigation or otherwise, occurs at the same time. So far, the country
seems to have been able to keep food production well ahead of population growth, and rice consumption per capita has increased by comparison with 1938 (Table I).

There is no real poverty in Thailand. The average farmer owns
2.4 hectares (6 acres) of land, which is more than enough to provide
for his family; should the need arise, he can find additional strips of
land for cultivation. Indebtedness on the land is less than $10.00 per
hectare (2.6 acres) or less than $5.00 per capita. These conditions
are, in general, 2 to 12 times better than in China, 1/3 to 1/2 better
than in India.

The diet of the lower-income groups among the Thais traditionally
consists almost entirely of rice accompanied by spices; a few auxiliary foods are also eaten. Such a diet provides energy values that are
nearly satisfactory but sufficient amounts of vitamins, minerals, and
valuable proteins are dangerously lacking. The rapid introduction of
mechanical hullers milling highly refined rice appears to be creating a
growing threat of beriberi, which ranks 10th among the causes of death
in Thailand. The government is aware of this situation and has attempted to introduce various measures to compensate for the nutritional losses incurred in milling rice, including parboiling and enrich-
ment. The government also recommended growing and eating more
pulses, of which only 41 thousand metric tons a year are now produced.
But here, also, traditional food habits impede the optimal utilization of
existing resources. All over the country the ratio of cereal to pulses

is high; this is true even in Chiengmai where pulses are grown for export. Eggs, most of which are sold for cash on the open market, could improve significantly the protein-to-carbohydrate ratio, but pregnant women and children are prevented from eating them by an age-old taboo.[1]

An important feature of Thailand's rice production is the large annual variation in the size of the crop, due to fluctuations in rainfall. Total paddy rice production in 1957 represented an index of 168 as against a prewar index of 100; the 1955 index of all agricultural production on the same basis was 176. During the next two or three decades, the cultivated area will grow as farmers take advantage of the margin of fallow land still available and irrigation, which is being expanded, will make double-cropping possible. "It is reasonable, therefore, to expect a fairly steady and rapid increase in Thailand's food supply during the next fifteen to twenty years. This availability of new land will give the farmers time to learn new agricultural methods that may be developed, but if the rise in population continues as it is now, problems of nutrition that will have been postponed will then loom with great severity."[9]

II. FOOD RESOURCES

A. GENERAL

The area of Thailand, including lakes and marshes, is about 51,000,000 hectares (126 million acres). Thailand is usually geographically divided into four parts: northern, central, eastern, and southern or peninsular.

Much of the north and east, which includes about 3/5 of the total area, cannot be used for agriculture because of the mountainous character of the terrain. In the east, the additional problem of scanty rainfall limits the arable areas to small valleys that must be irrigated.

The agricultural area is 9 million hectares (23.2 million acres) or a little less than 1/5 of the total.[8] Because of insufficient irrigation, very little of the cultivable area is double-cropped—not more than 20,200 hectares (50,000 acres) in 1955—most of it in the delta region where water can be raised from the rivers. Agriculture provides 45 per cent of the gross national product, and 85 per cent of the working population is engaged in farming and fishing as compared to 2.3 per cent in industry. Rice is the most important crop with 78 per cent of the total harvested area devoted to paddy rice. (Table 2)

Water is supplied by the rains and the river floods that follow. Rains are both orographic and cyclonic. In the central plains, large floods cannot occur if the typhoon rains do not fall in August and

September. If typhoon rains are scarce in September, drought can be
expected. The problem is to harness the rainfall into a profitable irrigation system; to obtain a good rice yield, the amount of water and the
timing of its arrival on the fields must be suitable for the various
stages of rice growing.

Records show that damage to crops occurs because of a) lack of
water during the plowing and sowing season in April and May; b) too
much water caused by the first heavy typhoon rains and the first rise
of the Menam River; or c) lack of water in the latter part of July and
the early part of August due to lack of rainfall.[8] A survey of the past
124 years showed that favorable water conditions have existed in 60 of
these years; in the remaining 64 the intensity and duration of the inundation was either too high and too long, thus flooding out the crops, or
too low and too short, so that the ground dried out before the crops
matured.

On the recommendation of European experts, it was decided to build
several irrigation projects in order to offset these conditions. The
most important of the projects is the Chainat Barrage which has been
strongly supported by the World Bank and by the Food and Agriculture
Organization. The Chainat project extends over 1,214,000 hectares
(3 million acres) in the 18 provinces that constitute the "rice bowl" of
Thailand. Of this area, 995,500 hectares (2,460,000 acres) will be irrigated by the end of 1960 and used for food production. The rest is
scheduled to be used for villages and town sites, fruit and vegetable
gardens, roads, railway lines, and canals.

Other irrigation projects are being developed in the Petchaburi
area, where the reclamation of 32,370 hectares (80,000 acres) is
planned. Four irrigation projects are expected to add 36,000 hectares (88,959 acres) to the land already under irrigation in the
north. Eight new projects have been developed to harness the water
supply of 3 local rivers in the northeast (which comprises 15 out of
the 71 provinces in Thailand), where soils are generally very poor.
The completion of these projects will bring the total area under irrigation to nearly 1.6 million hectares (4 million acres) in the plains.
In addition, tank irrigation in the mountainous northeast will develop
an additional 32,940 hectares (81,410 acres), with the United States
providing technical and economic assistance.[8] The area suitable for
double-cropping will thus be increased to 1/3 of the total cultivated
area (see map).[8]

B. CEREALS

Rice.   Rice cultivation varies from year to year. During 1957 it
covered 4.9 million hectares (12.2 million acres); in 1956 it totaled
5.9 million hectares (14.5 million acres). Generally, a crop of

between 4.5 and 5.5 million tons (before milling) is produced. As shown in Table I, rice production in postwar Thailand has considerably expanded. A total of 5,393,000 metric tons of milled rice was produced in 1957 and rice exports normally account for 32 to 51 per cent of the total value of exports. The output, given in Table I, was 90 per cent above the prewar average in 1956; exports have also shown an increase, surpassing the prewar level by 13 per cent (1,388,000 to 1,571,000 tons). However, it is interesting to note that the increase in export has been rather small in relation to the increase in production. This illustrates the expanded domestic consumption of rice—rice consumption reached an index of 133 in 1956 as compared to a prewar index of 100,* while a similar index of rice exports was only 89 in 1956— due partly to the population growth and partly to the increased use of rice for industrial purposes and livestock feeding.

The government policy concerning rice appears to be twofold: to promote the export of rice at good prices and thus acquire revenue for the government, and to stabilize domestic prices of rice for the benefit of the domestic consumers. Rice mills are permitted to sell rice freely for local consumption, but the entire surplus over domestic needs has to be sold to the government for export, domestic and export prices being entirely different.[4] The Rice Office of the Ministry of Agriculture can impose export quotas, as it did between August, 1957, and November, 1958, if there is a threat of shortage for domestic use. It is likely that the stabilization of prices of rice on the domestic market has had an influence on the prices of paddy at the farm level, although the latter has not been directly controlled. The Department of Economic Affairs has appointed some retail stores in Bangkok to sell rice at a moderate price to urban customers. Regarding the availability of rice to low-income groups, it must be noted that while the cost of living has risen to an index of 159 as compared to 100 in 1948 for all commodities, the cost of food has risen to only 152 and the cost of rice to 127.

Since 1954, the Rice Office has also handled all phases of research and extension work relative to rice farming. In addition to promoting seed selection and hybridization and experimentation on the use of fertilizers, the government has sold some fertilizers to rice farmers, first at half the market price and later at cost with free transportation.[4] The government has also undertaken pest-control work. At the same time, in order to encourage diversification, research work has been done on improving the cultivation of food crops and export crops other than rice.

Corn. Corn has shown an important expansion since World War II

---

*According to an estimate of the Thai Ministry of Agriculture, the domestic use of rice increased to an average rate of 3.7 per cent per year between 1947 and 1956.

both in terms of area sown (8,000 hectares in 1938 to 95,000 hectares
in 1957) and in terms of yield (index 100 in 1938 as compared to 234 in
1957). Corn is not a popular item in the daily fare of the Thai but it is
becoming an important export commodity—the area planted in corn
totals 1/12th of the area planted in rice. Corn lots are found mainly in
the Saraburi, Lopburi, and Nakorn Rajasimi Provinces.[7]

C. CASH CROPS

Tubers. Cassava is also an important cash crop although it appears
only occasionally on the farmer's tray. Formerly it was planted between rows of new tuber trees, but in the last few years it has become
a crop in its own right, especially in Cholburi and Rayong.

Pulses. Soya beans have been more extensively planted recently
—from 3,000 hectares (7,413 acres) in 1938 to 25,000 hectares (61,777
acres) in 1957—but have had a lower yield per hectare—index 100 in
1938 as compared with index 85 in 1957. The area of soya-bean production is found mainly in the north, around Chiengmai, Prae, and
Nan. Other small patches occur elsewhere. An average of 20,000
tons are produced every year, of which 7,000 are exported.

Mungbeans form a valuable crop. The seeds are eaten locally and,
in addition, starch made from these beans is used for making noodles.
The amount harvested every year is increasing considerably and mung-
bean export for noodle-making tripled between 1954 and 1957.

Peanuts and other groundnuts. Peanuts and other groundnuts are
among the most important crops grown because of their export value
and because of their by-products, oil and the seed cakes that are used
for animal food. In 1957, a total of 94,981 hectares (234,754 acres)
were planted in groundnuts, primarily in the Bangkok Plain. This was
an increase in planted area from 63,000 hectares (155,679 acres) in
1948. The yield per hectare was expressed by an index of 132 in 1957
compared to 100 in 1948, the total production almost doubled to well
over 100,000 tons, which allowed the valuable export of 20,000 tons of
nuts, 6,000 tons of cakes, and 1.3 million liters of oil.

Sugar cane. Sugar cane has also shown a great expansion since
the end of the war. The area planted increased from 58,000 hectares
(143,323 acres) in 1948 to 127,000 hectares (313,829 acres) in 1957,
the index of yield from 100 to 137, and the index of production from
100 in 1938 to 1,589 in 1957. The harvest areas include the Provinces
of Cholburi, Rayong, Lampang, Utaradit, Ubol, Udom, Nakorn Rajisma,
and Petchaburi. Sugar, a well-liked commodity in Thailand, also
comes from other sources, such as coconuts. There is not enough
sugar produced from all the sources to meet the demand of over 70,000
tons a year and approximately 35,000 tons must be imported.[4]

Coconuts. Coconuts are one of the major economic crops; they are grown all over the country and they furnish the people with fruit, sugar, oil, fiber, thatches, and drink. Coconut milk is an important ingredient in food recipes, but no accurate data are available to indicate home consumption of coconut or coconut products. Most growers are small holders.

Fruit and vegetables. A total of 676,000 hectares (1,672,000 acres) are under fruit production, with most of the fruit orchards situated on the banks of the Menam River near Bangkok. A large part of the fruit produced is eaten "out of hand," or served as dessert. In some instances such fruits as mangoes, durian, and bananas are eaten with specially prepared glutinous rice. Popular confections are prepared from fruits, and cooked, dried, and pickled fruits are also consumed in quantity. Only a few kinds of fruits, tangerines, oranges, and palm fruits are exported to markets of nearby countries.

Vegetables are grown in house compounds throughout the year; some are sold in nearby markets, but most are consumed by the family. These vegetables include chilies, spices (the Thai love "hot" foods), onions, garlic, cucumbers, cabbages, lettuce, eggplant, tomatoes, peppers, bamboo shoots, and green peas.

D. NONEDIBLE CASH CROPS

The primary nonedible cash crops are cotton and rubber. Rubber planting is confined mainly to the southern provinces, but some scattered patches occur in other provinces. Rubber production has increased four-fold from prewar output, through better yields rather than expansion of acreage. Domestic consumption is about 1,000 tons. Exports of rubber (130,000 tons a year up to 1955) bring valuable foreign exchange. Rubber's effect on diets is remote.

Cotton production has risen five-fold since 1938, mainly because the sown area has increased from 6000 hectares (14,827 acres) in 1938 to 41,000 hectares (101,315 acres) in 1957. Cotton supplies only local needs and has no impact on the foreign-currency earnings of the country.

E. ANIMAL PROTEIN RESOURCES[8,4]

In Thailand, from early times, animal proteins have come essentially from fish. If sufficient quantities were eaten regularly, the Thai diet could be considered a reasonably well-balanced one. Fisheries rank next to agriculture in extent and value among the basic industries of the country and have a three-fold importance: as a source of indispensable food; as a means of livelihood for a large part of the population; and as a source of revenue for the government.

Most numerous of the fresh-water fish are members of the carp family (**Cyprinidae**), and of these the most important are the **Puntius** ("Pla tapein"), the **Osteochilus** ("Pla prom"), and the **Dangila** ("Pla san"). Next in importance come the varieties of catfish. These include the Clarias ("Pla duk") and the Wallagonia ("Pla Khao"). In addition, there are many species of marine fish, but most of the fish eaten by the Thai are caught in the many rivers and canals ("Klongs").[6]

In spite of the abundance of fresh-water fish, Thailand is aware of the importance of perpetuating the supply. Three fish sanctuaries have been established: at Bungborapet, Kwan Payao, and Nongharn in the eastern part of the Korat Plateau. In addition, the government encourages pond fish culture, which, however, is still in its beginnings. Fish culture in the true sense of recent birth as far as food fish are concerned although fighting fish have been bred for a long time. Thousands of small fish ponds are maintained by farmers in various parts of the country, notably along the canals in the central plain. Since the ponds are deeper than the adjacent canals and are connected with them, they are used by the fish as refuge at low water. Such ponds often become crowded with fish and they can be "bailed out" as required. A fish pond 14 kilometers north of Bangkok carries out work that more closely resembles scientific fish culture. Several species of fishes are bred at this station. In addition, large quantities of carp fry are imported every year from China and reared by the Chinese community in Bangkok. Annual output of fisheries has been estimated at 200,000 tons of which 140,000 tons come from the sea and 60,000 tons are fresh-water products.

Control of fisheries. Both fresh-water and salt-water fisheries are under the control of the central government and all operations are subject to the granting of licenses and the payment of fixed annual fees. Exclusive privileges such as fishing in a given lake or the taking of turtle eggs on a given island may be granted to an individual on the basis of competitive bidding.[8]

Other animal proteins. Only a small percentage of the animal proteins consumed by the Thai are provided by domestic animals. There are approximately 5,640,000 head of cattle, 5,800,000 buffalo, and 6,000,000 swine in the country. However, water buffalo and cattle are chiefly used as draft animals. They are also a criterion of wealth. The center of cattle and water buffalo production is in the northeast. Government livestock stations are located in many parts of the country to maintain breeding herds of all classes of livestock. It is hoped that Thailand in the not too distant future will develop its livestock industry to the point where it can export animals on the hoof, and also refrigerated meat, to neighboring countries.[5]

F. SALT

Most of the salt is obtained from sea water, the chief salt pans lying around the head of the Gulf of Siam. As in other places, salt water is pumped onto the pans and then allowed to evaporate. In several places inland, chiefly in the eastern provinces, salt is also obtained from brine wells and from scrapings of the surface soil. In Ubon and Udom provinces, there are many localities where the surface soil is rich in salt.[8]

G. EXPORTS AND IMPORTS

Thailand is a food-exporting country and the amount of rice exported every year since 1954 has exceeded 1 million tons and brought an income of $140 million a year. Other food exports include groundnuts (20,000 metric tons) mungbeans (20,000), soya beans (8,000), tapioca flour (55,000), and salt.

However, Thailand has to import sugar and milk products, the latter almost exclusively for the foreign population.

H. FOOD INDUSTRIES, STORAGE AND TECHNOLOGY[3]

The food-processing industry can be said to be well developed for a Southeast Asian country. Probably the most important type of food processing is the fishery products industry. Fishermen do not distribute their catches directly to the consumers, but dispose of them through middlemen, who preserve the catch for marketing, mostly by salting.

Several methods of processing fishery products are in use. They include both the salting and drying process used for the most common fish, especially the Pacific mackerel, and also the long-dried process used for larger fish. Enzyme hydrolysis is used especially for small shrimp, which are ground and dried in the sun, making a shrimp paste very similar to that made in Malaya. Sometimes the same process is used in making a paste from heavily salted small fish, which are macerated and then sun dried. The liquid drawn off in this process is known as fish sauce. Carbohydrates, usually roasted and ground rice, are often added for flavoring to this hydrolyzed, salted paste. The mixture is called "phachon" if made of small fish, or "kungchon" if made of shrimp.[3]

Another important food-processing industry is rice milling. Steam or motor-driven mills are scattered all over the rice-producing areas of the country and only in a few remote localities does one still find the old method of milling by pounding in a wooden mortar.

Tapioca flour made from cassava is milled in about 200 small fac-

tories, mostly in Cholburi and Rayong. A few of these are modern factories, capable of producing 18 to 20 tons of flour a day, but most of the
factories lack modern machinery and equipment. However, a few larger
modern mills were being built in 1957 for completion around 1960, with
the purpose of producing tapioca flour of higher quality for the world
market.

Sugar is produced in a number of local sugar mills, which use open-
pan methods. Relatively few sugar mills produce plantation white sugar.
Some mills depend partially upon the supply of brown sugar produced
by scattered smaller mills; this procedure often results in considerable
loss of sugar. In an attempt to make the country self-sufficient in
sugar production, a number of modern sugar mills of large capacity are
being erected at Lampang and Utaradit by the semigovernmental sugar
corporation. The newly constructed mill at Cholburi has a capacity of
1,500 tons of cane per day, and another mill presently under construction is to grind 2,000 tons of cane per day. It is expected that Thailand
will produce enough cane sugar for her own consumption and may have
a small surplus for export after 1960.

The alcohol industry produces 40 million liters (10 million gallons)
of spirits per year, of which 45 million liters (1 million gallons) is
known as Mekong Whiskey.[3]

The fats and oil of Thailand could form the basis for increased industrial development. The only important production of edible oils is
from coconut oil, groundnut oil, and industrial rendering of lard.

There are 6 medium-size coconut oil factories, 4 in Bangkok and
2 in the south, and 10 small factories, located mainly in the south.
Of the 13,000 tons of oil produced, about 1/3 was refined. The equipment in most of the medium-sized factories is deemed to be reasonably
good, but owing to lack of technical knowledge processing is not always
satisfactory. The total quantity of copra extracted in 1957 was estimated at 22,000 tons. In many cases, copra making is done in a primitive way, with the result that the quality of the product is lower than
it need be. The success of the copra and coconut oil industry will depend both on the world prices for these products and on the efficiency
of the Thai in producing high-grade copra and in improving the extraction rate of the oil mills. The recent considerable rise in the world
price for copra and coconut oil (1959) should stimulate the production
of these commodities.[3]

There are 18 relatively small groundnut oil mills, mostly in the
Bangkok-Thonburi area. Most of these oil mills operate in a very
primitive way. The total production of groundnut oil in 1957 was estimated at about 5,500 tons and most of this was used without refining
for human consumption.

There are only a few primitive factories for the rendering of lard.
Although exact data is not available, it is probable that the production

for 1957 did not exceed 2,000 tons. Lard is a very popular cooking fat
in Thailand, but it is usually rendered at home.

Little information is available on refrigeration facilities in Thailand,
although there are several such plants in the major cities, especially in
Bangkok.

III. DIET TYPES[5,1,3,7]

A. GENERAL

Although the Thai's diets need improvement in terms of protective
substances, they are better than those of most other Southeast Asian
countries.

As already stated, the staple of diet is rice, which is increasingly
polished and milled mechanically, thus removing a considerable amount
of its nutritive value, and only in a few areas is the rice still milled at
home by wooden pestle in a wooden mortar. Unfortunately, in the
densely populated Menam Delta, many Thai farmers have taken advantage of the proximity of the commercial rice mills to have their families' rice supplies milled. The result is that delta farmers have the
highest incidence of beriberi in Thailand. In certain areas, Chinese-
owned rice mills are being replaced by government-controlled stand-
ardized mill systems, which might do a better job of keeping the
nutrient in the kernel.

The mills are popular not only because white rice is considered
more palatable, but also because they save time and labor. Since
these rice hullers have been introduced in many provinces of Thailand
the problem of maintaining the thiamine-to-calorie ratio above the
0.18 danger point has become of national importance. Several methods
have been recommended to re-establish this ratio. Encouraging hand
pounding is the most obvious one, but at the beginning of the planting
season when all members of the family are busy, the temptation to
send the rice to the mill, if one is available, is too great to be resisted,
and soon this labor-saving measure tends to become a permanent habit.

Parboiling by modern processes may well be the best solution for
the preservation of the vitamin content of rice milled in large mills,
but would be hard to popularize in rural areas. This process, which
consists of soaking the rice, followed by steaming or boiling, and then
drying, results in a final product very similar in appearance to ordinary white rice. However, this product is not acceptable to the Thai
farmer because the flavor is slightly different from the rice to which
he is accustomed.

Enriched rice is produced by adding a small portion of specially
treated rice grains (Premix) to a large bulk of milled rice. The

special grains, impregnated with thiamine and other nutrient supplements according to the needs of the particular area, are made comparatively resistant to washing and cooking losses by applying a final water-proof coating. The mix thus produced is fed into the rice coming into the mill at a fixed speed, usually one grain to 200 ordinary rice grains, but it would be difficult to induce small village millers to purchase this concentrate and mix it carefully with each individual lot of rice. Oddly enough, while rural families are reluctant to adopt enriched products, they have readily changed from home-pounded rice to the labor-saving but nutritionally inferior mechanically milled rice.

Still another method is to control the percentage of the rice removed by the hullers. At present, almost all mills process the rice finely, breaking it up badly. An education program in the villages might help to prevent the complete swing-over from the undermilled rice of the mortar and pestle to the highly refined rice that comes out of the mills. It might also be possible to devise ways and means for the villagers to prepare bran as an acceptable addition to the normal diet.

Finally, the danger of thiamine deficiency can be averted if the other factors in the diet include protective elements. Some rural areas have large supplies of fresh vegetables and fish, and may compensate the losses caused by milling, but other areas, particularly in the northeast, are lacking in these foodstuffs. The peasant of the northeast, for instance, does not have enough water to grow vegetables and must depend on dry fish during most of the year.

Pulses are a potentially rich source of both proteins and vitamins at present available but eaten only in very small quantities. Thai people eat them sprouted, as noodles, in sweet cakes, and in curry. These dishes are considered to be special and are eaten mostly on festivals or weekly market days, not as daily staple food as they are in India and many other parts of Asia and the Far East. Thai authorities hope to increase the quantity eaten if a large supply can be made available at a low cost, because these foods have prestige value and their flavor is popular. However, it is recognized that it would be a major undertaking to alter the food habits and agricultural patterns of Thailand to the extent needed to raise the consumption of pulses to the 36 grams per day per head, which is required to make the ratio of cereal to pulses protective.

Eggs, an important source of animal protein, also are eaten in very small quantities, although they could be produced in almost every homestead in the rural areas. Instead, they are used as cash crops.

In general, one may say that owing to the lack of education and proper knowledge of the nutritional value of native foods, the Thai people neglect to eat high-value foods that are readily available. This applies especially to the feeding of infants and children whose diets are badly in need of nutritious foods such as eggs in order to insure optimal growth and well being.

B. IN RURAL AREAS

A number of surveys of diets eaten by various groups of the Thai
population have been made. These surveys were based on a certain
number of families of varying economic status and included data on
the weight and amount of food consumed, and the number, age, and
economic position of persons in the family. Families were visited
after each meal was cooked and eaten. Each article of the diet was
noted and the amount weighed, the weights being recorded as "weight
cooked" and "weight left-over." Estimates of the nutritive value of
each diet in these surveys were based on published analyses of diets
in the Far East and in the United States.

The nutrition pattern of the rural Thai is, like that of most people
of the Far East, closely correlated with the annual cycle of activities
(Table 3).[1,5]

Rice begins to mature in November and the harvest goes on until
the beginning of February. Every daylight hour is used and threshing
continues far into the night. The harvest coincides with the matura-
tion of the best species of fish in the canals, so that families are
divided between harvesting and fishing, while some, especially the
younger children, stay home to take care of the babies and toddlers.

The hot, dry, post-harvest season is occupied by festivities, both
familial and religious, coinciding with the onset of the rains. Late in
May the preparation of the fields for the next rice cycle begins. During the busiest part of the year, food may be cooked once a day and
saved for the other meals, taken sometimes in the field, sometimes in
the home. While the fish and sweets must be protected from ants,
rice may be stored any place - providing the dogs cannot get at it.
These practices account for much food pollution.

During the least busy time of the year, food is prepared twice a
day, and in all meals rice is the main item. Everyone, including children 6 years of age, can cook rice. Breakfast is eaten at dawn
around 6 o'clock, usually consisting of rice and coconut milk obtained
by squeezing coconut gratings in water. Curry is often added to flavor
the rice. At lunch and supper, additional dishes, especially vegetables,
occasionally eggs, and roasted or boiled fish, all seasoned with fish
sauces, are served. Fruits are seldom included in the main meals
but are eaten at those in-between snacks that support the pleasure of
living among almost all oriental people.

Minburi. In the Minburi District of Pranakara Province, 40 kilometers from Bangkok, 12 families were investigated; well-to-do,
middle-income, and poor. The average daily consumption unit of the
12 families was 2,637 calories, in which carbohydrates accounted for
84 per cent or 496,50 grams, proteins for 11 per cent or 65,79 grams,
and fat for 5 per cent or 28.90 grams of the total calories. The calorie intake ranged from 1,896 to 3,764 with no correlation to economic

level. From this survey it would seem that the average diet of the people of Minburi is deficient in good-quality proteins, in fats, and in vitamins of the B-complex, while the number of calories appear to be sufficient. It is suggested that the people should be educated to balance their one-sided and vitamin-deficient diet by eating more eggs, fish, beans, vegetables, and fruit. Typical examples of these diets are given in Tables 4, 5, and 6.

Ubol Rajadhani Province in northern Thailand. Surveys carried out in this region indicate that the diet consists mainly of glutinous rice, small amounts of fermented fish, and fresh fish if available locally. Chicken and pork are eaten one or twice a week. Few vegetables are used in the diet, particularly in the dry season when no vegetable can be grown for lack of water. In the rainy season more vegetables are available. Leaves of trees are used as vegetables in this region and it is suspected that such leaves may contain significant amounts of oxalic acid. The daily diets contain small quantities of pulses, sometimes made into a sweet.

Home-milling of rice has been gradually disappearing in this province, as in many others, since rice mills have been installed. As a result, more and more beriberi cases have been admitted to the Ubol hospital. Diets are generally deficient in protein and in vitamin C, thiamine, and riboflavin, and signs of vitamin deficiency have been observed in the schools. Soya-bean products, like soya sauce and soya paste, are used as condiments in food. The experiments with soya milk conducted in different parts of Thailand show that the children like the taste of it and that it could become popular, but soya-bean growers are restricting their acreage in the area because of lack of demand in the markets.

Peanuts are grown locally in the Walin and Ammath Districts, and 30 pounds of unshelled peanuts cost only 50 cents. During May and June mushrooms are plentiful, and the local variety is highly appreciated in Bangkok. A small canning center has been established for canning or cottling mushrooms. Pork costs 10 cents a pound while in Bangkok it costs 25 cents. The farmers are not able to sell their pigs because of transportation difficulties.

In the Muang District of the same Province a dietary survey of 30 families gave the results shown in Table 7.

Chengmai Province. Twenty villages in the Sansai District, Chiengmai Province, were studied. Thirteen years ago this area was opened up by a new irrigation project; families from surrounding parts bought the land cheaply and received loans from the government's Cooperative Department to clear the jungles and start farming. As families gradually moved in, the farmers in each new village joined together to form their own registered cooperative. There is a Cooperative Department Office in the center of the area, with 6 officers who handle cooperative loans and advise the villagers.

Almost all the rice eaten in this region is of the glutinous variety.
Glutinous rice is soaked for 12 hours before steaming, which may affect the results of the dietary survey. Details of this diet are found in
Table 8. The average number of calories consumed was 2,083. Some
432 people among those surveyed were examined clinically; 10 of them,
or only 2.3 per cent, were found to show signs of beriberi; 5.8 per
cent had nutritional glossitis; and 7.6 per cent had nutritional hyperkeratosis. Thus, it was found that 68 people, or 15 per cent of the
sample, had some defective nutritional condition. The interesting
aspect of this study is that most of the people examined had the habit
of pounding the rice at home, which meant that the ratio of calories to
thiamine in their diet was well above the 0.18 danger point. Such a
diet is not likely to be associated with severe beriberi, and indeed the
only 10 people who showed signs of beriberi had, contrary to the usual
habit, all used rice from the mills. In other districts of the Chiengmai
Province where the diet is similar to that of the Sansai families just
studied, rice is processed by mechanical hullers. Soon after these
were introduced in the villages, an epidemic of beriberi occurred during which some 2,000 cases were reported.[1]

Cholburi Area, Panusnikon District.   Cholburi is a prosperous
province of Thailand, about 100 kilometers southeast of Bangkok. It
consists of 8 villages with 330 families and a population of 1,500,
mostly farmers with a somewhat low standard of living. Their chief
income is derived from rice production with the exception of a few
families who support themselves in part by constructing bullock carts.
The diet per capita per day provides 1,746 calories and includes 15
grams of animal proteins and 33 grams of vegetable proteins. The average consumption of rice, mostly home pounded, was 425 grams per
head per day, meat 5 grams, and varieties of small fish 69 grams.
Details of this diet can be seen in Table 9. Such a diet is very unbalanced, and is representative of the diets recorded in numerous groups
throughout the kingdom, even in Bangkok itself.[7]

C. DIETS IN SPECIAL GROUPS OF THE POPULATION

Armed forces.   Thai authors have found that incidence of nutritional disorders is very high in the navy. The most commonly observed deficiency disease was beriberi, followed by glossitis,
keratitis, and stomatitis. Analysis of the diets used in the navy showed
that caloric content was adequate; that vegetable protein intake was
higher, and animal protein lower, than recommended; and that the intake of calcium, thiamine, niacin, vitamin C, vitamin A, and riboflavin was below standard.

A survey of the dietary situation in the army was carried out in
1955-1956 in 16 units of provincial garrisons. The average weight of

the men was 55 to 65 kilograms, while the total caloric intake was at least 3,000 per capita, 80 per cent of which came from rice. In 13 samples, the number of calories rose to 4,000. The consumption of fats, animal proteins, calcium, and vitamin A was below standards recommended by the United States National Research Council.[8]

Children. Over half of the children do not eat a regular lunch. Schoolchildren either bring their lunch from home, go home for lunch, or buy lunch from vendors. Food so purchased mainly consists of rice mixed with soup containing 2 to 3 small pieces of meat. School-lunch programs are being considered. The diet of infants and pre-school children is much worse than the adult diet. Infants, on the whole, are given adult foods at too early an age. The most common type of supplements are cooked rice, ripe bananas, dried fish, pork, and other meat. Cow's milk is not available in the remote rural areas except in the form of sweetened condensed milk. Orphans or babies whose mothers have insufficient breast milk are fed either by the neighboring lactating women or fed with cooked rice with banana and other family foods as they can take them. Most infants are flabby, listless, underweight, and are apparently malnourished. The preschool and school children, especially in rural areas are found to be small for their age with generally retarded development. Their nutritional status is marginal.

IV. ADEQUACY OF FOOD RESOURCES

Since the diet is essentially based on rice production, anything that may interfere with the success of the rice crop adversely affects the diet, both because it reduces the main export product on which the acquisition of foreign currency is based, and also because it may reduce the domestic supply of rice. We have already alluded to the bad rice-crop years caused by lack of rain. It may be noted in passing that the successful development of irrigation schemes will probably offset the danger of shortages in the near future.

Rice-field pests present a big problem. Up to 1957, almost 10 per cent of all control work was undertaken by the government free of charge, and since only a very small force of trained men and a comparatively small budget were available, only a fraction of the total area could derive benefit from pest control. A small charge is now made for these services at least in some cases. Control of rice-field pests also is hampered by the farmers' conservatism and by the cost of chemicals and equipment. A further difficulty stems from the variety of paddy-field types that exist in Thailand - the transplanted paddy field, the broadcast paddy field, the floating paddy field, and the upland field - each requiring different techniques and methods of

insecticide application. Since sprayers and dusters are not manufactured locally, but must all be imported from countries where the terrain is different, such equipment is often not as well adapted to the
country as one would wish. Furthermore, all equipment has to be
easily portable since the country does not lend itself to mechanized
transportation. At present there is very little such equipment available. Finally, the farmers are not yet well enough educated to use the
pesticides toxic to man with safety.

While the Thai diet for the time being is not dependent upon livestock, the fight against livestock diseases and parasites is a problem
in this tropical country. An international immune belt for the eradication of rinderpest disease has been established in cooperation with the
neighboring countries of Vietnam, Laos, and Cambodia. Government
livestock stations are located in many places where breeding animals
are kept. Farmers can get free service from these animals if they so
desire, as well as education in methods of breeding, feeding care, and
management of livestock from the stations. While the higher authorities are well aware of the problems involved in improving livestock
and protecting the livestock capital against disease, modern methods
of animal husbandry are still in the beginning stage.

V. NUTRITIONAL DISEASE PATTERNS

Multiple vitamin and mineral deficiencies and cases of protein malnutrition occur in Thailand. In rural areas, 68 per cent of the school
children are free of caries of permanent teeth, but 54 per cent show
various signs of nutritional deficiency. This percentage increases in
the older age groups—only 6 per cent of the children under 6 years of
age show signs, as compared with 25 per cent of children above 15.
Hemoglobin values of less than 11.5 grams per 100 milliliters were
observed in 8 per cent of the children. Signs most frequently observed
included xerosis of the skin in 15 per cent of the cases; enlarged liver
in 9 per cent; dry, scaling hair in 8 per cent; leg ulcers in 6 per cent;
phrynoderma in 5 per cent; and bowed legs in 4 per cent. The average
weight and height of Thai children is given in Table 10.[4]

Beriberi is an important problem in Thailand whether it occurs in
small epidemics or sporadically. Many people present some mild
signs of the disease such as numbness of the feet or weakness when
walking. Signs of avitaminosis, including nutritional glossitis with
fissured tongue and atrophy of the papillae, hyperkeratosis, dry skin,
and areas of desquamation also are frequent, especially in children.

VI. CONCLUSIONS

While the Thai enjoy an abundance and variety of basic foods unknown to their neighbors, poor nutritional patterns based on tradition
and culture result in observable dietary deficiencies. The diet is
quite unbalanced, most calories being derived from rice, while the
consumption of protective foods is below minimum standards. Diets
do not seem to take advantage of available commodities such as fruits,
the consumption of which may not be accurately recorded.

The diet of infants and of pregnant and nursing women is particularly poor due, at least in part, to the numerous food taboos and prejudices that are still prevalent.

SELECTED REFERENCES

1. Chandrapanond, Amara, and Ritchie J. A Nutritional Survey in North Thailand
   and Its Implications with Regards to Beriberi. *Journal of the Dietetic Association*, Vol. 35, 1959.
2. De Young, Maurice. Village Life in Modern Thailand. Berkeley, University of
   California Press, 1952.
3. Food and Agriculture Organization. *Development of Food Industries and Food
   Technological Research No. 1138*. Rome, 1959.
4. Food and Agriculture Organization. Price Policies in Asia and the Far East.
   Bangkok, 1958.
5. Hauck, H. M., *et al*. Food Habits in a Siamese Village. (New York State College
   of Home Economics and South East Asia Program.) *Journal of the Dietetic
   Association*, Vol. 35, 1959, pp. 1144-1148.
6. International Cooperation Administration. Near East and South East Asia Conference. Beirut, 1959.
7. Thailand, Ministry of Health, Division of Nutrition. Personal communications.
   Bangkok, 1955-1959.
8. Thailand Past and Present. Ninth Pacific Science Congress, November 18-30,
   1957. Bangkok, 1957.
9. Thompson, W. S. Population and Progress in the Far East. Chicago, University
   of Chicago Press, 1959.

Table 1

Thailand: Population and Rice Production, Consumption and Exports,
1934-1938 Average and 1947-1957

Year[a]	Population Mid-Year (1,000)	Production	Domestic Consumption	Export
		(1,000 metric tons, milled rice equivalent)		
1934-1938, average ..	14,492[b]	2,832	...	1,388
1947.................	17,478	2,887	2,598	385
1948.................	17,808	3,579	2,674	812
1949.................	18,145	4,443	2,767	1,215
1950.................	18,488	4,345	2,876	1,508
1951.................	18,837	4,408	2,959	1,612
1952.................	19,193	4,761	3,035	1,413
1953.................	19,556	4,291	3,265	1,342
1954.................	19,925	5,355	3,471	1,018
1955.................	20,302	3,711	3,377	·1,228
1956.................	20,686	4,769	3,445[c]	1,239
1957.................	21,076	5,393	...	1,571
1958.................		7,128		

(a) Calendar years except for production figures which refer to crop years
(e.g. 1947 = 1946/47).
  (b) 1937.
  (c) Preliminary.

  Source: Population: United Nations, Demographic Yearbook; United Nations,
Population and Vital Statistics Reports. Rice production and exports: FAO,
Yearbook of Food and Agricultural Statistics and Monthly Bulletin of Agricultural
Economics and Statistics. Domestic consumption estimates: Ministry of Agricul-
ture, Thailand, Agricultural Statistics of Thailand, 1955.

Table 2

Thailand: Area, Yield and Production of Selected Crops, 1934–1938 and 1948–1952 Averages and 1953–1957

Period	Paddy	Maize	Soya beans	Groundnuts	Sugar cane	Tobacco	Cotton	Rubber
	Harvested area(a)(1,000 hectares)							
1934–38 av.	3,370	8	3	...	...	10	6	...
1948–52 av.	5,211	34	17	63	58	33	34	251
1953	5,931	47	24	72	83	53	40	275
1954	4,524	52	22	79	96	54	34	282
1955	5,356	55	21	78	103	56	32	291
1956	5,762	82	24	81	121	56	39	272
1957	4,576	95	25	95	127	61	41	...
	Yield per hectare (Index: 1934–38 or 1948–52 = 100)							
1934–38 av.	100	100	100	...	...	100	100	...
1948–52 av.	102	149	63	100	100	95	71	100
1953	108	177	71	114	129	107	75	86
1954	98	195	76	123	146	111	79	103
1955	106	200	74	127	150	115	93	111
1956	111	230	72	132	135	120	100	122
1957	97	234	85	132	137	125	98	...
	Production (Index: 1934–38 or 1948–52 = 100)							
1934–38 av.	100	100	100	...	100	100	100	100
1948–52 av.	157	620	350	100	379	299	350	323
1953	189	1,020	502	130	697	547	450	306
1954	131	1,240	550	153	934	578	400	373
1955	168	1,340	500	156	1,034	614	400	415
1956	190	2,296	550	168	1,467	640	550	426
1957	131	2,736	688	197	1,589	733	550	434

(a) Rubber: tappable area.

Source: FAO, Yearbook of Food and Agricultural Statistics, and Monthly Bulletin of Agricultural Economics and Statistics, except figures for acreages of rubber and yields of rubber, and sugarcane, which are derived from Ministry of Agriculture, Thailand, Agricultural Statistics of Thailand, 1956.

Table 3

Harvest Calendar

Crops	Harvest Period	Bulk of Harvest
Maize	July-Nov.	July
Rice	Oct.-Mar.	Nov.-Jan.
Sugar cane	Oct.-Mar.	Dec.-Feb.
Soybeans	Nov-Apr.	Mar.-Apr.
Groundnuts	Aug.-Nov.	Aug.
Sesame seed	Sept.-Nov.	Oct.
Coconuts	Whole year round	Dec.
Tobacco	Jan.-Mar.	Feb.
Cotton	Nov.-Feb.	Dec.
Rubber	Whole year round	June-Aug.

Source: Food and Agriculture Organization: World Crop Harvest Calendar. Rome, 1959.

Table 4

Family 5 adults 3 children (14 yrs., 12 yrs., 9 yrs.) Coefficient = 7.2

Nos. of Cooking Daily		Quantities Consumed in	Carbohy-drates in	Proteins	Fat	Calories
First	Cooked rice	3880	1244.32	51.58	16.30	5456.44
	Green bean pungent soup with fish	3940	162.33	151.69	124.90	2378.18
	Fried fish (Trichopodus pectoralis)	100	—	32.02	21.93	325.40
	Boiled duck's egg	50	0.25	7.12	8.0	105.0
	Riped banana	990	295.20	10.40	2.77	1128.60
Second	Cooked rice	2640	846.64	52.48	11.08	3712.64
	Roasted fish (Clarius batrachus)	160	0.14	28.26	7.60	122.14
	Fried sweet and salted fish	120	18.0	39.60	28.80	423.60
	Total daily quantities		2566.88	396.23	221.38	13652.0

Calorie value per person: 1896
Protein value per person: 55.03 grams
Fat value per person: 30.75 grams
Carbohydrage value per
person: 356.51 grams

Source: Ministry of Public Health; Division of Nutrition, Bangkok. Personal Communications, 1945-1959.

Table 5

Family 3 adults 2 children (14 yrs., 8 yrs.) Coefficient 4.4

Nos. of Cooking Daily		Quantities Consumed in	Carbohy- drates in	Proteins	Fat	Calories
First:	Cooked rice	3600	1154.52	68.03	27.61	5062,68
	Dried fish soup with coconut milk	1050	12.77	56.06	294.64	3220.08
	Roasted dry fish	40	—	4.42	0.46	32.54
Second:	Cooked rice	2980	955.69	60.25	12.49	4190.77
	Fish sour soup with vegetable	1730	121.27	94.63	24.05	1080.39
	Total daily quantities	—	2244.25	283.41	346.76	13586.46

Calorie value per person: 3087.83
Protein value per person: 64.41 grams
Fat value per person: 78.81 grams
Carbohydrate value per
person: 510.06 grams

Source: Ministry of Public Health; Division of Nutrition: Personal Communications, 1955-1959. Bangkok.

Table 6

Family 2 adults 3 children (12 yrs., 11 yrs., 9 yrs.) Coefficient 4.9

Nos. of Cooking Daily		Quantities Consumed in	Carbohy- drates in	Proteins	Fat	Calories
First:	Cooked rice	2910	933.28	56.72	12.21	3922.33
	Fried lettuce with fishes	1370	49.44	21.74	15.36	423.88
	Boiled ipomeoa leaves	150	5.46	6.38	0.06	49.50
	Red & green chillies with shrimp paste	30	—	7.02	0.84	39.80
Second:	Cooked rice	2450	785.72	47.78	10.29	3445.44
	Fried celery leaves with fish	710	29.88	9.26	8.92	223.09
	Total daily quantities	—	1803.88	148.90	47.68	8171.04

Calorie value per person: 1992.94
Protein value per person: 36.32 grams
Fat value per person: 11.63 grams
Carbohydrate value per
person: 439.97 grams

Source: Ministry of Public Health, Division of Nutrition: Personal Communication, 1955-1959. Bangkok.

Table 7

Average Daily Intake of Food Per Capita in 30 Families of the Muang District

Average daily intake of food per caput:

Rice (glutinous)...	510	
Sugar	0.5	"
Meat including fish, pork, chicken	40	"
Milk..	Nil	
Egg	1.0	"
Beans	8.0	"
Vegetable—leafy 13—non leavy 17.........................	30	
Oils and fats	1.0	"
Fruit...	3.0	"

Source: Ministry of Public Health, Division of Nutrition: Personal Communications, 1955-1959. Bangkok.

Table 8

Dietary Survey at Sansai, Chiengmai Province, 80 Families
(Including 432 Persons for Two Days)

Consumption Per Head Per Day

Weights are of the edible portion. Calories and protein calculated from FAO composition tables (1949). Thiamin calculated from FAO unpublished data.

	Weights (grams)	Calories	Protein (grams)	Thiamine (microgram)
Rice (home pounded mostly glutinous)	502	1802	35.6	502
Wheat and other cereals	7	24	.8	21
Pulses and nuts	4	14	.9	20
Vegetables, leafy	20	5	.4	12
Other, incl., roots, tubers	64	49	.8	42
Fruits	14	10	.1	8
Meat (Pork, chicken, beef)	32	106	5.0	106
Fish	15	20	2.8	6
Eggs	5	8	.6	5
Oils and fats	5	45	0	0
Total		2083	47.0	722

Source: Ministry of Public Health, Division of Nutrition: Personal Communications, 1955-1959. Bangkok.

Table 9

Sample Diets of the Cholburi Area

Actually consumed per capita per day:	Weight in
Rice (mostly home-pounded)	425
Meat	5
Fish (small varieties)	69
Beans and nuts	4
Vegetables: leafy	30
Non-leafy	41
Oil and fat	5
Sugar	1
Condiments	24

Food value of diet per capita per day:	
Calories	1746
Protein: animals	15
vegetables	33 "
Carbohydrate	349 "
Fat	13 "
Calcium	0.132
Phosphorus	0.228
Iron	7
Vitamins: A	2006 I.U
Thiamine	0.78
Riboflavin	0.46
Niacin	11.14
C	30

Source: Ministry of Public Health, Division of Nutrition: Personal Communications, 1950-1959. Bangkok.

Table 10

Average Weight and Height of Thai Children

Age	Weight	Height
Birth	3.1 Kg.	—
1 Month old	3.97 "	55.2 cm.
2 " "	5.09 "	57.1 "
3 " "	5.98 "	60.77 "
4 " "	6.7 "	62.5 "
5 " "	7.11 "	63.0 "
6 " "	7.48 "	65.6 "
7 " "	7.77 "	67.9 "
8 " "	7.87 "	68.8 "
9 " "	8.22 "	69.9 "
10 " "	8.4 "	69.9 "
11 " "	8.58 "	71.7 "
12 " "	8.76 "	73.3 "

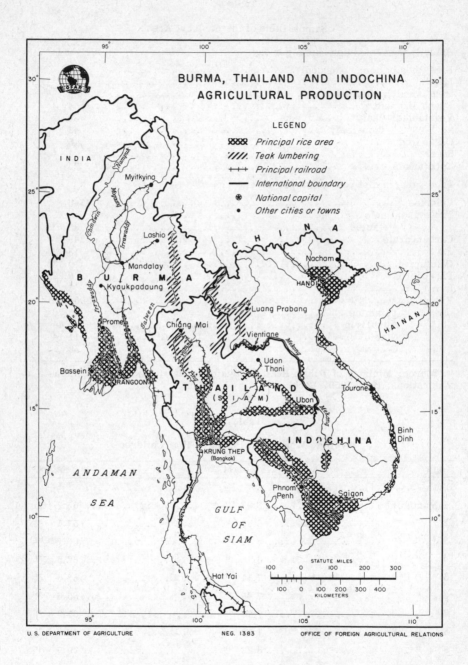

BURMA, THAILAND AND INDOCHINA
AGRICULTURAL PRODUCTION

LEGEND

- Principal rice area
- Teak lumbering
- Principal railroad
- International boundary
- National capital
- Other cities or towns

INDIA

Myitkyina

Lashio

B U R M A

Mandalay

Kyaukpadaung

C H I N A

Nacham

HANOI

Luang Prabang

Prome

Chiang Mai

Vientiane

HAINAN

Bassein

Udon Thani

RANGOON

T H A I L A N D

(S I A M)

Ubon

Tourane

Binh Dinh

I N D O C H I N A

KRUNG THEP
(Bangkok)

A N D A M A N

S E A

Phnom Penh

Saigon

G U L F

O F

S I A M

STATUTE MILES

100   0   100   200   300

KILOMETERS

100   0   100   200   300   400

Hat Yai

U. S. DEPARTMENT OF AGRICULTURE   NEG. 1383   OFFICE OF FOREIGN AGRICULTURAL RELATIONS

FEDERATION
OF MALAYA

I. GENERAL REMARKS[1,2]

Thanks to favorable economic circumstances, Malaya has been one
of the best-fed countries in Asia. However, its current economic prosperity is dependent to a high degree upon its cash crop of rubber and
the world demand for tin. There is a disturbing inadequacy of subsistence crops, which has resulted in the recent five-year plan (1956-
1960) designed to emphasize diversification of agricultural products
and increased production of cash crops. (The latest figures (1958)
available do not indicate any significant change.)

The population of Malaya is not homogenous, a situation which
bears upon production more than it does upon diets. The main ethnic
groups (which include Javanese, Boyanese, and other people of Indonesian stock) are: Malaysians, 48.4%; Chinese, 38.2%; Indians and
Pakistanis together, 11.7%; and others, including aboriginese, Europeans, and Eurasians, 1.7%. All of these groups eat rice but only the
Malays produce it, while the Chinese mill it and import it.

The total population according to the 1957 census was 6.3 million,
with an average density of 120 per square mile. This is a misleading
ratio, however, because four-fifths of the country is jungle and the
population is concentrated in the remaining one-fifth, thus giving a
density of approximately 600 per square mile.

The population grows at a rate of 2.75% a year, one of the highest
growth rates in the world; 65.5% of the people live in rural areas, but
there is a trend toward the cities, especially to Singapore.

While some Malaysians are found in the civil service, most are
farmers and cultivate the 900,000 acres of rice, 9,000 of which yield a
double crop. The Chinese are essentially urban and addicted to trade;
some of them, however, own small plantations, and others occupy posi-
tions of importance in the rice industry (processing, storage).

The relatively small acreage planted in rice, the most important
food staple of the country, contrasts with the 3.8 million acres planted
in rubber (which yielded in 1957 some 7,000,000 tons). Other food
crops include coconut, oil palms, pineapple, sugar cane, and fruit, but
in adding up all the acreage occupied by the secondary foods, the total
falls far short of the amount of land devoted to the cash crops.

Malaya has become a country of small holdings; farms seldom

exceed three or four acres. In general, methods of farming are primitive and inadequate. There is no satisfactory estimate of how much new land might be brought into cultivation for food crops.

The principal aims of the government's agricultural policy are the expansion of locally-grown food supplies, particularly rice; the replacement of old rubber trees with younger, high-yielding ones; the expansion and improvement of the local fruit industry; the maintenance of soil fertility; and a gradual diversification of the country's agriculture to make it less dependent on imports, and, consequently, exports.

II. FOOD RESOURCES

Rice. The total tillable land in Malaya covers some 5.5 million acres. The most important rice growing areas are in the states of Perlis Kedah, Perak, and Province Wellesley. Kelantan and Trengganu also have recently become rice-growing areas. On a smaller scale paddy is found in Selangor, at Panjong-Kerong, and in almost all other states. The cereal is cultivated under the wet system, considerably more productive than the dry; the climate and configuration of the land favor this type of cultivation (see Map and Table I).

Aware of the constant threat to the country's food supply, the government has endeavored to expand irrigation works. By 1956 there were 219,500 acres of improved paddy land and 55,600 acres of new land reclaimed for that culture. As a result paddy production rose from the 1948-1952 annual average of 635,000 tons to 800,000 in 1957-58 and 725,000 in 1959, yielding a little over 500,000 tons of milled rice, an amount that covered barely 60% of the need and left, in 1958, 350,000 tons to be imported.

The precariousness of Malaya's rice supply was illustrated in 1952 when a sudden and considerable increase in the world price of rice occurred. Export unit values of rice from Thailand increased by 30%, while simultaneously the prices of rubber and tin decreased by 42%. This was parried by a government subsidy protecting the retail price of rationed rice in the Federation of Malaya; in Singapore, where no subsidy was forthcoming, the retail price soared.

The government has continued to cushion rice prices by purchasing it from the producer. Table I gives production, imports, and purchases of rice and the cost of living index in recent years.[5]

At times, in order to replenish its stocks, the government has to pay above its minimum rate for rice, while farmers have to sell their crops for cash to traders at less than the government minimum because of their own indebtedness to the traders; still more often the cultivator uses **padi kumcha** or the mortgaging of an unharvested crop at exorbitant rates to obtain cash from a village money-lender. This system breeds famine and disease.

No other cereal is grown in Malaya in significant quantities.

Animal protein resources[1,7] Animal proteins are supplied to a small extent by land animals and to a larger extent by fish. The sources of land animal proteins are as follows: oxen, 285,000; buffaloes, 244,300; goats, 275,000; sheep 31,000; swine, 400,000.

Because of both an unfavorable climate and a lack of pastures, the cattle raising industry is underdeveloped. Most of the available land is used for rubber or paddy.

The production of fresh milk, which amounted to 90,000 tons at the end of 1957, is insufficient for the demand, especially of the Indian population. The bulk of the dairy products is imported with the result that the cost of these items is above the reach of the masses.

There are four types of cattle in Malaya: 1. the white-horn swamp buffalo (240,000 head), which are found mainly in the rice-growing areas of Perlis, Kedah, Trengannu and Malacca, where they are chiefly used for plowing the rice fields; they also supply a large portion of the fresh beef eaten in the country; 2. the curly-horned Murrah buffalo (4,300 head) which are kept for milk production by the northern Indians near the larger towns; most of the milk is sold as raw milk though a certain amount is turned into **ghee** (clarified butter); 3. the malayan oxen (200,000 head), small hardy animals which are found like the swamp buffaloes mainly in the rice growing areas; they are used for plowing, carting, and, meat; 4. the local Indian dairy oxen (85,000 head), a mixture of Indian breeds of cattle, which are found mainly around the larger towns and on estates with Indian laborers; the average milk yield is 100 gallons a year, although yields up to 300 gallons have been recorded.

Goats are reared for meat by Malaysians and Indians in most parts of the country. Sheep are raised chiefly in the dry areas of the east coast. Pig raising is almost entirely a Chinese monopoly. There are over 400,000 pigs in Malaya, an amount that is sufficient to meet all the Federation's requirements of fresh pork and also provide a surplus for export to Singapore. It must be remembered, however, that Moslems, who compose the largest part of the population, do not eat pork.

Poultry is kept by all nationalities both in the towns and in the countryside. Although there are a few large farms raising up to 10,000 birds, the majority is kept as small backyard flocks as a side line to other activities. It is estimated that there are at least 12 million birds in the Federation. In spite of a considerable increase in poultry raising during the past few years, local production is still unable to meet the demand for birds and eggs. There is thus a large import trade from Singapore and Thailand.

Fisheries.[7] Despite a long coastline, the fishing industry has not yet been fully developed. Malaya produces annually over 100,000 tons

of sea fish and imports a total of 6,200 tons of higher grades of fish
from Thailand, Sumatra, Singapore, and elsewhere. Usually a surplus
of over 17,000 tons, primarily of middle and lower-grade fish, is available for export. Thus the net supply for local consumption amounts to
nearly 100,000 tons annually. The equipment for catching these fish
comprises 19,400 sets of tackle and 23,400 boats operated by 51,000
fishermen. Only 5,641 of these boats are powered. Seventy per cent
of the fishermen are Malaysians, twenty per cent Chinese, and the rest
Indians, Thais, Eurasians, and others.

Considerable effort is being made to increase the supply of this
highly important source of animal protein. The government is encouraging greater production by introducing mechanized techniques,
canning, and scientific research. The Ministry of Agriculture has
arranged for a Japanese fishing company to assist in establishing a
tuna industry at Penang, and there is a Fish Research and Training
Institute at Malacca. A training scheme for fishermen in special
schools has been initiated by the government. Cooperative marketing
is encouraged in an effort to reduce the price gap between the prices
received by the fishermen who make the catch and those paid by the
consumer.

Analyses have been undertaken to shed some light on the water,
protein, fat, carbohydrate, ash, calcium, iron, and phosphorus content
of the various species of fish in Malayan waters.

Tubers, vegetables, and fruits. These are raised primarily by
the Chinese population, although many Malaysians keep a small plot
near the house. It has been estimated that 250,000 tons of cassava
roots are produced annually for local consumption. Other tubers,
such as yams, bring the total to 500,000 tons. Tapioca is also grown
extensively for the production of starch and for pig fodder.

Vegetables are grown mainly by the Chinese, who have achieved
high yields of leafy ones, lettuce, mustard, and cabbage (Cameron
Highlands). Some 500,000 metric tons of vegetables are grown annually. This production falls short of the need by 200,000 tons. During the annual fallow of the rice, crops such as ground nuts, maize,
beans, cucumber, and **lobak** (Chinese radish) are raised in some parts
of the country.

Fruits are abundant and are produced around the houses and near
the big cities. They include citrus fruits, bananas, and the durian, an
evil smelling fruit that is, however, extremely nutritious and contains
valuable proteins.

Bananas are increasingly favored as a cash crop in new and re-
planted rubber lands. The total area under cultivation in fruit is estimated at 250,000 acres. This includes acreage in pineapples, a crop
that was almost completely destroyed during the war but is now being
rehabilitated and annually supplies an average of 60,000 tons, or 27%
of the world's total production, the remaining 63% coming from

Hawaii. By 1960 an increase of 200,000 tons is planned. An estimated 500,000 acres of new land is suitable for pineapple, and the expansion of this industry is an important part of the Federation's development planning.

Fats. Fats come mostly from coconut oil. The total area under cultivation in 1958 was 517,000 acres, very nearly equal to that of pre-World War II. About 80% of this acreage consists of small holdings, mainly in the western coastal area. Production is low with vast differences in yield per acre, ranging from 500 to 2000 pounds. The total production in 1957 was 96,500 tons. The quality has been relatively poor, and the government is helping the growers to improve it.

Palm oil and palm kernel oil. This crop covered 116,000 acres at the beginning of 1958 with a production of 58,000 tons. More than 80% of the total acreage is distributed in some 60 estates. The residue of the palm kernels, after the oil has been expressed (14,781 tons in 1957), is used for livestock feed.

Sugar cane. Sugar cane, which was at one time an important Malayan crop, has practically disappeared. There are no sugar cane plantations and no commercial sugar mills in the country. The per capita consumption of sugar, excluding palm sugar, is estimated at 66 pounds per year. Imports are obtained from the United Kingdom and Hongkong.

Spices. Spice acreage in 1957 amounted to 51,000 acres. Chili, ginger, turmeric, clove, and nutmeg are grown for domestic consumption, while areca nut and pepper are exported.

Tea. In 1957, 9,000 acres were planted in tea. More than two-thirds of this acreage was in the highlands of the state of Pahang; the remainder was lowland grown, chiefly in Selangor. In 1957 5.2 million pounds were harvested. Intensification of this culture is planned for future years.

Cacao. Experiments are being made with cacao. It is believed that 300,000 acres of land can eventually be made available for this crop.

III. EXPORTS AND IMPORTS

As the foregoing has made clear, Malaya has to import large amounts of food. Table I shows the tonnage of rice that had to be imported each year between 1949 and 1957. Other foodstuffs, which include condensed and powdered milk and other dairy products, meat, preserves, sugar, flour, and beverages, must also be purchased from abroad and represent in value twice the cost of rice imports. Food exports include tea, pineapples, fresh and canned coconut oil, and palm oil and kernels.

IV. FOOD INDUSTRIES, STORAGE AND TECHNOLOGY[1,7,3]

Food processing is undertaken in over 1,800 small plants and factories, giving employment to nearly 5,000 people, 75% of whom are
Chinese. Over 7,500 tons of biscuits and 10 million gallons of soft
drinks are manufactured. Other food processing includes rice milling
and fish products. Both the salting and drying is done on the east
coast and various preparations of fish—fish meal and flour—are
made, some of which are becoming popular. A portion of this fish
processing, especially in the northeast, is done by the fishermen themselves by drying the fish on bamboo mats and pickling it in brine.

There is some refrigeration storage in the most important fishing
harbors, such as Malacca and Port Swettenham. In these ports, salt-
water storage is available to keep the fish from periods of glut for
periods of shortage.

All the big cities have some refrigeration capacity with a total estimated at approximately 200,000 cubic feet. There is no information
on the availability of refrigerated trucks or wagons on the railroads.

There is little information on storage facilities in general, although
some storage space is available to the government for imported rice.
Problems of food storage are considerable in hot and humid countries.
In Malaya, where the average humidity is high, these problems are
particularly acute. Research is being undertaken to find out the best
way to prevent silos from admitting not only water but also water
vapor when rice, flour, sugar, and other perishable goods are stored
for some length of time.

V. DIET TYPES[3,6,7,9]

A discussion of the diets of the population of Malaya should take
into consideration the varied ethnic groups mentioned at the beginning
of this chapter. Those of Malaysian stock and of the Moslem faith,
such as the Javanese and the Boyanese, have substantially the same
diet, with the exception that the Javanese tend to eat tempe, a fermented soya bean preparation which has a good nutritional value.*

The southern Chinese, whether they come from China proper or
are Malaya-born, usually keep the traditional Chinese cuisine, although some may show a Malay influence in their diets by adding hot
spices to their rice. Some of the Chinese are Buddhists and their diet
is strictly vegetarian. The Ceylonese and the southern Indians eat
the same type of foods. Only the preparation of sauces and spicing is

_____

*Information in this section has been given by Miss E. Cheeks of the
I.M.R.

different. All consume much milk and ghee when available. Diets also vary with the location of the population group (whether rural or urban) and with the economic level of the group (laboring class or middle class).

Among the laboring class all members of the family except school-grade children are employed. Incomes or salaries range from $30 to $60 a month.

The Chinese eat highly milled rice, but may not necessarily suffer the consequences as their diet is more varied than that of the Malays. The Malays use a highly milled rice, if it is available, but in some areas they still eat a home-pounded rice. Many Indians take the easy-to-come-by, highly milled rice. The parboiled rice which they ate in their own country was not available during the war years and has not been successfully developed since for lack of the necessary paddy drying equipment. There is, however, a growing demand for parboiled rice if it can be made palatable.

The various groups of aborigines, numbering not more than 100,000, have their own diets based on hunting and gathering.

In many parts of the Federation, particularly in some rural areas, children are sent considerable distances to school without any morning meal before leaving their homes. They, therefore, do not break their fast until they return home in the early afternoon, unless they can afford to buy food during the morning from canteens and itinerant vendors. It is perhaps not surprising that these children sometimes find it difficult to concentrate on their work in school and become listless and inattentive.

Members of the "middle class," which include school teachers, office workers, workers in industry, and those doing skilled work such as engineering, earn a better salary than the hourly-paid laborers. Their income may reach $150 to $200 a month. Thus, they can afford more meat, to go with the rice that is the basis of the diet for every-body. The middle-class people have a much greater variety in their choice of foods than have the laborers. There is a tendency to take a mid-morning snack, which may be quite a substantial dish purchased from a canteen, if, as is sometimes the case, no breakfast has been eaten in the morning. There is also a tendency to take a milk drink before retiring. The Chinese will sometimes take a supper dish, particularly if the dinner is a light meal eaten early for the purpose of going out for an evening's entertainment.

On the whole the diets of the Malayan people are superior to those of other Asian countries (see Table 2). The average food intake pro-vides 2,555 calories, 53% of which is of the cereal origin. Proteins of animal origin provide 10.8% of the calories. Meat, fish, poultry, and eggs supply 7.3%, which is the highest rate in Southeast Asia. It must be remembered, however, that these overall figures do not give an exact picture of the situation. The Chinese population, living under urban conditions, is more prosperous and is responsible for a considerable share of this favorable average, while the Malaysian and Indian groups, rural dwellers or laborers, do not fare as well.

A. MEALS EATEN BY THE LABORING CLASSES

Malaysians. The planning of meals, other than the purchase of food, is not a matter of great concern to the Kampong woman, who never thinks of varying the daily fare beyond the addition of eggs and —whenever possible—meat or fish, and blending a variety of seasonings for her curry dishes. Wood is the cooking fuel and boiling or frying the usual methods of cooking. These features are not conducive to an elaborate cuisine. Food is usually cooked in the cool morning well ahead of mealtime, and is served cool enough to be eaten with the fingers. For this reason the Malaysian housewife is reluctant to cook the vegetables at the last minute even if told that it preserves their nutritive value. Rice is washed several times, possibly because it does away with the unpleasant flavor that sometimes results from its unprotected storage between meals.

Most people have three meals a day and cooking may be repeated in the evening; lunch is usually taken to the field to eat during the day's work. In some cases only two meals a day are eaten, at morning and evening. Malays usually drink water, or coffee, if they can afford it. The typical diet of the Malaysian laboring class is:

Breakfast - Rice with a small portion of salt fish or **belachan** (prawn paste) as a flavoring.

Lunch - Rice and salt fish saved from that cooked the previous evening.

Dinner - Rice and salt, dried or fresh fish, occasionally buffalo meat, green vegetables, either purchased or collected from those growing wild.

Chinese. Laborers working on building construction will frequently patronize hawkers during the day. This adds variety to their menus, but the total amount of food so purchased is small. The typical diet is:

Breakfast - Rice with salt, dried or fresh fish, or soya bean curd, vegetables (generous portion) frequently served in the form of soup.

Lunch - Rice, fish, and vegetables saved from that cooked for breakfast.

Dinner - Rice, fish, and vegetables, sometimes an extra dish of meat or soya bean curd or a second vegetable, one of the dishes frequently in the form of a soup.

Indians. Food is cooked once a day, at night; the rice is kept from the previous night by pouring fresh water into the rice left in the cooking pot, so that the contents of the pot do not dry out. This water is then poured off in the morning and the rice and other items for lunch are packed up in a banana leaf to take to work.

Indian laborers sometimes take a bottle of cold tea with no milk to drink during the day.

Breakfast - Rice, **rasam** (a spiced sauce), and fried vegetables, usually brinjals (egg plant) saved from that cooked for the previous night's meal.

Lunch - Rice, **rasam**, fried vegetables, as for breakfast, saved from that cooked on the previous night.

Dinner - Rice, dried or fresh curried fish, **rasam**, and fried vegetables.

B. MEALS EATEN BY THE MIDDLE CLASSES

Malaysians.

Breakfast - Tea or coffee with sugar and no milk, bread with butter and/or jam. Sometimes fruit, sometimes rice cooked up from the previous night's meal.

Lunch - Rice, curry made from salt, dried or fresh fish or from soya bean curd or eggs, or fried fish served with spiced **sambal**, boiled or fried vegetables, or vegetables cooked with coconut cream.

Tea - Fruit drink, or tea or coffee with or without bread, butter and/or jam, or biscuits or cake. Sometimes fruit.

Dinner - Rice, curry, vegetables as for lunch.

Vegetables are normally only lightly cooked; sometimes cabbage or potatoes may be cooked with the curry in addition to the other vegetables.

Chinese.

Breakfast - Coffee, tea, or a fruit drink, or sometimes milk. Bread with butter and/or jam. Sometimes an egg or part of an egg. Sometimes fruit.

Lunch - Rice, meat, fish or soya bean curd dish, one or more vegetable dishes. Sometimes both dishes are lightly fried, but frequently one dish is in the form of a soup. Occasionally one dish is curried. More chili is taken with the meals of southern Chinese living in Malaya than of the same people living in China.

Dinner - Rice, one meat or fish dish, one or more vegetable dishes, usually one dish in the form of a soup. Slightly bigger meal than lunch in most cases.

Indians.

Breakfast - Coffee or milk. Bread with butter and/or jam or bread or a pancake made from whole-meal flour and other grains. Sometimes an egg.

Lunch - Rice, meat or fish curry, one or more vegetable dishes. Sometimes the meat or fish is fried and the vegetables are curried. Sometimes soup, occasionally tomato salad.

Tea - Tea, sometimes bread and butter or biscuits, cake, or curry
   puff (pastry with curried meat filling).
Dinner - Rice, meat or fish curry, one or more vegetable dishes.
   Sometimes soup. Sometimes fruit.

VI. ADEQUACY OF FOOD RESOURCES

A number of surveys have been made by the Division of Nutrition
of the Institute for Medical Research since this division was created
in 1946. It has been found generally that among the rice growing population immediately prior to the harvest, the nutritional standard was
low and the people were thin and depressed. After the harvest there
was a considerable change for the better. A coconut-growing community in fairly good economic conditions had health standards very
similar to those found in the rice growing community; the children
were lacking in spirit and were frequently thin and undersized.

On the other hand, in the fishing community the people were of
good physique and the children full of spirit. The intake of food per
capita was large compared with that of the other groups investigated.
A dietary survey of young Malays training in a police depot at Kuala
Lumpur showed a daily per capita intake of about 3,000 calories.[4] Investigation of a small Chinese community engaged in timber cutting
proved that the adult males were consuming well balanced diets yielding about 4,500 calories per capita per day.[9] Examination of Malay
special constables showed per capita daily intakes of up to 3,000
calories.

An important nutritional loss occurs in the rice after milling in the
small mills commonly used in the country. Studies made at the nutrition division of the Institute of Medical Research have shown that a
rate of 36% of broken grains is obtained from this type of milling,
leaving a ratio of thiamin in the rice of 0.4 milligrams per pound instead of the 0.7 minimum acceptable. Thus the extensive and increased use of the small, power-driven mills has led to an increase
in the consumption of badly-broken, highly-milled rice with greatly
depleted thiamin content. In the absence of an increased consumption
of other protective food substances, the risk of beriberi in communities
using this kind of rice is greatly increased.

In times of stress, such as the recent emergency, or in times of
war, the food situation in Malaya is bound to deteriorate rapidly.
Whereas the recent emergency has not drained the food resources too
heavily, World War II showed that the country is not equipped to withstand major challenges. No accurate data exists on the level of nutrition that existed between 1942 and 1945, but there is evidence that

malnutrition caused considerable damage in some groups where up to 30% of the people examined showed serious symptoms.

Milk and relief food supplies had to be distributed by the Department of Social Welfare and the Medical Department to pre-school age children and to children who did not attend school in order to correct these conditions right after the war.

VII. NUTUTIONAL DISEASE PATTERNS[9]

Protein malnutrition is found to exist to a more or less important degree among all Malay peoples. While it may vary from place to place, it is absent from no areas of the country. Classical kwashiorkor is not always found, but pre-kwashiorkor is very common. Dry, cracked skin, hyperkeratosis, depigmentation of the hair, oedema of the dorsum of the foot, enlarged liver, all these signs are found together or separately.

Beriberi is still found in subclinical forms showing isolated symptoms. However, the percentage of hospital admissions for it dropped from 0.7% in 1946 to 0.2% in 1955, while outpatients showed a still greater decline.

Between 1946 and 1955 the percentage of total hospital admissions for anemia dropped from 2.7% to 1.2%, while the percentage of outpatients examined rose from 3.4% in 1946 to 4.4% in 1955, indicating that causes of anemia are still present although they do not generally result in severe incapacities.

Iron deficiency plays an important role in the etiology of anemia in Malaya, as shown by a study based on the absorption and utilization of dietary iron isotopes in people living on poor-quality rice diets. Hemoglobin surveys made at different periods, but mainly in 1950, in Malaya showed a prevalent low level of hemoglobin in the samples examined (rubber estate laborers).

Infant mortality rates dropped from 102 per 1,000 live births in 1947 to 78 in 1955.

VIII. CONCLUSIONS

No gross malnutrition or starvation exists in the country. It has a relatively high level of nutrition compared to other countries of Southeast Asia. Nevertheless, there is an obvious prevalence of minor signs of malnutrition in certain places, and among certain groups during certain seasons. The factors involved in these foci of incidence are essentially poverty and ignorance.

The present level of nutrition is possible because of the prosperity brought to the country after the war by the boom in rubber and tin. This boom is essentially transitory and may be gravely threatened by synthetic rubber on the one hand and the uncertainty in the demand for tin on the other. Should there be a rise in the world price of rice and a drop in the price of such commodities as Malaya can export, a truly catastrophic situation might result, especially if the present population growth continues unabated. While its cash crops have lifted the diet of the Malayan population to a satisfactory level, it is highly questionable whether, left to itself and using only its own resources, the same satisfactory levels could be maintained without considerable cultural and agricultural changes.

SELECTED REFERENCES

1. British Information Services, Malaya: The Making of a Nation. New York, 1957.
2. Dobby, E. H. G. Settlement Patterns in Malaya. *Geographical Review*, Vol. 32, 1942, pp. 211-232.
3. Firth, Rosemary. Housekeeping among Malay Peasants. London, London School of Economics, 1943.
4. Thompson, Kenneth. Malaya. *Focus*, Vol. 9, No. 2, October, 1958.
5. Food and Agriculture Organization. Food and Agricultural Price Policies in Asia and the Far East. Bangkok, 1958.
6. Marx, R. E. Diets Not Adequate in Most of Asia. *Foreign Agriculture*, Vol. 22, No. 6, June, 1958, pp. 3-4, 22.
7. Federation of Malaya, Information Services. Fact Sheets on the Federation of Malaya. Kuala Lumpur, 1958.
8. International Cooperation Administration. Near East and South East Asia Conference, p. 108. Beirut, 1959.
9. Institute for Medical Research. Annual Reports. Kuala Lumpur, 1950-1958.
10. Directory of Singapore and Malaya 1958-1959. Singapore, *Straits Times*, 1959.
11. United States Department of Commerce, World Trade Information Service. Basic Data on the Economy of the Federation of Malaya. *Economic Reports*, *Part 1, No. 58-59*, 1958.

Table 1

Rice Availability in Malaya and Singapore

Year	Production*	Imports	Govt. Purchases	Cost of Living Index
1949	307	304	78	100
1950	436	294	58	110
1951	443	311	3	139
1952	341	284	9	141
1953	441	352	19	137
1954	408	198	3	129
1955	411	347	16	124
1956	420	363	52	125
1957	488	341	63	131

*In thousands of tons of milled rice or equivalent.
Source: Food and Agriculture Organization: Food and Agricultural Price Policies in Asia and the Far East. Bangkok, 1958.

Table 2

Calories Consumed per Capita per Day in the
Federation of Malaya and Singapore (1957)
(Percentage distribution by food groups)

Rice	44.5
Wheat	7.4
Maize and other grains	1.1
All grains	53.0
Dry beans and peas	2.0
Roots, tubers, starches	2.5
Sugar	9.5
Oilseeds (incl. soybeans and peanuts)	1.8
Oils and fats (excl. oilseeds and butter)	9.8
Vegetables	1.7
Fruits and Nuts (incl. coconuts)	8.9
Meat, fish, poultry, eggs	7.3
Milk and dairy products incl. butter	3.5
Grand total	100.0
Number of calories	2,555

Source: Foreign Agriculture: Diets Not Adequate in Most of Asia. Vol. 22, June, 1958.

Table 3

Harvest Calendar

Crops	Harvest Period	Bulk of Harvest
Rice:		
Main season wet paddy[a]		
West coast	Jan.–Apr. }	Jan.–Apr.
East coast	Feb.–Apr. }	
Off-season wet paddy		
West coast	July–Aug.	. . .
Upland dry paddy		
Whole of Malaya	Oct.–Nov.	. . .
Lowland dry paddy		
West coast	Nov.–Dec.	. . .
East coast	Jan.–Mar.	. . .
Sugar cane	Whole year round	. . .
Sweet potatoes and cassava	Whole year round	. . .
Citrus fruits	Whole year round	and Apr.–May Sept.–Oct.
Bananas	Whole year round	. . .
Pineapples (for canning)[b]	and Feb.–June Sept.–Dec.	Mar.–June
Palm kernels	Whole year round	. . .
Groundnuts	June–Aug.	June–Aug.
Coconuts	Whole year round	Jan.–Oct.
Coffee	and Feb.–May Sept.–Nov.	. . .
Cocoa		
West coast	and Apr.–May Oct.–Nov.	. . .
East coast	and Oct.–Nov. Apr.–May	. . .
Tea	Whole year round	. . .
Tobacco	July–Sept.	July–Sept.
Rubber	Whole year round	. . .

(a) Main season wet paddy forms the bulk of all paddy crops harvested, and the peak harvest period of this crop is from January to April.

(b) Pineapples for home consumption are grown and harvested throughout the year.

Source: Food and Agriculture Organization: World Crop Harvest Calendar, Rome, 1958.

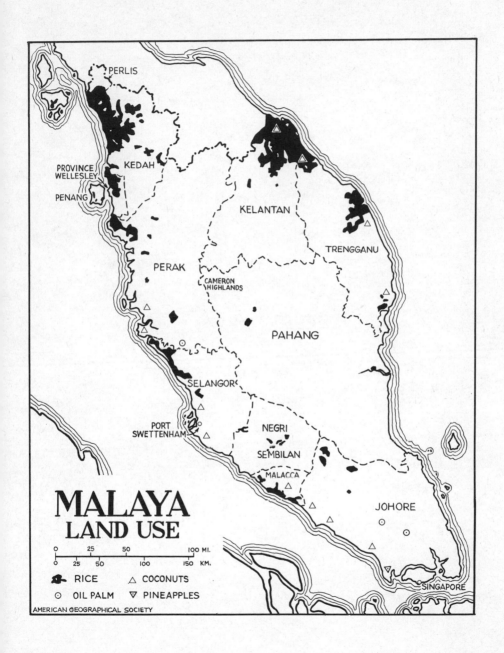

MALAYA
LAND USE

0	25	50
0	25	50

100 MI.

100   150 KM.

🦴 RICE   △ COCONUTS

⊙ OIL PALM   ▽ PINEAPPLES

AMERICAN GEOGRAPHICAL SOCIETY

PERLIS

PROVINCE
WELLESLEY

KEDAH

PENANG

KELANTAN

PERAK

TRENGGANU

CAMERON
HIGHLANDS

PAHANG

SELANGOR

PORT
SWETTENHAM

NEGRI

SEMBILAN

MALACCA

JOHORE

SINGAPORE

BURMA

I. GENERAL REMARKS

The Union of Burma occupies an area of 261,610 square miles
(677,544 square kilometers) extending from approximately 92° to
102° E. and from 10° N. to 28° N. It consists of a sparsely populated
mountainous west and north, and a densely populated delta, plus the
Arrakan and Tenasserim coastal strips.[10]
It is a monsoon country where rainfall is abundant but unevenly distributed. From the food-production point of view it can be divided into
four agricultural regions: lower Burma, central Burma, northern
Burma, and the Shan and Kayan regions.
Lower Burma, the main granary of the country includes 52.6 million
acres of cultivable land, of which a little over one-third is in actual
use. It receives 80 to 200 inches of rain a year.
Central Burma is a dry zone receiving less than 40 inches of rain a
year. It produces a variety of crops including some rice. Most of the
products are consumed locally, some are exported.
Northern Burma receives more water than central Burma and de-
votes two-thirds of its 371,000 cultivated acres to rice; another 4 million acres is cultivable but not cultivated. (See Map No. 1)
The Shan and Kayan regions are also well watered and produce some
temperate climate crops in addition to rice—they are the·main sources
of domestic animals and produce some cash crops (tea and spices).
The total population is estimated at slightly over 20 million, including approximately 800,000 Indians and Pakistanis and 300,000 Chinese.
About 45 per cent of the population is thought to be literate (71.7 per
cent among males and 21 per cent among females), an unusual level for
a Southeast Asian country. The birth rate is 47.5 per 1,000; the death
rate, 35.7, but there is only fragmentary data on infant mortality. The
average density of population is 73 per square mile, but distribution is
uneven: 28 per square mile in the northern mountain regions, and 215
per square mile in the delta. The standards of living are low and rank
after those of Japan, Ceylon, Thailand, and even Pakistan.
Burma's basic food staple is rice, of which enough is produced for
home consumption and for an export trade that is still the largest for
this commodity in the world, although it has diminished to two-thirds
of its prewar tonnage. In British days, timber and oil were also ex-

ported, but these are not available for trade any longer. This leaves rice as the sole basis for the country's economy. Wheat, flour, vegetables, oils, sugar, and dairy products have to be imported. While the avowed policy of the government in the first years of independence has been to develop the range of agricultural products by socializing the peasant society, the actual condition of agriculture has "dwindled towards a primitive economy not far advanced beyond the bare subsistence level, almost solely relying upon the raising of paddy".[22] While there were over 19 million acres under cultivation in Burma in 1936-1941, there were only 16 million acres cultivated in 1957 (see Table 3). The yield of paddy per acre was 30.58 baskets.* Burma had a rice-exportable surplus of over 3 million tons in 1939, while in 1958 it was slightly under 2 million, and in 1957, barely over 2 million. The reasons for this are multiple.

The Burmese cultivator, who became fairly prosperous when a world market for his rice had been opened by British shipping and by Indian or Chinese brokerage, lost his land to money-lenders at the beginning of the twentieth century following his improvident management of his newly-acquired resources.

Thanks to the war and to the disappearance of most money-lenders of foreign birth, who were fearful of reprisals, Burmese farmers recovered the physical possession of their holdings by default after 1945.[22] When, in 1948, all land was nationalized, although this nationalization was not put into effect immediately,† the farmers lost it again to the state. At the same time their crops suffered heavily at the hands of the twelve-odd political groups that, until 1955, fought for control of the country. This civil strife was responsible for the loss of 750,000 acres of farmland, destroying what little irrigation and drainage there was, as well as disrupting most facilities. Even at present (1960), security is not assured and the hold of the government over the country is, at best, uncertain.

The policy of the government is to finance industrialization by rice exports.[4] Hence, it must increase its revenue by export earnings, while stabilizing domestic prices to producers and consumers. By establishing an export monopoly, the government made sure that the profits are made available for the development of the country. In addition, this policy makes it possible to check any large fluctuations in the internal economy originating from abrupt changes in world prices for rice; at the same time, specific stabilization measures have been taken to guarantee a minimum price to growers of paddy and to protect consumers against undue increases in the retail prices of rice.[8]

Additional objectives of the government have been to expand the

---

*A basket is 46 to 50 lbs of rice.
†As of early 1959 there were only 1-1/2 million acres of nationalized land.

area under rice cultivation in order to increase export earnings, as
well as to increase the acreage planted in groundnuts, cotton, jute,
coconuts, tobacco, onions, and sugar cane in order to diversify agriculture and reduce expenditures on imports.

The problem of starvation is not as pressing in Burma as in other
countries of Asia or Southeast Asia. There is an average of two acres
of cultivable land for every member of the population; India has only
1.1 acre, Pakistan 1 acre, Ceylon 0.8 acre, and Japan 0.2 acre.[13] The
yield per acre is low, leaving little doubt that if an all-out effort were
made, Burma could easily support three times as many people as it
has at present (See Table 1). It is also important to remember that
probably alone of all Asian countries, Burma has no explosive growth
of population. The rate is 1.2 per cent per year as against 2.75 per
cent in Thailand, and 1.8 per cent in India. Thus, basically, the problem of food supply and distribution seems to be entirely manageable,
given reasonably peaceful circumstances.

II. FOOD RESOURCES

In 1959, approximately 14 million acres were in actual use. Various estimates exist on the amount of land that could be reclaimed for
the development of food production. These vary widely. Andrus[1]
quotes a Burmese estimate of 19 million acres, which some authors
question; while Stamp[18] quotes official sources as giving the figure of
60 million acres. Central Burma and lower Burma differ in many
features; land tenure, soil, climate, production, and potential. In
central Burma, where the land is subdivided into small holdings
owned and operated by single families, the soil needs irrigation, the
production is low; in lower Burma, the land lends itself better to industrial agriculture, the soil needs drainage, the area produces surpluses.

Cereals.   Rice is the most important food resource throughout the
country. Paddy covers 68 per cent of all cultivated land; in certain
areas the ratio rises to 95 per cent. In the dry zone, however, production is insufficient to meet needs and additional rice has to be locally
purchased from the State Agricultural Marketing Board (SAMB) stores.

In the old days farming was done on a family basis for subsistence
only; 20 to 30 acres providing work for one man, his household, and
his cattle. Typically, whatever land was not needed was left fallow.
Now, whenever possible, rice has been pushed as a monoculture, supplanting other crops in order to supply the government with its most
valuable export product.

Originally, the center of rice production was located in central
Burma, expecially in the districts of Kykukse, Yamathin, Schewebo,

Mandalay, Myktina, and Khatan. In the Shan States and in the Kayan regions some valleys also produce rice but not as a principal crop.

After the jungle was cleared in the late nineteenth and early twentieth centuries, paddy was increasingly grown in lower Burma in the well-watered Irrawaddy Delta. Paddy is also found in the lower valleys of the Sittang and Salween Rivers and on the coastal strips of the Arrakan and Tenasserim coasts. The rice of lower Burma supplies the export market.

Low unit yields (less than 1,300 pounds per acre)* are characteristic of Burmese agriculture. This is due largely to the abundance of farmland which encourages un-intensive farming techniques. In many areas, no rotation is practiced, and after two or three years, when the soil is exhausted, the farmer moves to another field. The output is achieved with little capital investment and little or no fertilizers and insecticides. Thus the considerable exports of rice in the past have been produced under methods characterized by the use of animal power, hand labor, and primitive tools. Table 1 gives the index yield of rice per acre in a number of countries.

This table shows that while yields have increased in almost all Asian countries, they have decreased in Thailand and India, and Burma's index rose but slightly.

Table 2 shows food production in Burma and the acreage sown between 1954-1955 to 1958-1959. Although a small increase in paddy acreage is shown, indicating perhaps some degree of recovery, the figures are smaller than those shown in previous years, appearing in Table 3.

Paddy culture in Burma is extremely sensitive to the variations of the weather. In 1958, insufficient rainfall in the cropping season and showers toward the end of the harvest caused a decrease in the matured acreage. The crops also suffer because of the reluctance of the inhabitants to use insecticides and to destroy rodents in certain parts of the country. In the same year, a sudden, increased activity of pests and rats, decreased the yield per acre by an estimated 6 per cent from that of the previous year.[7] Table 6 gives the harvest calendar for most food crops.

The main agent of the government's rice policy is the State Agricultural Marketing Board (SAMB), established in 1947. Table 4 indicates the relation of official paddy prices to wholesale agricultural prices, and to the general retail price levels during the decade of 1948-1957. This shows that on the whole, the price of wholesale paddy has remained static since 1948 in relation to the price of other agricultural commodities. However, the retail price index has increased from 100 to 115.[8]

While it is true that consumers have undoubtedly benefited from the

---

*Malaya: 1,594, U.S.: 2,292, Japan: 3,240, Spain: 4,093[22a]

price policy of SAMB, it is not certain that this has increased the per
capita consumption of rice during the same period. By the same
token, it has also prevented the producers from benefiting directly
from the subsequent increase in the world price for rice, which might
have meant increased consumption and a rise in the standard of living.

It is also doubtful whether the best possible use has been made of
this monopoly.[4] After the Korean war, the stocks of rice suddenly
reached unmanageable proportions. This occasioned the serious problem of rapidly decreasing foreign exchange, and the consequent im-
pairment of major development projects. The Burmese government
turned to financial barter agreements in order to move its surplus.
Inexperienced government missions charged with procuring goods in
exchange for the rice made hasty commitments in their barter agreements which resulted in excessive amounts of concrete reaching
Burma during the rainy season and in the delivery of cast-iron pipe
from Communist China by weight instead of by length. After 1956,
however, an effort was made to sell the rice for cash, and the incon-
veniences of the barter agreement are on the way to being erased.[8]

It is hoped that a Rice Production Expansion Committee (RPEC),
established in 1956, will finally succeed in raising the rice export
crop to 3 million tons by 1960. A parallel effort is being made in
quality control and better rice milling, storage, and shipping facilities,
though details are not available.

Millet and wheat are produced in Burma, in small quantities and
used for cakes and breads by the non-Burmese population (Indians and
Pakistani). The acreage devoted to these crops remains between
560,000 and 580,000, although it reached 700,000 in previous years.
The production does not exceed 71,000 tons in any year.[19]

Pulses. Land devoted to pulse production is reported to have been
854,000 acres in 1957-58 as compared to over 1 million acres in
1956-57. As a result, less than 200,000 tons were produced. These
pulses consist essentially of lentils, chick peas, and **dhall** (red or
yellow lentils).

Oil-producing grains. Oil-producing grains are the most important sources of fat in the Burmese diet. These grains include peanuts
and sesamum. The policy of the government is to increase the production of these fat-producing plants in order to gain self-sufficiency as
soon as possible. As a result, the acreage sown in nuts has increased
steadily over the last five years.

In 1957-1958, the harvest of shelled peanuts rose for the first time
to 195,000 long tons and reached 235,000 in 1958-1959 (see Table 2).

On the other hand, the sesame acreage has remained essentially
stationary, suffering even a small drop of 2 to 3 per cent in the last
three years. This resulted in a marked drop in sesame production,
from 55,600 tons in 1957 to 35,000 in 1958. It is deemed that 80 to
90,000 tons of vegetable oils are needed every year, of which less

than two-thirds are locally produced. This crop, which grows mainly
in the districts of Toungoo, Meiktila, Mandalay, Yamathin, Schwebo,
Sagaing, and the lower Chindwyn, is extremely sensitive to bad
weather and to drought.

Sugar.   Sugar is one of the few items showing a steady production
increase due to the commissioning of two new mills (see below). With
90,000 to 100,000 acres in sugar cane, the production of finished sugar
may be expected to reach 40,000 tons or more a year, far short, however, of the actual need.

Sugar Production	
Year	Tons
1952-53	21.098
1953-54	21.463
1954-55	16.512
1955-56	16.326
1956-57	26.950
1957-58	39.851

Animal protein resources.   The sources of animal proteins are
limited. Estimates on the number of cattle and other domestic animals
are subject to wide variations. It was believed that approximately 5 million cattle and 7 million buffaloes were in existence at the end of 1949.
Yet more recent data seem to have lowered the total of the two species
to a little over 3 million head.[7] All observers agree, however, that
there were fewer cattle and plow animals in Burma in 1959 than in
prewar days. As a result, the slaughter of cattle is now prohibited by
the government, in the hope of building up herds for domestic work.
As a source of food, these herds are of questionable value, producing
little milk and butter because of starvation and disease conditions.
The hog population is said to have increased in the last 10 years to
approximately half a million. There are a few sheep (21,000) and
goats (170,000), very seldom killed for meat. Mortality rates in all
herds of domestic animals are high.

Fish and fish products constitute the most important source of
animal protein in the Burmese diet. Although Burma has 1,200 miles
of coastline, deep-sea fishing has not been carried on extensively.
The Burmese traditionally prefer fresh or brackish-water fish, which
are generally marketed dry or salted.

Tidal waters of the delta provide promising fishing opportunities
and fish forms an important part of the cargo of many of the launches
plying the delta streams. The annual catch for which license fees are
collected is approximately 50,000 tons. It is generally estimated,[23]
however, that the total catch is at least five to six times this amount.
The government is encouraging an annual catch of 20,000 tons of deep-
water fishes to replace and supplement about 10,000 tons of canned
and dried fishes that have to be imported annually. To reach this goal,

it is fostering research and is inviting private firms to invest in Burmese fisheries. The principal firm now engaged in this deep-sea fishing is a joint Burmese-Japanese venture which employs ships mainly manned by Japanese fishermen.

III. EXPORTS AND IMPORTS

Before independence, Burma was one of the principal suppliers of certain food stuffs, especially rice, to India and the United Kingdom. In recent years, there has been a marked change in the number and relative importance of Burma's trade partners. Japan has emerged as a major supplier and customer, there has been a notable increase in the development of trade with communist countries. Although this trade may vary from year to year.

Rice shipment to barter countries has declined since 1956. Rice exports to the Soviet Union dropped from 212,000 tons in 1955-1956 to only 107,000 tons in 1956-1957. Shipment to China in the same period declined from 105,000 tons to 98,000 tons.

Pulses, following a peak export year in 1956 to 1957, dropped to approximately 66,000 tons in 1958 shipped mainly to Japan, Ceylon, and Hongkong. Export of oil cakes for cattle feed averages annually between 80,000 and 90,000 tons.

Food imports, however, remain an important item in the Burmese diet. The chief foods imported are fats which amount to an average of 30,000 tons a year. In spite of this, the per-capita consumption of oil is very much below desirable standards. The World Health Organization has indicated that the diet of the average Burmese is more deficient in fats than in any other single item. Import of milk and milk products is also important, expressing a deficiency in production. It is estimated at approximately 10,000 to 25,000 tons a year. Sugar and sugar preparations enter the import balance sheet at the rate of 15,000 to 20,000 tons a year; while fish and fish products amount to about 10,000 tons allowing, together with the home-grown fish, an approximate consumption of 23.6 pounds per capita per year, compared with 75 pounds in Japan. Spices enter the purchase program for 750 to 1,000 tons a year, while tea is represented by approximately 600,000 pounds a year. The agricultural commodity agreement concluded with the United States in February, 1956, provided a $21.7 million loan for the purchase of surplus United States agricultural products. By its terms, the United States must ship to Burma a total of $3.2 million worth of tobacco, dairy products, and dried fruit.[25]

IV. FOOD INDUSTRIES, STORAGE AND TECHNOLOGY[14]

What little food technology there is in Burma is devoted mainly to rice processing. There are approximately 840 food and beverage plants, including some 700 rice mills employing 25,000 workers and processing 14,000 to 15,000 tons of rice a day. The milling capacity is entirely commensurate with the rice production, yet two new rice mills at Pazundoung and Tyaukpyu, each with a capacity of 25 tons a day, have been put in operation since 1956, and two others with, respectively, 90 and 200-tons milling capacity a day, are being completed at Setsan and Rangoon. Approximately half of the rice mills are modern. The other half are obsolete and produce a finished product of poor quality. It has been reported that 40 per cent of the rice so produced was unsatisfactory and that the quality has further deteriorated since the war.

Prior to World War II rice storage was not a major problem. After the war, however, rapid changes in world market conditions forced the establishment of storage space for the reserves. This allowed the government to manipulate the domestic rice prices. Road, rail, and port facilities still leave a great deal to be desired. There is a chronic shortage of seasonal manual labor to handle rice cargoes. Loans have been made available to millers for the building of storage facilities. The first step in the program was to build 1,600 temporary thatched sheds, each of 300 tons paddy capacity, to be demolished as soon as permanent sheds were completed. In 1959, 302 of the 390 permanent silos planned for the year were commissioned, 235 of the 250 temporary silos planned were put into operation.

Fish and fish products comprise about 30 per cent of the food budget of a typical Burmese family. Yet there are no shore facilities of any consequence to handle, preserve, or process fish or sea foods, nor any proper distribution facilities to insure that fresh fish or sea food reaches interior consumers in good condition. Construction of a tuna cannery and fish-meat and fish-oil plants with three cold storage units was planned for Rangoon in 1959.

There is no organized meat packing in Burma due to the eating habits of the people, mostly vegetarians, and because as stated above, the livestock was considerably damaged during and after the war. A cattle-breeding center has been established near Magwe. Very little meat and meat products are imported. The meat offered on the market is poorly prepared and poorly handled. Almost all meat sold is freshly slaughtered. It was stated in 1953 that the only refrigeration facilities of significance ever owned by Burma were those left by the Allied forces after the war. These consisted of cars and barges that were later junked. The little progress made since those days does not solve the problem of protection of perishables.[2,7]

The people of Burma consume little milk and dairy products. No modern creameries exist, nor is any of the milk processed. Imported milk, in evaporated or powdered form, is used to supplement the indigenous supply of fresh milk.

Although it has 110 oil-extraction presses processing sesame, Burma is critically short of oil-producing plants—a situation that explains to some extent the fat deficit in the diet.

Among the recently developed industries is the refining of sugar. Two refineries with capacities of 22,500 and 15,000 tons have been put in operation at Pyinmana and Namti; these account for the increase in sugar production noted above.

At present, the principal fruit-growing region of Burma is in the Shan States. The fruit industry is too small to support modern plants for packing, storing, and processing of fruit or fruit products. As the fruit cannot be preserved or stored, it must be sold when ripe for domestic consumption.

In addition to the small industrial food-processing facilities mentioned above, some processing is also practiced at the cottage level.

There is no significant food hygiene in Burma. The maintenance of sanitation in the markets has always been and is still a considerable problem. Proper sanitation in temporary stalls in the immediate vicinity of bazaars is particularly difficult to enforce because these stalls are run by unauthorized extraneous vendors.[7]

V. DIET TYPES

The food habits of the people are limited to a diet of rice, vegetables, and spicy sauces, curry and saffron being the most important of the spices.

Burmese generally eat two meals a day: a breakfast at about eight in the morning and a dinner at five in the afternoon. There is no difference in the menu of the two meals. The rice is boiled, piled in a heap on a huge platter around which the members of the household gather, sitting on their heels. The curry sauce is placed in little bowls; each person has his own plate and helps himself. Few people are able to afford meat curries; besides, few are ready to disregard the law against taking life. Fish, however, is frequently used and is sold by non-Buddhists.[17]

Ordinarily, the curry sauce consists of a thin soup of vegetables in which chilis and onions figure largely. Young bamboo shoots, garlic, wild asparagus, stems of a number of aquatic plants, and fleshy arums are constantly used and may be seen for sale in every bazaar; tamarind and mango leaves are used by the very poor. Along with the rice, there is always some oil and salt and a variety of condiments, notably the **Nga-Pi**, a fish or shrimp sauce without which no Burmese would consider his meal complete.

Sometimes, the big, fierce, stinging **Ka-Gyin**, a species of red ant, is used along with the fish paste. At times it is fried in oil by itself. Roasted turtles and iguana eggs, dried fish, and fried ginger are delicacies.[15]

Bananas, wild pineapples, papayas, durians—the fruit that smells like advanced cheese, but tastes like hazelnut and rose—mangoes, letchis, and many others are found on Burmese trays of food.

Occasionally, roast meat cut into small slices and spitted on bamboo skewers is offered for sale. Cakes of rice are made in the following way: a special kind of rice called **koroknyin** is placed in a green bamboo with water; the bamboo is closed with a plug and put into the fire. By the time the bamboo is dry and begins to burn, the rice is cooked. Delicacies such as candied flowers are appreciated. The flowers are also plucked when covered with ants, then put into salt and water and used for flavoring. The rice is generally highly milled with attendant deprivation of thiamin; near Myirkina, however, perhaps due to the lack of mechanical equipment, villagers mill the rice by hand and so preserve its thiamin. In most villages, the daily consumption of vegetables is less than 100 milligrams per head, 50 per cent of which are of the leafy kind. Pulses are not popular and their consumption is usually below 50 milligrams a day.

Only Indians and Nepalese drink any significant amount of milk. These ethnic groups, however, rarely drink more than 200 or 300 grams a day. The daily ration of a Burmese is not above 5 grams a day. **Nga-Pi** consumption, which would provide some animal protein, varies from 0.15 gm in certain poorer areas to 40-50 gm a day in the richer communities.

Throughout the country, cooking habits are defective. Rice is extensively washed and boiled in a surplus of water which is thrown away after the rice is done. Vegetables, when available, are also poorly prepared. In most cases, they are boiled in water, which is discarded; in some cases, however, they are cooked with oil, salt and **Nga-Pi**, a method that preserves most of the nutrients.

The diets vary but slightly throughout the country, although in certain limited areas they include temperate-zone products such as millet and potatoes. The number of dietary surveys in Burma has been small and confined to few regions, but some information on the adequacy of the traditional diet is available. Table 5 gives an evaluation of the caloric intake and its distribution among the various nutrients. It shows that the average amount of calories consumed per day per capita is inadequate, not exceeding 2,020. Cereals provide 75.2 per cent of these, rice being responsible for 72.3 per cent. Dry beans and peas provide 2.5 per cent and sugar 4.7 per cent of the caloric intake. It is notable that meat and dairy products do not supply more

than 1.8 per cent, and meat, fish, poultry, and eggs combined supply no
more than 3.9 per cent. As a result, it can be said that the food resources of present-day Burma do not give the population an adequate
diet in terms of calories or even a well-balanced diet in terms of protective foods. The daily diet of most people lacks sufficient vitamin A,
thiamine, riboflavin, iron and calcium. Often the ascorbic acid content does not reach the standard 30-50 milligram consumption unit per
day. Expectant and nursing mothers often starve themselves because
they fear a rich diet may cause abnormal growth of the fetus, resulting
in painful labor. They favor polished rice, dried fish (in small amounts)
or mutton if available; some pulses may be eaten, but green vegetables,
fruit, eggs, and milk, even if they could be bought, are frowned upon.
The lack of thiamine is said to have caused fatal cases of beriberi in
breast-fed children. The weaning diets are primitive. From their first
day on, infants are fed on rice. Mothers chew it before giving it to the
infants, which helps digest the starch but increases the risk of disease
transmission. Better-situated families use home-made biscuits but
seldom milk or milk products.

The diets of the Chinese in Burma are somewhat richer in animal
protein and vegetables, probably because of the higher economic level
of the Chinese population.

Water is seldom drunk at meals but each one, when he has finished,
goes to the earthen jar full of water in the corner of the verandah and
rinses out his mouth. A certain amount of beer and spirits is drunk,
especially in lower Burma. There are "toddy" shops where liquor
can be found and Burma is not immune to alcoholism.

Not connected directly with food but important, nevertheless, is the
habit—of men, women, and children—of smoking cheroots. Chewing
betel is sometimes carried on simultaneously with smoking. Most
people, however, prefer to economize on enjoyment and chew in between smokes. The Burman usually slits his areca nut in half, smears
a little lime, white or sometimes tinted pink, on the betel wine leaf,
puts a little tobacco on top, rolls it up and stores the cud in the side
of his mouth, occasionally squeezing it between his teeth. One variety
of nut called the Taunggu Betel has effects very much resembling in-
toxication.[17] The connection between betel chewing and cancer of the
maxillary has been established.

IV. ADEQUACY OF FOOD RESOURCES

As has already been stated, the food resources of Burma are not
only adequate in terms of quantities for the existing population but
would be adequate even for a larger population, providing measures
were taken to increase production or to restore peace in the country.

As it is and under the present state of affairs, the malnutrition that exists stems from poverty.

The Central Research Nutrition Office has recommended and developed a national diet that would not conflict with traditional food habits and ingrained nutritional customs. Groups of people have been exposed to food indoctrination and wise recommendations have been issued.

"Eat with your undermilled rice every day one or more foods out of these three groups: (a) fish, Nga-Pi, shrimps, meat, chicken, eggs, milk or pulses; (b) leafy vegetables (dark green), tubers with red or orange flesh (e.g. sweet potatoes or young orange maize); (c) fruits with yellow or orange flesh, e.g. bananas, pawpaw, jackfruit, oranges, pineapple, mangoes; for vitamin C, Indian gooseberries and red peppers."[15]

Various posters are shown explaining the correct method of washing rice. UNICEF has provided some milk powder and fish-liver oil capsules for school children. In 1959, 250 million of these capsules were distributed.[9]

In times of stress, there is a shortage of food in places because of transportation problems from areas of surplus to areas of famine. However, if all the rice produced in Burma were locally consumed, instead of being collected for export, the problem of feeding the people could be solved. Furthermore increased food resources could be expected from improvement in the very primitive cultivation practices, in the quality of the seeds, and in the methods of fertilizing. The eventual results of these improvements cannot be predicted because various soils will not respond equally well to the same treatment and the cultivators understand these improvements in different ways. Their planning and attitude would influence results.

There has been little incentive for raising high quality rice in Burma. The present milling, allowing 40 per cent breakage, is such that any kind of rice meets that requirement. The practice of working the soil under water conditions and the lack of rotation of crops has depleted the soil, indicating the need for scientific fertilization.

Food production could also be increased by constructing a number of water drainage and irrigation projects, flood control in the middle and lower Irrawaddy Valleys, and irrigation in the south. Several projects are in the process of being realized, and great hopes are attached to pumping projects making use of the abundant water tables that exist in the dry areas. These have already begun in Pakokku and the Pegu region.[6]

A number of other projects covering not only production but also marketing and storing are being supported by the government, assisted by United States funds.

Among the larger projects, classification of land, development of uncontrolled water resources in lower Burma, and irrigation in central

Burma are promising. The creation of an animal husbandry is planned in the Shan, Kachin and Kayan States together with livestock disease services and insect and plant disease control.

Considerable resistance has been encountered in trying to overcome the Buddhist prejudice against taking life. The government has been purchasing small amounts of insecticide in recent years for the Armed Forces and Public Health Services, and it has encouraged greater utilization of such products by the railways and agricultural agencies responsible for storing agricultural products.

VII. NUTRITIONAL DISEASE PATTERNS

A four-month survey, the most important ever undertaken in Burma, has revealed that 60 per cent of the inhabitants suffer from nutritional deficiencies.[15] The survey covered representative population groups: school children, dock laborers, government clerks, nurses, social workers, pregnant women, and mothers. It was found that most Burmese are underweight (men—105 pounds, women—90 pounds) and that signs of minor or even major deficiencies occur in certain areas in 78 per cent of the people. The main deficiencies found included dental caries and irregularity of teeth, angular stomatitis, xerosis of the conjunctiva, anemia, phrynoderma, bleeding gums, and dry skin. School children showed deficiencies indicated in the following tables.[15]

Percentage Incidence of Deficiency
Signs Among School Children in Rangoon

Sign	Burmese		Chinese	
	Boys	Girls	Boys	Girls
Anemia	20.8	34.6	24.0	25.4
Angular Stomatitis	19.0	14.5	2.6	2.2
Caries	28.0	30.7	41.3	38.2
Xerophtalmia	3.3	6.7	0	0

Nutritional Condition of
School Children in Rangoon[15]

Type of Child	No. examined	Nutritional State (Per cent)		
		Good	Moderate	Bad
Burmese boy	1,497	8.0	77.8	14.2
Burmese girl	1,258	24.9	70.3	4.8
Chinese boy	622	20.1	76.5	3.4
Chinese girl	410	11.0	80.2	8.8

In the Lashio area many cases of goiter are observed, often accompanied by cretinism. Signs of mild beriberi are frequently encountered. Kwashiorkor has been known in Burma for a long time as **Noe Mget**, meaning the disease a child gets when his mother gets pregnant.

VIII. CONCLUSIONS

While nutrition in Burma could rise to a satisfactory level, the odds against this are considerable. Much of the rice grown comes from seed that has seen little improvement in recent centuries. Failure to use proper fertilizer and to accept the use of insecticides and pest control programs, will continue to limit production, and hence the earning capacity on which further development of the country is based. Although a vast number of projects have been written up and considerable interest has been at times aroused by Burma's plight, little if any improvement as expressed by improved nutrition is observable to date. It can be safely forecast that the dietary level in Burma is not going to rise, more because of economic policy and cultural factors than because of overcrowding and lack of agricultural resources.

Burma is a potential supplier of food for a growing population, but is at present handicapped by a low standard of living that is the aftermath of wars both foreign and civil and of a rather passive population, content to live in a traditional manner.

Changes in popular philosophy are under way, however. The trend is definitely toward a state-controlled, moderate standard of living, since food surpluses are earmarked for the financing of a hypothetical industrialization, fostered by an ideology that does not take into account the absence of technicians, raw materials, foreign markets, and domestic purchasing power.

SELECTED REFERENCES

1. Andrus, I. R. Burmese Economic Life. Stanford, Stanford University Press, 1947.
2. Burma, Department of Health. Annual Report for 1950. Rangoon, Government Printing Office, 1957.
3. Burma, Veterinary Department. Annual Report. Rangoon, Government Printing Office, 1953.
4. Bever, M. M. Burma Finds Barter Deals Unsatisfactory. *Foreign Agriculture*, Vol. 21, No. 5, May, 1957, pp. 19-20.
5. Cady, J. F. A History of Modern Burma. Ithaca, N. Y., Cornell University Press, 1958.
6. Survey of Nutritional Diseases in Burma. *Chronicle of the World Health Organization*, Vol. 7, No. 1, 1953.
7. Economic Survey of Burma. Rangoon, Government Printing and Stationery, 1958. *Ibid.*, 1959.

8. Food and Agriculture Organization. Food and Agricultural Price Policies in Asia and the Far East. Bangkok, 1958.

9. Food and Agriculture Organization. *Monthly Bulletin of Agricultural Economics and Statistics*, Vol. 8, 1959.

10. Government of Burma. The New Burma (Pyidawtha): Report on Long-Term Programme for Economic and Social Development. Rangoon, 1954.

10a. International Cooperation Administration. Near East and South East Asia Regional Conference. Beirut, 1959.

11. Knappen, Tippets, and Abbett. Economic and Engineering Development of Burma. (Vols. 1, 2.) New York, 1953.

12. Knoblauch, A. L. Agricultural Development: Basic in Burma. *Foreign Agriculture*, Vol. 19, No. 4, April, 1955, pp. 70-74.

13. Marx, R. E. Diets Not Adequate in Most of Asia. *Foreign Agriculture*, Vol. 22, No. 6, June, 1958, pp. 3-4, 22.

14. Pasfield, D. H. Some Rice Storage Problems and Their Solution in Burma. *Newsletter of the International Rice Commission*, Vol. 6, No. 4, December, 1957.

15. Postmus, S. Nutrition Work in Burma: Past and Present. *Proceedings of the Nutrition Society of London*, 1956.

16. Sarin, B. P. Clinical Observations on Kwashiorkor or Protein Undernutrition in Rangoon. *Indian Journal of Child Health*, Vol. 6, No. 6, June, 1957.

17. Shawyoi. The Burman: His Life and Nations. London, Macmillan & Co., 1910.

18. Stamp, L. D. Asia: A Regional and Economic Geography. New York, E. P. Dutton & Co., [1938?].

19. *The Statesman's Year-Book 1959*. London, Macmillan & Co. Ltd.; New York, St. Martin's Press; 1959.

20. Talbot Kelly, R. Burma. London, Adams & Charles Black, 1912.

21. Thompson, W. S. Population and Progress in the Far East. Chicago, University of Chicago Press, 1959.

22. Tinker, H. The Union of Burma. (2nd edit.) London, Oxford University Press, 1959.

22a. Trager, F. N. Toward a Welfare State in Burma. New York, Institute of Pacific Relations, 1958.

23. The 1953 Census of Industry. Rangoon, Government Printing Office, 1953.

24. United Nations Technical Assistance Administration. Social Services in Burma. TAA/Bur/16. October, 1955.

25. United States Department of Commerce, World Trade Information Service. Basic Data on the Economy of Burma. *Economic Reports*, Part 1, No. 58-13, 1958.

Table 1

Index of Rice per Acre in a Number of Countries

Country	Prewar	1957
Japan	100	122
Indonesia˙	100	108
China	100	119
Korea	100	131
Thailand	100	97
Burma	100	107
India	100	87
Malaya	100	187
Philippines	100	190
Ceylon	100	145

Source: Food and Agriculture Organization: Food and Agricultural Price Policies in Asia and the Far East. Bangkok, 1958.

Table 2

Food Production in Burma

1,000 Acres—Productions in Tons

	1954-1955		1955-1956		1956-1957		1957-1958		1958-1959	
	Acreage	Production	Acreage	Production	Acreage	Production	Acreage	Production	Acreage	Production
Rice	10161	5,803.3	10263	5,868.1	10,385	6,463.5	9,547	5,883	10899	6,350
Millet	560	66.0	560	69.0	580	71.0	520	70 (with wheat)	N.A.	N.A.
Pulses	1137	201.2	1049	232.6	1,127	238.8	854	199	"	"
Shelled peanuts	779	109.5	821	145.3	855	138.4	880	195	"	235
Sesame	1402	36.9	1421	44.8	1,466	55.6	1,420	35	"	N.A.
Sugar cane	57	916.4	66	855.5	75	1066.8	90	1,300	"	"
Cotton	370	23.4	422	18.3	399	15.8	354	11	"	"
Tobacco	110	46.7	104	39.6	121	48.8		32	"	"
TOTAL	14,576				15,008		13,665			

N.A. = Not available at time of writing.
Source: Statesman Year Book 1959. Food and Agriculture Organization Production Yearbook, Vol. 12, 1958.

Table 3

Burma: Acreages Sown to Main Crops, 1936/37-1940/41 Average and 1946/47-1957/58

(Thousands of acres)

Year	Paddy	Groundnut	Sesamum	Cotton	Pulses	Sugar Cane	Millet	Others Crops	Total
1936/37 to 1940/41 average	12,832	808	1,401	453	1,329	64	475	1,805	19,166
1946/47..........	8,242	573	1,262	171	852	38	603	1,715	13,456
1947/48..........	9,597	729	1,395	222	970	46	565	1,781	15,305
1948/49..........	10,128	706	1,385	219	968	56	583	1,738	15,783
1949/50..........	9,349	699	1,351	216	995	45	589	1,787	15,033
1950/51..........	9,467	693	1,321	221	974	42	626	1,760	15,104
1951/52..........	9,698	721	1,332	255	968	54	616	1,773	15,417
1952/53..........	10,331	744	1,328	344	1,060	65	598	1,843	16,313
1953/54..........	10,398	821	1,352	354	1,113	88	568	1,810	16,504
1954/55..........	10,161	779	1,402	370	1,137	57	560	1,911	16,377
1955/56..........	10,263	821	1,421	422	1,049	66	560	1,935	16,537
1956/57..........	10,386	855	1,466	399	1,127	75	580	1,971	16,859
1957/58(a)..........	10,160	880	1,420	354	854	90	520	1,958	16,236

(a) Provisional.
Source: Economic Survey of Burma, various editions.

Table 4

Burma: Relation of Official Paddy Price to Wholesale Agricultural Prices and to the General Retail Price Level, 1948-1957

(1948 = 100)

| | | Wholesale Agricultural Prices(a) | | | | | | General(b) Retail Prices | Price of Paddy as a Percentage of | |
Year	Paddy	Cereals	Pulses	Oilseeds	Other Food	Other Non-Food	All Commodities		All Agr. Commodities	Retail Prices
(1)	(2)	(3)	(4)	(5)	(6)	(7)	(8)	(9)	(10)	(11)
1948	100	100	100	100	100	100	100	100	100	100
1949	100	96	141	128	179	161	123	126	81	79
1950	100	98	118	118	109	196	115	109	87	92
1951	100	105	154	165	133	204	133	108	75	93
1952	100	99	177	115	120	155	114	97	88	103
1953	100	93	179	103	149	138	110	95	91	105
1954	100	94	147	121	112	157	110	86	91	116
1955	100	99	130	106	92	148	106	94	94	106
1956	100	99	148	115	113	143	109	119	92	84
1957	100	97	155	137	157	172	123	115	81	87

(a) Official series converted from base 1938-40 = 100.
(b) Official series converted from base 1939 = 100; in Rangoon.
Source: Government of Union of Burma, Quarterly Bulletin of Statistics.

Table 5

Calories Consumed per Capita per Day in Burma
Percentage Distribution by Food Groups

Rice	72.3
Wheat	.7
Other grains	2.2
Dry beans and peas	2.5
Roots, tubers and starches	0.5
Sugar	4.7
Oil seeds (incl. soya beans and peanuts)	2.0
Oils & fats (excl., oilseeds and butter)	5.8
Vegetables	1.3
Fruits and nuts (incl. coconuts)	2.3
Meat, fish, poultry & eggs	3.9
Milk and dairy products (incl. butter)	1.8
Grand total	100.0
Number of calories	2,020

Source: Marx, R. E.: Diets not Adequate in Most of Asia. Foreign Agriculture, vol. 22, June, 1958.

Table 6

Harvest Calendar in Burma

Crops	Harvest Period	Bulk of Harvest
Wheat	Mar.-Apr.	...
Maize:		
early	Sept.-Nov. ⎫	Nov.-Dec.
late	Dec.-Jan. ⎭	
Millet(a)	Jan.-Mar.	...
Rice:		
main crop	Nov.-Jan ⎫	
secondary crop:	⎬	Nov.-Jan(b)
I	Aug.-Sept.	
II	May-June ⎭	
Dry beans	Feb.-Apr.	...
Dry peas	Feb.-Apr.	...
Chick peas	Feb.-Apr.	...
Pigeon peas	Feb.-Apr.	...
Groundnuts:		
early	Aug. ⎫	
late	Dec.-Jan. ⎭	...
Sesame seed	Mid Aug.-End Sept.	...
Tobacco	Mar.-Apr.	...
Cotton	Oct.-Dec.	...

(a) Kunpyaung (Red Millet) is harvested as fodder crop in January-February.
(b) The harvest period for the main crop accounting for 85%.
Source: Food and Agriculture Organization. World Crop Harvest Calendar, Rome, 1959.

Map 1

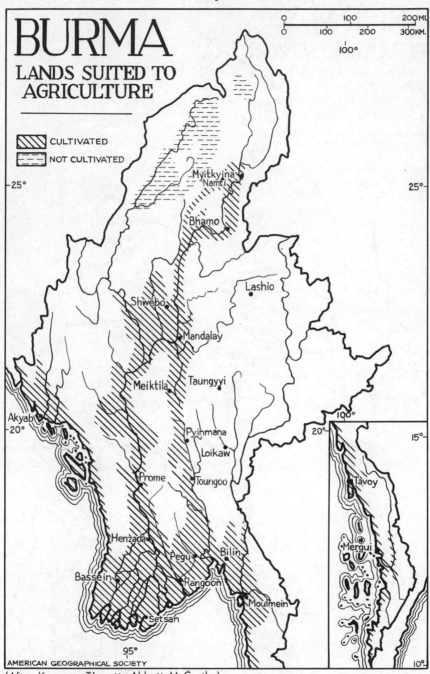

BURMA
LANDS SUITED TO
AGRICULTURE

⊠ CULTIVATED
☰ NOT CULTIVATED

100

200 MI.

300 KM.

100°

Myitkyina
Namti

Bhamo

Lashio

Shwebo

Mandalay

Meiktila

Taungyyi

Pyinmana

Loikaw

Prome

Toungoo

Henzada

Pegu

Bilin

Bassein

Rangoon

Setsan

Moulmein

Akyab

Tavoy

Mergui

100°

25°

25°

20°

20°

15°

10°

95°

AMERICAN GEOGRAPHICAL SOCIETY

(After Knappen Tippetts Abbett McCarthy)

Map 2

BURMA
POPULATION SUPPORT

FROM PRESENT
PRODUCTION OF
CULTIVATED LAND

IN PERSONS PER ACRE

| 0 | 50 | 100 | 150 MI. |

| 0 | 100 | 200 KM. |

NAGA
HILLS

MYITKYINA
1.36

UPPER
CHINDWIN
0.80

KATHA
1.4

SHWEBO
0.63

NORTHERN
SHAN STATES

CHIN
HILLS

LOWER
CHINDWIN
0.42

MANDALAY
1.14

SAGAING
0.41

ARAKAN
HILL
TRACTS
2.36

PAKOKKU
0.55

KYAUKSE
1.23

MYINGYAN
0.40

MEIKTILA
0.36

SOUTHERN
SHAN STATES

AKYAB
1.29

MINBU
0.72

MAGWE
0.53

YAMETHIN
0.88

0.97
KYAUKPYU

THAYATMO
0.76

KARENNI

1.49
PROME

TOUNGOO
1.44

TAVOY
1.75

SANDOWAY
1.19

THARRAWADY
1.49

SALWEEN
1.15

HENZADA
1.55

PEGU
1.35

BASSEIN
1.50

INSEIN
1:20

THATON
1.25

MERGUI
1.65

MAUBIN
1.25

HANTHAWADY
1.43

MYAUNGMYA
1.62

PYAPON
1.57

AMHERST
1.11

AMERICAN GEOGRAPHICAL SOCIETY

(After Knappen Tippetts Abbett McCarthy)

INDIA

L GENERAL REMARKS

Because the Indian population represents one-sixth of the human race, its tragic nutritional situation is of concern to the whole world. The task of presenting a reasonably complete and accurate picture of this situation in the few pages that can be devoted to it, is difficult.

The problem can be summed up thus: India's population is growing at the rate of 1.5 to 1.7 per cent a year, which means a current increment of between 5 and 7 million every year, to be followed by an increase of 10 to 12 million and more because of the geometrical character of the progression. As against this increase in population, food increases are slow and uncertain. According to Indian authors, very little if any land can be reclaimed for further development. However, Ford team experts who visited the country in 1959 believed that better water management could bring millions of acres into agricultural development. Yet, everybody agrees that boosting the yield of the present cultivated acreage is the primary task.

Against this background of inexorable population growth and food uncertainty, a number of additional subsidiary factors make the problem of feeding the Indian masses still more difficult to solve. The multiplicity of ethnic groups and languages, the diversity of cultures, the deeply-rooted prejudices for or against certain food stuffs, the depth of religious feelings—all these factors combine to make public education difficult.

The lack of financial resources and technical skills complicate the problem still further. In view of the foregoing, it is not surprising that the Ford team experts advocated emergency action and the creation of a high-level, coordinating, food-production authority. It was found that although India is making some progress in increasing food production, the present rate of increase must be tripled to meet the third Five-Year Plan target, which in turn is the bare minimum needed to feed the increasing population and to add a few ounces to the daily ration. If food production grows no faster than at present, the gap between supplies and need will be 28 million tons of food grains by 1965. To date, the government, well aware of this situation, has elaborated a program of reformatory measures which include price controls and marketing, land-tenure policy, and storage-building facilities

Food policies are implemented by the central and state governments.
The various civil services have so far been concerned mainly with preventing too sharp an increase of the prices of food grains to consumers
and with the control of inflationary tendencies. Price policies have also
to some extent recognized the need to prevent producers' prices from
falling too low. Thus minimum prices have been fixed at various times
for wheat, jowar, corn, rice, and grams, and in 1955 small quantities
of these grains were purchased by the government at the floor prices
in order to make the support effective. In addition, these price policies
have been backed by internal procurement of grains, prohibition of export in certain regions, controlled importation, control of circulation
of food stuffs, rationing of supplies during periods of scarcity, and the
sale of government reserve stocks through fair-price shops below market rates. In the face of constantly rising food-grain prices since 1955
(see Table 1) despite increases in production, controls are progressively being tightened.

The development of agricultural marketing was begun in 1935 by the
then government of India, and has been initiated in the states of Andhra,
West Bengal, Bihar, Bombay, Madras, Mysore, and the Punjab. The
basic objective of the marketing organizations is to create places where
the farmers will learn methods of pooling, processing, and grading
their produce and to give them an opportunity at the same time to get
an adequate share of the price paid by the consumer. These are becoming more effective since the abolition of intermediaries (Zamindars)
who for many centuries had, to a certain degree, strangulated the producers' economy.

The land policy of the government falls into four classes: abolition
of intermediaries; tenancy reform, which scales down rents to one-
fourth or one-fifth of the harvest, and recognize the rights of tenants
to acquire ownership of their land; ceilings on holdings; and a reorgan-
ization of agriculture to prevent the fragmentation of land in uneconomical parcels—a measure which favors at the same time the development
of cooperatives.

However effective some of these measures may have been, at the
end of 1959 the threat of a tragic gap between population growth and
food resources was still present and was creating the most serious
problem faced by the central government.

II. FOOD RESOURCES[10,11]

The total land area of India, is variously estimated at 806 million
acres, or at 1.3 million square miles (which means 812 million acres),
or at 694 million acres.

The discrepancy may arise from the fact that certain sources include the area occupied by Pakistan (118 million acres) in the total.
It seems, in any case, reasonably certain that the area actually sown
covers between 315 and 318 million acres, of which 44 million can be
sown twice, giving a crop area of about 362 million acres (see Table 2).

The total irrigated area is given as 56 million acres (1959-1960).
Irrigation is carried out by a variety of systems including tanks (10.2
million acres), wells (16.4 million acres), and a variety of other devices (5.1 million acres). Tank irrigation is common in central and
southern India where large quantities of rain water are stored in lakes
and in reservoirs during the rainy season and distributed during the
dry season of the year. In parts of Bombay and Madras, temporary
barrages are built across streams or small rivers to create additional
reservoirs. In these areas, wet season crops include rice, jowar, bajra,
corn, cotton, sugar cane, sesamum, and ground nuts. During the dry
season, the crops are wheat, barley, pea, gram, linseed, grape, and
mustard.

Well irrigation is common in the northwest; the farmers set up
various devices to help them lift water from wells ranging in depth
from 2 feet to over 50 feet.

The great bulk of agricultural land in India is deficient in organic
matter. (see Map No. 1) In most agricultural countries of the world
this want is usually met by returning farmyard manure to the land or
by using compost made from crop residues and similar organic waste
material. In India, however, cattle dung is largely utilized as village
fuel and only about 40 per cent of it is used for manurial purposes.

The agricultural season is divided in two: the **Kharif** season of the
monsoon, and the **Rabi** season of dry weather. The ground is generally
prepared for cultivation in April and May for Kharif crops and in late
October and November for Rabi crops. The chief Kharif crops are:
rice, jowar, bajra, corn, cotton, sugar cane, sesamum, and ground
nuts. The chief Rabi crops are: wheat, barley, peas, linseed, rape,
mustard, and—in South India—rice and jowar.

The harvest arrives on the markets as follows (see Table 28):
Kharif crops, November 1; Rabi crops, May 1; Rice, November 1;
Wheat, May 1; Sugar cane, November 1.

Table 3 gives a summary of the most important agricultural products, the acreage they cover, and the annual production.

Although a farm in, say the state of Uttar Pradesh would be above
the national average in size and might comprise five to six acres, it
would be operated in a typical manner by a "joint family" of five people, meaning that unemployed relatives would live on the income and
help out with the field work. This situation is common throughout the
country where there is critical unemployment of the farm population.
Such a farm would own two bullocks, two crude plows, one land leveler,

one cultivator-harrow, three hoes which may be used as spades, a
bullock cart, and a few hens.

Planting and fertilizing are done by hand. The principal crops in
this area are: wheat, sugar cane, sorghum, fodder, and even some
rice in patches. Water for irrigation comes from the Ganges through
a canal. Large mud containers are used for farm storage.

Such a family would live in a village with a population of 1,400 to
1,800. The village would be run by a village council (Panchayat) in
whose hands community development programs would basically repose.
There are more than 500,000 villages like this in India.

The yields are low: wheat; 8 bushels per acre against 25 in the
United States; corn, 13 against 50. Hens produce no more than 50 to 55
eggs a year, compared with 196 in the United States. Each cow delivers
around 300 pounds of milk a year, whereas a well-bred and well-kept
cow can produce 6,000. Full-grown pigs seldom exceed 100 pounds.

The total farm investment exclusive of land is estimated at $750.
In 1957, as a result of Foreign Aid, a number of farms in this area
received 250 pounds of nitrogen fertilizers for the first time, which
gave encouraging results. The crops are consumed in the village, and
adequate storage space would be needed if food production is to be increased. The nearest market beyond the village is in a town 15 miles
away which is a long distance to travel by bullock cart.

A. CEREALS (See Maps 4, 5, 6)

The most important cereals in India are rice, wheat, and the millets, of which there are many varieties. Starting in 1957 the government created separate rice and wheat zones. The southern rice zone
comprises the states of Kerala, Madras, Andhra, and Mysore. The
wheat zone is divided into a northern zone, an Uttar Pradesh zone,
and a western zone which itself includes Madya Pradesh, Rajasthan,
and the state of Bombay. This arrangement allows meeting the problem of chronically deficit states by permitting surplus ones in the same
zone to trade with them directly. It has also made it easier to enfore
restrictions on import and export between states and to cordon certain
deficit zones to protect them against the depletion that would result if
free trade were allowed.

The total contribution of these basic cereals to Indian diets has
fluctuated from 48.4 million tons in 1949-50 to 52.8 million in 1957-
58. The production of pulses—which are often included as food grains
in Indian statistics—has remained pegged at around 9.2 million tons
in the last ten years. This gives a maximum figure of 57.6 million
tons in 1949 and 62 million tons in 1959. An increase of approximately
8 per cent in food resources was matched by a population increase
during the same period of 12 per cent (358 million to 400 million).

Rice. Rice is eaten by more than half of the population of India. The chief areas of production are Assam, Bengal, the south, the west coast, and certain small areas in the remaining provinces. (see Table 4 and maps). The area planted in rice was 73 million acres in 1951-52 and rose from 79 million in 1958-59. During the same period, production passed from 21.5 million tons annually to 24.8 million. About one-third of this crop is irrigated, the bulk being sown in June and July and harvested in November and December. Unfortunately, rice yields per unit area are among the lowest in the world—one-fourth of Spain's and Italy's, one-third of Japan's, and one-half of China's.

At present, 76 research stations are attempting to improve these conditions, essentially by distributing better seeds. Out of 4,000 different types of rice, 455 superior strains giving 10 to 12 per cent better yields have been evolved, but they cover only a small percentage of the total rice area as follows: Andhra, 70 per cent; Assam, 8 per cent; Bengal, 10 per cent; Madya Pradesh, 16 per cent; Orissa, 10 per cent; and Uttar Pradesh, 12 per cent.

Rice farming practices vary considerably from region to region and even from place to place. During the last two years, the Japanese method has been tried with good results, and is practiced at present on 4 million acres; the Chinese method is also experimented with at 30 centers distributed throughout the rice areas of India. The mass of the farmers, however, are reluctant to change century-old methods and it requires relentless pressure by adequate teams to spread improvements of this nature to a significant degree.

Because of the number of different varieties and the diversity in soils, nutritional values of the diets change from place to place. For instance, the protein content of rice from Uttar Pradesh is 8.4 per cent, while it is only 5.98 per cent in Bombay. Other nutrients and especially minerals vary in similar proportions.[8] In the long run this is bound to have a significant influence on the health of the people consuming the rice. As generally found throughout Asia, the practice of mechanical milling is taking over the century-old practice of hand pounding, with the result that a larger proportion of the nutritional value of the rice is removed, especially in terms of thiamin. It has been shown that in certain parts of India machine milling removes up to 75 per cent of the thiamin from the kernel.

Wheat. Wheat comes from an area of 32 to 33 million acres, which represent a not inconsiderable development since 1951-52, when only 23 million acres were under this cereal. Thus the growth in wheat cultivation has been considerably greater than that in rice. During the same period, the amount produced rose from 6.2 million tons a year to 7.7 million. In 1958-59 further efforts resulted in a bumper crop of 10 million tons for the first time in India's history. Unfortunately, this progress is handicapped by the spread of virulent fungus disease, rust, which in normal years causes 5 per cent of the crops to be lost and

occasionally strikes in epidemic form with disastrous consequences.
Rust resistant varieties are being introduced, but these occupy only
60 per cent of the total wheat area in Madya Pradesh, 33 per cent in
Uttar Pradesh, and 70 per cent in the Punjab; these states produce 72
per cent of the total wheat production of India. Wheat is also eaten in
certain parts of Bihar and in the central provinces where it is transformed into unleavened bread with an extraction rate of 93 to 95 per
cent.

B. OTHER EDIBLE CROPS

Other edible crops in India include essentially the pulses, of which
gram is the most popular and important. There are various species
of these peas or grams, the Bengal gram, the black gram, the green
gram, the red gram, the lentil, and several others. Their nutritive
value varies considerably. The soya bean, for instance, has 40.1 per
cent protein content while the Bengal gram has only 22.3 per cent.
These pulses are found almost anywhere but there is a great concentration of pulse land in the northwestern part of the country where it
covers almost 55 million acres with a total production of between 9.5
and 11.4 million tons a year. (see Tables 3 and 4).

Fruits and nuts are not plentiful and their consumption appears to
be almost negligible, although mangoes, guava, cucumbers, watermelons, and bananas are eaten in season and are considered a delicacy.
The total area under fruit is estimated at over 3 million acres (see
Tables 2 and 5). The annual production of bananas between 1953 and
1956 came from 340,000 acres and yielded 1.8 million tons a year.
The area in papaya is said to be around 10,000 acres and the production 142,000 tons. Other fruits are listed in Table 5.

Roots and tubers are very popular. The sweet potato is grown on
450,000 acres with a production of 1.5 million tons; the European
potato is grown on 635,000 acres and produces just under 2 million
tons a year. Chilies and spices are present on all food trays. The
amount and place of production is shown in Table 6. These additional
condiments have an important nutritional significance, especially with
reference to minerals and vitamins. It has been found, for example,
that the chilis and the Indian gooseberries when dried and powdered
are a valuable source of vitamin C.

The Fruit Products Order under the Essential Commodities Act of
1955 insures the manufacture of fruit products of standard quality.
The food preserve industry is being developed; 23,000 tons of these
products were manufactured in 1958.

The total known area under vegetables covers approximately 1.5
million acres. As shown in Table 5 the most important vegetable-
growing states are Bombay, Assam, Uttar Pradesh, and Madya Pradesh,

but vegetable patches are found in many other states, especially
Madras, and Andhra. Many unlisted vegetables are also grown or
picked wild and they accompany the main dish of rice or the chapatties
(cakes made with wheat, see below), especially among the poorer
classes.

C. FATS

Fats in the Indian diets come essentially from vegetable oils. The
use of lard and suet is objected to by the major communities on religious grounds. At one time, ghee was being used for cooking purposes,
particularly in northern India, but on account of its increasing scarcity
and high cost, it has been gradually replaced by the partially hydrogenated oils. The main varieties of oil-producing seeds include ground
nuts, sesamum, rape, and mustard, linseed, castor seed, while coconut
oil and safflower oil are also used in certain regions of the country.
The total area under cultivation stands around 30 million acres. Bengal
and Bihar and part of the Uttar Pradesh area are partial to mustard oil
(see paragraph on disease patterns), Bombay to safflower seed oil, and
a large part of the central provinces, Mysore and Madras, to ground
nut oil.

Coconut oil is used exclusively on the west coast and sesame oil is
favored in southern India. Table 7 gives the acreage of the different
varieties of oil seeds by states and territories. These oils are mainly
used for preparing various spiced and curried foods and for frying
other foods.

D. CASH CROPS

India has a number of cash crops, notably coffee, tea, and sugar.
Coffee is confined to the hilly tracts from 1,000 to 6,000 ft. above sea
level in Mysore, Madras, and Kerala. The area in coffee increased
between 1951 and 1958, from 235,000 acres to 260,000. Production
also followed an upward trend during the same period from 21,000 tons
to 43,000 tons; at the same time, exports grew from 2,200 tons in 1951
to over 15,000 tons in 1956-57. Tea ranks as the largest item in India's
export trade. It earns every year a foreign exchange of about $250
million. The area under tea remained at 768,000 acres from 1948 to
1956, but the production in millions of pounds increased, rising from
577 million pounds in 1948[10] to 667 million pounds in 1956. The sugar
industry is the second largest in India next to the cotton-textile industry. The acreage under sugar cane, which was slightly above 4 million
in 1900, rose to 5 million in 1958, resulting in the production of 19
million tons of crushed cane in 1958. These outputs of sugar cane
yield an average 2 million tons of sugar every year. Table 8 gives the

acreage in sugar cane and Table 9 gives the production of sugar by state.

E. LIVESTOCK AND POULTRY

The large livestock population of India numbered in 1956 some 307 million head (see Table 10); approximately 160 million cattle, 45 million buffaloes, 38 to 40 million sheep, 56 to 58 million goats, 1.5 million horses, and 6 to 8 million other animals including pigs. This represented 19 per cent of the world's cattle, 50 per cent of the world's buffaloes, and 18 per cent of the goats. This large population unfortunately is more a liability than an asset in view of the limited land resources and the consequent competition between man and beast for food. Religious prejudices demand the preservation of sterile, valuless, aged animals. One of the basic recommendations of the Ford team, while recognizing the limitations imposed by beliefs concerning animal slaughter, includes the creation of a tax that would make the maintenance of useless cattle a burden to their owners. It is also recommended that all bulls not kept for breeding be castrated (this is not objected to by religious beliefs), that measures to control open grazing be enforced, and that plants for desicating fallen animals be established with incentive payments to owners for bringing in dead cattle.

Of the 200-odd million cattle and buffaloes, 72 million or 36 per cent are milch animals. Milk yields are low. Cows produce an average of 300 to 400 pounds a year and buffaloes 1,000 to 1,100 pounds. A few strains, however, such as the "Sahiwal" milch cow, yield up to 4,000 pounds a year, and Murrah buffaloes yield up to 3,000. The scarcity of food, the general poverty, the lack of organized cattle breeding, and the embryonic stage of the dairy industry explains these poor yields.

Although buffaloes form only 30 per cent of the milch animals, they account for 55.9 per cent of the total milk produced because of their high yields. Buffalo milk has a butterfat content of 6.5 to 7 per cent as against 4 to 5 per cent for that of the cow. Gross production of milk is estimated at slightly over 22 million tons a year of which 3 million are marketed. The rest is used for home consumption or fed to calves. Most of the milk-producing cattle are to be found in the Punjab and in the irrigated part of Rajasthan. Other cattle occur in the area extending southwest from the southern part of West Bengal to the Orissa-Andhra border and also in some of the northern districts of Bihar and Uttar Pradesh.

Between 58 to 72 per cent of the milk is transformed into the various milk products of which India is so fond. Intensive steps are being taken by most states to improve the cattle both as draft animals and as milk producers. These include the extension of milk-supply organizations to certain cities (especially Calcutta), setting up dry cattle farms, and training personnel (especially in Bihar).

In 1956, India had around 100 million head of poultry. Poultry is an important subsidiary industry of the poorer farmers, but due to neglect and starvation, the yield is low, limited, as noted, to slightly over 50 eggs per hen per year. Thirty-three centers of poultry development have now been established and 150 more are in the process of being created.

F. FISH

Fish could be an important item in the nutritional health of India. Fisheries are potentially rich but do not as yet yield a fraction of what they could, partly because of the caste system; fishing and the fishing trade are universally relegated to people of low castes who, from want of education, show extreme conservatism.

The production of fishes rose from 800,000 tons in 1950 to over 1.2 million in 1957. Approximately 70 per cent of the catch comes from the sea. (see Table 11). Most of it is represented by marine teleosteans, and herrings, sardines, anchovies, and the Pacific mackerel also are found in abundance (see Table 11a). Central Bombay is the most active fishing area (see Table 11b), landing over 250,000 tons of fish (1957). The next fishing state is Kerala. Great efforts are being made to mechanize and industrialize India's fishing techniques with the help and assistance of Norway, the United States, and the Food and Agriculture Organization. More than 800 mechanized boats out of 73,400 fishing craft operate on the Indian coast. Cold storage facilities have been increased and a central fishery technological research station functions in Kerala.

The fresh-water fishing industry is also being developed. Efforts have been made to import quick-growing varieties of baby fish. The total production of fish from tank and reservoir fish culture amounted to 357,566 tons in 1957.

III. FOOD RESOURCES BY STATES (see Tables 20 to 27)

Food resources vary considerably from state to state. In the following paragraphs a brief summary of them is given.

Andhra Pradesh. The state of Andhra Pradesh is one of the most important from the agricultural point of view. Some 42 per cent of the total area is sown and cultivated. It is essentially a rice and millet state where oil seeds are also extensively cultivated.

Assam. The total area sown and cultivated in Assam is estimated at slightly over 6 million acres, of which approximately 900,000 are sown more than once. Assam is a country of cash crops which include tea, jute, cotton, and tobacco. The main food crops are rice, rape, mustard, sugar cane, potatoes, pulses, maize, and oranges.

Bihar. Bihar is a fertile state, thickly populated. Rice is the most important crop occupying approximately 12 million acres or more than 50 per cent of the crop area. Corn, wheat, and barley are also extensively grown. Oil seeds like castor and mustard form an important part of the agriculture. After Uttar Pradesh, Bihar is the second most important sugar area in India. Cash crops include jute and tobacco.

Bombay. Bombay is one of the richest and most important states of India, both because of its agricultural production and because of its industries; it is also the largest. Slightly over 50 per cent of its area is under cultivation. The most important crops are the cereals, especially jowar followed by rice. Other millets and pulses include bajra, ragi, tur, and gram. The state is a food and deficit area.

Himachal Pradesh. The main agricultural wealth of this territory is derived from potatoes and fruits such as apples, peaches, almonds, nuts, and pomegranates. Seed potato is the chief cash crop; salt is another important item; but the territory does not contribute much to the nutrition of India's millions.

Jammu and Kashmir. This territory, famous for its scenery and its forests, is a poor agricultural producer. The soil is not very fertile and only 3.6 per cent of the total area can be cultivated. The main crops are rice, corn, and wheat. It is a food-deficit area.

Kerala. Kerala is a troubled state where, for a time, a communist government was in power. New land legislation has been passed by the Assembly, fixing a maximum holding of 50 acres of double-cropped land and establishing the maximum and minimum rates of fair rent, excess land to be surrendered to the government against compensation. An experiment of regrouping a number of families under **sarvodaya** (communal living) was attempted at the end of 1957. The main food crops are rice, tapioca, and sweet potatoes. The state has a deficit of approximately 700,000 tons of rice a year. The main cash crops consist of coconut, areca nuts, tea, coffee, cardamom, rubber, pepper, ginger, lemon grass, ground nut, and cashew nut.

Madhya Pradesh. Madhya Pradesh is the second largest state of India. About 36 per cent of the area is under cultivation while 20 per cent of it is covered by forests producing the best quality teak in India. The chief food crops are wheat, especially in Malwa, Narmada Valley, Satna, Chatarpur, and Bhopal, and rice which is mainly grown in Chattisgarh, Shahdol, Rewa, Thar, and Indore. Cash crops include cotton, sugar cane, and oil seeds found all over the state.

Madras. Madras is an important state, in size and in activities, both agricultural and industrial. Some 45 per cent of its area is under cultivation. Its main crops are rice, the millets, pulses, sugar cane, potatoes, sweet potatoes, and tapioca. The main cash crops consist of ground nut, cotton, coconut, tobacco, coffee, and a few others. Bananas

(500,000 tons a year), mangoes (200,000 tons a year), and citrus fruit (27,000 tons a year) are the most important fruit crops.

Madras is also a fishing state with an annual production of over 107,000 tons of fish.

Manipur. Manipur is a fertile, sparsely populated territory, producing enough rice for its needs on its 200,000 acres of cultivated land.

Mysore. Mysore is an agricultural state where 53.5 per cent of the acreage is under cultivation. The main resources are rice, jowar, bajra, maize, ragi, and wheat. Pulses and oil seeds are also grown. Cash crops comprise coffee, tea, and rubber. Inland fisheries are being developed, producing 3,500 tons of fish a year. Research is stimulated by 3 rural fishery demonstration units and 14 fish farms, and a number of improved seeds have been distributed as well as manure, compost, and other fertilizers. The results have been rewarding.

Orissa. Orissa is an important cattle state.

The Punjab. Punjab is the second largest wheat and gram producing area in India and it is third in barley and maize production. A little over 50 per cent of it is sown and cultivated under irrigation and dry farming methods in approximately equal amounts.

Rajasthan. Rajasthan is a poor state where cultivation is generally precarious. The region southeast of the Aravalli Mountains is higher, more fertile, and diversified in character than the rest of it. The main food crops of the state are: rice, bajra, jowar, pulses, and corn (Kharif crops); wheat, barley, and gram (Rabi crops).

The main cash crops include oil seeds, sesame, rape seed and mustard, linseed, and ground nuts, cotton, sugar cane, and tobacco. Approximately 40 per cent of the area is sown and under cultivation.

Tripura. Tripura is a territory of jungles and hills with little agricultural value. Its main products are paddy, jute, cotton, tea, and fruit such as pineapple, jackfruit, and others. Only 20 per cent of the territory is cultivated.

Uttar Pradesh. Uttar Pradesh is an active, populous, and important state. Approximately 55 per cent of it is cultivated, three-fourths under dry and one-fourth under wet cultivation. Ninety-three per cent of the cultivated area is in food crops: wheat, barley, gram, rice, jowar, bajra, and corn; the main cash crops are sugar cane, linseed, rapeseed, mustard, ground nut, cotton, and jute. At the end of June 1958, it was estimated that another 7.5 million acres could be made available for cultivation through reclamation measures, a situation that is not often encountered in Indian states. Uttar Pradesh is an important center of livestock breeding and improvement. At the end of June 1958 there were 6,000 stud bulls, 1,500 buffalo bulls, 1,700 rams, 716 bucks, and 215 boars. There were 11 state poultry farms and several cattle-breeding and research stations. There were approximately 35,000 acres of water under the control of the Department for Pisciculture.

West Bengal. West Bengal whose capital city is the overcrowded agglomeration of Calcutta, is among the states making considerable efforts to improve their agricultural returns. A state-wide campaign for the Japanese method of rice cultivation was undertaken during the last Five-Year Plan while breeding bulls were supplied to villages to improve animal strains. The state is also remarkable for the Greater Calcutta Milk Supply Scheme and the Milk Colony Units that are being established in the suburbs.

It is believed that by the end of 1960 over 185 tons of milk will be distributed daily in the city of Calcutta.

IV. EXPORTS AND IMPORTS

Although India exports a considerable amount of food (see Table 12), especially in the form of live animals and meat, fish, frozen vegetables, coffee, tea, and spices, it has to import some of the basic elements of its diets. Thus, in 1958, as in many other years, it had to import cereals and dairy products. These amounted together to over 1.5 billion rupees or 82 per cent of the total food import bill. Grain imports fluctuated widely between 1950 and 1958, 1951 being the worst year with an import of over 4 million tons of grain, and 1955 being a good year when only 700,000 tons were imported. The average import stands around 2 million tons a year (mostly wheat) (see Tables 13 and 13a). These grains, India gets mostly from the United States, Australia, Burma, and Viet Nam—Australia and the United States supplying wheat, Burma and Viet Nam supplying rice (see Table 13a). The government's policy of stocking supplies of grain has resulted in a considerable need for storage space (see below).

The central government supplies food grains to the states when production breaks down as happened when, in 1957-58, drought in the central and northeastern parts of the country particularly affected Assam, Bengal, Bihar, Orissa, eastern Uttar Pradesh, Madhya Pradesh, and Rajasthan. Table 14 gives the amount of wheat supplied to the states from April 1, 1958 to January 31, 1959.

V. DOMESTIC AND FOREIGN AIDS TO AGRICULTURE

In addition to the price policies, marketing facilities, zoning laws, land tenure policies, and storage facilities programs listed in section I, the government has embarked on a "grow more food campaign" which includes: loans to the states; improvement in land management through waste-land reclamation; soil conservation; mechanical cultivation wherever possible; seed supplies; irrigation projects for new wells, tanks and tubewells; construction of dams and channels; installation of waterlifting and pumping appliances; manure and fertilizer supplies; plant protection against pests; and improved techniques (Japanese and Chinese) of rice cultivation. In addition, the Ford team has made a number of recommendations which, if followed, may improve the picture.

India receives a considerable amount of foreign aid from various sources, the most important of which are the United States, the Colombo Plan, and the United Nations and its agencies. Total assistance from the United States authorized between 1951 and January 1959 amounted to $433.3 million.[12] In the early years of the Technical Cooperation Program, emphasis was laid on the development of agriculture, which occupied top priority in India's first Five-Year Plan and, according to the I.C.A.[7] should again have that priority in the next Five-Year Plan. Under this technical assistance, more than 300,000 tons of fertilizer were distributed, while 135,000 tons of steel for agricultural implements were supplied. By the end of 1958 $100 million had been spent by the United States in support of 27 joint projects in agriculture. Agreements that have been made or will be made soon regarding the shipment of food grains are said to be worth nearly $1 billion.

VI. FOOD INDUSTRIES, STORAGE AND TECHNOLOGY

The problem of food storage is dealt with in different fashion in the different states, although in most parts of India, there has been little such problem since much of the food is consumed when it is produced. Now that the government has embarked on a program of food stocking to meet food shortages, the problem of storing may become more acute. The Ford team has recommended that suitable local storage be built in each village to help buffer the grain market.[3] So far, private enterprises have been unwilling to put up the capital needed because food storage facilities may remain vacant for an undetermined length of time. The Indian government has begun to add to storage capacity and to buy land for more bins. A dispersed storage is envisioned so that supplies may be quickly available in case of crop failures.

The central government has also urged the states to set up warehouses for this purpose. This has already been done in over 200 centers, each warehouse having a capacity of 1,000 to 5,000 tons. In addition, the central government has established a Central Warehouse Corporation and has started warehouses and rented accomodations at nine strategically located places: Amravati, Gondia, Sangli, Gadag, Devanagere, Warangal, Moga, Chandauvri, and Baragarh. State warehouse corporations have been set up in 12 states so far, excepting Assam and Kerala.

As there is some uncertainty about the ability of Indian docks to handle the unloading of grain shipments from the United States, it seems urgent to improve godown facilities at harbors. Already 984 godowns are being constructed by large credit societies and 435 by marketing societies. The Central Warehouse Corporation has a credit of $14 million for its program which is said eventually to aim at creating 100 centers of national importance with a total capacity of 3 to 3.5 million tons. In addition, grants in aid will help local societies to construct 4,000 godowns at farming centers to prevent distress in case of emergency.

The food industry is still in its infancy in India. It is limited to the production of salt, the refining of sugar (1.8 million tons a year), of vegetable oils (1.8 million tons), and the manufacture of biscuits and confectionery (20,000 tons).

Eight hundred and ten licensed factories manufacture food products, the most important of which are in Amritsar, Bombay, Calcutta, Delhi, and Lucknow. These usually concentrate on vegetables and fruit, of which 28,000 tons were produced in 1958. But it is hoped that by 1961 the annual output of the factories mentioned above will rise to 50,000 tons.

A Central Food Technological Institute in Mysore studies food processing and conservation, food engineering, and all other aspects of food technology. Processing of rice is an important village industry. About 65 per cent of the paddy is thus processed. These facilities come under the Rice Milling Regulation Act of 1958. The government of India has also directed that these licensed establishments restrict their milling to removal of no more than 5 per cent of the bran. The sugar industry is another important cottage industry, using nearly 60 per cent of the total cane crop. In addition, there are four varieties of palm sugar including date, palmyrq, coconut, and sago supplying raw material for mills that employ or will soon employ over 150,000 people. Six firms are licensed to fabricate complete sugar plants in cooperation with foreign manufacturers. This is going to be increased during the course of the third Five-Year Plan.

India is one of the most important producers of oil seeds in the world. The five major sources are: ground nuts, castor, sesame, rape and mustard, and linseed. The production of oil from these five oil seeds is shown in Tables 7 and 7a. In addition to these major cash crops, India has an important acreage in opium and produces fiber for the jute industry.

There is no detailed information available on cold storage facilities. It is known that such plants exist in Bombay, Mangalore, Calicut, Cochin, Quilon, Trivandrum, Madras, and Calcutta and that additional plants are being installed in many other places. Some of these plants have been provided under the various foreign aid programs.

VII. DIET TYPES

A. GENERAL

The task of discussing diets in India is a formidable one. While research in nutrition can be traced back to 1881, it was only following
the Conference on Far Eastern Countries on Rural Hygiene of 1937
that intensive work in the field of nutrition started. Being a conglom-
eration of nations, cultures, resources, and traditions, it might seem
presumptuous to speak of an Indian diet at all. There should be in the-
ory at least three important factors that govern diets: natural resources, social classes, tradition. Patwardhan,[8] however, whose
knowledge of Indian nutritional problems is second to none, remarks
that although to a casual observer the diets of the people appear to be
materially different in composition and nutritive value, the differences
are, actually, superficial and originate chiefly in the different methods
of preparation of various foods and not so much in the average composition of the diet. Basically the dietary habits conform to certain well-
known patterns. Most interest is concentrated on the habits of the
poorer classes. This is natural for two reasons: they comprise at
least 80 per cent of the population; and, because of the limitation of
their economic power, their chances of providing themselves with adequate nutrients are minimal.

The common characteristics of all Indian diets are their extremely
high cereal content, and their marked deficiency in protective food
stuffs. Inadequacy of minerals and of most of the important vitamins
is to a great extent a consequence of these two primordial characteristics.

Tables 15 to 18 give a comparison of the caloric structure of the
"average" Indian diet at different times. From a reading of these
tables, one gets the impression that the nutrition of the Indian masses
has deteriorated since the pre-World War II era. Patwardhan reports
that according to 132 surveys made between 1931 and 1942, the average
caloric intake amounted to 2,560 calories per consumption unit per day
(in 92 surveys, the caloric intake was between 2,000 and 3,000, in 28
surveys, it was between 3,000 and 4,300, in 17 surveys it stood between
1,100 and 1,500). This deterioration is in accordance with what we know
of the increasing gap between food needs and food resources. However,
the origin of these calories has not changed; now, as always, 70 to 80
per cent of the calories come from cereals and pulses, but there seem
to be much less of them. Then as now, the amount of protein consumed
every day was and is generally low. In the majority of the pre-World
War II surveys, it stood at between 51 and 100 Gms. But, in the 17 surveys made among the poorer population, it was between 20 and 50 Gms.
Then as now, most of the protein in the diets came and comes from
vegetable sources. The average figure of 7.3 of the total protein in the

diet that came from animal origin is not reached today. Most of the fat is derived from oil seeds and a small amount from butter or milk products. The trend, as stated above, shows a gradual replacement of the animal fats by vegetable fats; thus, while the amount of fat in the diet has not changed greatly its quality has dropped.

The most popular cereal in India is rice, although others have been gaining since the war. Of the total amount of rice consumed in India a large proportion is of the parboiled type. In certain regions and in a few communities, raw milled rice is preferred and eaten. This practice can be traced to social or religious prejudices against parboiled rice; also, certain groups resent its sometimes offensive odor. Parboiling occurs either on a large scale in the mills, or in small quantities in the consumers' homes. Parboiled rice is preferred in Madras and on the west coast. The method consists in soaking paddy in cold or luke-warm water for varying lengths of time. This is followed by steaming until the grain becomes soft and partly or wholly cooked. The excess water is drained off and the paddy spread out to dry. The parboiled paddy is then hulled, giving the rice its special appearance and flavor. The grain then appears slightly colored and is harder to the tooth than the original rice grain.

It has been demonstrated that parboiled rice retains a considerable amount of vitamin B_1 even when highly milled. Explanations for this phenomenon have been numerous but the net result is that this age-old practice could be usefully utilized for preserving valuable nutrients.

Rice can be prepared in other ways. The paddy can be wetted, mixed with about four times its volume of pre-heated sand in a frying pan, and kept on an open fire. The temperature of this sand reaches 230° to 240° C. The paddy is then rapidly stirred with an iron ladle and after two or three minutes thrown over a wire sieve which removes the sand, leaving behind the parched rice which has swollen and burst out of the cracked hull during parching. The final product which has different names in local vernacular is very tasty and is used as food for convalescents.

Another method consists in steeping the paddy in warm water; the temperature of which stays at 60 to 70° C. After remaining overnight the mixture is cooled to room temperature, and the water is drained off. Small amounts of this paddy are heated in shallow pans until the husks crack, then it is spread on a wooden mortar and pounded. The product is then dried and eaten after frying in oil or ghee mixed with spices. Quite often the above mentioned product does not enter the menu of the regular meals, but is part of the snacks so popular in Asia that serve as a moral lift between the main meals. Another practice commonly found in India is the washing of the grain of rice in plenty of water before cooking. The first washing is responsible for a loss of 40 to 50 per cent of the thiamine and the draining of the water after cooking is responsible for additional losses. However, this practice is not general. Some families know how to prepare palatable rice while not throwing away the water, and in many parts of India, rice-water is used for breakfast. Among the most primitive tribes, rice is cooked to glutinous paste.

Next to rice, millet and wheat are the most popular cereals. There are a number of varieties of millets and numerous recipes to prepare bread, cakes, and pancakes with various flours. During the war, it became difficult to import rice in India and imports of wheat made up the yearly deficit. As a result, the consumption of wheat has certainly increased in many parts of the country. Indian bread known as chapatti is prepared according to various methods. The simplest consist in mixing the flour with the required quantity of water and kneading the mixture till a dough is obtained. The chapatti is then baked in a shallow pan or on an open fire. One side gets baked in about two minutes and the other side is then turned over for the same treatment, the chapatti is then placed on the fire and manipulated by hand or by tong. It then separates in two layers and is ready to eat.

Another method consists in preparing the dough with a little oil or ghee. It is then baked in a pan and eventually looks like a pancake **Paratha**; another method of preparation, **purie**, is a chapatti fried in deep fat, usually ghee, over an open fire. Because of these added ingredients, purie is the food of the rich.

Pulses of various kinds are common all over India. They enter the menus in different forms, sometimes mixed with the pancake flours, or entering into the composition of certain breads. The most common practice is to soak the gram with the husks and with beans in water from 12 to 24 hours, then to tie the soaked grain in a wet cloth. The tied bundle is allowed to stand at room temperature for another one or two days when most of the grain germinates. The easily-removable husk is then taken off and the germinated legume is either eaten raw or consumed after cooking with spices.

Soya beans have excited a good deal of interest among nutrition workers. This bean is cultivated to some extent in Bengal, Bihar, and Orissa, but Indian experts do not consider it of outstanding value for the population of the country. Pulses are consumed in the north more than in the south in the form of a gruel, sometimes cooked, sometimes served as a delicacy between meals. In Bengal, they are soaked, boiled, or parched, and they form more than 80 per cent of the protein intake of most of the population.

Milk is always boiled before being drunk. Milk by-products are important items of the diet. These include ghee, butter, buttermilk, and local products known as **khoa**, **rabadi**, **malai**, and **channa**. Ghee is a butter fat from which the water has been removed by heating. The procedure varies in its details but the end result is very much the

same and akin to ordinary butter. The milk is brought to boil and allowed to remain at that temperature for five minutes or longer. It
cools slowly and when warm to the touch, is inoculated with preformed
curd. Fermentation results, after which an equal quantity of water is
added. The mixture is churned in a metallic or earthen vessel by a
wooden churner. In half an hour the butter separates, and is then removed and pressed. Buttermilk, a by-product of butter, is very popular and contains most of the nutrients of milk except the fat. It is eaten
mixed with rice especially in the south, while in the north, it is drunk.
Curd is another by-product of milk which is greatly appreciated. Malai
is the cream which rises to the top of slowly heating milk, rabadi is
whole milk boiled down to a thick consistency and sweetened. Khoa is
whole milk concentrated in open pans to a granular curd still containing
some water; it is the basis of several Indian sweets. Channa, made by
curdling milk either by rennet or by adding mineral or organic acids,
is a specialty of Bengal although sometimes prepared in Bihar and
Orissa.

The consumption of vegetables in the Indian diet is very low; they do
not provide even as much as 1 per cent of the total caloric intake. It is
however impossible to compute the amount of green-leaf vegetables
that are picked up in the fields, boiled or eaten raw during meals or
between meals. The majority of families in the lower income groups
use them as an adjuvant, possibly to swallow mouthfuls of cooked cereals or pulses.

The average intake of fats and oil is very low. The use of butter as
a spread is confined to the upper-middle-class families. Fats are used
for cooking and, as stated above, the hydrogenated oils are gradually
replacing the expensive butter or ghee. The use of mustard oil is popular in Bengal, Assam, Orissa, Bihar, and the eastern portion of Uttar
Pradesh, while ground-nut oil is popular over large areas where this
nut is extensively cultivated. Gingelly or sesame oil is used in Madras
state more than anywhere else, while the consumption of coconut oil is
restricted to the west coast.

The very little meat that is eaten in India, which provides a slightly
more than 0.5 per cent of the caloric intake, originates usually in
"mutton," fish, chicken, or exceptionally pig. When it appears on the
table of the medium or well-to-do classes, this meat is found in curry.
It is the nonavailability of these flesh foods that make many nonvege-
tarians appear as vegetarians. Fish, because of its low price, is more
popular than the more expensive items, especially along the coast and
in the inland parts of Assam, Bengal, Orissa, and Bihar. Dried fish is
not very popular; appreciable amounts of it are exported abroad (see
Table 12). Eggs, because of their high price, are usually sold by the
masses, rather than used as food. Poultry keeping is confined to limited areas of the country and especially to the poorer classes. Many
hindus, especially in the north, do not like chicken because they object

to all scavenger animals. This is extended in certain cases to eggs, while, as Planap remarked, others abstain from eating eggs because it would be tantamount to destroying life.

Condiments of all kinds and spices such as turmeric, coriander, rapeseeds, chilis, black pepper, and many others are quite extensively used and are important not only because they make dishes attractive but also because they carry minerals and vitamins.

The majority of the people have only two principal meals a day (although a small percentage may have breakfast, a mid-day meal, and a night meal). Breakfast consists of some porridge or gruel accompanied by chilies or some rice left over from the evening with chilies or **achars.** Then the worker may or may not take with him a snack of rice or a piece of unleavened bread with an onion or a small amount of green-leaf vegetable to eat during his day in the field. In the evening, rice is cooked, together with boiled vegetables or pulses, and on some rare occasions there may be a meat or fish curry.

B. VARIATIONS IN DIETS

As stated above, the main variations in diets are related to natural resources, traditional culture, and economic status. In Assam, a rice state where the cooking fat is mustard oil, dried fish may be consumed with lentils, red gram, and a few other pulses.

In Bihar, also, rice is the cereal of choice, irrespective of income. However, Bihar is an ambivalent state and wheat stands next in order of popularity. The rice consumed is of the parboiled variety. The poorer classes have a fondness for a mixture of flour made of parched cereals and pulse called **sattu.** In northern Bihar, some corn is introduced in the diet either baked in the tender stage with a little fat, or ground into flour and cooked into chapatties. Consumption of vegetables is low. During the winter, boiled sweet potatoes and boiled water chestnuts are popular. Little meat is eaten, and only on rare occasions. Sometimes even rat meat or the meat of crocodiles is consumed among the poorer, semi-aboriginal families. Dried flowers are eaten as a supplement to cereals in the very poor strata of the population. Although Bihar is a milk-producing state, consumption of it is low because of its great cash value.

Rice is the most popular cereal in most parts of the state of Bombay, especially along the coastal region. There are large areas of the state where other cereals come into prominence especially jowar in Karnatak and bajra in the southern part of Maharashtra. In the northern part of Maharashtra, however, wheat and jowar are both preferred. In Gujrat, rice, wheat, and millet are consumed in varying proportions.

The state of Madhya Pradesh can be divided into three different regions based on the popularity of wheat in the north, jowar in the center, and rice in the south. Millets are generally boiled to a porridge, sometimes with pulses. Small millets are also favored by the poorest classes in the villages where they are sometimes accompanied by dried flowers boiled and eaten in place of cereals. Consumption of fruit and vegetables is small; ground nut oil is used for cooking.

Punjab is a wheat state, though rice makes some small inroads from time to time among certain people. The consumption of milk is higher than in other states, but yet unsatisfactory.

In Madras, rice and millets are preferred and the consumption of wheat occurs only in the richer homes. Raji, the millet of the poorer people, is common. **Sholam** is another of the small millets, which is ground into a flour, then boiled or steamed in small balls or **bolus**. This is consumed along the coast by the lower social classes. As usual, where the standard of living is low and the consumption of the better vegetables or pulses is insignificant, there is an increase in the intake of chilies, tamarinds, condiments of all sorts. Consumption of milk is negligible, gingelly oil is the popular cooking fat.

In Orissa, rice is the main cereal. The great majority of the people eat it parboiled and home-pounded. The various types of millet are found to be popular among the lower classes and corn is occasionally eaten. While the most popular pulses are the same as for the rest of India, non-leafy vegetables such as plantains, potatoes, tubers, beans, and water lily roots are more generally eaten in Orissa than elsewhere. Mangoes and jackfruits are popular. Mustard oil and gingelly oil are the cooking fats. Fish is the most important fresh food, as one would expect in a maritime state.

In Andhra Pradesh, rice is the most popular cereal in the northern, eastern, and southern portions of the State, while jowar (sholam) is the staple cereal in the rest of it. A certain amount of raji is also consumed. The red gram and the Bengal gram are the most popular pulses. Ground-nut oil and gingelly oil are the cooking fats. No animal food is taken by the masses and milk is hardly ever drunk. In Mysore, the most popular cereal seems to be raji, but few surveys have been carried out.

In Uttar Pradesh, rice is the most popular cereal; in Kerala, rice and pulses, cooked in coconut oil, form the basic menu. Fish is the most important flesh eaten. The poorer classes of people supplement their cereal food with tapioca which can be made into various forms of curry.

Considerable dietary variations occur, however, within the range of social classes. Well-to-do families have, of course, a larger variety of diets than the poorer ones, but their increased adequacy is not the result of a reasoned dietetic effort but the accidental outcome of their greater purchasing power. As one rises in the economic level, the amount of animal proteins (flesh or milk) increases.

In northern India, for example, the well-to-do, identified with the upper caste people, eat wheat and rice while the poorer, equated to the lower castes, are content with barley and millet. As stated above, many well-to-do Hindus do not consider fish as meat and since it is an expensive item, they make rather an abundant consumption of it.

In central India it was found (Planalp) in a given area that poor families, representing 40 per cent of the population, have three meals a day, mainly based on cereals. The breakfast consists of rice leftovers from the previous evening, heavily spiced with chili or pickles; the second meal consists of boiled vegetables or pulses with a meat curry, sometimes accompanied by bread; and the meal is based on vegetables, curry, rice, with meat or fish. (There is no doubt that this represents an unusually favorable picture of Indian diets as "poor" classes comprise far more than 40 per cent of the Indian population.)

Wealthy families, representing approximately one-fourth of the population under study, have more substantial meals: for breakfast a paratha accompanied by vegetables or curry with pickles and tea; a typical second meal includes meat or fish, vegetable or pulse curry and rice; and the evening meal is the same as the second meal.

There is some uniformity in the infant feeding and weaning habits of southern India. Less data are available for the north, but it may be assumed that they are similar. Breast feeding is started on the third day after birth because most women believe that the milk flow begins at that time. During the intermediate period, the baby is usually entrusted to a neighbor acting as a wet nurse. It is reported that some Moslems remaining in India feed their babies on honey and date pulp during that period.

The time at which supplementary feedings are given babies varies. In Mysore, 75 per cent receive supplements during their first year, while in Hyderabad only 5 per cent receive them. It is also found that in urban areas there is a tendency to start the supplements earlier than in rural areas. These supplementary foods may consist of animal milk often diluted with water, but cereal foods are the most common. The children receive rice products, pancakes, or steamed cooked cakes of unleavened bread without any special preparation. About 75 per cent of the infants are completely weaned by the end of two years. The abrupt switch from mother's milk to starchy foods results in some forms of protein malnutrition or kwashiorkor.

VIII. ADEQUACY OF FOOD RESOURCES

As has been stated above, even in normal times food resources are inadequate for the teeming population of India. A diet survey made during 1945-48 by the Indian Council of Medical Research shows this inadequacy in each of the nutritional fields.

Table 19 shows the gap that exists at the individual level between adequacy and availability. A number of recommendations alluded to in the first paragraph of this chapter have been made by the Ford team, to bridge this gap. These can be summarized thus: the growing of vegetables and fruit must be promoted as rapidly as possible, overcoming the different problems involved, such as finding sites for gardens and obtaining good seeds; information on the culture requirements of these items must be given to the villagers; the grazing of livestock and the pilfering of robbers must be controlled; educational material on the way to cook and preserve these vegetables must be made available.

In terms of broad policy, two types of action can be envisaged: short-range and long-range. Short-range projects are based on relief by shipment of United States surpluses to India. It looks like a tailor-made solution to feed India's people and at the same time relieve the United States of the burden of storage of an increasing amount of food. Yet, this solution is viewed with no enthusiasm either in India or in the United States. The Indians fear that payment of these surpluses in rupees might have an inflationary effect, putting too much control of the Indian currency into foreign hands. It is also believed that Indian farm output might be reduced if the pressure of necessity is relieved. In the same vein, it is feared that arrival in India of huge quantities of foreign grain might upset the market and cause farmers to diminish production. The problem of dock handling of arriving grain and further storage has already been mentioned. Finally, it is feared in India that American surpluses might not be inexhaustible and that an easy dependency might develop in the country instead of a courageous attitude of facing up to the problem.[12]

In the United States, objections are raised on the basis of the considerable cost that would be involved in shipping, doubts about the ability of India to store and protect the supplies, and the fear that dumping American grain on the foreign market might have an unfavorable effect on other grain exporters.

Long-range measures are therefore more popular. Actions recommended as essential involve five basic points:

a) better soil and water conservation;

b) procurement of chemical fertilizers in the amount of 1.5 million tons of nitrogen, 750,000 tons of phosphoric acid, and 200,000 tons of potash which, according to Ford experts, would mean a nine-fold increase in the use of nitrogen, and considerably larger increases in the use of the other fertilizers;

c) improvement in cereal production, including plant protection, more equipment such as tractors and sprayers, and the enlargement of cultivator-educational teams;

d) distribution of improved, rust resistant seeds and of corn hybrid;

e) adequate development of livestock.

IX. DISEASES CAUSED BY DIETS

The problem of deficiency diseases in India is enormously complicated and there is very little statistical evidence on their distribution.
Map No. 3, drawn after Patwardhan, gives an impression of what the
distribution of some of them may be.

Full or partial cases of kwashiorkor have been observed in various
parts of the country. The patients come mostly from the poor classes
of people living on diets that are both qualitatively and quantitatively
inadequate. As elsewhere in tropical areas where the disease has been
described, it occurs in children receiving a faulty diet after weaning,
essentially based on starchy foods among families which cannot afford
to purchase milk.

Vitamin A deficiency is common, manifested by thickening and fold-
ing of scleral conjunctiva, by Bitot spots, and by keratomalacia. The
latter symptom is said to be common in Calcutta where it has been
observed by certain authors in 10.5 per 10,000 persons. Night blindness is also often found in the children of the poorer classes of India,
although the point is made that not all cases of night blindness are the
result of vitamin A deficiency. Dry and rough skin is frequently encountered among children, often associated with xerosis of the eye.
Indian authors, however, do not believe that vitamin A deficiency is
the only cause of this symptom but believe that it may also be correlated with fatty acid deficiencies. Angular stomatitis, scrotal eczema,
and glossitis also occur, indicating probably important deficiencies in
nicotinic acid and riboflavin. Thiamine deficiencies are prevalent among
the rice-eating population. The most important centers of occurrence
are the districts of Ganjam, Vizagapatam, Godavari, Krishna, Guntur,
and Nellore. In addition, a few circumscribed areas of beriberi occur
in Bengal and Assam.

Wherever parboiled rice is used, beriberi is practically unknown.
As elsewhere in the Far East, there appears to be a correlation between the incidence of the disease and the distribution of modern rice
mills doing mechanical hulling. In addition to too-thorough milling,
the practice of washing the rice and of allowing the cooked rice to remain overnight may also be responsible for a considerable loss of
thiamin in the diet. Pellagra occurs sporadically throughout India, although it is more common in the parts of the state of Madras where
beriberi is endemic. Patwardhan remarks that pellagra does not affect large numbers of people at one time but that cases occur continu-
ally in small numbers.

Vitamin C deficiency, is not one of the common manifestations of
malnutrition although the usual intake of vitamin C in poor Indian diets
is low. Rickets and osteomalacia are found, contrary to some claims
that they do not occur. It seems that most cases are concentrated in
the state of Bombay. Other surveys report an incidence of rickets as

being between 0.2 and 1.6 per cent in Orissa, while 3.2 per cent of the children of Uttar Pradesh are afflicted. Osteomalacia also occurs, since the conditions that result in rickets in the early part of life do not cease to exist. These cases are particularly common in the Punjab but have not been described in other parts of India. Simple goiter is endemic in the Himalayas and south Himalayan regions.

Other dietary diseases commonly found in certain areas of India are urinary calculi, especially in the bladders of young children, epidemic dropsy, the cause of which has now been identified as the use of mustard oil in cooking. This apparently is due to **Argemone mexicana,** a plant whose seed oil is used to stretch or adulterate gingelly oil.

Lathyrism due to the consumption of **lang dahl** or **Lathyrus sativus,** is a problem of considerable importance in view of the popularity of this cheap and resistant legume. In periods of famine or scarcity, it forms a staple article of the diet in certain regions. The government has at various times taken steps to mitigate the danger or even suppress the consumption of this food. Finally, fluorosis must also be cited as a disease occurring in many parts of the country against which no preventive measures have been taken.

X. CONCLUSIONS

The Ford team considered that, in order to absorb the 45 million people expected to be born in the next five years in the rural areas, a public work program of projects requiring primarily hand labor, such as contour bunding, land leveling, surface drainage, and irrigation by wells and tanks, should be carried out. At present India is using only a small portion of its potential water supply; judging by the one-fifth to one-fourth increase in crop yields that have been obtained on irrigated land as compared to non-irrigated land, it is recommended that considerable effort be made towards better water management. The Ford experts believed that intensification of expenditure of time and effort on water management would be preferable to construction of large-scale irrigation projects. It is also believed that millions of acres could be reclaimed and made more productive by drainage improvements and it is hoped that this will be given a high priority in the next plan.

This intensification of efforts should be concentrated on certain crops and certain areas. Rice and wheat should receive more attention than other crops in areas particularly suited to this kind of culture. As the result of all these recommendations, it is believed that a target of 100 to 110 million tons of food grains might be achieved by 1965—1966. This target would permit a slight improvement in consumption and also meet the nutritional demands of the increased population.

SELECTED REFERENCES

1. Food and Agriculture Organization. Food Balance Sheets 1952-1953; *ibid.*, 1954-1956.
2. Marx, R. E. Diets Not Adequate in Most of Asia. *Foreign Agriculture,* Vol. 22, No. 6, June, 1958, pp. 3-4, 22.
3. Government of India. Report on India's Food Crisis and Steps to Meet It. (Report sponsored by the Ford Foundation.) 1959.
4. Indian Council of Medical Research, The Nutrition Research Laboratories. Annual Reports. 1953-54, 1954-55, 1955-56, and 1956-57.
5. Indian Council of Medical Research. Report of Work Done in States. New Delhi, 1950-1956.
6. Results of Diet Surveys in Indian 1935-1948. New Delhi, 1951-1953.
7. International Cooperation Administration. Near East and South Asia Regional Conference of Food and Agriculture Officers, April 20-25, 1959, p. 94. Beirut, [1959].
8. Parhwardhan, U. N. Nutrition in India. *The Indian Journal of Medical Sciences,* Vol. 4, 1952.
9. Rao, K. S., Swaminathan, M. C., Swarup, S., and Pathwardhan, U. N. Protein Malnutrition in South India. *Bulletin of the World Health Organization,* Vol. 20, 1959, pp. 603-639.
10. *The Statesman's Year-Book 1959.* London, Macmillan & Co., Ltd.; New York, St. Martin's Press; 1959.
11. Directory and Yearbook 1959-60. *Times of India.*
12. Food Demand Crisis in India. *Washington Post and Times Herald,* February 29 and March 1, 1960.

Table 1

Price Indices in India

Price Level

The movement in the price of some items is shown by the following table of index numbers of wholesale prices: (Base 1952-53: 100)

	1956		1957		1958
	January	December	January	December	January
All commodities. . . .	95.3	107.9	107.2	107.0	106.0
Food Articles	89.4	104.8	103.2	104.0	122.5
Cereals	80.0	97.0	95.0	98.0	97.0
Pulses	76.0	87.0	86.0	80.0	80.0
Rice	77.0	93.0	91.0	102.0	101.0
Wheat	85.0	94.0	94.0	86.0	86.0
Jowar.	83.0	127.0	119.0	109.0	108.0
Bajra	98.0	133.0	132.0	117.0	114.0
Ragi.	60.0	97.0	97.0	100.0	103.0
Gram	57.0	77.0	78.0	73.6	64.0
Arhar.	85.0	82.0	83.0	86.0	74.0

The price position was difficult June to Sept. 1958.
Source: The Times of India: Directory and Yearbook, 1959-1960.

Table 2

Classification of Area

(Thousand acres)

States and Territories	Forests		Area Not Available for Cultivation		Uncultivated Land Excluding Fallows		Fallowland		Total Cropped Area	
	1954-55	1955-56	1954-55	1955-56	1954-55	1955-56	1954-55	1955-56	1954-55	1955-56
STATES										
Andhra Pradesh	12,614	13,992	11,429	10,584	7,788	7,643	7,112	6,563	29,739	30,399
Assam (A)	12,042	12,042	14,077	14,077	3,638	3,638	889	889	6,003	6,003
Bengal (West)	2,087	1,916	3,880	3,831	1,904	1,817	1,596	1,129	14,750	15,317
Bihar	9,126	9,676	5,224	5,066	2,916	3,000	6,196	6,471	23,750	24,498
Bombay	15,214	15,946	19,384	10,329	11,263	10,973	7,540	7,567	69,347	69,910
Jammu & Kashmir	1,400	1,398	1,739	1,672	708	655	403	665	1,849	1,840
Kerala	2,515	2,433	1,033	968	1,017	1,030	443	504	5,233	5,466
Madhya Pradesh	33,675	33,489	11,365	11,491	18,002	18,111	6,062	5,876	42,403	43,392
Madras	4,491	4,488	5,534	5,547	3,663	3,610	3,935	4,205	17,116	16,967
Mysore	6,851	6,288	4,531	4,145	6,687	6,886	3,847	3,579	25,589	25,208
Orissa	8,799	8,799	6,274	6,274	6,466	6,466	3,008	3,008	14,958	14,958
Punjab	836	843	7,753	7,781	2,509	2,381	1,770	1,490	22,157	23,500
Rajasthan	3,433	3,478	16,535	16,282	21,974	21,609	15,182	14,734	29,505	31,006
Uttar Pradesh	8,643	8,713	11,002	10,985	7,813	7,536	3,513	3,638	51,395	51,925
TOTAL STATES	121,726	123,501	119,760	118,032	96,348	96,355	61,496	60,318	353,728	360,389
TERRITORIES										
Andaman & Nicobar Islands	37	39	16	16	15	16	2	2	12	15
Delhi	(a)	4	79	85	46	48	11	12	298	323
Himachal Pradesh	400	400	157	159	1,020	1,022	57	45	1,041	1,047
Laccadive, Minicoy and Amindivi Islands	*	*	*	(a)	*	(a)	*	*	*	7
Manipur	37	37	(b)	(b)	91	91	(a)	(a)	218	218
Tripura	1,574	1,573	66	96	469	447	46	37	557	564
TOTAL TERRITORIES	2,048	2,053	318	356	1,641	1,624	116	96	2,126	2,174
TOTAL INDIA	123,774	125,554	120,078	118,388	97,989	96,979	61,612	60,414	355,854	362,563

*Not available.　(a) Less than 500 acres.　(b) Included under forests.　(A) Including North-East Frontier Agency.
Source: The Times of India: Directory and Yearbook, 1959-60.

Table 3

Food Areas and Production in India

Area and Production

*Includes sugar cane

Crops	Area in '000 Acres		Production in '000 Tons*		Average Yield Per Acre in Lbs.	
	1956-57	1957-58	1956-57	1957-58	1956-57	1957-58
Rice	79,320	79,027	28,282	24,821	799	704
Wheat	33,580	29,657	9,314	7,654	621	578
Barley	8,726	7,531	2,827	2,175	726	647
Maize	9,197	9,762	3,009	3,064	733	703
Jowar	40,367	41,411	7,249	8,056	402	436
Bajra	27,884	27,453	2,885	3,565	232	291
Ragi	5,831	5,897	1,715	1,716	659	652
Small Millets . .	12,230	11,979	1,964	1,759	360	329
Total Cereals .	2,17,135	2,12,717	57,245	52,810	591	556
Gram	24,265	22,405	6,264	4,754	578	475
Redgram	5,686	5,598	1,954	1,396	770	559
Black gram . . .	4,362	3,297	393	328	202	223
Green gram . . .	3,243	3,359	319	279	220	186
Horse gram . . .	4,026	3,887	350	327	195	190
Lentil	1,287	1,235	188	171	320	310
Khesari	2,287	1,805	272	219	266	179
Peas	2,403	2,741	571	574	532	469
Moth	4,675	4,142	369	286	177	155
Other pulses . .	5,981	6,186	823	882	308	319
Total Pulses . . .	58,215	54,655	11,503	9,216	443	378
Total Foodgrain . .	2,75,350	2,67,372	68,748	62,026	559	520
Sesamum	5,446	5,268	442	363	182	154
Groundnut	13,450	14,457	4,200	4,271	699	662
Rape & Mustard . .	6,311	6,050	1,026	905	364	335
Linseed	4,156	3,318	384	271	207	183
Castor seed	1,415	1,325	124	97	199	165

	3,057	3,021	6,151	6,451	6,000	2,001
Sugar Cane · · · · · · · · · ·						
Tobacco · · · · · · ·	1,029	926	294	252	639	610
Cotton · · · · · ·	19,893	20,158	4,735	4,753	93	92
Jute · · · · ·	1,908	1,754	4,288	4,088	899	932
Mesta · · · · ·	733	726	1,478	1,211	807	667
Sann-hemp · · · ·	609	—	125	—	458	—
Pepper · · · · ·	2,209	2,290	273	264	277	258
Ginger · · · · ·	393	388	150	140	855	808
Chillies · · · ·	1,476	1,534	342	355	519	518
Turmeric · · · ·	1,550	—	1,527	—	2,206	—
Tea · · · ·	782	—	6,67,727	—	880	—
Coffee · · · ·	260	—	68,143	—	336	—
Rubber · · · ·	184	—	48,795	—	483	↑
Banana · · · ·	3,63,787	—	1,601	—	10,414	—
Papaya · · · ·	11	—	142	—	27,774	—
Potato · · · ·	702	785	1,674	1,981	4,342	N.A.
Sweet Potato · · · ·	374	—	1,128	—	6,748	—
Tapioca · · · ·	609	—	1,759	—	6,467	—
Indigo · · · ·	9	—	0,100	—	25	—
Opium · · · ·	59,313	—	13,495	—	19	—
Lac · · · ·	—	10,023,000	13,15,000	—	—	—

*Note: Data for 1956-57 and 1957-58, relate to Partially Revised and Final Estimates respectively and are subject to revision: (a) Production of rice is in terms of cleaned rice; groundnut as unshelled nuts; sugarcane as raw sugar or gur; cotton as lint in thousand bales (of 392 lbs.) and jute and mesta as dry fibre in thousand bales (400 lbs.); coconut as thousand nuts (the average yield being in the number of nuts). (b) Area and production of pepper, ginger, and turmeric are in terms of 100 acres and 100 tons respectively. (c) Area and production of tea, coffee, and rubber are in terms of 1,000 acres and 1,000 lbs. and those of tea and rubber relate to calendar years. (d) Acreage under opium is in terms of acres and production in maunds (of 82 2/7 lbs.) This also applies to lac.

Source: The Times of India: Directory and Yearbook, 1959-60.

Table 4

Area Under Different Food Crops

(Thousand acres)

States and Territories	Rice 1954-1955	Rice 1955-1956	Wheat 1954-1955	Wheat 1955-1956	Barley 1954-1955	Barley 1955-1956	Maize 1954-1955	Maize 1955-1956	Jowar 1954-1955	Jowar 1955-1956	Bajra 1954-1955	Bajra 1955-1956	Ragi 1954-1955	Ragi 1955-1956
STATES														
Andhra Pradesh	6,371	6,376	60	77	9	8	475	476	6,145	6,294	1,640	1,579	808	785
Assam	4,195	4,217	7	7	—	—	38	38	6,145	—	—	(a)	—	—
Bengal (West)	9,833	10,158	141	155	107	109	117	126	4	4	(a)	10	24	24
Bihar	12,024	12,209	1,597	1,444	899	778	1,612	1,347	7	5	9		374	348
Bombay	4,062	4,005	2,850	3,217	36	36	504	548	17,736	17,258	9,578	8,807	638	669
Jammu & Kashmir	452	459	275	275	50	50	283	293	3	1	31	31	11	10
Kerala	1,941	1,944	(a)	—	—	—	1	1	12	12	1	1	11	10
Madhya Pradesh	9,363	9,417	5,716	5,976	410	415	1,013	1,034	5,350	5,183	517	529	36	35
Madras	5,266	5,251	4	4	1	1	16	16	1,771	1,777	1,338	1,399	948	946
Mysore	2,293	2,298	666	870	11	9	27	32	6,399	6,501	1,389	1,315	2,021	1,976
Orissa	9,518	9,403	13	13	1	1	62	61	17	17	11	11	305	304
Punjab	654	674	4,434	4,609	617	497	948	985	722	700	2,446	2,581	20	20
Rajasthan	157	169	2,069	2,310	1,274	1,339	1,341	1,292	2,748	2,690	8,042	7,940	(a)	(a)
Uttar Pradesh	9,090	8,928	9,295	9,875	4,808	4,813	2,594	2,379	2,506	2,224	2,884	2,768	483	468
TOTAL STATES	75,209	75,508	27,127	28,832	8,223	8,056	9,031	8,628	43,420	42,066	27,936	26,971	5,668	5,585
TERRITORIES														
Andaman & Nicobar Islands	7	9												
Delhi	2	1	67	70	13	12	4	3	26	55	47	54	—	—
Himachal Pradesh	110	111	322	322	73	77	276	278	—	—	(a)	(a)	43	42
Laccadive, Minicoy & Amindivi Islands	—	—												
Manipur	217	217	1	1			(a)	(a)					—	—
Tripura	404	407	—	—			(a)	(a)					—	—
TOTAL TERRITORIES	740	745	390	393	86	89	280	281	26	55	47	54	43	42

States and Territories	Small Millets		Total Cereals		Gram		Red Gram		Other Pulses		Total Pulses		Total Foodgrains	
	1954–1955	1955–1956	1954–1955	1955–1956	1954–1955	1955–1956	1954–1955	1955–1956	1954–1955	1955–1956	1954–1955	1955–1956	1954–1955	1955–1956
STATES														
Andhra Pradesh	2,951	2,721	18,449	18,316	299	311	422	441	2,955	2,786	3,676	3,538	22,125	91,854
Assam	5	7	4,245	4,269	7	7	6	7	173	174	186	188	4,431	4,457
Bengal (West)	6	10	10,232	10,586	438	468	57	57	1,536	1,424	2,031	1,949	12,263	12,535
Bihar	773	762	17,295	16,903	1,384	1,359	469	382	4,156	3,762	6,009	5,503	23,304	22,406
Bombay	1,123	1,100	36,527	35,640	1,361	1,620	1,523	1,517	3,860	3,531	6,744	6,668	43,271	40,308
Jammu & Kashmir	17	17	1,111	1,126	9	(a)	9	9	55	—	9	9	1,120	1,135
Kerala	35	34	2,000	2,002	(a)	9	9	9	55	55	65	64	2,066	2,066
Madhya Pradesh	3,628	3,654	26,033	24,243	3,388	3,500	1,013	997	4,021	4,093	8,422	8,590	34,455	34,833
Madras	1,632	1,612	11,026	11,006	4	4	143	149	920	917	1,067	1,070	12,093	12,076
Mysore	1,454	1,277	14,260	14,278	377	385	629	662	2,095	2,022	3,101	3,069	17,361	17,347
Orissa	117	111	10,044	9,921	58	58	33	35	1,049	1,188	1,140	1,281	11,184	11,201
Punjab	24	42	9,865	10,108	5,886	5,678	—	—	604	633	6,490	6,311	16,355	16,419
Rajasthan	221	209	15,582	15,949	2,168	2,809	—	30	2,994	2,977	5,196	5,816	21,048	21,765
Uttar Pradesh	1,748	1,474	33,408	32,929	6,567	6,573	1,605	1,471	2,825	2,811	10,997	10,875	44,405	43,804
TOTAL STATES	13,734	13,030	2,10,348	2,09,276	21,946	22,801	5,944	5,757	27,243	26,373	55,133	54,931	2,65,481	2,64,207
TERRITORIES														
Andaman & Nicobar Islands	—	—	7	9	—	—	—	—	—	—	—	—	7	9
Delhi	—	—	159	195	81	83	—	—	8	8	89	91	248	286
Himachal Pradesh	65	65	839	895	20	18	—	—	56	58	76	76	965	971
Laccadive, Minicoy & Amindivi Islands	—	—	—	—	—	—	—	—	—	—	—	—	—	—
Manipur	—	—	218	218	—	—	—	—	—	—	—	—	218	218
Tripura	—	—	404	407	—	—	—	—	2	2	2	2	406	409
TOTAL TERRITORIES	65	65	1,677	1,724	101	101	—	—	66	68	167	169	1,844	1,893
TOTAL INDIA	13,799	13,095	2,12,025	2,11,000	22,047	22,902	5,944	5,757	27,309	26,441	55,300	55,100	2,67,325	2,66,100

Source: The Times of India: Directory and Yearbook, 1959–60.

Table 5

Fruits and Vegetables of India

Item	Acreage	Area
Mango	1,460,000	Uttar Pradesh, Andhra, Bombay, Madhya Pradesh, Bengal, Bihar, Madras, Mysore, Kerala.
Citrus	223,000	Mosambi, Malta, Santra, Kagzshi, Lime, etc.
Jackfruit	164,000	Bihar, U.P., Kerala, Madras.
Guava	69,000	U.P., Bihar, M.P., Bombay.
Grapes	1,600	Bombay, Andhra, Madras, Himachal Pradesh.
Custard apple	110,000	Andhra, Bihar, M.P.
Pomegranate	2,000	Bombay, U.P.
Letchis	21,000	Bihar, U.P.
Pineapple	21,000	Assam, Bihar, Bengal, U.P., Kerala.
Apples	3,300	Hills of U.P., H.P., Punjab, Madras, Kashmir.
Pears	1,200	Hills of U.P., Bihar, Delhi.
Peaches	1,200	Hills of U.P., Punjab, Kashmir.
Sapotas	758	Bombay, Andhra.
Figs	746	Bombay, U.P.
Phalsa	250	Uttar Pradesh
Dates	889	U.P., Bombay, M.P.
Apricots	630	U.P., H.P.
Walnuts	474	U.P., H.P., Punjab, Kashmir.
Suran	1,300	Bombay.
Aroids	52,000	Assam, U.P., M.P., H.P.
Yams	400	Bombay
Gurds	2,800	Assam, M.P., Andhra.
Cucumber	12,000	Assam, U.P.
Water melon	2,300	U.P., Andhra, Assam.
Musk melon	37,000	U.P., Punjab, Andhra, Bombay.
Squash	1,600	Assam, U.P.
Lady's finger	50,000	Assam, Bombay, M.P., Bihar.
Brinjal (eggplant)	91,000	Assam, Bombay, M.P.
Other summer vegetables	175,000	Madras, Punjab, Andhra.
Beans	22,000	Assam, M.P.
Carrot	62,000	U.P., Bombay, Assam.
Beetroot	4,000	U.P., Assam.
Radish	44,000	Assam, U.P., Madras.
Turnip	16,300	Assam, U.P.
Cabbage	37,500	Assam, U.P., Punjab, Delhi, Bombay.
Cauliflower	45,000	Assam, U.P., Punjab, Delhi, Bombay.
Brussel sprouts	700	Assam, U.P.
Lettuce	1,000	Assam, U.P.
Celery	100	Assam, U.P.
Spinach	2,800	Assam, U.P.
Parsley	600	M.P., U.P., Assam.
Methi	2,100	U.P., Bombay, Assam.
Onions	54,000	Bombay, Andhra, Assam, Bihar.

Source: Compiled from The Times of India: Directory and Yearbook, 1959-60.

Table 6

Area Under Spices, Condiments and Plantation Crops

(Thousand acres)*

States & Union Territories	Pepper		Ginger		Chillies		Tea		Coffee		Rubber	
	1954-55	1955-56	1954-55	1955-56	1954-55	1955-56	1954-55	1955-56	1954-55	1955-56	1954-55	1955-56
STATES												
Andhra Pradesh	—	—	12	18	441	436	—	—	(a)	(a)	—	—
Assam	—	—	—	—	8	8	385	386	—	—	—	—
Bengal (West)	—	—	13	13	16	17	195	195	—	—	—	—
Bihar	—	—	—	—	50	41	1	1	—	—	—	—
Bombay	—	—	10	13	332	339	—	—	—	—	—	—
Jammu & Kashmir	—	—	—	—	—	—	—	—	—	—	—	—
Kerala	2,060	2,140	250	258	11	10	96	97	26	27	166	168
Madhya Pradesh	—	—	11	22	100	88	—	—	—	—	—	—
Madras	4	4	10	8	156	143	69	69	43	46	2	2
Mysore	59	52	18	19	282	266	5	4	160	167	4	4
Orissa	—	—	15	14	24	24	—	—	(a)	(a)	—	—
Punjab	—	—	3	6	84	69	9	9	—	—	—	—
Rajasthan	—	—	1	2	66	41	—	—	—	—	—	—
Uttar Pradesh	—	—	—	—	8	7	6	6	—	—	—	—
TOTAL STATES	2,123	2,196	343	373	1,578	1,489	766	767	229	240	172	174
TERRITORIES												
Andaman & Nicobar Islands	—	—	—	—	—	—	—	—	—	—	—	—
Delhi	—	—	—	—	1	1	—	—	—	—	—	—
Himachal Pradesh	—	—	25	27	1	1	2	2	—	—	—	—
Laccadive, Minicoy & Amindivi Islands	—	—	—	—	—	—	—	—	—	—	—	—
Manipur	—	—	—	—	—	—	—	—	—	—	—	—
Tripura	—	—	—	3	2	2	11	12	—	—	—	—
TOTAL TERRITORIES	—	—	25	30	4	4	13	14	—	—	—	—
TOTAL INDIA	2,123	2,196	368	403	1,582	1,493	779	781	229	240	172	174

*Area of Pepper & Ginger are in terms of 100 acres.　　(a) Less than 100 acres.

Table 6 (Continued)

Area Sown Under All Crops

(Thousand acres)

States & Union Territories	Net Area Sown		Area Sown More Than Once		Total Area Sown	
	1954-55	1955-56	1954-55	1955-56	1954-55	1955-56
STATES						
Andhra Pradesh	27,312	27,899	2,427	2,500	29,739	30,399
Assam†	5,118	5,118	885	885	6,003	6,003
Bengal (West)	12,727	13,122	2,023	2,195	14,750	15,317
Bihar	18,979	18,610	4,705	5,888	23,684	24,498
Bombay	66,462	67,092	2,885	2,818	69,347	69,910
Jammu & Kashmir	1,674	1,533	175	307	1,849	1,840
Kerala	4,363	4,477	870	989	5,233	5,466
Madhya Pradesh	38,191	38,584	4,212	4,808	42,403	43,392
Madras	14,354	14,171	2,762	2,796	17,116	16,967
Mysore	24,787	24,376	802	832	25,589	25,208
Orissa	13,854	13,854	1,104	1,104	14,958	14,958
Punjab	17,421	17,794	4,736	5,706	22,157	23,500
Rajasthan	27,325	28,303	2,180	2,703	29,505	31,006
Uttar Pradesh	41,572	41,671	9,823	10,254	51,395	51,925
TOTAL STATES	314,139	316,604	39,589	43,785	353,728	360,389
TERRITORIES						
Andaman & Nicobar Islands	12	14	(a)	1	12	15
Delhi	230	217	68	106	298	323
Himachal Pradesh	679	679	362	368	1,041	1,047
Laccadive, Minicoy & Amindivi Islands	*	7	*	*	*	7
Manipur	218	218	*	*	218	218
Tripura	479	481	78	83	557	564
TOTAL TERRITORIES	1,618	1,616	508	558	2,126	2,174
TOTAL INDIA	315,757	318,220	40,097	44,343	355,854	362,563

†Including North-East Frontier Agency.   (a) Less than 500 acres.   *Not known.

Source: The Times of India: Directory and Yearbook, 1959-60.

Table 7

Area Under Oilseeds in India

(Thousand acres)

States & Union Territories	Groundnut 1954-55	Groundnut 1955-56	Sesamum 1954-55	Sesamum 1955-56	Rape & Mustard 1954-55	Rape & Mustard 1955-56	Linseed 1954-55	Linseed 1955-56	Castor Seed 1954-55	Castor Seed 1955-56	Total Oilseeds 1954-55	Total Oilseeds 1955-56
STATES												
Andhra Pradesh	3,067	3,041	708	674	2	2	74	89	902	886	4,753	4,692
Assam	—	—	14	14	290	280	3	3	4	4	311	301
Bengal (West)	—	—	11	11	205	224	80	90	—	—	296	325
Bihar	—	—	63	44	234	190	246	232	30	29	573	495
Bombay	5,139	4,447	892	739	73	71	525	549	220	314	6,849	6,120
Jammu & Kashmir	—	—	—	—	50	60	14	14	—	—	64	74
Kerala	36	37	50	47	(a)	(a)	—	—	(a)	(a)	86	84
Madhya Pradesh	810	654	1,223	1,106	322	334	1,232	1,293	21	20	3,608	3,407
Madras	1,772	1,772	380	374	2	2	—	—	35	34	2,189	2,182
Mysore	2,108	2,050	213	220	13	12	118	116	119	114	2,571	2,512
Orissa	61	61	257	253	126	126	26	26	53	53	523	519
Punjab	136	134	64	65	631	669	28	28	—	—	859	896
Rajasthan	126	105	1,324	982	532	622	167	167	3	3	2,152	1,879
Uttar Pradesh	291	283	1,292	1,197	3,520	3,649	839	815	7	5	5,949	5,949
TOTAL STATES	13,547	12,584	6,490	5,726	6,000	6,241	3,352	3,422	1,394	1,462	30,783	29,435
TERRITORIES												
Andaman & Nicobar Islands	—	—	—	—	—	—	—	—	—	—	—	—
Delhi	—	—	—	—	5	2	—	—	—	—	5	2
Himachal Pradesh	1	—	2	2	9	9	2	2	—	—	14	14
Laccadive, Minicoy & Amindivi Islands	—	—	—	—	—	—	—	—	—	—	—	—
Manipur	—	—	—	—	—	—	—	—	—	—	—	—
Tripura	—	—	9	10	11	10	—	—	—	—	20	20
TOTAL TERRITORIES	1	—	11	12	25	21	2	2	—	—	39	36
TOTAL INDIA	13,548	12,584	6,501	5,738	6,025	6,262	3,354	3,424	1,394	1,462	30,822	29,471

Source: The Times of India: Directory and Yearbook, 1959–60.

Table 7a

Production of Oilseeds

The following table gives the actual production - in thousand tons - of oilseeds during the seasons 1956-57 and 1957-58:

	1956-57	1957-58
Groundnut	4,200	4,271
Castor seed	124	97
Linseed	384	271
Sesamum	442	363
Rape and mustard	1,026	905
Total	6,176	5,907

	Average Indian Production (Lakh Tons)	As Percentage Of World Production
Groundnut	42.00	36
Castor seed	1.24	26
Linseed	3.84	15
Sesamum	4.42	26
Cotton seed	13.00	13

The actual production of oil from the five major oilseeds has been estimated as follows:

(000 Tons)

	Groundnut	Castor	Sesamum	Rape and Mustard	Linseed	Total
1953-54 ..	847	37	165	246	103	1,398
1954-55 ..	938	39	184	291	114	1,566
1955-56 ..	878	39	143	242	123	1,440
1956-57 ..	954	39	138	293	123	1,547
1957-58 ..	970	31	138	293	123	1,555

Source: The Times of India: Directory and Yearbook, 1959-60.

Table 8

Area Under Cash Crops

(Thousand acres)

States & Union Territories	Sugar Cane		Tobacco		Cotton		Jute		Mesta	
	1954-55	1955-56	1954-55	1955-56	1954-55	1955-56	1954-55	1955-56	1954-55	1955-56
STATES										
Andhra Pradesh	176	178	308	318	1,218	1,195	—	—	179	189
Assam	60	64	24	23	35	35	282	780	3	5
Bengal (West)	57	61	41	40	(a)	(a)	551	780	141	199
Bihar	327	379	28	36	12	11	270	270	31	45
Bombay	213	220	211	254	9,908	10,869	—	—	90	96
Jammu & Kashmir	3	3	(a)	(a)	—	—	—	—	—	—
Kerala	17	17	14	16	19	22	—	—	—	—
Madhya Pradesh	71	76	38	39	2,356	2,324	—	—	22	21
Madras	126	122	103	108	823	921	—	—	1	1
Mysore	112	155	11	11	2,449	2,798	—	—	39	38
Orissa	59	59	7	7	25	25	87	111	21	23
Punjab	414	452	13	16	1,189	1,282	—	—	1	1
Rajasthan	53	64	44	49	509	590	—	—	—	—
Uttar Pradesh	2,292	2,620	—	—	120	136	34	33	—	—
TOTAL STATES	3,980	4,430	842	917	18,663	20,208	1,224	1,561	528	618
TERRITORIES										
Andaman and Nicobar Islands	—	—	—	—	—	—	—	—	—	—
Delhi	5	7	1	1	1	1	—	—	—	—
Himachal Pradesh	3	3	2	2	(a)	(a)	—	—	—	—
Laccadive, Minicoy & Amindivi Islands	—	—	—	—	—	—	—	—	—	—
Manipur	—	—	—	—	20	21	—	—	—	—
Tripura	6	6	1	1	—	—	19	20	—	—
TOTAL TERRITORIES	14	16	4	4	21	22	19	20	N. A.	—
TOTAL INDIA	3,994	4,446	846	921	18,684	20,230	1,243	1,581	528	618

(a) Less than 500 acres.
Source: The Times of India: Directory and Yearbook, 1959-60.

Table 9

Sugar Production

States	Sugar Cane Crushed (1,000 Tons)		Sugar Produced (1,000 Tons)	
	1956-57	1957-58	1956-57	1957-58
Uttar Pradesh	11,152	9,485	1,080	942
Bihar	3,327	2,770	312	275
Bombay	2,070	2,857	240	320
Andhra	1,542	1,571	142	153
Punjab	640	874	58	82
Madhya Pradesh	502	347	49	34
Mysore	465	712	42	73
Madras	710	734	65	64
Rajasthan	185	152	18	14
Kerala	134	101	12	8
Orissa	44	42	3	4
West Bengal	93	59	8	6
ALL INDIA	20,864	19,704	2,029	1,975

Source: The Times of India: Directory and Yearbook, 1959-60.

Table 10

Livestock Statistics in India

The following table shows the estimates of livestock population for 1956:

(In thousands)

Area	Cattle	Buffaloes	Sheep	Goats	Horses & Ponies	Other Livestock	Total Livestock	Poultry
STATES								
1. Andhra Pradesh	10,958	5,743	7,428	3,601	96	708	28,534	14,058
2. Assam	5,247	478	32	1,103	16	306	7,182	8,712
3. Bengal (West)	11,587	772	667	5,298	30	345	18,699	13,189
4. Bihar	14,331	3,387	990	6,422	119	709	25,958	8,690
5. Bombay	20,231	5,427	4,000	7,155	245	407	37,465	10,548
6. Jammu & Kashmir	1,757	374	1,465	814	96	2	4,508	2,166
7. Kerala	2,536	515	100	918	2	125	4,196	6,763
8. Madhya Pradesh	22,560	4,995	898	5,220	253	425	34,351	5,383
9. Madras	9,859	2,066	7,173	3,965	19	569	23,651	10,153
10. Mysore	8,997	2,642	4,151	2,606	42	254	18,692	7,899
11. Orissa	8,036	884	679	1,924	6	114	11,643	5,225
12. Punjab	5,943	3,852	1,164	1,871	100	445	13,375	1,411
13. Rajasthan	12,127	3,452	7,373	8,734	113	700	32,499	461
14. Uttar Pradesh	22,938	9,781	1,903	6,258	352	1,416	42,648	2,178
TERRITORIES								
1. Andaman & Nicobar Islands	5	6	*	4	*	14	29	57
2. Delhi	120	115	7	22	7	35	306	71
3. Himachal Pradesh	1,171	219	633	598	5	6	2,632	53
4. Laccadive, Minicoy & Amindivi Islands	*	*	*	*	*	*	*	*
5. Manipur	143	17	†	6	1	36	203	*
6. Tripura	317	41	3	109	1	41	512	365
TOTAL INDIA	158,863	44,766	38,666	56,628	1,503	6,657	307,083**	97,372

*Not known. † Less than 500. **Includes poultry.

Source: The Times of India: Directory and Yearbook, 1959–60.

Table 11

Fisheries in India

Production

Production is shown by the table below. About two-thirds of the catch are marine-fishes.

'000 tons

Year	Marine	Inland	Total
1950	571	233	804
1951	525	215	740
1952	520	212	732
1953	572	234	806
1954	579	236	815
1955	586	240	826
1956 ....:...........	707	289	996
1957	862	352	1,214

Table 11a

The following table shows the figures by species:

Groups & Species	1955 Metric Tons	1956 Metric Tons	1957 Metric Tons
MARINE FISH			
Flounders, halibuts, soles, etc.	5,595	9,122	3,687
Cods, hakes, haddocks, etc.	3,190	1,308	1,138
Herrings, sardines, anchovies, etc..	123,970	114,014	292,999
Tunas, bonitos, mackerels, etc.	64,883	56,831	139,356
Miscellaneous marino teleosteans ..	271,007	356,015	278,348
Sharks, Rays, skates, etc........	20,451	21,856	23,080
Crustaceans	106,626	159,552	136,812
A Total Marine Fish	595,722	718,698	875,420
B Fresh water fishes	243,300	293,552.7	357,566
C Grand total	839,022	1,012,250.7	1,232,986

Table 11b

Production of Fish by State

The total landing of marine fish by State is shown below (where available):

(In Metric Tons)	1956	1957		(In Metric Tons)	1956	1957
1. West Bengal & North Orissa	158,82	4,509		11. North Kerala (Malabar)	78,405	
2. South Orissa		3,757				
3. North Andhra		29,673		12. Mysore		76,090
4. Central Andhra	52,476	5,499		13. South Bombay I (up to Ratnagiri)	25,901	11,945
5. South Andhra		5,290				
6. North Madras		20,521		14. South Bombay II		51,078
7. Central Madras (Palk Bay)	55,208	13,974		15. Central Bombay	324,127	258,467
8. South Madras (Gulf of Mannar)		14,097		16. North Bombay		2,763
				17. South-east Saurashtra		24,448
9. West Madras & South Kerala	133,736	51,820 112,278		18. South-west Saurashtra	29,792	5,451
10. Central Kerala		176,920		19. North Saurashtra		2,508

Source: The Times of India: Directory and Yearbook, 1959-60.

Table 12

India's Foreign Trade in Food (1958)
(In Rupees)

Items	Export	Import
Live animals for food	1,312,000	387,863
Meat & meat preparations	7,413,631	205,428
Dairy products	3,206,910	69,475,991
Fish and fish preparations	57,928,775	20,632,237
Cereals	2,018,419	1,488,358,430
Fruits & vegetables	211,552,013	174,256,804
Sugar & sugar preparations	36,963,443	184,752
Coffee, tea, choc., spices	1,525,757,019	30,543,166
Fodder and animal feed	75,876,186	18,168
Misc. food preparations	1,505,796	2,068,936
	1,923,535,092	1,786,131,775
Beverages : alcoholic	10,233	5,602,667
: non alcoholic	21,609	4,157
Oil seeds, oil nuts, etc.	3,425,154	104,830,849
Animal & veg. oils & fats	82,410,495	43,947,059

Source: The Times of India: Directory and Yearbook, 1959-60.

Table 13

Import of Food Grains in India, 1950-58
(In thousand of Tons)

1950	2.100
1951	4.700
1952	3.900
1953	2.000
1954	0.808
1955	0.700
1956	1.420
1957	3.580
1958	3.173

Table 13a

Countries from which imports were obtained from 1955 to 1957 with quantity (in million tons) and C & F value (in lakhs of rupees) were as follows: The figures are provisional:

Country	1955		1956		1957	
	Quantity	Value	Quantity	Value	Quantity	Value
U. S. A.	0.129		0.423		2.868	
Australia . . .	0.306		0.617		0.161	
Argentina . . .	—		—		—	
Canada	—		—		0.011	
U. S. S. R. . .	—		0.40		—	
Pakistan . . .	—		0.020		0.012	
Burma	0.265		0.274		0.609	
Viet Nam . . .	—		—		0.007	
China	—		0.046		0.014	
TOTAL . .	0.700	33,11	1.420	56,34	3.582	16,218

Countries from which imports of individual grains were made in 1957 were as follows:
(In thousand tons)

	Wheat	Rice	Millets
China	—	14	—
U. S. A.	2,674	194	—
Australia	161	—	—
Burma	—	509	—
Viet Nam	—	7	—
Pakistan	—	12	—
Canada	11	—	—
TOTAL	2,846	736	—

Source: The Times of India: Directory and Yearbook, 1959-60.

Table 14

Wheat Supplied to Various States
(April 1, 1958 - January 31, 1959)

Andhra Pradesh ....   25,000 Tons
Andaman and Nicobar Islands ....   1,000 "
Assam ....   61,000 "
Bihar ....   637,000 "
Bombay ....   388,000 "
Delhi ....   39,000 "
Himachal Pradesh ....   2,000 "
Kashmir & Jammu ....   45,000 "
Kerala ....   4,000 "
Madhya Pradesh ....   107,000 "
Madras ....   71,000 "
Mysore ....   34,000 "
Orissa ....   14,000 "
Punjab ....   44,000 "
Rajasthan ....   66,000 "
Tripura ....   3,000 "
Uttar Pradesh ....   467,000 "
West Bengal ....   583,000 "

Source: The Times of India: Directory and Yearbook,
1959-60.

Table 15

Comparison of Indian Average Caloric Intake Since and Before World War II

	Total Caloric Intake	Total Protein	Animal	Vegetable	Fats
1956-57	1,890	50.4	5.3	45.1	25.7
1954-55	2,030	—	—	—	?
1952-53	1,710	46.6	5.7	40.9	22.4
Pre W.W. II	2,560	73	7.23	—	23.5

Source: Computed from:
     Food and Agriculture Organization, Food Balance Sheets 1952-53,
        1954-46.
     Foreign Agriculture, Vol. 22, June, 1958.
     Pathwardhan, U.N.: Nutrition in India. J. Med. Sci., Bombay.4, 1952.

Table 16

India's Food Balance Sheet, 1952/1953
(1000 metric tons unless otherwise specified)

Commodity	Production	Change in Stocks	Foreign Trade Gross Exports	Foreign Trade Gross Imports	Available Supply	Per Capita Consumption Kg. Per Year	Per Capita Consumption Grams Per Day	Per Capita Consumption Cal. Per Day	Per Capita Consumption Protein Per Day Grams	Per Capita Consumption Fat Per Day Grams
	(1)	(2)	(3)	(4)	(5)	(13)	(14)	(15)	(16)	(17)
Cereals										
Wheat	7500			1739	9239	19.7	54.0	194	5.3	0.7
Barley	2928				2928	4.3	11.8	39	1.3	0.2
Maize	2870				2870	6.2	17.0	62	1.4	0.2
Jowar	7359			146	7505	17.2	47.1	162	4.8	1.6
Bajra	3192				3192	7.2	19.7	68	1.9	0.6
Ragi	1337				1337	3.0	8.2	27	0.5	0.1
Small Millets	1925				1925	4.6	12.6	43	1.2	0.4
Rice (paddy)	34347			267	34614	57.6	157.8	568	10.6	1.1
Total						119.8	328.2	1163	27.0	4.9
Roots and Tubers										
Potatoes	1992				1992	3.9	10.7	7	0.2	—
Cassava	1255				1255	3.4	9.3	10	0.1	—
Sweet potatoes	919				919	2.5	6.8	7	0.1	—
Total								24	0.4	—
Sugar (gur)	5099		90		5009	11.7	32.1	113	0.3	—
Pulses, Seeds and Nuts										
Gram	4208			10	4218	8.3	22.7	78	5.0	0.5
Other pulses	4980			42	5022	11.3	31.0	107	6.9	0.7
Groundnuts (in shell)	2929		16		2913	0.5	1.4	5	0.3	0.4
Sesame seed	471		2		469	0.3	0.8	5	0.1	0.4
Coconuts	2002			1	2003	2.9	7.9	5	0.1	0.4
Total								200	12.4	2.4

Vegetables									
Fruits	6126	43	140	6223	12.6	34.5	20	0.2	0.1
Meat									
Beef	97			97	0.3	0.8	1	0.1	0.1
Pork	24			24	0.1	0.3	1	—	0.1
Mutton	114			114	0.3	0.8	2	0.1	0.2
Goat	158			158	0.4	1.1	1	0.2	0.1
Buffalo	75			75	0.2	0.5	—	0.1	—
Poultry	44			44	0.1	0.3	—	—	—
Total					1.4	3.8	5	0.5	0.5
Eggs	59		2	61	0.2	0.5	1	0.1	0.1
Fish	825	25	4	804	2.0	5.5	3	0.5	0.1
Milk									
Cow	9072		109	9181	19.7	54.0	33	1.8	1.7
Buffalo	9950			9950	24.3	66.6	67	2.7	5.0
Goat	400			400	0.8	2.2	2	0.1	0.1
Total							102	4.6	6.8
Oils and Fats (pure fat content)									
Groundnut	638	69		569	1.3	3.6	32	—	3.6
Coconut	149		29	178	0.3	0.8	7	—	0.8
Sesame	144	29		144	0.3	0.8	7	—	0.8
Linseed	105	9		76	0.1	0.3	3	—	0.3
Rapeseed	251			242	0.7	1.9	17	—	1.9
Total					2.7	7.4	66	—	7.4
Total							1710	46.6	22.4

Animal 5.7
Vegetable 40.9

(a) Round weight.
Source: Food and Agriculture Organization: Food Balance Sheets, 1952–53, 1954–56.

Table 17

Food Balance Sheets in India Based on Average for 1954/55, 1955/56, (Prov.) 1956/57

Commodity	Production	Change in Stocks	Foreign Trade		Available Supply	Per Capita Consumption				
			Gross Exports	Gross Imports		Kg. Per Year	Grams Per Day	Cal.* Per Day	Protein Per Day Grams	Fat Per Day Grams
	(1)	(2)	(3)	(4)	(5)	(13)	(14)	(15)	(16)	(17)
Cereals										
Rice (paddy)	40605		74	674	41205	66.1	181.0	652	12.1	1.6
Wheat	9046			1482	10528	21.3	58.3	203	5.7	0.8
Barley	2867				2867	4.2	11.4	37	1.3	0.2
Jowar	7776		3		7773	17.1	47.0	161	4.7	1.5
Bajra	3278				3278	7.1	19.6	67	1.9	0.5
Maize	2881		1		2880	6.0	16.5	60	1.4	0.2
Ragi	1753				1753	3.7	10.3	34	0.7	0.2
Small millets	2187				2187	5.0	13.8	47	1.3	0.4
Total						130.5	357.9	1261	29.1	5.4
Roots and Tubers										
Potatoes	1774				1774	3.2	8.9	6	0.2	—
Cassava (Tapioca)	1813				1813	4.7	12.9	14	0.1	—
Sweet potatoes	1278				1278	3.3	9.1	9	0.1	—
Total								29·	0.4	—
Sugar (gur)	6261		48	252	6465	14.7	40.3	141	0.4	—
Pulses, Seeds and Nuts										
Gram	5753		20	5	5738	10.9	29.8	103	6.6	0.6
Other pulses	5505		40	10	5475	11.8	32.4	112	7.2	0.7
Groundnuts (in shell)	4107		24		4083	0.5	1.3	5	0.2	0.4
Sesame seed	505		1		504	0.2	0.7	3	0.1	0.4
Coconuts	2539			1	2540	5.5	15.0	9	0.2	0.8
Rapeseed	979				979	0.2	0.5	3	0.1	0.3
Linseed	399				399	0.1	0.2	1	—	0.1
Total								236	14.4	3.3

Meat									
Beef	106			106	0.3	0.8	1	0.1	0.1
Pork	29			29	0.1	0.2	1	—	—
Mutton	115			115	0.3	0.8	2	0.1	0.2
Goat	177			177	0.5	1.2	2	0.2	0.1
Buffalo	81			81	0.2	0.6	—	-0.1	—
Poultry	53			53	0.1	0.4	—	—	—
Total				6	1.5	4.0	6	0.5	0.4
Eggs	81	23	6	87	0.2	0.6	1	0.1	0.1
Fish	893		4	874	2.0	5.6	3	0.5	0.1
Milk									
Cow	8199		321	8520	17.7	48.5	30	1.6	1.6
Buffalo	9661			9661	22.8	62.4	63	2.5	4.7
Goat	531			531	1.1	2.9	2	0.1	0.1
Total							95	4.2	6.4
Oils and Fats (pure fat content)									
Groundnut oil	929	77		852	2.2	5.9	52	—	5.9
Coconut oil	141		22	163	0.2	0.5	4	—	0.5
Sesame oil	157	22		157	0.3	1.0	9	—	1.0
Linseed oil(a)	115			93	0.1	0.3	3	—	0.3
Rapeseed oil	296			296	0.8	2.1	18	—	2.1
Total					3.6	9.8	86	—	9.8
*calories							1890	50.4	25.7

Total .... Animal 5.3

Vegetable 45.1

(a) Average of 1954/55 and 1956/57.

Note: Population figures for the years 1954/55 to 1956/57 have been revised on the basis of a new series of mid year estimates published by the Registrar-General, making the necessary adjustments to obtain estimates for the beginning of each year as follows:

1st January 1954 377.1 million   1st January 1956 387.4 million
"   " 1955 382.4 "   "   " 1957 392.4 "

Source: Food and Agricultural Organization: Food Balance Sheets, 1952-53, 1954-56.

Table 18

Origin in Per Cent of Calories in an Average Indian Diet
(U. S. Foreign Agriculture Service, 1957)

Rice 33.6%

Wheat 9.6%

Millet, etc. 20.4%

Dry beans & peas 11.4%

Roots, tubers 3.0%

Sugar 6.3%

Oil seeds (incl. soya beans & peanuts) 1.0%

Oil fats (excl. soya beans & butter) 3.5%

Vegetables 8%

Fruits & nuts 2.3%

Meat, fish, poultry 6%

Milk & dairy prod. 7.5%

Total 100.00%

Number of calories   2,030

Source: Foreign Agriculture, Vol. 22, June, 1958.

Table 19

Adequacy of Food Consumed

Items	Actual Intake In Ounces		Needed
Cereals	16.6	.....	14
Pulses	2.3	.....	3
Leafy vegetables	0.9	.....	4.0
Other vegetables	4.1	.....	6.0
Ghee and vegetable oil	0.9	.....	2.0
Milk & milk products	3.3	.....	10.0
Meat, fish & eggs	0.9	.....	4.0
Fruits and nuts	0.6	.....	3.0
Sugar & jaggery	0.7	.....	2.0
Condiments	0.4	.....	—

Source: Indian Council of Medical Research: Results of Diet Surveys in India, 1935-48, New Delhi, 1951-1953.

Table 20

Food Resources by State

ANDHRA

Rice	3,049,000	Tons
Jowar	1,131,000	"
Corn	111,000	"
Pulses	273,000	"
Sugar cane	525,000	"
Chilis	112,000	"
Oil seeds	1,238,000	"
Tobacco	131,000	"
Bajra	308,000	"
Ragi	220,000	"
Small millets	430,000	"
Onions	169,000	"

In addition, there are 12 million cattle, 17 million buffaloes, and 14 million heads of poultry.

ASSAM

Autumn rice	376,000	Tons
Winter rice	1,244,000	"
Spring rice	11,000	"
Rape & mustard	56,000	"
Sugar cane	86,000	"
Potatoes	115,000	"
Pulses	27,000	"
Corn	7,000	"
Wheat	1,500	"

The production of individual cash crops is as follows:

Tea	367,000,000	Lbs.
Jute	1,000,094	Bales (1 Bale = 400 Lbs.)
Cotton	8,249	Bales (1 Bale = 392 Lbs.)
Tobacco	6,900	Tons

Source: Compiled from The Times of India: Yearbook and Directory, 1959-1960.

Table 21

Food Resources by State (Continued)

BIHAR

Rice	2,000,198	Tons
Wheat	137,000	"
Barley	107,000	"
Corn	383,000	"
Sugar Cane	3,673,000	"
Potatoes	251,000	"
Tobacco	7,000	"
Jute	1,000,378	Bales

BOMBAY

Rice	1,367,800	Tons
Wheat	508,000	"
Jowar	3,275,000	"
Bajra	1,000,000	"
Tur	362,000	"
Gram	164,100	"

Important crops include cotton, ground nut, sugar cane, and tobacco.

DELHI

Delhi is essentially characterized by its administrative situation and white collar worker population. 60% of its territory is under cultivation, producing both food and cash crops.

Wheat	17,000	Tons
Jowar	4,000	"
Bajra	10,000	"
Gram	2,300	"
Barley	612	"
Corn	776	"
Sugar Cane	6,500	"
Cotton	142	"
Oil seeds	189	"

Source: Compiled from The Times of India: Yearbook and Directory, 1959-1960.

Table 22

Food Resources by State (Continued)

KERALA

Rice	400,000	Tons
Pulses	17,000	"
Tapioca	1,569,000	"
Bananas	311,000	"
Sugar cane	327,000	"
Pepper	27,000	"
Ginger	13,000	"

Import cash crops include:

Rubber	21,000	"
Coffee	3,000	"
Tea	30,000	"

MADHYA PRADESH

Rice	3,264,000	Tons
Wheat	1,702,000	"
Bajra	89,000	"
Corn	187,000	"
Barley	131,000	"
Gram	991,000	"
Tur	252,000	"
Jowar	1,082,000	"

The production of cash crops was:

Cotton	569,000	Bales
Sugar cane	167,000	Tons
Ground nuts	198,000	"
Castor oil	2,400	"
Sesame	66,000	"
Rape & Mustard	55,000	"
Linseed	130,000	"
Tobacco	4,000	"

Source: Compiled from The Times of India: Yearbook and Directory, 1959-1960.

Table 23

Food Resources by State (Continued)

MYSORE

In 1957:

Paddy	1,025,000	Tons
Jowar	197,000	"
Bajra	133,000	"
Corn	7,500	"
Wheat	71,000	"
Other cereals and small millets	152,000	"

In addition, there are 8,000,966 cattle, 2,000,669 buffaloes, 4,000,000 sheep, 2,000,584 goats and 7,000,668 poultry.

In 1958:

Rice	2,128,000	Tons
Jowar	3,924	"
Corn	9,548	"
Ragi	63,052	"
Wheat	2,761	"
Barley	138	"
Gram	7,800	"
Sugar Cane	100,000	"
Tobacco	2,710	"
Sesame	19,964	"
Ground nuts	17,166	"
Mustard	20,537	"
Linseed	2,519	"
Castor	4,134	"

In addition, cash crops include:

Cotton	2,148	Bales
Jute	244,000	"
Millet	10,954	"

ORISSA

Cattle	7,888,000
Buffaloes	893,000
Sheep	681,000
Goats	1,446,000
Pigs	108,000
Fowls & Ducks	3,900,000

Source: Compiled from The Times of India: Yearbook and Directory, 1959-1960.

Table 24

Food Resources by State (Continued)

PUNJAB

Paddy	277,000	Tons
Corn	651,000	"
Jowar	45,000	"
Bajra	240,000	"
Wheat	1,814,000	"
Gram	1,866,000	"
Barley	186,000	"
Sugar Cane	580,000	"
Ground nuts	43,000	"
Cotton	735,000	"

Considerable effort is being made to increase the production of raw sugar.

Cattle	5,948,000	Head
Buffaloes	3,810,000	"
Sheep	1,230,000	"
Goats	1,911,000	"
Other livestock	470,000	"

RAJASTHAN

At the end of 1957.

Bajra	537,000	Tons
Jowar	212,000	"
Corn	324,000	"
Wheat	1,315,000	"
Barley	710,000	"
Rice	86,000	"
Small millets	29,000	"
Grams	1,171,000	"
Tur	6,000	"
Other pulses	384,000	"

Cash crops yielded:

Oil seeds	283,000	"
Cotton	168,000	"
Sugar Cane	679	(in terms of gur)
Tobacco	5,000	Tons
Dry chilis	11,000	"
Potatoes	4,000	"

There are a large number of ponds, lakes and rivers providing an unknown amount of fresh water fish.

The total number of cattle was:	12,000,000
Breeding bulls	3,500,000
Breeding cows	4,400,000
Young stock	4,000,000
Buffaloes	3,500,000
Sheep	7,372,000
Goats	8,730,000
Pigs	72,000
Poultry	457,000

Source: Compiled from The Times of India: Yearbook and Directory, 1959-1960.

Table 25

Food Resources by State (Continued)

TRIPURA

Rice	154,000	Tons
Pulses	275	"

Cash crops amount to:

Sugar cane	3,864	Tons
Jute	10,121	"
Tea	4,992,000	"
Cotton	1,600	"

In addition there are:

Cattle	302,000
Buffaloes	40,000
Sheep	6,700
Goats	100,000
Other various types of livestock	40,000

UTTAR PRADESH

Rice	2,300,000	Tons
Barley	1,600,000	"
Bajra	500,000	"
Kodon	164,000	"
Corn	986,000	"
Peas	529,000	"
Potatoes	600,000	"
Wheat	3,114,000	"
Jowar	439,000	"
Mandua	89,000	"
Sawan	62,000	"
Gram	1,500,000	"
Arhar	1,000,000	"
Other pulses	119,000	"
Sugar cane	3,500,000	gurs

Cash crops were represented by:

Oil seeds	1,500,000	Tons
Cotton	46,000	Bales
Jute	157,000	"
Tobacco	15,000	Tons

Table 26

Food Resources by State (Concluded)

WEST BENGAL

The production of principal crops in 1958 was as follows:

Rice	3,758,000	Tons
Wheat	44,000	"
Sugar cane	119,000	"
Jute	1,500,000	"

Source: Compiled from The Times of India: Directory and Yearbook, 1959-1960.

Table 27

Comparative Indian States' Food Production
In Round Figures

States	Size (Sq. Mi.)	Pop. (In Millions)	Total Food Grain Prod. (In Millions T.)	Percentage of Total
Andhra	105,963	38 m.	5,259	9.1
Assam	47,000	10 m.	1,641	2.8
Bihar	67,000	43	2,825	4.9
Bombay	190,641	58	6,700	11.6
Delhi (terr.)	—	2	32	0.5
Himachal P. (terr.).	10,904	1.3	—	—
Jammu & Kashmir (terr.).	85,861	5.4	—	—
Kerala	15,035	15.5	400	0.6
Madhya Pradesh	171,201	30.5	7,701	13.4
Madras (terr.)	50,111	36.	4,658	8.0
Manipur (terr.)	8,628	.6	—	—
Mysore	74,861	23.4	3,000	5.2
Orissa	60,136	17.6	2,487	4.3
Punjab	47,456	19.3	5,600	9.6
Rajasthan	132,147	18.9	3,213	5.6
Tripura	4,116	1.0	0.155	
Uttar Pradesh	113,409	75.2	8,500	14.9
West Bengal	33,945	31.5	5,417	9.5

Compiled from: The Times of India: Yearbook and Directory, 1959-60.

Table 28

Harvest Calendar in India

Crops	Harvest Period	Bulk of Harvest
Wheat:		
Bihar	Mar.-Apr.	
Bombay	Feb.-Mar.	
Madhya Pradesh	Feb.-Mar.	
Punjab	Apr.-May	
Uttar Pradesh	Mar.-Apr.	
Rajasthan	Apr.-May	
India consolidated	Mar.-May	Mar.-Apr.
Barley:		
Bihar	Mar.-Apr.	
Punjab	Mar.-Apr.	
Uttar Pradesh	Mar.	
Rajasthan	Mar.-Apr.	
India consolidated	Feb.-Apr.	Mar.-Apr.
Maize:		
Bihar	Sept.-Oct.	
Bombay	Sept.-Oct.	
Punjab	Sept.-Nov.	
Uttar Pradesh	Aug.-Sept.	
Rajasthan	Sept.-Nov.	
India consolidated	Aug.-Nov.	Sept.-Nov.
Millets:		
a) Ragi (Eleusina Coracana):		
Andhra	Sept.-Jan. (K) and Mar.-May (R)	
Bombay	Oct.-Nov.	
Madras	Oct.-Neb. (D)	
Mysore	Oct.-Dec.	
Bihar	Sept.	
b) Bajra (Pennisetum Typhoideum):		
Andhra Pradesh	Sept.-Dec.	
Bombay	Oct.-Nov.	
Punjab	Oct.-Nov.	
Rajasthan	Sept.-Oct.	
Uttar Pradesh	Oct.-Nov.	
Madras	Oct.-Feb. (D)	
India consolidated	Sept.-Feb.	Sept.-Dec.
Jowar (Sorghum vulgare):		
Bombay	Nov.-Dec.(K) Jan.-Feb. (R)	
Andhra Pradesh	Jan.-Apr. (K)	
Madhya Pradesh	Nov.-Dec.(K) Feb.-Mar.(R)	
Uttar Pradesh	Oct.-Nov.	

Source: Food and Agriculture Organization: World Crop Harvest Calendar, Rome, 1959.

Map 1

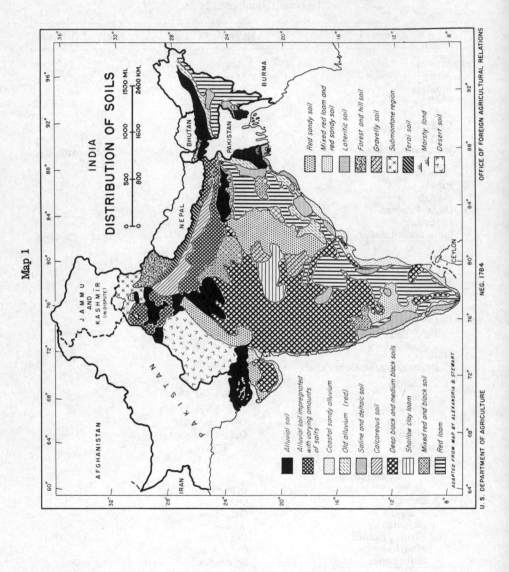

INDIA

DISTRIBUTION OF SOILS

	Alluvial soil
	Alluvial soil impregnated with varying amounts of salts
	Coastal sandy alluvium
	Old alluvium (red)
	Saline and deltaic soil
	Calcareous soil
	Deep black and medium black soils
	Shallow clay loam
	Mixed red and black soil
	Red loam

	Red sandy soil
	Mixed red loam and red sandy soil
	Lateritic soil
	Forest and hill soil
	Gravelly soil
	Submontane region
	Terai soil
	Marshy land
	Desert soil

ADAPTED FROM MAP BY ALEXANDRIA B. STEWART

U. S. DEPARTMENT OF AGRICULTURE   NEG. 1784   OFFICE OF FOREIGN AGRICULTURAL RELATIONS

AFGHANISTAN

PAKISTAN

IRAN

JAMMU AND KASHMIR (IN DISPUTE)

NEPAL

BHUTAN

PAKISTAN

BURMA

CEYLON

0   500   1000   1500 MI.
0   800   1600   2400 KM.

Map 2

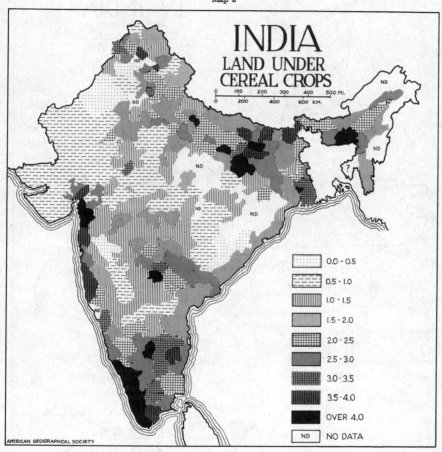

INDIA
LAND UNDER
CEREAL CROPS

0   100   200   300   400   500 MI.
0   200   400   600 KM.

	0.0 - 0.5
	0.5 - 1.0
	1.0 - 1.5
	1.5 - 2.0
	2.0 - 2.5
	2.5 - 3.0
	3.0 - 3.5
	3.5 - 4.0
	OVER 4.0
ND	NO DATA

AMERICAN GEOGRAPHICAL SOCIETY

Map 3

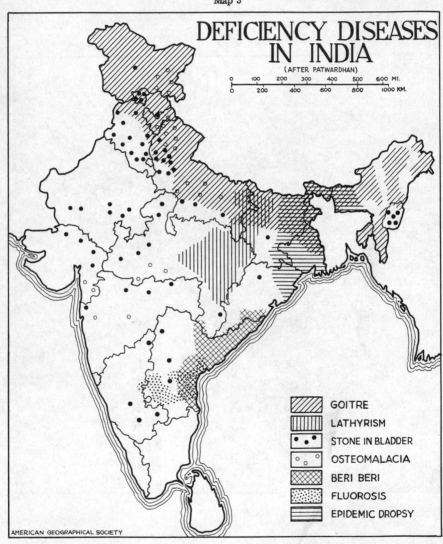

DEFICIENCY DISEASES
IN INDIA
(AFTER PATWARDHAN)

	GOITRE
	LATHYRISM
	STONE IN BLADDER
	OSTEOMALACIA
	BERI BERI
	FLUOROSIS
	EPIDEMIC DROPSY

AMERICAN GEOGRAPHICAL SOCIETY

Map 4

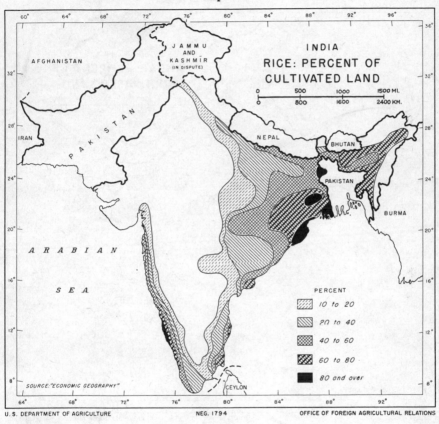

INDIA
RICE: PERCENT OF
CULTIVATED LAND

PERCENT

10 to 20
20 to 40
40 to 60
60 to 80
80 and over

SOURCE:"ECONOMIC GEOGRAPHY"

Map 5

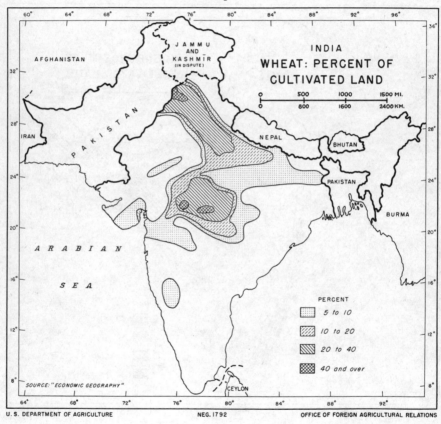

AFGHANISTAN

JAMMU
AND
KASHMIR
(IN DISPUTE)

INDIA
WHEAT: PERCENT OF
CULTIVATED LAND

500   1000   1500 MI.
800   1600   2400 KM.

IRAN

P A K I S T A N

NEPAL

BHUTAN

PAKISTAN

BURMA

A R A B I A N

S E A

PERCENT

5 to 10

10 to 20

20 to 40

40 and over

SOURCE: "ECONOMIC GEOGRAPHY"

CEYLON

U.S. DEPARTMENT OF AGRICULTURE   NEG. 1792   OFFICE OF FOREIGN AGRICULTURAL RELATIONS

Map 6

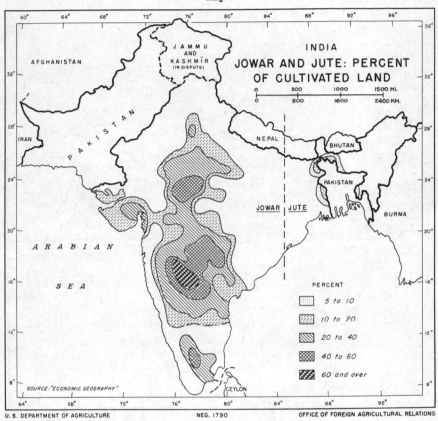

INDIA
JOWAR AND JUTE: PERCENT
OF CULTIVATED LAND

AFGHANISTAN

JAMMU
AND
KASHMĪR
(IN DISPUTE)

IRAN

P A K I S T A N

NEPAL

BHUTAN

PAKISTAN

BURMA

JOWAR JUTE

A R A B I A N

S E A

PERCENT

5 to 10

10 to 20

20 to 40

40 to 60

60 and over

SOURCE: "ECONOMIC GEOGRAPHY"

CEYLON

500   1000   1500 MI.
800   1600   2400 KM.

Map 7

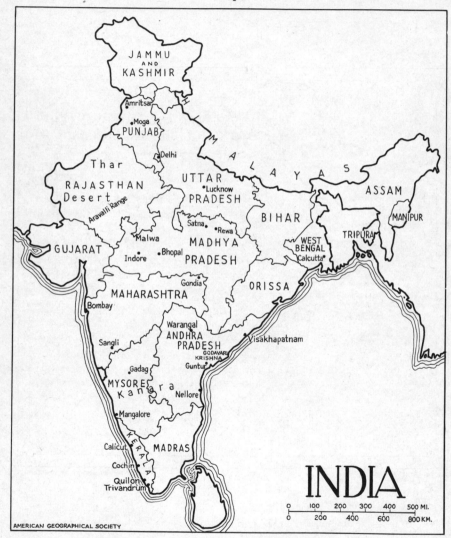

JAMMU
AND
KASHMIR

•Amritsar

•Moga
PUNJAB

•Delhi

Thar

RAJASTHAN
Desert

Aravalli Range

H
I
M
A
L
A
Y
A
S

UTTAR
PRADESH

•Lucknow

BIHAR

ASSAM

MANIPUR

Satna•
•Rewa

Malwa
GUJARAT
Indore• •Bhopal

MADHYA
PRADESH

WEST
BENGAL

TRIPURA

Calcutta•

Gondia•

ORISSA

MAHARASHTRA

Bombay

Warangal

Sangli

ANDHRA
PRADESH
GODAVARI
KRISHNA

Visakhapatnam

Gadag•
Guntur•

MYSORE

Kanara

Nellore•

•Mangalore

KERALA

Calicut•

MADRAS

Cochin•

Quilon•
Trivandrum

INDIA

| 0 | 100 | 200 | 300 | 400 | 500 MI. |
| 0 | | 200 | 400 | 600 | 800 KM. |

CEYLON

I. GENERAL REMARKS

Ceylon is an island in the Indian Ocean, off the southeastern tip of India. It lies between 9° 55' and 5° 55 N. and 79° 42' and 83° 53 E., and covers an area of 25,330 square miles (65,600 square kilometers). The food problems of Ceylon are dominated by two facts, stemming respectively from geography and history.

The geographical factor is represented by the mountains in the center of the island that stop the moisture-laden clouds driven northward by the southwest monsoon. As a result, the land to the northeast of the mountains, "the dry zone," does not receive more than 75 inches of rain a year, while the "wet zone" in the southwest receives up to 200 inches. The land use, the type of settlement, and the economy of the island are dominated by this situation. Most of the cash crops are grown in the southwest, while most of the essential food—rice—is grown in areas needing irrigation.

The historical factor has developed from this geographical situation. Throughout the centuries, invaders coming from India conquered the dry zone and destroyed its carrying capacity by ruining the irrigation works. The Ceylonese rulers reestablished their authority by regrouping in the south, chasing out the invaders, and rebuilding the irrigation systems.

Under the British, rubber and tin were developed and greatly benefited from improved technology, shipping, and markets. Earnings allowed the maintenance of irrigation in the dry zone and the purchase of food abroad (rice, sugar, chili). This prosperity camouflaged the island's severe dependence on exports to feed its people.

With the achievement of self government, a considerable readjustment of Ceylon's economy had to be made. Self-sufficiency in food had to be attained. The Colombo Plan is trying to solve this problem for Ceylon and other Asian countries placed in a similar situation.

The population of the island amounts to $9\frac{1}{2}$ million people (1960 estimate) with an overall density of 355 per square mile, unevenly distributed: 69.3 per cent are Singhalese, 23 per cent Tamils, 6.3 per cent "Moors" (Muslims). The Tamil group lives predominantly in the north and at present is engaged in a separatist movement. While population concentrations reach 1,600 per square mile in the fertile southwest,

certain areas of the north, northeast, and northwest are almost uninhabited. The rate of growth (2.8 per cent a year) is one of the highest
in the world. Eighty-five per cent of this population lives in the rural
areas, but produces a little more than one-third of the food needed. The
remaining two-thirds have still to be bought, and to be paid for by
goods, the demand for which often fluctuates widely.

About 60 per cent of the total land area is not available for agriculture. Of the remaining 40 per cent, only a little more than one-half is
actually farmed, plantations and cash crops occupying 60 per cent of
all the cultivable land per person theoretically available for Ceylon's
population actually dwindles to an inadequate one-fifth of an acre,
yielding subsistence crops.[12]

Agriculture contributes more than half of the gross national product
and provides half of the total employment. Tea, rubber, and coconuts
comprise 95 per cent of foreign-exchange earnings. Food imports constitute more than 40 per cent of the total import bill. Over 50 per cent
of the total grain supply has been imported in recent years, and all the
sugar has to be obtained from abroad.

Confronted with this situation, the government has adopted the following policies: boost the production of cash crops by replanting and
rehabilitation, increase domestic production of food to lessen dependence upon purchases abroad, bring additional land into cultivation, improve the yield per acre, and diversify agriculture. The program is
implemented through extensive price supports, subsidies for fertilizers, distribution of improved seeds, and resettlement of farmers on
new land.[4]

The government has also undertaken to stabilize the cost of living
by selling rice under a rationed scheme at a subsidized price. The
guarantees mentioned above have in recent years also been applied to
corn, millet, sorghum, mustard, sesame, chili, tamarind, black pepper,
pulses, groundnuts, red onions, etc. All these are known in Ceylon as
"highland foods." So far these policies have been reasonably successful; 1954 and 1955 were boom years, but 1956 was disappointing, the
national income dropping 6 per cent because of a drop in production
caused by drought and a drop in business caused by world prices. This
downward trend continued in 1957, first because of $7\frac{1}{2}$ months of
drought, then because of floods, and in 1958 because of another drought
so severe that wild elephants from the nearby jungle, in quest of water,
invaded the planted areas and added their destruction to the damage
caused by lack of moisture. This showed once more the critical sensi-
tivity of Ceylon to the vagaries of climate and the fluctuation of world
prices—and pointed to an arduous road toward self sufficiency.

In Ceylon a typical moderately prosperous farm might comprise 1
acre of rice and 1 acre of coconut. Let us assume that a family of six
lives on the farm. The two plots are separated by as much as two or
three miles. The farmer keeps in touch with the agents of the Depart-

ment of Agriculture; he uses a selected variety of seed and also chemical fertilizers under the government's scheme to increase food production. As a result, his annual yields per acre would have increased from 10 or 12 bushels twenty years ago to 70 bushels (in two crops) now. He does his plowing with a tractor, but if the tractor is unavailable, he may hire a team of bullocks. After plowing, the farmer may hire a dozen women from the village to complete the work of soil preparation. This is part of a working scheme organized by the government to help the various farmers with planting. These women uproot and transplant seedlings for a charge of $14 per acre, an operation that lasts two days. Irrigation is done by the family. It takes approximately a full day to harvest an acre of rice, using 12 people hired for the purpose. Another day is needed to collect the harvested grain and carry it to the threshing ground. There is little work to be done on the acre of coconut trees, which yield an annual crop of 1200 nuts that are collected six times a year. The nuts may bring an income of $25 to $30 a year, but the farmer has to purchase his chili, onions, potatoes, dried fish, tea, sugar, and fresh vegetables. The total yearly income of such a prosperous farm amounts to $480 and the total expenditure for raising the crop and for purchasing essentials for survival amounts to $457.

II. FOOD RESOURCES

A. GENERAL

In the eighteenth and nineteenth centuries, before the Industrial Revolution, Ceylon was a land of plenty, supplying itself in abundance with cereals, animal protein, fruits, and vegetables.[15]

The description of the food resources of the country by Portugese navigators who came to the island in those days are astounding to those who see Ceylon now as a land of malnutrition and hunger, towards which vessels have to sail from all corners of the world to bring the necessities for the next meal. Of the island's total area of approximately 16,200,000 acres, approximately 3.7 million acres are under cultivation, with approximately 3 million more available. In 1957,* more than 90 per cent of the cultivated area was devoted to four crops: tea (575,000 acres), rubber (660,000 acres), coconut (1,075,000 acres), paddy (1,343,551 acres). Although the first three crops occupy essentially the same acreage every year, the area in rice is expanding. Minor crops, including palmyra trees, cinnamon, citronella, cacao, cardamon, and tobacco, are grown on the remaining 10 per cent.

---

*1958 figures just available show no significant differences.

B. CEREALS

Rice is the chief cereal grown in Ceylon. There are two growing seasons—the long (Maha) during the northeast monsoon, and the short (Yala) during the southwest monsoon. Most of the rice is grown in the northwestern part of the wet zone, between the mountains and the coast, though it is found in all provinces. During the Maha, 60 per cent of the producing acreage is rain-watered and 40 per cent irrigated; during the Yala the proportion is reversed. The yield reaches an average of 31 bushels (1,400 to 1,500 lbs.) per acre during the Maha but varies from 58 bushels, (2,668 lbs.) in the well-watered Kegalla district to 22 bushels, (1,013 lbs.) in the arid Mannar district. The total amount produced each year has increased, as a result of various measures described later, from 340,000 metric tons in pre-World War II days to 892,000 tons in 1958. The area planted in rice, which stood at around 825,000 acres in 1934-1938, increased to 1,240,000 in 1958, and the yield per acre rose from 900 lbs. to 1,585 lbs. in the same period. Yet these increases do not allow more than 200 lbs. per capita production per year. To give farmers a further inducement for increasing paddy, the Paddy Land Act came into force on February 1, 1958. This transferred many of the prerogatives of landlords to the Commissioner of Agrarian Services, and to local "cultivation committees." These committees are comprised partly of government officials and partly of elected members. They have the right to appoint tenants and to evict those who do not maintain satisfactory standards of production. The tenant cultivator, on the other hand, is given the right of permanent transferable and inheritable occupation of paddy land. The rent received by the land owner is to be determined by the Commissioner and is not to exceed one-fourth of the total yield of paddy.[10a]

The Cooperative Agricultural Products and Sales Society (C.A.P.S.) offers credit to its members at reasonable rates of interest, but this source filled only 10 per cent of the cultivators' credit needs in recent years. In addition, a subsidy of 100 rupees (20 dollars) per acre is given to individual farmers to bring new land under paddy. The government also resettles cultivators on land in the dry zone reclaimed through construction or repair of irrigation systems, and much of this land will be used in paddy. To keep prices to the consumer down, ration books are issued to the entire population with the exception of children under one year. All producers of paddy have been entitled to the food ration since 1956, but they usually draw their ration only when there is a crop failure. The amount of rice allowed under rationing started in 1948 with one to two measures (a "measure" is approximately 2 lbs.) per adult per week. Many consumers have supplemented their ration with purchases of rice on the free market. The government, in order to fight the high cost of living determined by the cost of rice on the free market, began to make imported rice available to consumers at cost.[10a]

Sales to consumers are made by the Department of Agriculture and Food, which has a monopoly on rice, wheat, flour, and sugar. Table 1 gives the data for milled-rice on production, imports, domestic purchases, distribution of rice rations at subsidized price, and amount purchased on the free market.

In 1954, the rationed rice was almost solely imported rice. Since 1954, however, 20 per cent to 50 per cent of the domestic crop was also purchased by the government and used with the imported rice to provide for domestic consumption. After 1957, 68 per cent of the total supply of rice was distributed and rationed. The deal between the government and the producers is handled by the Cooperative Agricultural Production and Sales Society, which is responsible for marketing. The cooperative is paid a commission by the Department of Agriculture and Food for its service but has to bear the cost of transporting the rice from collection points to the Department's stores. The marketing department mills the rice on a contract basis.

It is believed that despite some shortcomings, the arrangements described above have moderated the cost of living, have brought great benefit to the farming community, and have increased production. In addition to the inducements mentioned above, the government is practicing a policy of price support to agriculture, known as the "Guaranteed Price Scheme." Since 1948, the paddy producer has been free to sell his rice to any buyer rather than solely to the government. Moreover, the government has undertaken to guarantee a minimum price of 8 Rs. ($1.60) per bushel, and this figure was raised to 12 Rs. in 1957. The guarantee is for five years, which gives further security to the producer. This guarantee was eventually extended to other foods, including corn, kurakkan, sorghum, red onions, mustard, sesame seed, chili, green gram, tamarind, black pepper, cow peas, ground nuts, and turmeric.[8]

Cereals other than rice include corn, kurakkan, sorghum, and menneri, the acreage and production of which are indicated in Table 2. Corn is produced during the two-crop season, but yields are higher during the short monsoon. It is grown mainly in Uva Province, but also in North Central Province, Central Province, and Southern Province during the Yala. Kurakkan is a crop of the North Western and North Central Provinces during the Maha, but is produced in Uva after the Yala. Sorghum is almost entirely an Uva crop, and is produced almost equally during Maha and Yala. In all, the production of secondary cereals or "highland foods" amounts every year to between 25,000 and 30,000 tons which, together with other minor cereals not listed above, works out to no more than 6 to 7 lbs. per capita per year.

C. ROOTS

The most important root crops are manioc and sweet potatoes. The
rural population has always included these items in its diet rather than
the Western potato. The production of manioc and sweet potatoes is
summarized in Table 3. Both are produced in all provinces, but predominantly in the northwest and south. From the figures in the table,
it can be seen that the availability of this item of diet does not exceed
45 lbs. per year per person.

D. PULSES

Pulses, with their high protein content, should be an important part
of any submarginal diet. Table 4 gives the production of pulses in Ceylon in the past years. Converted into weight, the total annual production of pulses in the past has fluctuated between 3,000 and 5,000 tons,
allowing a per-capita ratio of 6 lbs. a year—not enough for the average
2 ounces a day an adult Sinhalese should have. Table 4, however, shows
a sudden increase in the production of cow peas in 1956-1957; most of
this was produced in the Northwestern Province, probably as a result
of a combination of good weather and price-support inducements.

E. OTHER FOODS AND SPICES

Among the "highland foods," Ceylon produces vegetables and some
of the spices that the people of the East, and especially the people of
Ceylon, are so fond of. Table 5 indicates the amounts produced.

F. ANIMAL PROTEIN RESOURCES

These come essentially from meat and fish. Tables 6 and 7 give
details of this production in recent years. The figures given in Table 6
are only crudely indicative, as some animals are slaughtered illegaly
without licences and thus do not appear in the table. The Buddhist objection to taking life reduces the meat consumption to a minimum in
Ceylon, since only a minority of the population departs at times from
its vegetarian habits.

There is great interest in the island in animal husbandry, and the
government has encouraged the formation of livestock breeders' associations in several districts. The agricultural district officers and
the veterinary surgeons (of whom there are too few) are members of
the directing body of these associations.

The National Milk Board is said to be expanding rapidly. It operates
a milk-collection scheme and is about to provide marketing facilities
for large sections of the country. The livestock farms of the Depart-

ment of Agriculture produce more than 600,000 gallons of milk each year and supply superior breeding stock to farmers. However, the milk supply is insufficient to provide more than 2 or 3 ounces of milk per person per day.

The production of poultry and eggs is encouraged in two poultry-breeding stations, one at Karandagolla, the other at Welisara, near Colombo. The Animal Husbandry Extension Service has promoted a meat-processing factory.

Fish forms an important part of the diet of the population. Fisher-men are found all along the inhabited parts of the coast, but the main centers of production are in the north. Table 8 shows that around 38,200 tons of fresh fish are now caught every year, a notable increase from 25,000 to 30,000 tons brought ashore a decade ago. Of this amount, 5,000 to 6,000 tons are processed by drying (see Table 9). This catch does not allow a consumption of more than 6 lbs. per person per year. The balance of the needs is met by imports allowing a total consumption of 24 to 26 lbs. a year (per capita consumption in Japan is 75 lbs.) A by-product factory turns out shark liver oil, fish meal, dried fish, fish oil, and fish manure. Fresh-water fishing is now being developed under FAO guidance, and fish farms at Polonnaruwa, Wathupitiwela, and Narahenpita reflect the efforts of the government to encourage fishing, to improve the fleet, and to teach the men. The registration of fishing craft, started in 1954, was at first unpopular but is becoming better understood.[8]

G. CASH CROPS

Cash crops are essentially tea, rubber and copra. Table 10 shows the acreage and production of these three most important items. Cey-lon is the second largest producer of tea in the world, being surpassed only by India; its production accounts for over 30 per cent of the world's total marketable supply of tea. Since the end of World War II, European ownership of tea estates has declined, and by 1957 some 40 per cent of the tea acreage was owned by Sinhalese and 46 per cent by Europeans; 14 per cent was jointly owned. The tea estates are located in the high-lands at 6,000 feet or more, and they supply approximately 1,000 tea manufacturers.

Rubber is controlled by a Rubber Control Act which is the result of an international agreement.

Coconuts are essentially a culture of the Madampe, Rajakadaluwa, and Marawila areas. The crop is very sensitive to drought. Yields vary considerably between 2,000 nuts and 4,000 nuts per acre, with an average production of 2,400 for the country as a whole. Ceylon's estate copra yields an average 68 per cent of oil, which fills domestic needs and permits an export trade of 92,000 tons of oil a year.

H. SUGAR AND SALT

Ceylon is not a sugar-producing country and must import what it needs for local consumption and industry. The soil and climate, however, would lend themselves in several areas to sugar cane development. The establishment of two sugar refineries is in the offing.

Salt is manufactured by solar evaporation of sea water under a government monopoly which buys all the salt for resale. The production of salt varies considerably; for example, it was 22,000 tons in 1947, 106,000 tons in 1956, and 17,000 tons in 1958. Consumption, however, is remarkably uniform at 13 to 14 lbs. per capita per year. The nation's demand is about 49,000 to 50,000 tons annually, including the needs of industry.

I. REGIONAL FOOD PRODUCTION

The geographer, ethnologist, and administrator each recognizes different regions in Ceylon. In terms of food resources, it seems best to divide the island into two major regions on the basis of climate—the wet and the dry. The wet zone itself can be subdivided into wet-zone lowlands and wet-zone highlands. The dry zone comprises three subtypes—the arid belts (rainfall 25-50 inches), the dry zone proper (rainfall 50-75 inches), and the Jaffna Peninsula in the north.[6]

The wet zone lowlands are well watered by seven rivers (Deduru, Maha, Kelam, Kolu, Bentota, Giu, Nilwata) and by the abundant downpours of the southwest monsoon. Paddy cultivation is here the backbone of the economy but its dominant position is rivalled by coconut production and village industries. In addition a number of minor crops, such as papaya, plantain, and curry, are found in individual plots. This is a very densely populated area (1,000 to 1,100 per square mile) and the holdings are small.[17]

The highlands are the home of the cash crops and estate villages. The heart of the region is the tea country, in certain areas mixed with rubber plantations. The villages depend for a great part of their food upon their own gardens which grow, thanks to the reliable rainfall, fruits, coconuts, and vegetables.

The arid belts, found in the northwest and in a stretch of coast in the south-southeast, grow no food, and are virtually uninhabited.

The dry zone proper is characterized by seasonal rainfall followed by long periods of drought. It is sparsely populated (16 persons per square mile) by Hinduist Tamils in the northern half and Buddist Sinhalese in the southern half. In the ancient days, the dry zone was the seat of a well-developed irrigation network, using a tank system which is still operational.[18] The history of Ceylon was partly written there. In this area, the water tank is the root of life, and governs the size of the population by the amount of land it can moisten. The food grown is paddy mixed with some "chena" shifting agriculture. Plots are 2 to 4 acres in size and carry some corn and chili in addition to the basic rice. However, spices, salt, dried fish and other commodities have to be bought. On the east coast, rainfall is limited to the time of the northeast monsoon. In certain villages Tamil and Muslims live together in a laborer landlord relationship. Paddy fields stretch out over large distances, forcing the farm hands to spend their nights in crumbling shelters in the fields in order to be on the job at dawn, and to protect the fields against wild animals raiding from the nearby jungle. At the border between the southeast and the southwest, the two types of culture mix; the large paddy estates get smaller and are soon replaced by undersized plots owned and worked by the farmer; chena agriculture is also found there and as usual, supports only a meager, half-starvation level of subsistence.

The Jaffna Peninsula, although dry in terms of rainfall, has plenty of underground water. This is tapped through wells, and hard work is needed to bring it to the surface. Yet the peninsula is densely settled; clusters of population bring the density to 900 or more inhabitants per square mile. Many villagers are landless and large holdings are uncommon. The average holding is less than one acre. Paddy and curry are grown, and the palmyra palm plays an important role in the economy, providing food, drink, fodder, and even shelter.

J. EXPORTS AND IMPORTS

Ceylon, as we have seen, is an importer of food and an exporter of cash crops. In 1958, imports reached a value of $345,000,000 and exports a value of $341,000,000, but in previous years the imports had regularly been less than the exports.

Ceylon exports tea, coconut oil, copra, cinnamon, cocoa beans, areca nuts and cardamon, and imports rice, wheat flour, sugar, chili, fruits, vegetables, and dairy products. Its main trading partners are the United Kingdom, India, China, Burma, the United States, and Australia.[22,8a]

K. FOOD INDUSTRIES, STORAGE AND TECHNOLOGY

Food storage in Ceylon is primarily designed to shelter rice and other commodities purchased from abroad. It was stated in 1958 that six new warehouses of 3,000 tons capacity each had been completed at Kalmurai, Akkaraipattu, Mullartvu, Anuradhapura, Jaffna and Kogala, thus adding 18,000 tons of storage capacity to the already existing 60,000 tons distributed throughout the country in 20 stores. Further, 15 storehouses for rice and paddy, with a total capacity of 55,000 tons, were under construction in different parts of the island.

In September, 1958, a storehouse with a capacity of 32,000 tons was opened at Boosa, sufficient for the storage of a three-month supply of rice and flour for the entire Southern Province. This will facilitate the unloading of food shipments arriving at Galle. Six more of these district granaries are planned—at Kandy, Kurunegallo, Jaffna, Badulla, Chilaw, and Ralnajura—at a combined capacity of 95,000 tons.[9]

There is little published information on the refrigeration facilities of the island, with the exception of the Mutwal (Colombo) Cold Storage Plant and byproduct factory just completed with Canadian aid. This plant has a 550-ton capacity; it can quick-freeze 10 tons of fish every 24 hours and can also produce 25 tons of ice a day.

The food industries are primitive. The most important ones are grain and coconut milling. There were about 600 private and 5 government-owned paddy-hulling plants in 1956,[8] but the machinery is said to be obsolete (see Table 12).

Ceylon's coconut industry is extensive. It provides an average of 60,000 to 65,000 tons of dried coconut for export (mainly to the United Kingdom, the Commonwealth and Germany) processes some 122,000 tons of coconut oil (of which about half is used for food and local industry, the remainder exported), and manufactures oil cake (poonac) for domestic livestock feed. Oil cake was exported before World War II but the government discouraged the practice in order to build up Sinhalese herds. Other by-products of coconut manufacture include toddy or sap, obtained from the palms of the maritime provinces, the palmyra palms of the Northern and Eastern Provinces, or the "Kitul" palms of the hill country. Some of the toddy is consumed fresh and sweet. Some is fermented. Sales are controlled by government license and the consumption amounts of more than 5 million gallons consumed in the Jaffna peninsula under a different system.[8] By-products of these various palm saps are arrack and vinegar, manufactured by nine private distilleries (in the Kalvtara district) and one government distillery (at Seeduwa). The production amounts to 700,000—900,000 gallons a year. The government buys the products of the private industry and adds it to its own production. This is placed in vats and allowed to mature for periods of 1 to 6 years. The liquor is then sold to taverns which themselves are rented annually to the highest bidder. The concessionaire has the privilege of retailing to the local customers. Consumption of arrack averages 1,500,000 gallons a year. Other beverage industries include malt, beer and gin.

The sugar industry is still in infancy but experts are convinced that sugar cane could be successfully grown in Ceylon; the government is establishing a sugar refinery (Kautalu Sugar Corp.) with a capacity of 200,000 tons a year.[8]

The food-canning industry produces a number of fruit preserves. In 1958 the marketing department of the Ministry of Food produced 416,088 cans (30 oz.) of a variety of pineapple products. Papayas, passion fruit, wood-apples, mangoes, and limes were also processed in variable amounts as jams and jellies.

The slaughter of cattle and goats, the control of milk supplies, and the sanitary control of food for sale in shops are unsupervised by the personnel of the Department of Health, except in the municipalities of Colombo, Galle, and Kandy. In 1957, of 800 samples of milk examined, 43 per cent showed adulteration. In February, 1956, certain food and drug regulations relating to the control of food were made operative in all towns under the administration of local authorities. Prior to this, the regulations were enforced solely within the Municipality of Colombo. Regulations relating to the control, manufacture, and sale of ice cream has also been compulsory since 1957. In spite of these efforts, there is a high proportion of adulterated food sold in public places in Ceylon.[1,13,4]

III. DIET TYPES

A. GENERAL

Although the population is composed of different ethnic and religious groups, the dietary habits do not vary greatly—the differences are more a matter of detail in the mode of preparation of the dishes than in staple foods preferred. The Sinhalese, by virtue of their Buddhist faith, have the more restricted diet since in most cases, (there are exceptions) they do not eat meat. The Muslims use a wider range of foods, for their religion permits them to eat beef and they do not have any strong objection to milk. The Tamils, following the Hindu principles, drink milk whenever they can get it but refrain from eating flesh.

The following can be considered the typical daily fare as demanded by custom. Four meals a day are the general rule—a morning meal, a midday meal, a late-afternoon meal, and a night meal. Of these, the midday meal and night meals are the chief ones, the other two being light. In the morning, the main items of food are usually prepared from rice flour devoid of proteins are vitamins. These preparations are known as "appas," "idiappas," "pittu," or "rotti". For the last two, grated coconut is used. Alternative preparations—also made from rice—are "Kiri-bath" (milk rice) and "congee" (rice gruel). On occasion, bread or "rotti" made from wheat flour may be substituted. Accompanying the cereal preparation is usually a **sambol,** generally made of onion and chili, ground together with an array of spices and with or without grated coconut. In place of the sambol, or in addition to it, curries of meat, fish, vegetables may be taken. Sometimes an entire meal may consist of boiled yam or sweet potatoes with a sambol. Bananas are sometimes included in the morning meal. At the end of the meal sweetened tea, or occasionally coffee, is generally drunk— with or without milk. At the midday meal, the main food is boiled rice.

Along with the rice go curries made from meat (beef, mutton, pork, fowl), or eggs, fish, or vegetables, with fruits or jams to which many spices and condiments are added. The base of most curries is an emulsion made from grated coconut. The final dish usually has gravy but at times it may be dry. The leafy vegetables are often prepared in the form of a mellum, a preparation of shredded vegetable leaves cooked with grated coconut and spiced. The number of auxiliary dishes served with the rice varies, of course, according to economic circumstances, but there is often a dish from each of the main food categories, such as vegetable or fruits, with occasionally meat or fish and pulses.

The late-afternoon meal is a light one; some sweetmeats, usually made from rice flour and sugar or treacle, is eaten and sweetened tea is drunk as in the morning. The night meal is similar to the midday meal.[13]

Clearly, protective foods form a very small part of the Sinhalese diet. Ceylon is one of the countries in the world where consumption of milk is lowest, amounting to approximately two ounces per day per person, as compared with seven ounces in India and 35 ounces in the United States.

Some Ayurvedic physicians often prohibit some essential article of food in certain diseases, as for example, milk in chronic nasal catarrh, citrus fruit in influenza, meats (especially beef) in chronic coughs and tuberculosis. Certain fruits such as mangoes are frowned upon during the hot season, still further reducing the diet.

Authors who have computed the nutritional values of Sinhalese diets vary only slightly in their estimates; they agree that the bulk of the people consume between 2,000 and 2,065 calories daily, 57% of which comes from cereals. This represents the lowest ratio found in Southeast Asia. However, coconuts, not animal proteins, make up the difference between Ceylon's and other countries' rate of carbohydrate caloric intake. As shown in Table 13, very few calories of animal origin are found in the average Ceylonese diet.

According to a computation made in 1955, the diet described above supplied nutrients in the amounts shown in Table 14. These figures, which apply to the mass of the population, make interesting comparison with the figures given in Table 15 for middle class households. In Table 14, supplies of iron, niacin and vitamin C may be regarded as marginal, and those of calcium, riboflavin, and vitamin A are probably below requirements. Translated into terms of quantities of each nutrient, the basic Sinhalese diet develops as shown in Table 16.

A number of dietary surveys have been conducted in Ceylon. One of the most recent was undertaken in 1956 by the Census Department and the Medical Research Institute,[7] at the request of the Ministry of Agriculture and Food. Its purpose was to discover the adequacy of food intake and the main sources of this food in order to facilitate the planning of food production and distribution. Another survey, undertaken in 1957 under the auspices of the World Health Organization and the Food and Agriculture Organization,[4] essentially confirmed the figures given in Table 14. As was readily admitted by its authors, the first of these two surveys does not give a comprehensive picture of the food situation. It concerned itself chiefly with families enjoying a monthly income of $100 or more, located in the city of Colombo. Because the investigation lasted only a week, it could not reveal the seasonal variations in the availability of fruits and vegetables. It was shown that, of the total quantity of rice consumed per family per month, 36% was of the highly milled variety which is poor in thiamine, riboflavin, and nicotinic acid. Among the 15 varieties of leafy vegetables which appeared in the diets, the one eaten in the largest amount was cabbage. Fats came from coconut oil, with some butter. As shown in Table 15, consumption of all items of nutrients was adequate among the people of this income group, and so was the total caloric intake. The vitamin inadequacy found in the type of rice used was obviously compensated by other foods. However, while the **average** showed satisfactory consumption, a number of these families were below average in their consumption of one or more of items; Table 17 indicates the percentage of the households where these inadequacies were found. It is of interest to note that a deficiency of every nutrient except ascorbic acid occurs in a large percentage of these households; only 42% of the families were found to have an adequate consumption in all nutrients. Table 18 gives the source of nutrients as percentage of total consumption, from the figures computed by the Department of the Census and Statistics. This table indicates that in the higher income brackets cereals provide a smaller supply of calories compared with milk and milk products. In June, 1956, another survey was carried out by the same authority to assess the consumption of milk in the city of Galle. The results, shown in Table 19, show the expected correlation between level of income and milk consumption.

B. DIET OF PREGNANT WOMEN AND INFANTS

It was found by Clements and Bocobo[4] that most women do not modify their regular diet when they become pregnant. Some of them regularly attend pre-natal clinics where a pound of skim-milk powder is given to them every week, yet there is evidence that a considerable percentage of these women do not use this skim milk but distribute it among other members of their family. Women of the better classes claim that, when pregnant, they modify their diet to include a larger consumption of proteins, especially milk. Some pregnant women have a predilection for "king coconut," a fruit which, according to folklore, has particular value under these circumstances. There seem to be few taboos regarding what pregnant women should or should not eat, but precisely because pregnant women do not modify their diet during pregnancy, the result is that about 50% do not eat enough food and the majority of these probably do not consume enough proteins. It is also found that practically all pregnant women have some degree of anemia, with a hemoglobin level well below what is expected in well-nourished, healthy women. Most Sinhalese women aim at breast feeding their infant for as long as possible but it was found that probably not more than 15% have sufficient milk to sustain the growth of the infant until the end of the first year. From that time on, most of the infants are fed the same diets as adults. As a result, it can be said that two-thirds of the children coming to Colombo hospitals are found to be malnourished. Only 60% of boys attending schools and 63.7% of girls have been found to have a satisfactory nutritional status. The rest had varying symptoms of malnutrition.[4]

IV. ADEQUACY OF FOOD RESOURCES

A. IN NORMAL TIMES

There can be no "normal" times for a country like Ceylon, which is dependent upon the world market to feed 50% of the people at home. As long as the island needs to import 400,000 to 500,000 tons of polished rice a year and 165,000 tons of other meal and flour, altogether representing at least 30% of the total caloric consumption,* Ceylon will be in a critical situation. As indicated above, a considerable effort is being made at present by the government to reach self sufficiency.

Table 20 summarizes the needs of the island if self sufficiency is to be achieved. (Figures have been rounded.)

B. IN TIMES OF STRESS

Inadequate in peace time, Ceylon's food economy is still more vulnerable to the circumstances brought about by war or recession—as can be demonstrated by the history of the past 30 years. After 1939, and again after the Korean War, international trade turned sharply against Ceylon's agricultural exports. During World War II Japan's conquest of Burma and the losses suffered by British merchant shipping ended in a disastrous shortage of food in Ceylon.

---

*Since 57% of the caloric consumption comes from cereals, and half of these must be imported, this estimate would seem to be justified.

V. DISEASE PATTERNS

Although there is no gross malnutrition in Ceylon, under the present circumstances signs of undernutrition are prevalent. Beriberi, pellagra, scurvy, rickets, and a number of unspecified avitaminoses occur every year in Ceylon. The total number of these cases listed under nutritional disorders was more than 360,000 at the last census (1957).[1] Moreover, it is found that 18.54% of all defects discovered on the occasion of school medical inspections are attributable to malnutrition.

The Government has initiated two milk programs; one consists of a free midday meal, including a glass of milk, given to school children; the other consists of free milk deliveries to pre-school children and mothers.

Twenty-four per cent of the boys and 27.6% of the girls are substandard in terms of weight and height. Angular stomatitis, erosion of the tongue, Bitot spots, and phrynoderma are common.[4] Kwashiorkor also occurs, as shown by the number of children in children's wards of most hospitals who exhibit clinical signs of the disease. However, since most of the children afflicted with an acute stage of the disease would probably be hospitalized, the incidence should be considered small.

VI. CONCLUSIONS

Clements and Bocobo find that most families with incomes of less than $7 a month have an inadequate intake of proteins and calories from time to time and, for some of these families, the deficiency is considered to be more or less constant. It is generally accepted that poverty due to a variety of causes is the basis for this inadequate food intake and that it affects primarily women and children; the state of nutrition of adult males appears to be satisfactory. It can also be concluded that about 50% of pregnant women do not eat enough food and that the majority of these probably do not consume enough proteins. Half of the infants do not get enough food to eat, due mainly to unsatisfactory breast feeding and to the inability of mothers to purchase enough infant food. At least 20% of the children of preschool age and most school children would benefit by having more to eat.

Any increase in food production substantial enough to provide Ceylon a better living for her rapidly increasing population requires irrigation of the dry zone. In ancient times Ceylon had a prosperous economy based on the agricultural development of this zone, which at that time was irrigated. With the disruption of the irrigation systems as a result of invasions and wars, the island has shifted toward a commercial economy based on tea, rubber, and coconut plantations, that flourished under the British and is still prevalent.

It is believed that the land available for further development in the dry zone is approximately 3,000,000 acres, of which 2,000,000 acres could be irrigated. From 1948 to 1953 irrigation was brought to 165,000 acres of primarily uncultured land, and improved irrigation facilities were provided for 125,000 acres of paddy land already used.[12]

Another 125,000 acres are expected to be added at the end of 1960. It is believed that the surface water available for irrigation in the dry zone is sufficient to provide for one crop per year on 3.6 million acres, if the land is efficiently used. Plans call for irrigation of about 2 million acres and there should be enough water for two crops a year on half or more of these 2 million acres. If all these plans are carried out and if at the same time a considerable effort is made to rehabilitate the present livestock, hopes for an increase in milk production may not be unreasonable. The problem is rendered still more important in view of the existence of 3 million vegetarians whose animal proteins would have to come from milk. The problems created by tradition and culture combine with those created by the availability of food supplies.

Improvement of food resources could come faster in Ceylon than in most other countries of Southeast Asia. The Ceylonese are more literate than most of their neighbors; 57% of all persons aged 5 and over (71.1 of males, 43.8 of females) can read and write. This should make it easier to devise extensive plans for agriculture which can be put across and which will be suitable for the greater part of the population.

Yet it appears highly unlikely that any agricultural development in Ceylon during the next two or three decades could enable the highlands to supply their people with a larger proportion of their total food needs. All possible increase in food supply rests with the development of the dry zone.

With an annual growth rate nearly 3%, Ceylon's population will number 18 million by 1975 and 21 million by the end of 1980. Even if Ceylon more than doubled its food production, it would need to double the amount of food imports. Since there will be almost no increase in the acreage devoted to export crops, the question of how to finance the imports of food will be crucial.

In view of the lack of mineral resources, the future Ceylon can contemplate would be to produce as much of her manufactured consumer goods as possible so as to reduce imports. However, it is likely that complete food sufficiency will never be attained and one may question whether it would be wise to reduce the proportion of land now devoted to export crops.

SELECTED REFERENCES

1. Administration Report of the Director of Health Services for 1956. Part IV, Education, Science and Art (B), Colombo, Government Press, 1957.
2. Ang, I. R. Soil and Water Conservation and Settlement Schemes in Ceylon. *Journal of the Soil Science Society of the Philippines*, Vol. 9, No. 3, 1957.
3. Around the World Program. Ceylon. New York, American Geographical Society, 1956.
4. Clements, F. W. and Bocobo, D. L. Report on Nutrition in Ceylon. F. A. O. Report No. 9206, December, 1957.
5. Cullumbine, A. A Survey of Disabling Illness in Ceylon. *Bulletin of the World Health Organization*, Vol. 7, No. 4, 1952.
6. De Silva, S. F. A Regional Geography of Ceylon. Colombo, The Colombo Apothecaries' Company, Ltd., 1954.
7. Department of the Census and Statistics. A Report on a Dietary Survey of Upper Income Households in the City of Colombo. Colombo, Government Press, 1957.
8. Department of the Census and Statistics. Ceylon Yearbook 1957, 1958. Colombo, Government Press.
8a. Dept. etc. Statistical Abstract of Ceylon 1958 and 1959. Colombo, Government Press, 1958 and 1959.
9. Department of Food Comm. Adm. Report for 1958.
10. Farmer, B. H. Pioneer Peasant Colonization in Ceylon. New York, Oxford University Press, 1957.
10a. Food and Agricultural Organization of the United Price Policies in Asia and the Far East, Bangkok, 1958.
11. Food and Agricultural Organization of the United Nations. Food Balance Sheets, 1954-56 Average. Rome, 1958.
11a. International Cooperation Administration. Near East and South East Asia Conference, Beirut.
12. MacFadden, C. H. Ceylon and the Colombo Plan. Focus, Vol. 5, No. 7, 1959, Page 89, 1955.
13. Medical Research Institute, Deputy Director of Health. A Note on the Typical Daily Fare Consumed in Ceylon. Personal Communication, 1953.
14. Ministry of Finance. Economic and Social Development of Ceylon. A Survey 1926-1954 Presented to Parliament 1955. United Nations, ESA.
15. Ministry of Food and Cooperative Undertakings. Department of Information. Ceylon Food Plan. Colombo, Daily News Press, March, 1950.
16. Oliver, H. M., Jr. Economic Opinion and Policy in Ceylon. London, Cambridge University Press, 1957.
17. Ryan, B. Socio-Cultural Regions of Ceylon. *Rural Sociology*, Vol. 15, No. 1, 1950.
18. Ryan, B. The Agricultural Systems of Ceylon. *Rural Sociology*, Vol. 20, No. 1, 1955.
19. Sarkar, N. K. The Demography of Ceylon. Colombo, Government Press, 1957.
20. United Nations, National Planning Council. The Ten Year Plan, 1959. Ceylon. (Ec 8 ESA).
21. United Nations. Technical Assistance Administration. Development of Small Scale Industries in Ceylon. TAA/CEY/5, January, 1956.
22. United States Department of Commerce, World Trade Information Service. Basic Data on the Economy of Ceylon. Washington, D. C., Government Printing Office, 1957.

Table 1

Relationship Between Factors Influencing Rice Availability in Ceylon

(Thousands of metric tons)

				Distribution[d]		
Year	Pro-duction[b]	Imports	Domestic Purchases[c]	Rationed	Unra-tioned	Wheat and Wheat Flour Imports[a]
			Rice (in terms of milled)			
1949	354	403	8	377	9	213
1950	337	498	4	377	23	225
1951	337	402	16	392	77	302
1952	443	406	23	375	7	294
1953	336	410	8	355	16	405
1954	477	402	106	460	18	282
1955	544	385	270	579	9	304
1956	413	491	160	644	2	258
1957	484	523	204	678	2	271

[a] Almost exclusively wheat flour (grain equivalent).
[b] Figures shown e.g. for 1949 include production in maha season of 1948/49 and in yala season 1949.
[c] By the Marketing Department.
[d] By the Food Supplies Department.
    Source: FAO; Government of Ceylon, Statistical Abstract of Ceylon, Quarterly Bulletin of Statistics, Administration Report of the Acting Commissioner for Development of Marketing for the Calendar Year 1950. Administration Report of the Food Commissioner for 1950 to 1957. Administration Report of the Commissioner for Development of Marketing for 1956.

Table 2

	1954-55		1955-56		1956-57	
Item	Acreage	Produc-tion (bushels)	Acreage	Produc-tion (bushels)	Acreage	Produc-tion (bushels)
Corn	37,646	282,646	39,008	248,569	42,295	358,104
Kurakkan	109,259	720,950	98,723	506,225	102,656	901,961
Sorghum	3,762	39,594	3,263	18,034	4,157	34,559

Table 3

| | 1954-55 | | 1955-56 | | 1956-57 | |
	Acreage	Production (tons)	Acreage	Production (tons)	Acreage	Production (tons)
Manioc	166,788	246,525	206,596	191,166	126,639	158,090
Sweet potato	40,882	53,115	30,741	45,842	30,248	26,172
Potato	756	512	623	464	404	157

Table 4

| Item | 1954-55 | | 1955-56 | | 1956-57 | |
	Acreage	Production (bushels)	Acreage	Production (bushels)	Acreage	Production (bushels)
Green gram	11,861	85,417	10,015	59,772	10,442	73,512
Cow peas	7,989	54,456	5,661	36,205	7,163	216,989

Table 5

| Items | 1954-55 | | 1955-56 | | 1957-58 | |
	Acreage	Production (tons)	Acreage	Production (tons)	Acreage	Production (tons)
Chillies	32,677	18,036	28,413	18,903	44,025	14,079
Mustard	4,603	736	3,724	696	7,315	1,607
Onions	17,361	43,966	17,166	40,944	77,426	49,112
Ginger	5,642	4,349	5,438	3,601	5,754	3,322
Tumeric	4,528	1,637	3,155	1,420	6,083	1,520
Pepper	18,131	5,937	20,104	5,146	20,087	6,098
Cardamon	23,945	2,186	11,558	2,238	12,255	2,125

This table indicates a slow but steady upward trend in certain foods, many of which are under price support. The increase in area and production of onions is particularly striking.

Source: For Tables 2, 3, 4, and 5: Dept. of Census and Statistics. Ceylon Yearbook, 1957; Idem, 1958. Colombo, Government Press.

Table 6

Animals Slaughtered for Food[a]

					Number
	Cattle	Buffaloes	Sheep	Goats	Pigs (swine)
1938	112,949	14,289	7,631	93,909	..
1944	93,918	5,351	2,157	72,845	..
1945	82,617	3,084	1,118	53,853	..
1946	92,385	9,200	3,087	39,551	..
1947	111,322	8,642	10,527	56,938	5,478
1948	131,298	7,650	12,272	79,775	..
1949	127,775	9,054	11,138	69,440	..
1950	147,458	10,453	36,497	114,657	..
1951	151,790	10,282	48,923	108,673[b]	..
1952	119,878	7,227	..	124,792[b]	..
1953	161,952	128	490	153,346	..
1954[c]	173,790	209	190,068		15,579
1955[d]	174,845	1,406	193,439		13,538
1956[e]	174,917	2,013	183,213		20,281
1957[f]	177,770	2,170	112,709	36,708	19,821

[a] Local bodies that have licensed slaughter houses only furnish these figures.
[b] Includes sheep.
[c] Does not include figures for 149 Village Committees.
[d] Does not include figures for 49 Village Committees.
[e] Does not include figures for 44 Village Committees, 6 Town Councils, 2 Urban Councils and 1 Municipal Council.

[f] Does not include figures for 75 Village Committees, 8 Town Councils, 4 Urban Councils and 1 Municipal Council.

Source: Dept. of the Census and Statistics: Ceylon Yearbook, 1957; idem, 1958. Colombo, Government Press.

Table 7

Livestock[a]

	Buffaloes	Meat Cattle	Sheep	Swine	Goats
1938	543,259	1,127,150	62,526	36,685	232,542
1944	518,761	1,005,630	60,637	75,750	271,596
1945	561,007	1,058,254	50,137	58,367	284,119
1946	521,958	1,079,522	63,788	74,092	306,391
1947	624,168	1,115,807	55,303	84,501	326,386
1948	658,468	1,133,481	55,469	95,094	369,712
1949	656,052	1,248,747	57,349	103,767	400,653
1950	522,418	1,105,447	43,627	74,198	370,091
1951	567,672	1,112,360	72,600	74,638	411,320
1952	627,072	1,188769	84,481	69,743	445,664
1953	655,558	1,228,718	103,923	74,370	498,977
1954	706,644	1,277,310	94,994	83,275	563,912
1955	794,708	1,432,755	88,883	43,257	491,324
1956	789,421	1,450,156	65,063	43,158	471,298
1957	700,548	1,448,558	64,464	72,679	464,365

[a] From returns furnished by the Revenue Officers.

Source: Department of the Census and Statistics: Ceylon Yearbook, 1957; idem, 1958. Colombo, Government Press.

Table 8

Production of Fresh Fish(a)

Cwt.

| | 1956 | 1957 | | | | | | Small Shore-Seine Fish | | |
	Total	Total	Thora	Paraw	Blood Fish	Shark and Skates	Rock Fish	Group 1(b)	Group 2(c)	Other Varieties
Ceylon	765,312	732,345	17,758	45,005	69,931	67,012	103,748	112,537	278,365	37,989
Western Province	77,429	51,599	3,974	3,394	4,660	3,568	6,764	6,140	18,941	4,158
Colombo-Moratuwa	17,861	10,133	569	781	937	268	2,063	141	5,195	179
Beruwela	18,036	17,094	937	810	1,263	1,096	1,929	4,176	6,722	161
Negombo	41,532	24,372	2,468	1,803	2,460	2,204	2,772	1,823	7,024	3,818
Southern Province	64,908	66,715	2,531	3,481	19,767	7,454	8,695	3,769	18,442	2,576
Balapitiya	23,553	24,920	827	1,086	10,074	241	2,349	1,282	8,461	600
Dodanduwa	2,765	2,364	70	211	784	—	256	611	346	83
Galle	671	1,948	286	134	249	29	668	—	537	45
Matara	20,612	19,013	523	1,187	5,888	3,684	2,479	876	2,881	1,495
Tangalla	17,307	18,470	825	863	1,769	3,500	2,943	1,000	6,217	353

Jaffina	118,800	105,047	1,728	9,820	1,032	12,576	23,202	20,187	30,403	6,099
Kankesantural	23,489	45,537	—	2,443	—	10,863	5,115	3,397	21,388	2,318
Point Pedro	18,586	25,568	1,145	2,288	75	3,907	9,460	1,854	5,604	1,235
Mannar	57,743	61,752	153	2,626	2,732	3,121	4,075	11,925	36,978	142
Arippu and Silavathurai	11,235	5,425	183	780	48	861	1,859	372	1,247	75
Mullaittivu	25,390	33,200	2,212	2,277	1,208	2,305	3,661	3,086	16,171	2,280
Eastern Province	146,609	121,927	2,956	8,065	11,686	6,611	23,120	20,473	41,771	7,246
Trincomalee	38,567	22,948	1,227	1,155	4,473	2,127	5,907	1,486	5,880	693
Mutur	8,789	16,961	5	3,371	685	588	4,874	515	5,967	956
Batticaloa	55,273	34,942	641	1,760	2,572	1,841	6,210	5,000	11,727	5,191
Kalmunai	43,980	47,076	1,083	1,779	3,955	2,055	6,129	13,472	18,197	406
North-Wester Province	221,123	215,578	2,876	9,831	28,724	15,746	17,797	41,334	87,410	11,860
Kalpitiya	98,899	83,738	702	4,762	17,486	8,954	9,464	1,923	39,124	1,323
Mundel	91,346	98,644	751	2,667	8,073	3,925	4,889	33,997	37,773	6,569
Chilaw	36,878	33,196	1,423	2,402	3,165	2,867	3,444	5,414	10,513	3,968

(a) Excluding trawler landings.
(b) Kumbala, Bolla, Katuwalla, Angila, Parati, Savalaya, etc.
(c) Herrings, Sardines, Hurullo, Sudaya, Halmassa, etc.

Source: Department of the Census and Statistics: Ceylon Yearbook, 1957; idem for 1958. Colombo, Government Press.

Table 9

Production of Cured Fish

Cwt. (dried weight)

| | 1956 Total | 1957 | | | | | | Small Shore–Seine Fish | | |
		Total	Thora	Paraw	Blood Fish(a)	Shark and Skates	Rock Fish	Group 1(b)	Group 2(c)	Other Varieties
Ceylon	114,176	149,962	253	3,185	5,480	10,959	12,836	25,945	88,134	3,170
Western Province	2,595	1	—	—	—	—	—	1	—	—
Colombo–Moratuwa	—	—	—	—	—	—	—	1	—	—
Beruwela	5	—	—	—	—	—	—	—	—	—
Negombo	2,590	—	—	—	—	—	—	—	—	—
Southern Province	248	342	5	28	87	37	28	42	53	62
Balapitiya	—	—	—	—	—	—	—	—	—	—
Dodanduwa	—	—	—	—	—	—	—	—	—	—
Galle	—	—	—	—	—	—	—	—	—	—
Matara	—	—	—	—	—	—	—	—	—	—
Tangalla	248	342	5	28	87	37	28	42	53	62

Northern Province	45,956	47,591	171	1,873	768	4,650	7,268	8,198	24,318	345
Jaffina	19,824	17,582	171	1,519	–	2,659	4,392	1,197	7,589	55
Kankesanturai	858	662	–	–	–	369	26	208	59	–
Point Pedro	824	1,160	–	–	–	41	211	–	899	9
Mannar	15,896	16,673	–	70	768	1,342	1,974	4,864	7,655	–
Arippu and Silavathurai	2,133	1,426	–	44	–	60	312	–	1,010	–
Mullaittivu	6,421	10,088	–|–	240	–	179	353	1,929	7,106	281
Eastern Province	21,235	13,633	8	223	125	264	822	4,930	7,218	43
Trincomalee	6,269	1,858	–	4	66	113	256	113	1,282	24
Mutur	1,374	1,474	–	68	11	29	141	94	1,131	–
Batticaloa	4,035	1,782	–	80	–	20	194	714	746	19
Kalmunai	9,547	8,619	8	71	48	293	231	4,009	4,059	–
North-Western Province	44,152	88,395	69	1,061	4,500	6,008	4,718	12,775	56,544	2,720
Kalpitiya	26,801	48,476	69	1,061	1,777	3,869	1,973	32,415	36,011	529
Mundel	15,287	38,705	–	–	2,610	2,139	–	10,315	19,477	2,191
Chilaw	2,064	1,214	–	–	113	–	4,718	45	1,056	–

(a) Balaya, Atawalla, Kelawalla, Alagoduwa.
(b) Kumbala, Bolla, Katuwalla, Parati, Anglia, Savalaya.
(c) Herrings, Sardines, Hurullo, Sudaya, Halmessa, etc.

Source: Department of the Census and Statistics: Ceylon Yearbook, 1957; Idem for 1958. Colombo, Government Press.

Table 10

Cash Crops Production

Items	1955 Acreage	Produc- tion	1956 Acreage	Produc- tion	1957 Acreage	Produc- tion
		1000 (lbs)		1000 (lbs)		1000 (lbs)
Tea	575,000	380,013	565,518	375,578	575,000	397,775
Rubber	659,000	93,830	660,985	95,383	659,247	98,164
Coconut	1,075,000	2,400	1,075,000	2,582	1,075,000	2,400

Source: Department of the Census and Statistics: Ceylon Yearbook, 1957; idem 1958. Colombo, Government Press.
Department of the Census and Statistics: Statistical Abstract of Ceylon, 1958; idem, 1959. Colombo, Government Press.

Table 11

Imports

Items	1955	1956	1957
Sheep (for food) units	17,000	16,000	16,000
Goats (for food) "	24,000	20,000	18,000
Fish and fish preparations (tons)	34,000	38,700	36,000
Condensed milk (lbs)	13,675,000	12,433,000	15,856,000
Milk foods "	3,562,000	5,310,000	4,304,000
Powdered milk "	1,439,000	2,073,000	2,591,000
Skim milk "	2,510,000	835,000	11,303,000
Butter "	2,404,000	2,487,000	2,310,000
Eggs "	4,474,000	4,481,000	5,695,000
Malted milk "	10,271,000	10,393,000	13,490,000
Rice (polished & broken) (tons)	360,000	462,000	489,946
Meal & flour "	176,000	163,000	165,000
Biscuits "	67,000	65,000	65,500
Fruits & jams Apples Grapes Tamarind } "	6,613	5,501	4,200
Potatoes (not sweet) "	29,984	28,792	28,500
Dhall (pulse) Green gram (peas) Chick peas Black gram (peas) Lentils } (pulses) "	29,000	44,268	50,788
Onion Garlic } (tons)	29,200	29,950	29,800
Sugars "	134,000	180,000	120,000

This table shows to what considerable extent Ceylon is dependent upon its imports for its food.
Source: Department of the Census and Statistics: Statistical Abstract of Ceylon 1958; idem, 1959. Colombo, Government Press.
United States Dept. of Commerce, World Trade Information Service; Basic Data on the Economy of Ceylon, Washington, D. C., 1957.

Table 12

Food Industries in Ceylon (1952)

Item	No. of Establishments	Personnel
Salt	12	428
Milk products	4	34
Grain milling	67	931
Confectionery and canning	22	924
Distilleries & breweries	9	464
Aerated water	32	707
Coconut milling	75	7,747

Sources: Department of the Census and Statistics: Ceylon Yearbook, 1957; idem, 1958. Colombo, Government Press. Department of the Census and Statistics: Statistical Abstract of Ceylon 1958; idem, 1959. Colombo, Government Press.

Table 13

Sources of Caloric Intake in an Average Sinhalese Diet in Percent

Rice	43.3
Wheat	10.9
Other cereals	3.0
Pulses	3.9
Roots and tubers	3.3
Sugar	7.6
Oilseeds	.2
Oils and fats (excl. oilseeds & butter)	3.8
Vegetables	1.0
Fruits & nuts (incl. coconut)	17.8
Meat, fish, poultry, eggs	3.4
Milk & dairy products	1.8
Total	100.0

Source: Clements, F. W. and Bocobo, D. L.: Report on Nutrition in Ceylon. Food and Agriculture Organization Report #9206, December, 1957.

Table 14

Nutrients in Average Sinhalese Diet

Calories	2,000
Protein	42.2 Gm.
Vitamin A	266 I.U.
Riboflavin	0.6 mg.
Thiamin	0.931 mg.
Niacin	10.5 mg.
Vitamin C	65.2 mg.
Iron	13 mg.
Calcium	299 mg.

Source: Clements, F. W. and Bocobo, D. L.: Report on Nutrition in Ceylon. Food and Agriculture Organization Report #9206, December, 1957.

Table 15

Nutrient Intake Among Middle Class Households in Ceylon

		% of Adequacy
Calories	3,271	149
Proteins	84 Gm.	133
Calcium	762 mg.	123
Iron	20 mg.	222
Vitamin A	3,210 I.U.	124
Thiamine	1,395 mg.	134
Riboflavin	1,409 mg.	126
Nicotinic acid	16 mg.	123
Ascorbic acid	122 mg.	488'

Source: Department of the Census and Statistics; A Report on a Dietary Survey of Upper Income Households in the City of Colombo. Colombo, Government Press, 1957.

Table 16

Food Intake; Ceylonese Average 1954-56

Item	Gm. per Day	Calories per Day	Protein per Day	Fat per Day
Wheat flour	64.2	222	7.5	1.1
Corn	2.1	7	.2	.1
Millets	6.8	23	.6	.2
Other grains	2.9	10	.3	.1
Paddy	265.7	954	18.9	2.9
Potatoes	12.1	9	.2	—
Yams, sweet potato	14.0	13	.2	.1
Manioc	66.5	72	.6	.1
Sugar	43.7	169	—	—
Green grams	3.4	12	.8	.1
Other pulses	14.9	51	3.3	.3
Coconut	74.7	280	3.0	11.4
Vegetables	114.5	25	1.6	0.2
Fruit	10.5	5	.1	0.1
Pork	.4	1	—	0.1
Beef	6.3	9	1.0	0.5
Buffalo	0.1	—	—	—
Mutton & goat	0.7	0.1	0.1	0.2
Poultry	0.5	—	—	0.1
Eggs	3.3	5	0.4	0.4
Fish	33	33	3	2.6
Milk & Butter	36.04	36	1.4	11.6
Oils and Fats	19.9	87	—	0.3
Total	796.24	2,023.1	43.2	32.5

Of the proteins consumed, 5.9 are animal and 37.3 are of vegetable origin. There are, however, seasonal, regional and class differences.

Source: Clements, F. W. and Bocombo, D. L.: Report on Nutrition in Ceylon. Food and Agriculture Organization Report #9206, December, 1957.

Table 17

Percentage of Households Whose Consumption is Below Requirements

Calories	9%
Proteins	20%
Calcium	36%
Iron	3%
Vitamin A	41%
Thiamine	32%
Riboflavin	30%
Nicotinic acid	32%
Ascorbic acid	—

Source: Department of the Census and Statistics: A Report on a Dietary Survey of Upper Income Households in the City of Colombo. Government Press, 1957.

Table 18

Source of Nutrients as Percentages of Total Consumption

In the Higher Income Nutrients Brackets

Source	Calories	Protein	Calcium	Iron	Vitamin A (Pre formed)	Thiamine (Vitamin)	Riboflavin (Vitamin B$_2$)	Nicotinic Acid	Ascorbic Acid (Vitamin C)
		Gm.	mg.	mg.	I.U.	mg.	mg.	mg.	mg.
1. Cereals	41	37	5	29	–	38	21	49	–
2. Beverages	1	1	1	1	–	1	5	6	–
3. Vegetables	2	3	11	13	20	10	6	4	47
4. Roots and tubers	2	2	8	3	11	6	2	4	10
5. Dried pulses	3	9	5	11	1	11	5	5	–
6. Fruits	3	1	3	3	8	6	3	2	33
7. Nuts and seeds	12	4	3	7	–	8	8	3	–
8. Oils and fats	11	–	1	–	15	–	–	–	–
9a. Fish	2	14	8	3	2	2	4	10	–
9b. Meat and meat products	2	10	1	7	15	6	10	14	1
10. Spices and condiments	1	2	9	12	9	–	–	1	8
11. Milk, milk products, eggs, &c.	8	14	40	3	19	9	33	–	1
12. Miscellaneous	12	3	5	8	–	3	3	2	1
All Sources	100	100	100	100	100	100	100	100	100

Source: Department of the Census and Statistics: Ceylon Yearbook, 1957; idem 1958. Colombo, Government Press.

Table 19

Percentage of Households Consuming Fresh Milk

Income Group	
0 — $ 225 annually	17
225 — 600	40
600 — 825	65
825 — 1050	50
1050 — 1275	65
1275 — 1500	69
1500 — over	80
all groups	43

Source: Department of the Census and Statistics: Ceylon Yearbook, 1957; idem, 1958. Colombo, Government Press.

Table 20

Food Deficits in Ceylon

Item	Produced (tons) (average)	Needed From Abroad (average imported)	Total
Rice	540,000	500,000	1,040,000
Other cereals	31,000	165,000	196,000
Roots and tubers	280,000	38,000	318,000
Pulses	3,000	55,000	58,000
Coconuts	810,000	—	—
Vegetables	319,000	40,000	359,000
Fruits	26,000	7,000	33,000
Sugar (refined)		144,000	144,000
Pork	1,000		1,000
Beef	20,000		20,000
Buffalo	400		400
Mutton and goat	2,000		2,000
Poultry	1,000		1,000
Eggs	9,000	1,000	10,000
Fresh fish	33,000		33,000
Dried & salted fish	6,000	31,000	37,000
Canned fish		2,000	2,000
Cow's milk	79,000		79,000
Buffalo's milk	24,000		24,000
Milk products		9,000	9,000
Copra	255,000		255,000
Coconut oil	122,000		122,000
Butter		1,000	1,000
Desiccated Coconut	60,000		60,000

Compiled from: Department of the Census and Statistics. Ceylon Yearbook, 1957; idem, 1958; Statistical Abstract of Ceylon, 1958; idem 1959. Colombo, Government Press.

Table 21

Harvest Calendar in Ceylon

Crops	Harvest Period	Bulk of Harvest
Maize:		
Yala	Apr.-May ⎫	Sept.-Oct.
Maha	Sept.-Oct. ⎬	
Millets:[a]		
Yala	Apr.-May ⎫	Sept.-Oct.
Maha	Sept.-Oct. ⎬	
Rice:		
Maha	Feb.-Apr. ⎫	Feb.
Yala	Aug.-Sept. ⎬	
Potatoes:		
Maha	Jan.-Mar. ⎫	Jan.-Mar.
Yala	Apr.-June ⎬	
Sweet potatoes:		
Yala	Mar.-Apr. ⎫	Sept.-Nov.
Maha	Sept.-Nov. ⎬	
Cassava[b]	Mar.-May	...
Cow peas:		
Yala[b]	Apr.-June ⎫	Oct.-Nov.
Maha[c]	Oct.-Nov ⎬	
Mustard:		
Yala	Feb.-Mar.	...
Pepper:		
Maha	Mar.-May	...
Cardamons:		
Maha	Aug.-Dec.	...
Cacao	...	Apr.-June and Oct.-Dec.
Tobacco:		
Maha	Mar.-May ⎫	...
Yala	Aug.-Oct. ⎬	
Tea	Whole year round	...
Rubber	Whole year round	...

[a] Comprising Kurakkan—Eleusine Coracana L.; Meneri—Panicum miliaceum L.; Little millet; Amu—Paspalum serobiculatum L.; Thana—Setaria italica L.; German millet; Sama, also called Hin—Meneri and Shamai—Panicum miliare Lank. Common millet.
[b] In wet zone.
[c] In wet and dry zones.
Source: Food and Agriculture Organization: World Crop Harvest Calendar. Rome, 1959.

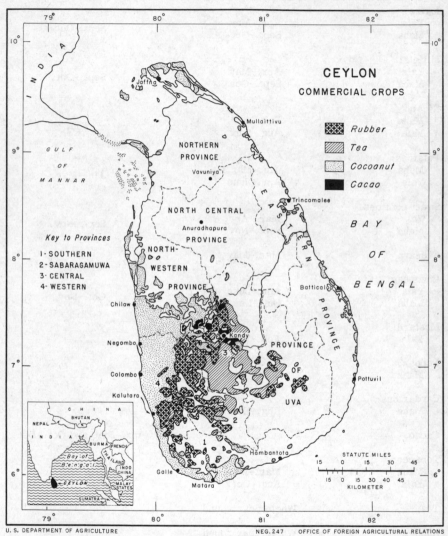

CEYLON
COMMERCIAL CROPS

Rubber
Tea
Cocoanut
Cacao

Key to Provinces
1 - SOUTHERN
2 - SABARAGAMUWA
3 - CENTRAL
4 - WESTERN

INDIA

GULF
OF
MANNAR

Jaffna

Mullaittivu

NORTHERN
PROVINCE

Vavuniya

NORTH CENTRAL
PROVINCE

Anuradhapura

NORTH-
WESTERN

PROVINCE

Chilaw

Negombo

Colombo

Kalutara

Trincomalee

BAY

OF

BENGAL

Batticaloa

EASTERN PROVINCE

Kandy

PROVINCE
OF

3

UVA

Pottuvil

4

2

1

Hambantota

Galle

Matara

STATUTE MILES
15   0   15   30   45

15   0   15   30   40   45
KILOMETER

CHINA
NEPAL   BHUTAN
INDIA
BURMA   FRENCH
Bay of   THAILAND   INDO
Bengal   CHINA
CEYLON   MALAY
STATES
SUMATRA

PAKISTAN

I. GENERAL REMARKS

Pakistan was born, an independent country, in 1947; it is formed of two geographic units separated by over 1,000 miles (1600 kilometers) of Indian territory. With the exception of cultural background and the religion of most of the people, the two units are entirely dissimilar. West Pakistan has a sparse population, East Pakistan is densely crowded; West lacks water, East has too much and the threat of floods creates emergencies almost every year. Yet, in 1957 and in 1958, it so happened that floods threatened food supplies in West Pakistan and there was drought in East Pakistan. Language is varied: Urdu is spoken in West Pakistan, Bengali in East Pakistan. Moslems comprise 85% of the people; Hindus, all living in East Pakistan, comprise 13%.

West Pakistan is located between 24° and 37° N. and between 61° and 75° E. East Pakistan is located between 20°45' and 26°30' N. and between 88° and 92°30' E. The western unit has an area of 310,236 square miles (803,508 square kilometers), the eastern 53,501 square miles (138,567 square kilometers), giving to the country a total area of 364,737 square miles (944,665 square kilometers). The population is estimated at 85 million people, making it one of the largest Moslem states in the world. Only 15% of the population is literate, and the economic level is very low—per capita income hardly reaches $50.00 a year.[5]

While West Pakistan has 85% of the territory, it has only 42% of the population. It is largely an arid land except in the far north and along the banks of the Indus River. It has a large irrigation system, with a number of canals, on which it depends for survival—hence the bitterness of the quarrels with India, whose geographic position allows it to command the flow of waters in the life-giving canals of Pakpattan, Dilpapur, Mailisi, Eastern Sadiqia, Fordwah, Kain, and Bahawal.[9] An equitable division of the waters between India and West Pakistan is of life or death importance, since over half of West Pakistan gets less than 10 inches of rainfall a year and most of the rest less than 20 inches. Due to intense heat the rate of evaporation is high. Irrigation farming with inadequate drainage often causes excess salinity, which has already caused abandonment of extensive acreages in the Punjab.

East Pakistan, on the contrary, is an alluvial flood plain, cut by a
large number of waterways that often change their courses. Houses
have to be built on elevated terrain for protection against the floods.
Crops are limited to cultures, such as rice and jute, that can survive
in standing water. In certain parts of the southeast, a very primitive
agriculture still remains, based on the slash and burn method.

Farms are, of course, generally different in East Pakistan and in
the Punjab (West Pakistan), but in both the farmers go to their fields
by day and return to villages at night. The Punjab is a semiarid region
where agricultural production is entirely dependent upon irrigation. A
typical farm[4] covers 10 to 12 acres, but there is not enough irrigation
to make use of all the land. Occasionally, a well supplements the canal
water supply. The farmer is usually a tenant and his equipment consists of a plow and a drag to level the ground and break up the clods.
He may have a team of bullocks and perhaps a bullock cart with which
to travel. His labor force typically consists of his own family, of one
or two boys of working age. He may also have one or two milking buffalo to supply his milk and ghee. His crops are wheat, gram, oil seeds,
rape and mustard, and green fodder crops. His net income averages
less than $100 annually.

In East Pakistan a typical farm does not exceed 3 acres, usually
fragmented into many plots, and located within a mile of the village.
There the farmer raises spring and summer paddy rice on nearly 85%
of his land. On the balance he grows jute, sugar cane, and occasionally
pulses, mustard, and vegetables. If he is lucky, he has fruit trees also.
He has 10 to 12 hens and a few ducks, and occasionally he may catch a
fish from the rice fields. He produces over 2,000 pounds of rice in a
good year and can feed all his family. If nothing destructive happens,
he may even collect $50.00 cash money at the end of the year. This
farmer cooperates with the other farms of his village in a system of
trading for seeds, work of the bullocks, and laborers. He is beginning
to be reached by improvement programs and to receive chemical fertilizers, which may eventually raise the yield of his acreage.

II. FOOD RESOURCES

A. GENERAL

Pakistan is largely an agricultural country; 70% of the national income comes from agriculture and 80% of the people are engaged in
farming; 90% of export trade is based on agricultural products. One of
the best sources on the country[5] states ''The area now comprising
Pakistan was formerly a substantial producer of food. Now only in
years of exceptionally good harvest, does Pakistan produce enough food

to meet domestic requirements allowing for some international exchange in foodstuffs. The population is increasing faster than the domestic food production. Crop yields per hectare already low, have declined in recent years. Increasing agricultural production is second to none among the problems of Pakistan." Figures in recent years amply justify this statement. As shown in Table 1, production figures have steadily declined in the decade between 1948 and 1958.[13] With an annual increase of population of nearly 1 million people, an additional 160,000 tons of food grains are needed every year to provide the minimum food requirements. At the end of 1959, there was no indication of a trend toward increased production.

The reasons for this situation are multiple. Centuries of subdivision of holdings in obedience to the inheritance laws have resulted in smaller and smaller plots, occasionally widely scattered, which are uneconomical to operate. In addition, money lenders and an intricate structure of mortgages on the land deprive the worker of a great percentage of his profits. The country is particularly vulnerable to natural disasters. Droughts in West Pakistan and floods in East Pakistan alternate in time and space to cause critical conditions. It is also claimed that food grains from East Pakistan are smuggled across the Indian border. Severe measures are being taken to obviate this depletion. Soil erosion, insects, inadequate and poor supplies of seeds and poor agricultural practices all contribute to the precariousness of the food supplies.

The government is endeavoring to keep the prices of rice and wheat stable by establishing central stocks for distribution in dearth areas. But it has found itself in the dilemma of either favoring the producer, which results in a rise in prices, or favoring the consumer, which results in a lowering of the prices with consequent lag in output. The price policies for wheat and rice have mainly been in the interest of the consumer. Wheat is procured directly from the cultivator and rice is purchased in the form of milled rice from the miller, although paddy may also be procured from the growers and milled on commission. The three methods for government procurement are: (a) compulsory levy, by which cultivators must sell their surplus to the government; (b) selective procurement, by which cultivators are required to declare their stocks of grain; and (c) voluntary procurement, in which the producer brings his crop to the government for purchase at the government price.[2]

As already stated, the geography of food is entirely different in the two "wings" of the country (see map). West Pakistan produces mainly wheat and, in addition, bajra, barley, gram, jowar, corn, rape and mustard, sugar cane, tobacco, cotton, and wool; its Punjab Province is the country's best dairy region. Over 16 million acres of land are irrigated. To supplement the water coming from the complicated network of canals, villages use water from wells, which provide irrigation for approximately $\frac{1}{2}$ million acres. East Pakistan produces rice, often of the floating type, that grows during the rains at the rate of one foot a day and reaches a height of 25 feet, necessary to keep it above the water. In addition, the east "wing" has cash crops such as jute and tea.

B. CEREALS[13]

Rice. Rice, the most important cereal food in the country, occupied 22,450,000 acres in 1958, an increase from 21,499,000 in 1948—which represents 45% of the total cultivated area. Production figures, however, are somewhat discouraging; production fluctuated between 8.4 million tons in 1948 and 8.8 million tons in 1958. An effort is being made to increase the yield. But, as noted above, many factors influence the success of the rice crop. In 1958 the deficit was 1 million tons in East Pakistan alone, probably caused by drought in the northern districts. This had to be met by internal as well as foreign procurement.

Wheat. Most of the wheat comes from a sown area of between 10 and 12 million acres. This represents approximately 40% of the crop area in the West Pakistan. The area sown has not increased greatly from 1948 to 1958 (see Table 1) and the production remained almost stagnant at less than 4 million tons a year, with 10% fluctuations over and under this figure.

The wheat crop is subject to severe vicissitudes because of locusts and other pests, floods and water shortages. In 1957, floods affected the northern part of West Pakistan and disrupted communications. As a result, arrival of wheat on the markets suffered a marked slowdown and a deficit of 720,000 tons eventually developed.[8,9,10] West Pakistan had to apply for 840,000 tons of wheat under the I.C.A. aid program. It is stated in official Pakistan sources that the United States government took considerable time in authorizing the necessary operations, thus obliging the Pakistan government to purchase around 300,000 tons of wheat from other sources with their own funds. However, food from the United States finally arrived in January, 1958. The following year a crop of 3.9 million tons was expected, when India decided to stop supplies of water to the Sutlej canal system, over which it has control. Wheat growers became panicky and started hoarding their stocks, creating difficulties for the government, which needed again to find wheat, this time, 700,000 tons.[9,10] These were requested from the United States government. The Pakistan government is, year after year, depending on foreign sources to feed its growing population.

Other cereals. Other cereals produced in West Pakistan include the millets, of which bajra is the most popular; its area of production (see Table 1) has shrunk in the last decade from 2,331 acres to 2,000 and the output from 394,000 tons to 350,000. The sown area of jowar showed a slight increase from 1,185,000 acres in 1948 to 1,300,000 in 1958. The yield, however, has dropped from 242,000 tons in 1948 to

235,000 in 1958. The sown area of barley, also a West Pakistan crop, has declined over 100,000 acres, from 658,000 to 535,000 with consequent loss in production from 191,000 tons to 125,000.

C. OTHER EDIBLE CROPS

Pulses. Gram (chick pea) is the most important of the pulses. The area under cultivation increased 10% between 1948 and 1958, but the yield dropped significantly—only 725,000 tons were harvested in 1958 as against 804,000 in 1948 (see Table 1).

Fruits and vegetables. Fruits are available, although not in large quantities. West Pakistan produces oranges, grapefruits, guavas, papayas, mangoes, ground cherries, custard apples, melons, and tomatoes. Some vegetables are also produced: potatoes, sweet potatoes, onions, carrots, turnips, cauliflower, green beans, radishes, cabbages, eggplants, cucumbers, rutabagas, red peppers and garlic. In East Pakistan, the chief fruits are bananas, mangoes, melons, papayas, grapefruits, and pineapples. One can also find blackberries, gooseberries, guavas, jackfruits, lemons, limes, oranges, plums, and pomegranates. Potatoes are a common vegetable in East Pakistan. Other vegetables include beans, beets, cabbages, carrots, cauliflower, peppers, cucumbers, gourds, lettuce, onions, peas, radishes, spinach, and tomatoes. Coconut and pulses are available throughout the year.

Sugar cane is one of the successful crops. The area under cultivation in both "wings" has grown from 708,000 acres in 1948 to 1,100,000 in 1958 with an increase in production from 1,043,000 tons of raw sugar "gur" to 1,250,000 in 1958.

Fats and oils. Pakistan is not able to supply itself with cooking fats and oils. East Pakistan produces only 50% of its own requirements, chiefly from mustard and rape seeds. So far coconuts have not been used for oil production. In West Pakistan the production of hydrogenated cotton-seed oil has increased in recent years.

D. CASH CROPS[7,8]

In terms of foreign exchange—so badly needed to meet food deficits—the most productive cash crops are jute and cotton, followed by tea. Pakistan is the world's most important producer of raw jute. The crop is grown only in East Pakistan, covering 1,877,000 acres in 1948, but declining to 1,300,000 in 1958 because of the increased planting in food grains. This resulted in a drop in foreign-exchange earnings. Cotton is a West Pakistan crop, often rotated with cereals and pulses. Most of the acreage is in the Punjab, accounting for 50% of the total. Tea grows in East Pakistan on the lower slopes of the Himalayas, in the Sylhet District, and in the hills of Chittagong and Tippera. There are 122 tea estates in Pakistan, of which 56 are owned by Europeans, covering 76,000 acres and producing 53 million pounds a year. Domestic consumption has tripled since Partition (1947), rising from 9 million pounds to 30.5 million pounds in 1957. As a result, exports have dropped and so has the earned foreign exchange.

E. ANIMAL PRODUCT RESOURCES[5,8]

An important producer of hides and skins, the country has approximately 25 million head of cattle, 3/5 of which are found in East Pakistan. Five million buffalo, 9 million sheep, and 14.5 million goats roam in West Pakistan. Unfortunately, these animals are suffering from malnutrition and therefore produce very little milk or meat and are a poor source of power.[5] Cows in East Pakistan do not provide more than 3 to 15 pounds of milk a day; in West Pakistan 50 or more pounds are obtained on certain government farms. As in India, there is considerable competition between man and beast for the available food. A number of high-grade buffalo and cows are raised on 17 large military dairy farms in West Pakistan. The buffalo milk is processed to produce ghee or canned milk; it is sometimes sold pasteurized or homogenized.

The country has approximately 23 million chickens and 5 million ducks; 3/4 of which are in East Pakistan. As a result of this low ratio of poultry to people, eggs have little significance in the diet.

With 850 miles of coastline, both on the Arabian Sea and on the Bay of Bengal, Pakistan has access to fish,[5,8] an important source of animal protein. Unfortunately, modern methods of fishing have made little headway, and fishing is confined to the coastal waters. In 1957, East Pakistan landed 215,544 metric tons of fish while West Pakistan, in whose coastal waters sharks, skates, rays, and sardines are prevalent, landed 67,256 tons. There is a bright prospect in shrimps—180,000 pounds were caught in 1957. Most of the rivers, lakes, tanks, ponds, and the rice fields of East Pakistan yield fresh-water fish.

Surveys conducted by the Central Fishery Department confirm the great potential resources of fisheries. A big handicap results from the lack of powered fishing boats and modern gear, little organization in the fishermen's community, and unsystematic ways of marketing. The government has introduced a number of measures to overcome these difficulties.

F. EXPORTS AND IMPORTS

Although Pakistan was at intervals self-supporting in food grains and even exported some of its rice, it has in recent years been an importer of food. In 1955, 434,000 tons of rice had to be imported, 201,722 of which were supplied by the United States. Yet, in the same

year, 219,140 tons were exported, a rather surprising occurrence.[13]
In 1956, over 900,000 tons of food grains had to be imported, which
included 475,000 tons of wheat and nearly 425,000 tons of rice. Of
these, over 200,000 tons of rice and over 400,000 tons of wheat were
supplied by the United States. In 1957-1958 imports had to be made in
West Pakistan to the extent of over 300,000 tons of rice and over
600,000 tons of wheat.[8]

In 1957, East Pakistan had a deficit of some 440,000 tons of rice
which had to be imported (see Table 2).

Some 100,000 tons of refined sugar are produced, resulting in a
need for 90,000 tons to be imported.[13] Certain foodstuffs, such as fish,
tea, oil cakes, fruit and vegetables are exported. The exact amount of
the nutrients that leave the country is not accurately known.

G. POSSIBLE MODIFICATION OF FOOD RESOURCES

Some of the factors that could modify the food resources are of domestic origin, others are of foreign origin. In Pakistan, agriculture
is the responsibility of the provincial departments, with the central
government exercising certain powers in coordination and support,
because of the limited financial resources of the two halves of the
country. The delineation of responsibilities between the central and
the provincial governments is not clear. The central government has
adopted a policy of extending land and loans for food agricultural-de-
velopment projects. The main goal is to attain self-sufficiency by producing more food grains through large-scale irrigation and land-reclamation projects, and by increasing yields through subsidized distribution of improved seeds and fertilizers and through eradication of
pests.[4] In West Pakistan, land-reclamation projects are being given
high priority with the establishment of water and power development
authorities. Serious efforts are being made in East Pakistan to increase the irrigation well and pumping stations.

Shortly after martial law was declared in 1958, a land-reform commission was appointed to consider the problems of ownership and tenancy of agricultural lands. The first action taken in West Pakistan was
to limit the size of holdings; no person can own an area of more than
500 acres of irrigated land or more than 1,000 acres of unirrigated
land.[4] Compensation for excess land retained by the government is
based on a productivity index. What effect this will have on the over-
all food situation is not known yet. Following recommendations from
the United States, additional programs for land reform, improved facilities and services, and rural credit with reasonable rates of inter-
ests have been offered. These should give the needed incentive to food
production. It is believed that improved marketing facilities and services might reduce the spread between retail prices and the producer's
prices.

The Japanese experts who came to Pakistan at the request of the government in 1956, under the Colombo Plan, to teach methods of rice cultivation are credited with producing local increases of 50 to 100% per acre. In 1958, over 114 experiments were conducted in East Pakistan at 26 centers and in 57 villages.[8] These concentrate on improvement in soil fertility based on the studies of soil composition and on the appropriate use of fertilizers. Improvement of yield through the application of imported fertilizers is, of course, dependent upon the capacity of obtaining foreign exchange. In 1956, over 50,000 tons of fertilizers were imported. This has increased to 132,000 tons in 1957, and 200,000 tons were scheduled to arrive in 1959.[5] An American-sponsored fertilizer factory at Daudkhel is said to produce approximately 50,000 tons of fertilizer.[5] Definite progress has been made in the expansion of fisheries. The export of shrimp to the United States has increased foreign exchange.

H. FOOD INDUSTRIES, STORAGE AND TECHNOLOGY

The existing food storage capacity in West Pakistan is approximately 100,000 tons, in Karachi. In East Pakistan, a 150,000 ton storage capacity exists. It is now the policy of the government always to keep on hand 100,000 tons of rice reserve, and storage for these 100,000 tons is being completed.

The development of a food-processing industry is embryonic. Out of 120 registered plants, only 11 for canning foods and vegetables employ as many as 20 people.[5]

As already stated, Pakistan produces approximately 100,000 tons of refined sugar. Of the 14 sugar mills in the country, 5 have been established by the government, at Jauharabad and Charsaddi in West Pakistan and at Rangpur, Thakurgon, and Diwanganj in East Pakistan. At the end of 1959, a Premier Sugar Mill at Mardan had a capacity of 50,000 tons a year, but most of the sugar is produced in primitive units on the cane fields themselves. The product is called "gur" (brown sugar), and the yield is low.

There is only one fish canning factory, a little shrimp factory at Karachi. Abundant resources in sardines and tuna could become the basis of a canning industry.

An evaporated-milk plant at Okera in East Pakistan is owned and operated by the army. A number of dehydration plants were established during World War II at Peshawar but are not operating now.[5]

A considerable quantity of edible oil ("Vanaspati") is obtained from crushing cotton seeds which is used as a substitute for "ghee" two days a week by the army. Among other miscellaneous technological developments there is a factory at Karachi that manufactures cans from imported tin plate. A Vegetable-Fruit Preserve Association has been organized with headquarters at Lahore. The Food Products Control Order of 1951 defines the required conditions for sanitation and quality in food processing, but the majority of the plants, even the largest, do not meet the requirements of the order.

III. DIET TYPES[5]

A. GENERAL

The diets of Pakistan, although somewhat different in the two halves of the country, have a common character—they are low in calories and inadequate in protective nutrients. The different sources consulted give slightly different estimates but all point in the same direction. According to food balances computed by the Foreign Agriculture Service of the United States for 1954-1955, the average per capita consumption of food for the entire population of East and West Pakistan amounted to 2,124 calories per day, (see Table 3). Cereals provided 71% of the calories, sugar and milk 7% each, and pulses, 5%. Meat fish, and eggs together contributed only 3%, oils and fats only 2%. These figures are at slight variance with those given by the Food and Agriculture Organization for 1954-1957 (see Table 5) and by the Foreign Agriculture Service of the United States for 1955-1956 (see Table 4).

According to the Foreign Agricultural Service source for 1955-1956, the total caloric intake did not exceed 1980 (68.2% from cereals, 8.3% from sugar, 8.7% from milk and milk products, and 4.2% from beans and pulses). Meat, fish and eggs contributed 3.8% and fats 2%. Based on a 3-year average, the total caloric intake, published by the Food and Agriculture Organization in 1958, was 2,000 (total protein, 47.3 grams, of which 8.3 were derived from animal proteins). The average fat intake was 25.2 gm. per day according to FAO (see Table 5). Whatever the exact average is, there is no doubt that the Pakistani diets are among the poorest in the world, as undoubtedly many low-income groups in the country are well below the figure stated above.

Rice, basic food of East Pakistan, is usually eaten as plain boiled rice ("khushka") with the excess water thrown away or as sweets ("zarda," "kheer," or "firni").[5] Wheat, basic food of West Pakistan, is treated much in the same way it is in India, as chapattis, in pancake form ("paratha"), as doughnuts ("balushahi"), or soaked in syrup ("jalebi"). It is also baked in patties filled with vegetables or made into a sweet pudding ("halwa") or vermicelli ("suvayan").[5]

Pulses and legumes are used with other foods, gram flour is fried in oil ("missi roti") or cooked in water to form a porridge ("pakora").[1] Other vegetables are eaten boiled and fried and sometimes made with

a salad ("raita"). A special carrot pudding ("halwagajar") is said to
be a great delicacy. Pickled vegetables and fruit ("achars" and "chut-
neys") are popular condiments. Preferred meats are chicken ("mur-
ghi") and goat and mutton of which "kebab" is prepared. Meat is mixed
in curried meat balls ("korma") and various dishes are prepared from
the feet, head, and brains of domestic animals. Fish ("machli") is a
favorite. Milk and milk products are similar to those prepared in India
(see that chapter), and eggs are liked but are too expensive for the majority of people.

Many combinations of these foods exist, mostly based on rice ("pi-
lavs" or "biryanis"), sometimes with split peas or beans ("khishris"),
or vegetables and dahls ("bhajias"). In West Pakistan, wheat flour is
added, resulting in a "samosa".[5] Pakistanis like their food highly
spiced, especially with curry whose powder, when fresh, is said to contain vitamins A and C.

The food is washed down with hot tea, sweetened and, if possible,
with milk. Cooking is done in butter, if available, or vegetable oil,
which is preferred for fish and gram flour. Animal fat, as it most often comes from the pig, is unacceptable to Moslems. Some vegetables
(radishes, carrots, and cucumbers) are eaten raw. Sea foods, exclusive
of fish and shrimp, are not popular. The well-to-do have a wider range
of foodstuffs and often add European dishes or delicacies to their basic
Pakistani fare.

B. SPECIAL DIETS

A nutrition survey of the armed forces[5] found that their dietary intake was good (see Table 6). The rations supplied are sufficient in proteins, iron, thiamine, and niacin. Caloric intake is consistent with the
activity level. Dietary intake of riboflavin by the rice-eating troops of
East Pakistan was slightly lower than that of the wheat-eating troops
of the same area. Some of the units did receive suboptimal amounts of
vitamin C and vitamin A, due to the availability of fresh fruits and
vegetables. Edible food wastage was found to be 4% in the army and
10% in the navy and air force.

There is little information on the diets of pregnant women and infants. The adult male certainly has a priority in helping himself to the
available fare, which in the lower-income group must result in considerable malnutrition in the other members of the family. This is especially damaging for pregnant women and infants.

IV. ADEQUACY OF FOOD RESOURCES

The food resources are inadequate at all times. Tables 7a and 7b
show the amount of food grain that the government had to procure between 1948 and 1958. It can be seen that wheat has been needed in

amounts varying from 809,000 tons in 1949 to 175,000 tons in 1956 and that rice has been needed in large amounts almost every year. In West Pakistan, poor soil, dependence on irrigation works that are not all under the country's control, pests, flood or droughts and primitive farming methods are reasons enough to jeopardize food supplies. In East Pakistan, the soil is more favorable but excess water limits agricultural possibilities to certain varieties of rice. The density of the population has overtaken the carrying capacity of the land and natural disasters are not uncommon.

The prospect is bleak, since the population is growing fast and no new factor is in sight that might narrow the gap between the needs and the yields.

V. NUTRITIONAL DISEASE PATTERNS

There are no adequate statistics on which to base a description of nutritional diseases in Pakistan. Certainly the most common disease is rickets; its late form, osteomalacia appears especially in women as a result of the deprivation of sunshine caused by the seclusion of purdah.

According to Bohidar,[1] who made a survey of 344 school children between the ages of 5 and 10 in the Bargarh Community Project, 50% showed signs of nutritional deficiency and over 50% showed signs of some chronic concomitant diseases. Out of 4,000 children examined at the hospital there, 1,268 showed signs of malnutrition; 1,068 of them had other diseases, mainly gastrointestinal. Commonest of these diseases were anemias, hypoproteinemia, and avitaminosis A, B, and D. Many patients suffered from multiple deficiencies. It is stated that malnutrition, especially protein malnutrition in children, remains a major problem. Epidemic dropsy is common in East Pakistan where most of the cooking is done with mustard oil.

SELECTED REFERENCES

1. Bohidar, R. D. Nutritional Disorders in Children. *Pakistan Medical Journal*, Vol. 8, No. 7, July, 1957, pp. 5-14.
2. Food and Agriculture Organization. Food and Agricultural Price Policies in Asia and the Far East. Bangkok, 1958.
3. Marx, R. E. Diets Not Adequate in Most of Asia. *Foreign Agriculture*, Vol. 22, No. 6, June, 1958, pp. 3-4, 22.
4. International Cooperation Administration. Near East and South Asia Regional Conference of Food and Agriculture Officers, April 20-25, 1959. Beirut, [1959].
5. United States, Inter-Departmental Committee on Nutrition for National Defense. A Nutrition Survey of the Armed Forces in Pakistan. *Journal of Nutrition*, Vol. 68, Suppl. No. 2, July, 1959.

6. Misra, S. M. Pellagra: Its Nature, Diagnosis, and Treatment.... *Pakistan Medical Journal*, Vol. 8, No. 11, November, 1947, pp. 27-38.
7. Pakistan: Facts and Figures. Karachi, Pakistan Publications, 195?.
8. Pakistan 1957-1958. Karachi, Pakistan Publications, 1959.
9. *Pakistan News Digest*, Vol. 6, No. 11, June, 1958.
10. *Pakistan News Digest*, Vol. 6, No. 13, July, 1958.
11. *Pakistan News Digest*, Vol. 6, No. 16, August, 1958.
12. *Pakistan News Digest*, Vol. 6, No. 12, June, 1958.
13. United States Department of Commerce, World Trade Information Service. Basic Data on the Economy of Pakistan. *Economic Reports, Part 1, No. 58-6,* 1958.

Table 1

Area and Production, Crop Years 1948 and 1956-58

(Area in thousands of acres; production in thousands of tons except as noted).

Crop	Area 1948	Area 1956	Area 1957	Area 1958	Production 1948	Production 1956	Production 1957	Production 1958
Rice................	21,499	21,904	22,444	22,450	8,408	7,209	9,001	8,800
Wheat...............	10,686	11,289	11,807	11,400	3,993	3,315	3,639	3,400
Bajra (millet)........	2,331	2,199	2,207	2,000	394	348	366	350
Jowar (grain sorghum)	1,185	1,297	1,353	1,300	242	252	246	235
Gram (chickpeas)	3,003	3,345	3,378	3,400	804	720	724	725
Maize (corn)(a)	952	1,059	1,060	1,000	376	449	454	450
Barley...............	658	580	543	535	191	148	133	125
Rape & mustard	1,512	2,008	1,965	2,000	267	321	311	315
Sugar cane	708	967	1,017	1,100	1,043	1,204	1,226	1,250
Jute 1,000 bales(d)	1,877	1,634	1,230	1,300	5,483	5,592	5,514	6,000
Cotton do (e)	2,653	3,537	3,591	3,600	1,267	1,738	1,737	1,750
Tea million lb.	73	77	76	76	34	52.5	54.6	53
Tobacco do	164	195	201	180	142	201	201	190

(a) For crop year ending June 30.
(b) Estimated.
(c) Production in terms of raw gur.
(d) Bale of 400 pounds.
(e) Bale of 392 pounds.
Source: U.S. Dept. of Commerce, World Trade Information Service: Basic Data on the Economy of Pakistan. Part 1, No. 58-6, 1958.

Table 2

Imports of Rice in East Pakistan in 1957

From:	Amounts (in Tons)
Italy	20,049
Burma	141,612
U.S.A.	173,081
Thailand	61,358
S. Vietnam	19,759
Cambodia	2,951
West Pakistan	23,000
Total	441,810

Source: Pakistan 1957-1958. Pakistan Publications, 1959.

Table 3

Pakistan: Food Consumption 1954—1955[a]

	Calories Per Person Per Day		
Item	Number	Percentage of Total	
Grains	1503		70.8
Rice (milled)		45.3	
Wheat		19.2	
Other		6.3	
Sugar	158		7.4
Pulses	104		4.9
Gram		3.4	
Fruits and Nuts	57		2.7
Oils and Fats (and oilseeds)	40		1.9
Vegetables	30		1.4
Roots, tubers and starches	21		1.0
Meat	32		1.5
Fish and eggs	33		1.5
Milk	146		6.9
Total	2124		100.0
Plant Products	1910	90.0	
Animal Products (including mutton tallow)	214	10.0	

[a] These data, ".....refer to food consumed. They are not necessarily identical with amounts of food available for consumption because not all planted food crops are harvested, nor are all foods growing wild harvested."

Source: U.S. Dept. of Agriculture. Foreign Agriculture Service: Pakistan Food Balance, 1954-55. As quoted in Inter Departmental Committee on Nutrition in National Defense, A Nutrition Survey of the Armed Forces of Pakistan, 1959.

Table 4

Calories Consumed per Capita per Day. Pakistan 1955–56

Rice	43.1
Wheat	18.4
Other grains	6.7
Dry beans and peas	4.2
Roots, tubers etc.	0.8
Sugar	8.3
Oil seeds (incl. soya beans)	—
Oil & fats (excl. oilseeds and butter)	2.0
Vegetables	1.5
Fruits and nuts	3.8
Meat, fish, poultry & eggs	2.5
Milk & dairy products	8.7
Grand total	100
Number of calories	1,980

Source: Foreign Agriculture, June, 1958 Derived from Food Balances, Consumption Year 1955–56, for Countries in South Asia, East Asia and Oceania. Foreign Agriculture Service, October, 1957.

Table 5

Food Balance Sheets Based on 3 Years Average 1954—1957

| | Production 000 T. | Foreign Trade | | | | Per Caput Consumption | | | | |
		Change in Stocks	Gross Exports	Gross Imports	Available Supply	Kg. Per Year	Grams Per Day	Cal.* Per Day	Protein Per Day Grams	Fat Per Day Grams
	(1)	(2)	(3)	(4)	(5)	(13)	(14)	(15)	(16)	(17)
Cereals										
Wheat	3420			514	3934	40.6	111.1	387	10.9	1.4
Barley	138				138	1.1	3.0	10	0.3	0.1
Maize	452				452	4.3	11.9	43	1.0	0.1
Jowar	242				242	2.5	6.9	24	0.7	0.2
Bajra	357				357	3.7	10.2	35	1.2	0.5
Rice (paddy)	12632		144	304	12792	98.3	269.1	969	18.0	1.9
Total						150.5	412.2	1468	32.1	4.2
Sugar										
Sugar (refined)	101			90	191	2.5	6.7	26	—	—
Sugar (gur)	1251				1251	12.7	34.8	122	0.3	—
Total								148	0.3	—
Pulses and Nuts, etc.										
Gram	696				696	3.6	9.9	34	2.2	0.2
Other pulses	415				415	5.3	14.5	50	3.2	0.3
Rape, mustardseed	309				309					
Linseed	12				12					
Sesamumseed	36				36					
Cottonseed	608				608					
Total								84	5.4	0.5

Fruits	...	...	...	(33.2)	(90.9)	52	0.5	0.3
Meat								
Beef	...	...	...	(2.7)	(7.5)	17	1.1	1.4
Buffalo	...	...	...	(0.6)	(1.7)	1	0.2	—
Goat	...	...	...	(0.8)	(2.3)	3	0.3	0.2
Mutton	...	...	...	(0.4)	(1.1)	3	0.1	0.2
Total				(4.5)	(12.6)	24	1.7	1.8
Eggs								
Hen	...	...	...	(0.2)	(0.5)	1	0.1	0.1
Duck	...	...	...	(0.2)	(0.4)	1	—	0.1
Total						2	0.1	0.2
Fish	273	27	246	3.1	8.5	5	0.7	0.2
Milk								
Cow	...	...	...	(24.5)	67.2	42	2.3	2.2
Buffalo	...	...	...	(25.4)	69.6	70	2.8	5.2
Goat	...	...	...	(6.4)	17.4	13	0.7	0.8
Total						125	5.8	8.2
Oils and Fats								
Rapeseed oil			97	1.2	3.4	30	—	3.4
Sesamum oil			13	0.2	0.5	4	—	0.5
Linseed oil			4	0.1	0.1	1	—	0.1
Cotton seed oil			42	0.5	1.4	13	—	1.5
Ghee			...	(1.5)	(4.2)	37	—	4.2
Total				3.5	9.6	85	—	9.7

Total 2000 47.3 25.2

Animal 8.3

Vegetable 39.0

Figures are at variance with U.S. estimates. See Table 1.   Note: Figures in parentheses are based on previous years' reports.
Source: F.A.O. Food balance sheets 1954–56 averages. Rome 1958.

Table 6

Pakistan: Average nutrient intake (per man per day). Corrected for conservative vitamin losses in cooking[a]

Unit	Average No. Men in Mess	Calories	Protein Gm.	Fat Gm.	Calcium mg.	Iron mg.	Vit. A I.U.	Thiamine mg.	Riboflavin mg.	Niacin mg.	Vit. C mg.	Salt Gm.
I. Army												
Lahore, Med.[b]	178	3278	85	93	543	18	659	2.78	1.26	26	16	10.4
Lahore, Inf.[b]	85	3466	87	117	626	24	763	3.80	1.20	27	39	9.6
Quetta[b]	50	3208	78	90	604	21	5294	2.80	1.17	26	47	12.0
Bahawalpur[b]	50	3911	94	153	634	24	2629	3.83	1.36	29	126	19.9
Muzaffarabad[b]	143	3358	86	89	604	23	2768	2.87	1.20	26	14	7.2
Comilla, E. Bengal[c]	73	3649	90	102	423	19	1744	2.39	0.99	22	50	16.0
Army average	97	3478	87	107	572	22	1904	3.08	1.20	26	49	12.5
Lahore boys	124	3718	109	111	1163	22	2753	3.50	2.25	29	50	11.6
II. Navy, PNS Jhelum												
Wheat-eaters	122	3451	99	102	558	21	4188	2.49	1.26	24	263	11.6
Rice-eaters	28	3675	91	99	483	17	4188	1.59	1.08	17	263	14.7
Vegetarian[b]	6	3989	99	138	1251	19	5304	3.00	1.96	21	340	24.3
Vegetarian[c]	10	4213	91	135	1176	15	5304	2.10	1.78	14	340	26.7
Navy average	166	3555	97	104	609	19	4298	2.34	1.28	22	270	13.5
III. Air Force												
Peshawar[b]	356	3300	89	98	490	21	5218	2.55	1.14	25	69	4.9

(a)See Table 3.
(b)Wheat-eaters.
(c)Rice-eaters.

Source: Inter Departmental Committee on Nutrition for National Defense: A Nutrition Survey, of the Armed Forces of Pakistan, Bethesda, Md., July, 1959.

Table 7a

Government Procurement of Meat. Pakistan 1948-1958

Year Beginning 1st May	Total Production (1,000 long tons)	Quantity Procured[a]		Procurement Price (Rupees per per maund f.a.q.[b]
		(1,000 long tons)	(% of production)	
1948	3,321	398	12.0	9.5
1949	3,993	809	20.3	9.5
1950	3,885	249	6.4	—
1951	3,950	297	7.5	7.5
1952	2,972	178	6.0	9.0
1953	2,390	291	12.2	12.5
1954	3,599	467	13.0	9.25
1955	3,162	381	12.0	8.75
1956	3,336	175	5.2	10.0
1957	3,605	237	6.6	11.5
1958	3,659	...	...	11.5[c]

[a] All the procurement takes place in West Pakistan, where over 99 per cent of the total output is grown.

[b] One maund equals 82.28 pounds or 37.32 kilogrammes; f.a.q. stands for "fair average quality."

[c] For three months after harvest, 12.5 rupees.

Table 7b

Pakistan: Government Procurement and Procurement Prices of Rice, 1947/48-1957/58

Year (July-June)	Total Production (1,000 long tons, milled rice)		Quantity Procured (1,000 long tons, milled rice)		Procurement Price (Rupees per maund, milled rice)		Imports Into East Pakistan (1,000 long tons)[a]
	East Pakistan	West Pakistan	East Pakistan	West Pakistan	East Pak-Med	West Pak-Kangni	
1947/48	6,736	648	81	281	12.5-13.4	9.5	
1948/49	7,673	735	122	214	12.0-13.4	9.5	
1949/50	7,378	793	9	245	12.5	9.5	
1950/51	7,343	852	19	220	12.5	9.5	
1951/52	7,034	722	15	192	12.5	9.5	219
1952/53	7,335	816	26	421	14.0	10.5	130
1953/54	8,245	907	125	349	14.0	11.5	8
1954/55	7,590	821	—	—	—	—	—
1955/56	6,384	821	32	23	18.0	—	536
1956/57	8,185	820	—	—	—	—	453
1957/58	7,598	889	...	...	17.5	16.0	...

[a] Including imports both from West Pakistan and from abroad.

Source: Food and Agriculture Organization: Food and Agricultural Price Policies in Asia and the Far East, Bangkok, 1958.

Table 8

Harvest Calendar

Crop	Harvest Period[a]	Bulk of Harvest
Wheat	Mar.–June	Apr.–May
Barley	Mar.–June	Apr.–May
Maize	Aug.–Dec.	Oct.–Nov.
Bajra (millet) [b]	June–Nov.	Nov.
Jowar (sorghum) [b]	Aug.–Nov.	...
Rice:		
Autum	July–Sept.	July–Aug.
Winter	Sept.–Jan.	Oct.–Dec.
Summer	Apr.–May	Apr.–May
Sugar cane [b]	Oct.–June	Dec.–Feb.
Potatoes:		
Autumn	Dec.–Feb.	...
Spring	Apr.–May	...
Hill crop	June–Nov.	...
Onions [b]	Mar.–June	Apr.–June
Garlic [b]	Feb.–May	Feb.–Apr.
Chick-peas	Mar.–May	Apr.
Lentils [b]	Feb.–Apr.	...
Dry beans:		
Mash (Phaseolus Mungo) [b]	Oct.–Feb.	Nov.–Feb.
Mung (Phaseolus aurens) [b]	Oct.–Feb.	Oct.–Dec.
Fruits [b][c]	—	—
Groundnuts	{ Mar.–Apr. and Sept.–Dec. }	...
Linseed [b]	Feb.–Apr.	Mid Feb.–Mid Mar.
Rapeseed and mustard seed	Jan.–Apr.	...
Sesame seed:		
Winter [b]	Oct.–Jan.	Nov.–Dec.
Summer [b]	Sept.–Oct.	...
Tea	Mar.–Dec.	July–Early Oct.
Tobacco [b]	Mid Feb.–July	Mid Feb.–Mar.
Tobacco, late sown	Sept.–Dec.	...
Cotton	Sept.–Jan.	Oct.–Dec.
Sunnhemp [b][d]	Sept.–Apr.	Feb.–Apr.
Jute [b]	July–Oct.	Aug.–Sept.

[a] It is difficult to draw a line of demarcation between the months of "harvest period" or "bulk of harvest." In Pakistan there are two crop seasons, viz. Kharif (or Bhadoi) and Rabi. Kharif crops may be broadly defined as crops which are sown late in Spring or in the beginning of Summer, and harvested in Autumn or early Winter. Rabi crops are sown in Autumn, and harvested in the following Spring or early Summer.

[b] Source: Crops, Vegetables and Fruits in Pakistan, Fact Series n. 2, May 1955.

[c] Mangoes, lime, pears, pomegranates, and dates are ripe during July–September. Bananas, peaches, grapes, phalsa, and Jaman mature during June–July. Guava is harvested almost all the year round in one or the other region of Pakistan. Oranges, lemons and pommelos are ready for harvest during November–January. Bers ripen in March–April, loquats in April–May, mulberries in about April, and papaya during February–May.

[d] Sunnhemp is grown as Bhadoi as well as Rabi crop. The bulk of harvest comes from Rabi sunnhemp.

Source: Food and Agriculture Organization: World Crop Harvest Calendar, Rome, 1959.

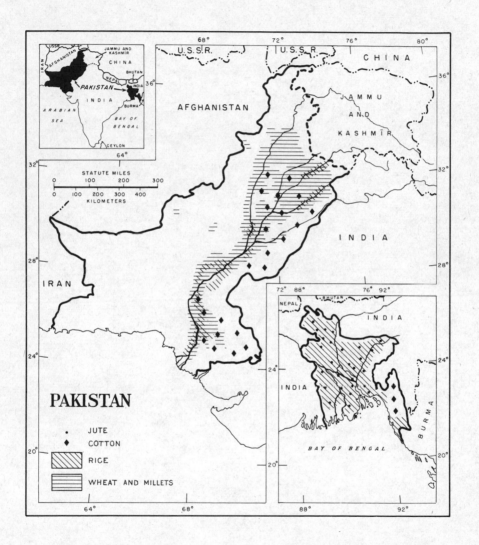

STATUTE MILES
0   100   200   300

0   100   200   300   400
KILOMETERS

PAKISTAN

- JUTE
- COTTON
- RICE
- WHEAT AND MILLETS

BAY OF BENGAL

AFGHANISTAN

I. GENERAL REMARKS

The kingdom of Afghanistan is known by ancient Afghan writers as "Aryana." Its old city of Balkh, formerly called Bactria, is said to date back to 3500 B. C.

Afghanistan is a landlocked country. It forms the northeastern part of the Iranian Plateau and is located between 60° 30' E. and 75° E. and between 29° 30' N. and 38° 30' N. Its area is estimated at 699,300 square kilometers (270,000 square miles). Its longest boundary is with the Soviet Union. It also adjoins Iran on the west, Pakistan on the east and the province of Sikiang in China on the north.[4]

Because of its strategic location, Afghanistan has been the object of many conquests and has served as passage for many invading armies. These events have left their mark on the population, culture, and language.

Although no census has ever been carried out in Afghanistan, the population is estimated at 12 million, distributed in the following ethnic groups: Pakhtuns (Pashtuns), 60 per cent; Tadjiks, 30 per cent; Uzbecks, 5 per cent; Hazarah, 3 per cent; Hindus and others, 2 per cent.

The first two groups thus form 90 per cent of the total population and belong to the same ancient stock; they differ only in language, the former speaking Pashtu, mostly in the south, and the latter speaking Farsi, mostly in the north. The two languages are the official tongues of the country. A third, Uzbecki of Turkish origin, exists only in the unwritten form.

More than $2\frac{1}{2}$ million of this population are nomadic and lead a pastoral life on the steppes, often crossing over to Pakistan and India in the winter. Some 95 per cent of the population is engaged in agricultural or pastoral activities which produce more than 65 per cent of the gross national product. The per capita income is estimated at $30 a year. Afghanistan is one of the most underdeveloped countries of the world; the ruggedness of the terrain creates considerable transportation difficulties, which result in isolation and inbreeding of small groups. The food supply does not move around the country and the diets are largely dependent upon local production. Western observers describe its people as vagrants in quest of food to put in the pot and twigs of kindling wood to make the pot boil. In addition to ruggedness, the second most important characteristic of the country is its need for water. Rainfall is scanty and unevenly distributed. It occurs mostly between February and April but varies from year to year and from one area to another. The average is estimated at 250 mms. and never exceeds 380 mms., and in the Seistan desert area totals are less than 150 mms. About two-thirds of the cultivated area of the country is under irrigation.[4]

For centuries, food supplies have depended upon one of four types of irrigation: perennial, by gravity flow from surface canals, perennial, from pits and wells in which the water is lifted by animal power, perennial from underground channels (karez system)*, and nonperennial from seasonal torrential floods. However, it has been stated that the waters of several rivers and streams are not fully utilized.

II. FOOD RESOURCES

A. GENERAL

Agricultural production consists primarily of wheat, fruits, nuts, cotton, sugar beets, and vegetables (see Table 1).[6]

Some 69 per cent of the country consists of barren mountains or desert land, 20 per cent is used as pasture land, 3 per cent is in forest, 5 per cent is at present under cultivation, and another 3 per cent is potentially productive. Although agriculture supplies most of the food, livestock raising provides the most important element of the national income through the export of the world-famous Karakul pelts.

Of the total area under cultivation, 75 per cent lies north of the Hindu-Kush Range in the valley of the Oxus River. The most productive agricultural land and the most thickly-populated area is found in the valleys tributary to the Kabul River between the central plateau and the Pakistan border. To the southwest, the Helmand River supplies water to new lands being developed by large projects designed to supply hydroelectric power, to control floods, and to reclaim 202,000 hectares (500,000 acres) for nomads to settle as farmers. It is now reported that the nomads do not want to stop roaming and that salt in the ground has rendered much of the newly irrigated land useless.[5] The salinity of the soil is widespread, especially in the south where land farmed under dry conditions yields only one crop, after which it is left fallow for two or three years.

There is little commercial agriculture and subsistence farming by families is encountered almost everywhere and is carried out under very primitive conditions. Land is plowed by wooden plows drawn by oxen, the crops are harvested by sickle, and occasionally the grain is threshed by threshers drawn by oxen. There are not more than 30

---

* An underground tunnel protecting water from evaporation.

tractors in the whole country. Little or no fertilizer is used although
organic matter is applied in some of the irrigated areas.

In the greater part of the country there are two crop seasons. During the main season, from autumn to the spring of the following year,
the principal food crops of wheat and barley are grown, together with
gram, a certain kind of oilseed, and some varieties of peas and beans.
This harvest is called "bahari" (spring), since the crops are harvested
in spring. The other season is shorter and the crops are sown in spring
and harvested in autumn. The crops grown during this season are paddy, corn, cotton, certain varieties of millet, sugar beet, coilseed, and
some vegetables. This harvest is called "tirmahi" (autumn). In the
loftier regions of the country, there is generally but one harvest, the
"tirmahi."

Land-tenure practices in Afghanistan have for centuries been de-
vised to facilitate the remuneration of the military and the upkeep of
the successive administrations. However, in recent years, the system
has tended to protect the interest of cultivators whenever possible.
There are four main categories of ownership: government domain,
privately-owned land, communally-owned land, and religiously-owned
land. About 25 per cent of the cultivated land is worked by tenants who
are usually paid a percentage of their harvest (one-fifth in the areas
under irrigation, one-fourth in the dry farming areas).

There is a relatively small number of absentee owners. It is assumed that the size of the vast majority of holdings is about 2 hectares
in the irrigated areas and 3 hectares in the dry-farming zones. A
number of land owners, however, own about 5 hectares and a few have
several hundred hectares. Tribes may jointly own large areas of
grazing land, especially in the Herat and Helmand areas.

A typical farmer in the Kabul area farms from 1 to 2 hectares. He
lives in the village nearby and has to go to his fields every day. He
may have 4 to 12 hens and a rooster, all of which scratch a living from
the ground and suffer from malnutrition. He may own an ox. In that
case, he hires the services of another man for plowing and other land
preparations. The farmer uses a one-handled wooden plow with a steel
point, a wooden plank for dragging, and an upright type of wooden leveller. He probably also has a donkey on which he goes to the bazaar to
sell or buy his commodities, his wife riding the donkey and the farmer
walking beside her.

Such a farmer has a cash income of less than $80 a year, derived
from the sale of his principal crop, wheat, which is, on the average,
severely injured by rust one out of every three years. A third of the
land is fallow in the summer because it is too depleted to produce a
crop every year. The soil of the farm is probably completely void of
organic matter. He may also sell alfalfa grown in small plots, of which
he gives only a small amount to his animals, their main diet being
straw. Some farmers may have a small plot of potatoes and even a

small vineyard. The grapes are sold in the form of fresh fruit or as
raisins. Fuel is scarce, even more so than food. It consists usually of
cattle dung mixed with straw, alfalfa roots, and other crop residue.
Meals are cooked only once a day with the implication of pollution and
scarcity.[3]

In the Helmand Valley, settlement projects vary from 3 to 6 hectares
per family, all irrigated. The family comprises 4 to 5 people. The
work requires two men. In addition to land and building there are a
pair of oxen and a few wooden tools. The average gross income of such
a farm is $500 per year, out of which taxes and fees for irrigation must
be paid.

Villages are arranged to accommodate about 40 families, and no
settler needs to walk more than half a mile to get to his field. In the
village, each settler gets 0.5 hectare of land for his house, vegetable
garden, and fruit trees. At the center of every sixth village or so is a
school, a playground, and a market place where the leaders and the
agricultural extension agents for the surrounding villages are housed.
Requirements for leases include pledges of continuous presence on the
land, self-farming, compliance with agricultural extension service
regulations, possession of draught animals and tools, and good character.

In some of the old settlements orchards predominate; in most of the
newer settlements wheat, corn, clover, and alfalfa are the main crops.
The scarcity of commercial fertilizers still limits the development of
these settlements.

The country can be divided into five agricultural regions.

(1) The Hindu-Kush Mountains, the Hazarajat Plateau, and the
Herat area have much in common in terms of food resources. Wheat
is the staple food and it is grown in rotation with barley under dry
farming and irrigation. Rice, vegetables, fruits, cotton, and silk are
also produced. This is the great grazing zone for the Karakul sheep
and the native sheep—the habitat of the nomads.

(2) The Kataghan and Badakhshan regions are mostly irrigated
areas where only in the uplands a little dry farming is done. This is
primarily a cotton and secondarily a sugar-beet area. However some
lowland rice is grown as an additional crop as well as a few oil seed
plants and wheat, barley, corn, and vegetables.

(3) The northwestern region also depends on irrigation; less than
20 per cent is dry farmed; this is essentially a cotton area, with some
fruit production. A large number of Karakul sheep are raised in the
foothills of the Hindu Kush.

(4) The Kabul and Samt-I-Mashriqui region in the eastern provinces
is mainly an irrigated area where cultivation, practiced in patches on
the plains, is intensive. This is the rice-producing area, but some
sugar cane is grown and processed in Jalalabad. Many vegetables are
also grown here, and among the fruits dried apricots form an impor-

tant export item. Oranges and lemons are also found. Livestock is
represented by cattle, with a scattering of sheep.

(5) The southern region depends entirely on irrigation through
underground channels. This is primarily a wheat-barley-sorghum
zone, but vegetables (eggplant, tomatoes, squash, onions, peas, and
beans) are also found. The area is renowned for quality fruits, especially sweet apricots, known as "shakarpara." Camels, goats, and
sheep are also found here.

B. CEREALS

Cereal crops occupy about 75 per cent of the 3 to $3\frac{1}{2}$ million hectares of land under cultivation in Afghanistan.

Wheat is said to cover 2 million hectares, though reports vary.
The production in normal years is 870,896 tons according to government estimates quoted by F. A. O. experts, more than 2 million tons
according to United States government experts (see Table 1). This
crop is grown in the Hindu Kush, Hazarajat Plateau, and Herat areas
in rotation with barley. Barley flour is used as a "stretcher" with
wheat. The annual barley crop is said to amount to some 280,000 tons.
More than 30 varieties of wheat and 10 varieties of barley are grown
in the country, often interplanted in the same fields. These cereals
are also found as summer crops in the Kabul region and the eastern
provinces. In the southern region some cereal patches are sown after
the June monsoon and harvested in July.

Rice. Half of the rice produced in the country is grown in the
Jalalabad and Sarobi plains of the eastern provinces. A lowland variety is grown in the Bamian and Herat districts in irrigated, terraced
areas. Rice is transplanted in May and harvested in October. It is
frequently infested by a borer and other rice pests. The amount of
the total annual average rice production, again, is in doubt; United
States government experts place the 1957 output at 274,000 tons (see
Table 1) but F. A. O. sets the figure at 58,000 tons, of which 40 per
cent comes from this region and 10 per cent from the Khanabad area,
where it is grown as a secondary crop.

Corn is often included in rotation with rice in the same agricultural
areas. The total production is estimated at 600,000 to 700,000 tons by
U. S. experts and at 174,000 tons by F. A. O. specialists. About 60 per
cent of it is grown in the Bamian and Herat areas, and like rice, corn
is often blighted by pests.

Other cereals include millet and sorghum grown as summer crops
in the Kabul area in the eastern province, in the Kandahar area, in the
zone watered by the Arghandab and Helmand rivers, and in the southern region. In the latter, these crops are sown after the monsoon.

C. VEGETABLES AND FRUITS

Vegetables are grown in small patches by most farmers under both dry and wet farming conditions everywhere, but particularly near the large cities where they can find a market. Pest-free potatoes are found in the vicinity of Kabul; eggplant, tomatoes, squash, onions, peas, okra, and watermelons are planted throughout the country but in unknown quantities.

Fruits and nuts are important assets in the food production of Afghanistan. A great variety of fruits, some of which are exportable, are found in almost all regions with the exception of the Kataghan and the Badakhshan areas. Nuts comprise mainly almonds, pistachios, and walnuts; fruits are of many types, among them cherries, plums, (tamsoq), apricots, apples, pears, figs, grapes, and pomegranates. There is, however, little citrus fruit except in the Samt-I-Mashriqi area where oranges are grown. Pineapples are also to be found there. Orchards occur along terraced highlands in the vicinity of Herat, which contributes 25 per cent of the total production, while Kabul specializes in apricots, and Kandahar in the luxury quality of fruit. Yields could easily be doubled in all areas, as growers do little pruning. However, the value of grafting is known. Some of the fruit is locally consumed, some is dried, (especially apricots), and some is sold and exported fresh, mainly to Pakistan. The total production from all areas, which was estimated at 682,000 tons in 1957, is handled by a single fruit agency, the "sherkat"* Pashtun, which collects all the crops for distribution.

With the exception of olives, which grow wild in Samt-I-Junubi, Afghanistan is short of fat-producing plants; some cotton seeds, however, are used for this purpose. No figures are available as to annual production.

D. CASH CROPS

These consist essentially of cotton, sugar beets, and tobacco. Cotton is mainly grown under irrigation in the Herat area, the Kunduz valley, and Kataghan province, but it is found also in the northwest, in parts of the Mazar-I-Sharif provinces. It is reported that in some areas as much as 40 per cent of the crop is destroyed by pests. After Karakul pelts, cotton is the most important earner of foreign-exchange in Afghanistan. The yearly output is estimated at 55,000 tons of raw cotton, yielding about 20,000 tons of ginned cotton, of which 6,000 to 12,000 tons (about 15 per cent of the total exports) are exported every year.

Sugar beets were introduced under irrigation in the Kataghan area

---

*Company.

as early as 1934. Climatic and soil conditions permit an 8-month
growing season. In 1956 3,800 hectares were known to be planted, but
the area is said to be under constant expansion. The yield is low, 13
tons per hectare, and according to F. A. O. could easily be increased
to 48 tons. A sugar mill at Baghlan with an annual capacity of 7,500
tons does not as yet operate at capacity because of an inadequate supply of sugar beets. A second refinery, for cane sugar, exists at Jalalabad and it is hoped that by these means the country may reach self
sufficiency in sugar by 1961. Up to the present, only about 5,000 tons
are produced every year, and this amount fulfills only about half of the
needs.

A third cash crop is tobacco, with production estimated at between
6,000 and 7,000 tons per year, 25 per cent of which comes from the
Herat area where it is grown as a secondary crop on unirrigated, fallow land. About half of the crop is produced in the Kabul area and in
the eastern provinces, where it is grown under dry farming conditions.
All of the tobacco is consumed locally, either as leaf smoked in water-
pipes, or as snuff.

Mulberry trees must be mentioned, since they support a not inconsiderable silk-worm industry. The trees are grown principally in
Kataghan province, where an effort is being made to improve cultivation. Opium poppies are grown in Badakhshan and in small quantities
in Herat. Afghanistan produces an unknown but significant quantity of
good honey in Samt-I-Junubi and Jalalabad. Most of this is marketed
in the big cities, especially Kabul.

E. ANIMAL PROTEIN RESOURCES

Livestock-raising constitutes the most important part of the national economy. Animals raised are mainly sheep, goats, cattle, donkeys, camels, and horses; water buffaloes, mules, and yaks are kept
in certain small areas. There are no accurate statistics of the livestock population but estimates are given in Table 2.

Karakul sheep, raised mostly in the northern area (Maimana),
Mazar-I-Sharif and Kataghan provinces, are of considerable importance, both for export of whole pelts and for wool used in carpet manufacture. This industry takes place in the northwestern steppes and in
the northern foothills of the Hindu Kush, where the largest concentration of Karakul sheep is found. However, in recent years, an effort has
been made by the government to transfer at least part of this activity
to the Herat and Kataghan areas. Karakul lambs are killed at birth
and their pelts are exported as luxury furs. The wool of the mature
Karakul sheep is mixed with other carpet-wool types to weave the
Afghan carpets which are a considerable item of export. The Karakul
Export Company of Afghanistan has a practical monopoly on Karakul
pelts. This trade has recovered losses incurred after 1950 and has

done even better recently. More than $2\frac{1}{2}$ million skins are now exported every year. The average value of individual pelts has fluctuated from $14.00 to $6.50 a piece. Many Karakul raisers are inclined to keep the lambs, raising them for meat and also for clandestine export, but this practice is being strongly discouraged.

Native sheep play an important role in nutrition, as the fat of their tails is used in cooking instead of butter. Forty per cent of the sheep and goat herds converge in the summer on the Hazarajat plateau. The mutton-producing Turkish breed and the wool-producing Ghiljai, Gadic, and Baluchi breeds are also kept for their meat, milk, and hides. Herds are found around Herat and large sheep concentrations occur in northern Kataghan and in Badakhshan; in the summer, the herds are driven to the cooler areas of Sheva, Eysh, Piyadzy, and Khargasi, and then return to Badakhshan. Goats are kept in the Jalalabad region. About 30 per cent of the carpet–wool type of sheep are found in the Khandahar area. Most of the wool is exported. Only 150 tons of wool are said to be processed in Kandahar. In the southern region goats and camels provide milk, transportation, and meat.

All Afghan cattle are of the **Bos indicus** type with or without hump. They are chiefly used for work in the fields but their milk is collected and their meat eaten when they are old. The cattle areas include Herat, the Kataghan and Samt-I-Mashriqi, which support 20 per cent of the cattle population of the country. Dairy cattle (and some water buffalo) are concentrated in the Jalalabad area, and cattle are also found in Kandahar, Ghakhansur and the Hazarajat plateau. Though there is no accurate information on the milk or meat supplied from these sources, it is known that both camel milk and yak milk are drunk, but most of the yak milk is turned into butter. The meat of these animals as well as that of donkeys is also eaten on occasion.

Additional animal proteins come from poultry, which is a cottage industry in the river valley areas but is seldom found in the mountains. The birds are not scientifically raised and they live by scratching the land. They are small and have a low egg-laying capacity. Their meat and eggs are eaten only on rare occasions, the greater part being sold in the cities for cash.

F. EXPORTS AND IMPORTS

Afghanistan has had to import wheat from time to time, depending upon the volume of domestic production; for example, some 40,000 tons of wheat flour were imported from the United States in 1957. Mainland China started making substantial shipments of tea in 1956. Total food imports have an average value of 3 million dollars a year; the country is, however, usually capable of supporting its own inadequate level of food consumption.

Exports of foodstuffs are limited to fruit. The quantity shipped is unknown but the value is 8 to 10 million dollars a year.

G. FACTORS CAPABLE OF IMPROVING FOOD RESOURCES

United States aid has been intensive in Afghanistan. The policy as stated in 1959 has been to assist in producing exportable items which will improve foreign exchange, to feed the people, to improve forest and pasture, and to improve irrigation. To carry out these manifold activities, projects were set up to demonstrate the benefits to be derived by the use of fertilizers, improved seeds (especially rust-resistant wheat), and so forth. A village–worker training program was organized, and scholarships to send students abroad were made available.

All the local planning is done through village tribal chiefs and committees under the direction of an extension supervisor and village extension workers. A big drive has been made to establish more orchards on individual farms and to promote the use of fertilizers. Finally, a regional insect-control project started in 1957 seems to have given good results under the leadership of the Ministry of Agriculture; chemical insecticides have been provided by the United States Operations Mission.

Among the factors capable of improving the food resources irrigation is foremost. It is at present mainly done by canals using water stored in the Arghandab and Helmand dams. A major irrigation project in the Helmand valley is now being developed by an American firm responsible for the construction of several dams. This project irrigates 116,900 hectares of already-cultivated land and 239,000 hectares of reclamated wasteland. Another project is reported to have as its objective the reclamation of 200,000 additional hectares. The government makes an effort to resettle families in these various projects.

It is believed that the cultivated areas of Afghanistan could be increased by more than 15 per cent, without counting the Helmand Valley project. This could be done by the erection of dams in suitable locations, by improving the existing canal systems in the Kunduz, Khanabad, and Talikan areas, by introducing centrifugal pumps to lift the water from streams, and by developing underground water resources in the northwest for watering the livestock as well as for irrigation.

It is believed that the use of modern machinery for the development of agricultural resources in Afghanistan is premature and ill advised because of the smallness of the holdings, the high cost of machinery, and the difficulty in providing fuel and upkeep. On the other hand, there is an abundance of low-cost farm labor. Better yields could be obtained by more efficient farm management, by increased use of fertilizers (200 tons of ammonium nitrate and superphosphate were imported in 1957), and so forth. It was stated in 1957 that the continuation of this work is handicapped by acute shortages of skilled personnel. Other

improvements would result from the protection of crops against the
many insect pests and diseases already mentioned.[1,4]

Finally, Afghanistan receives financial assistance from a number of
communist countries, but especially from the Soviet Union, which nego-
tiated a first loan of $100,000,000 in 1955, and recently extended credit
in the amount of $22,400,000, all to be used for development projects.[2]

H. FOOD INDUSTRIES, STORAGE AND TECHNOLOGY

There is little food technology in Afghanistan other than the sugar
factories mentioned previously and the oil plants processing cotton
seeds in the Kunduz area. Two grain warehouses with a capacity of
20,000 tons each (in Pul-I-Khumri and Kabul), a flour mill, and a bakery are said to have been built with Soviet loans.

III. DIET TYPES

Before discussing diet types and nutritional values in Afghanistan,
it must be pointed out that there are no accurate data available either
on birth rate or on number of school children, and that there are no
adequate figures on food and agricultural production. The standards of
living are very low, about 80% of the farm workers are mostly paid in
kind. Some of them live on the farms permanently and they and their
families are fed with handouts; once a year they get a share of the
crops, which may vary from 10 to 15% to provide "pocket money."
Other families live in the villages but are fed on the farm and also receive their wages in kind, mostly in wheat, oats, or barley. In addition
to the difficulties caused by the lack of information and statistics, the
diversity of the population groups, isolated one from another by the
ruggedness of the terrain, is conducive to a number of diets rather
than to one basic general type. Certain groups of the population have
never been investigated and it is impossible to find out at present what
women, pregnant women, and small children eat. As a result, no balanced food sheet for the country exists.

Most of the people live on unleavened bread occasionally supplemented by fruit, rice, and meat. In a few areas, broad beans and mulberries form the basis of the diet. According to Dols, the northern and
western part of the country seems to have a sufficient food supply. The
Khandahar district has a single diet particularly rich in fruit, with an
abundance of cereals and vegetables. In the northern part of the eastern province, the food supply seems to be less satisfactory.[1] In the
east, wheat bread is the basic staple food of the population, but rice is
consumed when income allows its purchase. Dairy products are represented by cheese and skimmed milk. The main source of fat is the fat

tail of the sheep (dumba). Onions are the principal vegetables; no potatoes are available. Green tea and unrefined sugar are consumed. Meat is also eaten, usually chicken or beef, depending on its availability on the farm.

In the valleys of central Afghanistan, the staple food is again wheat bread, with sheep milk, soft cheese, and occasionally some meat. In this area, few fruits and vegetables are eaten. Most people eat three meals—breakfast, lunch, and supper—but when food is short this is sometimes reduced to two. Often the noon meal consists of a piece of bread with some wild vegetable or clover eaten in the field.

In the city of Kabul, particularly in winter, the food situation is bad. This is caused essentially by the rapid growth of the town in the last fifteen years which has created unemployment. The difficulty of transportation, particularly in winter, has often resulted in a lack of milk and milk products in the city areas.[1] This fact, combined with the low wages paid and the little cash available, creates serious situations in many families. There is a wider spectrum of diets than in the countryside, ranging from very satisfactory for certain classes of people to very poor for those who live in the slums. The well-to-do have a varied diet which includes game, poultry, meat, fish, eggs, rice, potatoes, vegetables, fruit, and bread. The middle class is also adequately fed, although with a narrower range of items. It is believed[1] that 30 to 35% of the population of Kabul belongs to these two classes. However, the balance of the population comprises many people who have crowded into the city in the past 15 years. Their diet is quite unsatisfactory, based on some bread, occasionally potatoes, dried fruit, onions, and sometimes yogurt. When these are combined into meal the people deem themselves fortunate. Meat is only exceptionally available. Sometimes bread is dunked in syrup or maize bread is prepared with onion; soup is often eaten with wild mint and letchies. Wheat bread is often replaced by a bread containing a mixture of wheat, barley, peas, beans, and several wild vegetables. Bread from other cereals, such as sorghum, is also used. Occasionally beans are added. The very poor people who live in smaller towns eat wild rhubarb and other wild plants, often cooked, and long periods occur when people are reported to have nothing to eat but the bark of trees.

There is, however, more information on the diets consumed by certain special groups of the population—for example, those eating at schools, student hostels, university cafeterias, and the like. These particular classes of people enjoy a very satisfactory diet.[1]

In the student hostels, particularly, where the food is provided by the government, three meals providing a total of 3,963 calories are offered daily; these include 113 grams of total protein and 19.4 grams of animal protein. The calcium supply amounts to 450 milligrams. This diet, too high in calories and proteins, is also unsatisfactory in terms of vitamin A derived solely from leafy vegetables such as spin-

ach, lettuce, carrots, and cabbage. It is believed that these foods insure a sufficient supply of absorbic acid and that the rest of the nutrients such as iron and elements of the B complex are supplied in
satisfactory amounts.

Students living at the University also receive three meals at government expense, while those not living at the University get only one free
meal. Table 3 gives the amount of calories, proteins, and calcium received in these diets. It can be seen that on the whole the diet is better
than that found in the student hostels.

Another privileged group is the students in the training schools for
sport teachers, whose diet is also satisfactory. The basic diet in hospitals is given mainly to the personnel but also to some patients; again,
it is too high in calories and proteins and barely sufficient in calcium
and vitamin A (see Table 4).

IV. ADEQUACY OF FOOD RESOURCES

Although Afghanistan can support its population at the semi-starva-
tion level, its food resources are inadequate at all times to supply a
balanced and sufficient diet.

In normal times, an estimated 20% of the crops grown in the country
are infested annually with insect pests, some 50% of the stored grain
in Mazar-I-Sharif and Samt-I-Masahriqi is known to be infested with
the khapra beetle. A long list of pests has been compiled and locust
officers when available are sent to the field from Kabul to combat locust infestation. F. A. O. and foreign agencies such as the International
Cooperation Administration supply toxicants for this purpose. In times
of war, the situation would undoubtedly grow worse, as the country
would be deprived of the possibility of importing food, especially wheat.
Many sections of the population would depend upon the occupying powers
for handouts or succumb to mass starvation.

V. NUTRITIONAL DISEASE PATTERNS

There is very little accurate information on the prevalence and
incidence of diseases caused by unsatisfactory diets in Afghanistan.
Even Afghan scientists are undecided as to whether deficiency diseases
exist as a general problem or occur only patchily. According to the
Ministry of Public Health, goiter is widespread in the high mountain
regions of the eastern and central provinces. and measures are under
consideration to supply iodized salt.

In the northern part of the eastern province, beriberi has been reported on a large scale. It is also stated that instructions were given

to modify the method of milling, with improved results. In the central valleys of Afghanistan, scurvy has been observed in winter. However, according to Dols, the most important deficiency disease found in the Kabul area is rickets, and dental caries has been found in 70% to 80% of the children in the primary schools. There are many cases of serious undernutrition due to lack of sufficient caloric intake but, detailed information is not available. It is believed that the death rate during the two first years of life is high, but no exact figures can be obtained.

VI. CONCLUSIONS

It is almost impossible to draw conclusions in view of the lack of accurate information on diets in Afghanistan. However, on the basis of what is known, it seems certain that a large percentage of the farm population is subject to diet insecurity because of dependence upon poor transportation, unfavorable weather, and other factors. It is very likely that if the weather is bad during the most difficult season for transportation, a considerable amount of undernutrition—if not outright malnutrition—must exist. It is also known that a large part (almost 50%) of the Kabul population is undernourished in terms of both calories and protective elements. A number of projects are afoot to improve the food resources and eventually the diets of the country. There is here no limitation to available land and no serious population pressure.

SELECTED REFERENCES

1. Dols, M. J. L. Report on Nutrition and Supplementary Feeding in Afghanistan. F. A. O. 9/6465. 1957.
2. Hunter, E. The Past Present (A Year in Afghanistan). London, Hodder and Stoughton, 1959.
3. International Cooperation Administration. Near East and South East Asia Conference. Beirut, 1959.
4. Lateef, N. A. Characteristics and Problems of Agriculture in Afghanistan. *Background Country Studies No. 5.* F. A. O. 4/2575. 1957.
5. Afghanistan to Develop a Valley Authority with $22,400,000 in Soviet Aid. *New York Times* February 15, 1960.
6. United States Department of Commerce, World Trade Information Service. Basic Data on the Economy of Afghanistan. *Economic Reports, Part 1, No. 58-7,* 1958.

Table 1

Estimated Production of Principal Crops, 1953 Through 1957.[a] Afghanistan

(thousands of metric tons)

Crop	1953	1954	1955	1956	1957
Wheat	2,281	2,090	2,018	2,100	2,100
Rice	316	279	284	250	274
Maize (corn)	602	618	570	730	654
Barley	n.a.	278	283	280	n.a.
Sugar, refined	3.4	4.9	5.4	6.1	n.a.
Cotton, ginned	14	13	20	20	20
Fruits	n.a.	n.a.	n.a.	n.a.	682

N.A. Data are not available.
[a] Fiscal years, March 21 through March 20.
Source: U.S. Dept. of Commerce, World Trade Information Service, Part I #58-7. Basic Data on the Economy of Afghanistan. 1958.

Table 2

Estimated Livestock Resources in Afghanistan 1957

Karakul sheep	5 million
Native fat tailed sheep	9 "
Goats	6 "
Cattle	2.5 "
Donkeys	800,000
Horses	500,000
Camels	300,000
Mules	200,000
Yaks	2,000

Source: Lateef, N. A.: Characteristics and Problems of Agriculture in Afghanistan. Background Country Studies #5, Food and Agriculture Organization 4/2575/57.

Table 3

Average Diet Provided by University Cafeterias. Afghanistan 1957

	Grams	Calories	Protein, Gm.	Animal Protein, Gm.	Calcium mg.
Bread	600	1590	54.9	—	162.0
Butter and fats	50	400	—	—	—
Sugar	36	138.6	—	—	—
Meat and bone	220	190	20.5	20.5	5.6
Fluid skim milk	415	166	14.8	14.8	500
Potatoes (retail weight)	350	210	5.9	—	21
Vegetables (spinach, etc. retail weight)	300	90	5.3	—	100
Rice	25	90	1.7	—	2.5
		2874.6	103.1	35.3	791.1

Source: Dols, M.J.L.: Report on Nutrition and Supplementary Feeding in Afghanistan. Food and Agriculture Organization 9/6465. 1957.

Table 4

Average Diet Provided by Hospitals. Afghanistan 1957

	Grams	Calories	Protein, Gm.	Animal Protein, Gm.	Calcium mg.
Meat and bone	354	303.4	32.55	32.55	8.9
Rice	230	320	15.40	—	23
Bread	600	1828.5	63.15	—	186.3
Vegetables (retail weight)	345	48.3	4.83	—	115
Sugar	29	115	—	—	—
Fats and butter	48	384	—	—	—
Fruits	115	53	0.60	—	11
Salt	7	—	—	—	—
Tea	1.8	—	—	—	—
		3052.20	116.53	32.55	344.2

Source: Dols, M.J.L.: Report on Nutrition and Supplementary Feeding in Afghanistan. Food and Agriculture Organization 9/6465. 1957.

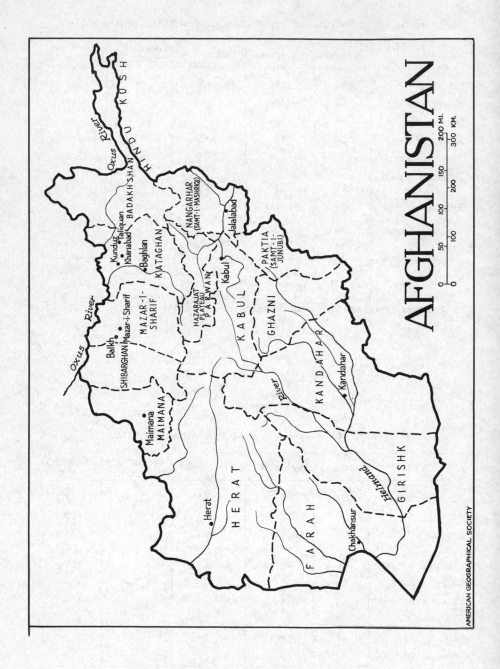

AFGHANISTAN

HINDU KUSH

Oxus River

BADAKHSHAN

Kunduz
Taliquan
Khanabad
Baghlan
KJATAGHAN

NANGARHAR
(SAMT-I-MASHRIQI)

Jalalabad

Oxus River

MAZAR-I-
SHARIF

HAZARAJAT
PLATEAU
PARWAN

Kabul

PAKTIA
(SAMT-I-
JUNUBI)

Balkh
Oxus River
SHIBARGHAN Mazar-i-Sharif

KABUL

GHAZNI

Maimana
MAIMANA

KANDAHAR

Kandahar

River

HERAT

FARAH

Helmund

GIRISHK

Herat

Chakhansur

0   50   100   150   200 MI.
0   100   200   300 KM.

PART II. THE MIDDLE EAST
AND EGYPT

INTRODUCTION

The following pages contain a survey of the food supplies, diet, and nutritional level in selected countries of the Middle East, namely, the countries of the Arabian Peninsula, Egypt, Iran, Iraq, Israel, Lebanon, Syria, and Turkey. There are many differences in the food supply situation of these countries but there are also certain basic similarities; the most important aspects of the situation are discussed in the paragraphs below.

I. GENERAL REMARKS

The basic pattern of agriculture in the Middle East has been characterized as one in which rather small areas of intensive cultivation, chiefly on irrigated land, alternate with vast areas of extensive grain production and with equally large areas devoted to nomadic and semi-nomadic livestock raising.[6] Foodstuffs are the main crop, even in countries such as Egypt where nonfood agricultural exports are vital to the economy.[1] The aim of feeding the local population exclusively on domestic produce, a goal common to all countries of the region, has not yet been achieved by any country; it probably will not be reached until substantially greater progress is achieved in the agriculture of the region.

Factors retarding the development of agriculture in the Middle East include unfavorable climatic and other physical conditions and defects in the social and economic structure of the countries.[6] The most important of the physical factors, unquestionably, is the scantiness and irregular distribution of rainfall. Social and economic factors affecting agriculture and food supplies include overpopulation in relation to arable land, a high rate of population increase, a surplus of agricultural labor, the use of primitive agricultural methods, and inequitable systems of land ownership and tenure. The problems created by the inadequacy of rainfall and the present attempts to increase available supplies of water and acreage of irrigated land are discussed at some length in each of the country-by-country studies below. In several countries, including Turkey, Iraq, and Syria, the acreage of cultivated land has been extended in recent years to include marginal dry-farming areas particularly susceptible to the periodic droughts affecting the area.

Agriculture is the means of livelihood of the majority of the inhabitants in all the countries under consideration. This is true both in the densely populated and intensively cultivated countries, such as Egypt and Lebanon, and in the sparsely populated and extensively cultivated countries, such as Syria, Iraq, and Iran. Between 60 and 80% of the inhabitants derive their livelihoods from farming and animal husbandry; in some of the countries studied a considerable proportion of this agricultural population is surplus, with few alternative sources of employment available. This high degree of rural underemployment is associated with a degree of poverty that leaves no surplus available for even the most desirable agricultural improvements.[6] Despite advances in production and increases in national incomes reported for recent years, it is difficult to show that the living standards of the bulk of the population, that is, of the lower income urban groups and the rural inhabitants, have improved to any marked extent.[13]

Agricultural technology in the Middle East is, in general, at a primitive level. Simple agricultural implements are used to till the soil, there is little or no selection of seeds or of breeding animals, the use of fertilizers is at a minimum, and most harvesting is done by hand.

Introduction of modern agricultural techniques, in some instances, has had unfavorable results. For example, the displacement of abundant and cheap agricultural labor in an overpopulated country, consequent to the introduction of mechanized agricultural methods, has resulted in economic loss instead of gain. Also, some types of farming machines that were introduced have been found to be unsuited for use on Mediterranean soils. The use of such machines has even caused severe soil erosion.[10]

The antiquated land holding systems that were, until very recently, prevalent everywhere, served to accentuate the poverty of the majority of the inhabitants and to retard agricultural progress.[2] Land reform and land redistribution programs are in operation in most of the Middle Eastern countries, such as Egypt, Syria, and Iraq and, to a limited extent, Iran. Where land is owned by the farmer, it may be subdivided excessively into small, uneconomical holdings, as is the case especially in Turkey.[6]

International technical aid in agriculture and nutrition has been provided primarily by specialized agencies of the United Nations, including U.N.I.C.E.F., F.A.O., and the W.H.O., as well as by the United States I.C.A. under the so-called "Point Four" Program. Technical aid offered by the USSR has increased in quantity and scope in recent years, especially in Syria, Egypt, and Yemen, but details of these programs were not available.

Perhaps the most ambitious of the international aid programs is

the Mediterranean Development Project sponsored by the Food and
Agriculture Organization. This long-range project, in which countries
bordering upon the Mediterranean participate, aims at raising agricultural production and, consequently, living standards, by improving
agricultural practices, encouraging reforestation, and generally raising the level of productivity of the depleted and eroded Mediterranean
soils. Several pilot projects are in operation, one of these in Turkey.

II. PRODUCTION

Agricultural production has been increasing at a rapid rate in the
Middle East despite the limiting influence of the factors discussed
above. Increases in production have been stimulated by increasing
the use of oil revenues and other foreign exchange earnings for the
expansion of irrigation, by the greater availability of technical and
economic aid for development from international agencies or private
enterprises, and by the strong nationalistic urge for economic development that followed political independence.[11] At the same time, however, the population of the area has been increasing rapidly, from an
index of 69 in 1937 to 112 in 1958, with 1953 as 100. This rate of increase is likely to continue and may be accelerated by the increase in
health facilities. The differences between total and per capita production both of agricultural crops in general and of food crops in particular is shown in Table 1. Thus in Egypt, for example, although total
food production in 1958-1959 had increased by 18% over 1952-1954
production, the increase was only 2% on a per capita basis, whereas
in Iraq, Lebanon, Saudi Arabia, Syria, Turkey, and Yemen the per
capita food production was lower than in 1952-1954.[15]

The pattern of food production is overwhelmingly one of cereal cultivation; in nearly all the countries studied cereal crops occupied
more than half of the cultivated acreage. Wheat and barley are the
most important cereals grown, with wheat predominating in all countries except Egypt and Iraq.[1]

Market gardening is of considerable importance in Israel; in other
places it is a feature only in the neighborhood of large towns. Elsewhere, vegetables tend to be limited in variety and amount and, except
for onions and one or two other common vegetables, are available
only on a seasonal basis.[1]

Fruits indigenous to the Middle East reportedly include olives,
grapes, apricots, figs, pomegranates, cherries, peaches, and carobs.
Bananas, oranges, and sugar cane have been imported from the south
and apples and strawberries from countries to the north.[1] Olives
occupy one half to one fourth of the total fruit area and are used as
food and as a source of cooking oil, while the crushed stones are

valuable fodder. Dates are an important food in the southern portions
of the Middle East, and the northern limits of date palm growth divide
the Mediterranean zone from the drier south. Dates have a high sugar
content, relative resistance to contamination with pathological bacteria,
and long-keeping qualities, all of which make them an ideal food for
nomadic and seminomadic peoples.[1]

Animal husbandry is an ancient and important occupation in the
Middle East. Throughout the area livestock raising is carried out in
mountain or desert regions where the lack of water or of good soil
make conditions unfavorable to the growing of crops. The level of
animal nutrition is generally low because of poor breeding practices,
poor pastures, and inadequacy of water supplies. As a result livestock yields are low, particularly yields of meat and milk. The extension of cereal cultivation to former marginal pasture land in Turkey
and Iraq has further depressed the level of animal nutrition in these
countries.

Except in Israel, sheep are the predominant farm animals since
they are better adapted to the semiarid climate. Goats are kept in
large numbers in Arab countries because they can subsist on poorer
pastures than sheep. Unfortunately, goats are most destructive to
grazing lands and are held to be a major factor in the soil erosion
that is a serious problem in most of the countries studied. Cattle are
less numerous and are usually kept as draft animals, while dairy
herds are to be found only in the vicinity of large cities. This does
not apply to Israel, where almost all livestock is maintained for dairy
purposes and most of the milk produced is cow's milk.[16]

The slow development of marketing and distribution systems makes
the movement of supplies from farm to market a wasteful and costly
process, which keeps retail prices high and restrains increases in
domestic consumption of food.[6]

III. EXPORTS AND IMPORTS

Except in Iran and Iraq, where oil is the most significant source of
wealth, agriculture is the dominant segment of the economy in the
countries studied. Agricultural exports are the big earners of foreign
exchange, and an agricultural pattern has emerged that emphasizes
the production of surplus items for export while, except in Israel,
maintaining internal consumption for the majority of the people at
subsistence levels. Each country has endeavored to develop specialty
export surpluses such as cotton (Egypt and Syria), bread grains
(Syria and Iraq), rice (Egypt), dates (Iraq), coffee (Yemen), citrus
fruits (Israel and Lebanon), apples (Lebanon), and olive oil (Syria and

Lebanon).[11] These are critical export items on which the various countries depend for securing badly needed foreign exchange.

Imports of food are not as important as exports, but in almost all the countries imports are necessary to supplement domestic production of basic food items, especially grains. Grain imports are of special importance in poor crop years; in 1960, for example, even countries such as Syria, which normally produces a surplus of grains, had to import wheat from the United States. Imports include, in addition, minor food items not grown or produced in the Middle East, as well as several luxury items for the well-to-do classes.

IV. DIET TYPES

Although agricultural production has increased rapidly in recent years, the actual consumption of food in most countries has failed to keep pace with expanded production. This may be attributed to the low purchasing power of the predominantly rural population[3] as well as to the fact that the lack of transportation and distribution facilities tend to keep retail prices at a high level.[6] Nevertheless, there has been some increase in the available intake of energy-producing foods, such as grain and cereals, but the consumption of protective foods still is at a very low level throughout the Moslem countries of the region.[3]

A satisfactory analysis of food consumption is not possible at present in view of the incomplete and imperfect data on food supplies and food utilization currently available. Average consumption levels of certain foods are low in comparison with other regions, but there are wide differences in food consumption from country to country and in different areas or population groups within a country.[6] For example, in the larger cities the food intake of the well-to-do may be comparable to that in any city of the United States, but it is completely different from the monotonous, poorly balanced, and often severely restricted diet of the poor in the rural areas of the same country.[2]

Food balance sheets that estimate the quantities of food produced, imported, and exported and the quantities available for human consumption on a per capita basis, after deducting nonfood uses, are available only for Egypt, Israel, and Turkey. Food consumption analyses for other countries are only rough estimates of the supplies of food but are presented since they are the only information available. In studying available data on total consumption per capita, consideration must be given to the very great variations in individual consumption ascribable to differences in economic level, to regional distribution of production, and to seasonal availability of foods.[5] Available food consumption data for the countries covered in this study is contained in Tables 2 and 3.

The diet patterns of Middle Eastern countries have certain basic similarities that reflect the influence of geographic and climatic conditions, cultural patterns, and the character of the people. Food habits of Moslems are governed by the dietary laws of Islam, which prescribe certain periods of fasting and impose numerous food taboos. Similar taboos are prescribed by the Mosaic law observed by many of the inhabitants of Israel. Diet patterns also are influenced by the absence of modern means of food preservation, transportation, and refrigeration and by the severe climatic conditions, all of which determine the way in which perishable food products are processed.[14] Perishable foods are, in general, consumed in the season and in the locality where they are produced.[5]

Wheat is the most widely consumed cereal in all the countries studied, but maize, barley, rice, and millet are important staples in some areas.[12] Cereals provide a major portion of the caloric intake in the average diet, with percentages ranging from 43% in Israel to 71% in Turkey, as contrasted with only 38% in the United States. Cereals also provide most of the protein intake, ranging from 40% of proteins in Israel to 71% in Turkey, as compared with only 17% in the United States.[12]

Wheat is eaten primarily in bread or as **burghul**. The wheat flour used is of low extraction rate, except in Israel and the large urban centers of Moslem countries. The wheat flour often is mixed with maize, barley, or millet, and distinctive regional varieties of bread are a common cultural feature. The predominant type of bread baked is a flat, round loaf that serves not only as the main article of food but often as the plate and eating utensil as well. Burghul is used extensively in several countries, especially Turkey, Syria, and Lebanon. It consists of parboiled wheat that is sundried and then crushed into either fine or coarse varieties. Coarse burghul is used in the same ways as rice; the finer varieties are used as stuffing for meats or vegetables, or in soups or porridges.[2]

Corn constitutes the chief staple of diet in some countries, usually in specific areas such as the delta region of Egypt and the Black Sea coast of Turkey. In both of these countries the substitution of wheat for corn in the diet is being encouraged by official government measures[12].

Rice is popular everywhere, but its high cost limits consumption to the inhabitants of producing areas and the well-to-do. It is served alone, with meats in a stew, or is used as a stuffing for various vegetables.

Lentils and other legumes are relished and cooked in a variety of ways. They are of nutritional importance as a source of good quality vegetable proteins in diets largely based on cereals.[12] They may be cooked with oil or butter, in a stew with other vegetables, or may be made into a soup.

Vegetables are universally popular but, except in Israel, are everywhere produced and consumed in inadequate amounts. Onions appear at almost every meal, either raw or cooked with the main dish. Other popular vegetables include tomatoes and eggplants as well as cucumbers, green and red peppers, squash, and cabbages. Most of these vegetables are eaten raw or parboiled and served in a salad; a common practice is to stuff them with rice, burghul, or meats.[9] The intake of vegetables shows wide seasonal and regional variations.[12]

The intake of fruits also shows wide seasonal variations, except for fruits such as dates, raisin grapes, and apricots, which can be preserved by drying in the sun. In Iran, Syria, and Turkey, there is an abundance of fruits during the harvesting season, but lack of facilities for preservation, storage, and transportation limit consumption.[12] In Lebanon and Israel fruit is produced in exportable surpluses, and fruit production is important in the agricultural economy.

Consumption of sugar is rising rapidly in many countries, an increase associated with the growing habit of drinking tea and soft drinks containing large amounts of sugar.[12] From a nutritional standpoint this is an undesirable development.

Throughout the Middle Eastern countries consumption of meat and meat products is at a very low level, although meat dishes are extremely popular. Meat contributes only about 2% of the total caloric intake, compared with 21% in the United States. The main reason for the low consumption lies in the low purchasing power of the majority of the inhabitants and the relatively high cost of meat, which is produced everywhere in quantities too small to satisfy local demands. This may seem strange in an area where animal husbandry is an important occupation and the animal population is among the highest in the world, but to the herdsman the animals represent capital that is not to be wasted by slaughter. Several kinds of meat are proscribed by religious law or local custom, and the ritual slaughter necessitated by the codes of both the Moslem and Hebrew religions add to the cost of meats.

The principal kind of meat in the Moslem countries is mutton and beef and, to some extent, goats, camels, and buffaloes,[12] while in Israel poultry supplies the major portion of the meat intake. In some countries of the area beef is consumed to a greater degree in towns than in rural areas, and the same applies to poultry and eggs, which are usually produced in the villages but are sold and eaten in the towns. Meat is eaten raw, stewed, or broiled, or it may be used as a stuffing for vegetables and pastries.

Considering the extent and variety of coastal and inland waters, fish as a food is remarkably scarce, being used in appreciable amounts only in Israel. In Moslem countries fish may be an important component of the diet only among certain limited population groups, such as the inhabitants of the Black Sea region in Turkey, the population of the delta lakes region in Egypt, and the marsh dwellers of southern Iraq. Fish is an excellent source of animal proteins, and an increase in its consumption would provide a much-needed increase in animal protein intake, but the lack of transportation and refrigeration facilities limits such an expansion of consumption.[4]

The difficulty of transporting and preserving fresh milk under the climatic conditions of the Middle East has led to the adoption and use of milk products with better keeping qualities. One of the most common of these is fermented milk (yoghurt or leben), which is prepared by boiling fresh milk and fermenting it with a "starter" culture. The yoghurt or leben is eaten alone, as an accompaniment to numerous dishes, or diluted with water to make refreshing drinks. Fat is converted to butter, which is either sold fresh or, more frequently, boiled to make ghee, or samn. When butter is made from yoghurt instead of fresh milk it has an acid flavor. Often ghee is made with a mixture of fats, usually butter fat and the fat of fat-tailed sheep. The buttermilk left after butter-making is frequently curdled by boiling, and then is strained and rolled into balls that are salted and dried in the sun. This product keeps indefinitely in dry places and is a favorite, especially with the nomadic inhabitants.

Numerous types of cheese are made in the various countries but, in general, white cheese made from sheep and goat milk is the most common. Often the freshly made cheese is salted and packed in containers, after which it is kept in a cool place to ripen. Where no cool storage is available, surplus milk may be converted into hard cheese and packed in goat skins.

V. NUTRITIONAL LEVEL

The nutritional level of the Middle Eastern countries discussed in these reports, with the possible exception of Israel, cannot be considered satisfactory for the majority of the inhabitants. At the present time there is no marked general shortage of calories in the region, although inadequate caloric intake occurs in certain groups and the intake may show seasonal variations. Diets are, in general, deficient in proteins of high biological value and in certain essential vitamins and minerals.[12] One evidence of this may be found in the high infant mortality rates and the high death rates in the 1 to 4-year age group, both of which are believed to be due, at least partly, to nutritional diseases. Figures quoted for infant mortality are as high as 250 per 1,000 live births, while the death rate in the 1 to 4-year age group may be as high as 35 per 1,000 children.[12]

Clinical and subclinical disease due to malnutrition is common throughout the region. No conclusions can be drawn, however, on the exact prevalence of such diseases in different countries, since very few clinical surveys of population groups have been made and hospital statistics are of limited value in assessing the incidence of disease in areas in which the hospitals are situated.[12] The deficiency diseases most frequently reported include rickets, vitamin A deficiencies, ariboflavinosis, and nutritional anemia associated with parasitic infestation.[2] Some diseases, such as pellagra, may be limited in their distribution by the dietary patterns peculiar to certain regions in a country.[5] Parasitic infestations, especially intestinal bilharzia, appear to contribute to the causation of this disease in Egypt.

Rickets is a common disease throughout the area, although the active disease is not often found in children old enough to play in the sun. A record of surveys shows a very similar incidence of this disease in various countries. Avitaminosis A occurs, but it appears to be less prevalent here than in certain other parts of the world, such as Southeast Asia. Mild forms of ariboflavinosis are widespread, whereas scurvy, although rare, is sporadically seen and may be of importance in limited areas or at certain seasons.[12]

Kwashiorkor has been reported among poorer social groups in Egypt and Israel, and it is probably prevalent elsewhere in the Middle East although statistics are lacking.[7] Anemia seems to be associated most often with hookworm and, to a somewhat smaller extent, with bilharziasis and malaria. The intake of iron appears to be insufficient to compensate for the chronic loss of blood caused by the helminthic infestations.

The primary causes of the bad nutritional situation in the Middle East were summarized in a report of the Food and Agriculture Organization Standing Advisory Committee on Nutrition in the Middle East in 1948, and are just as valid today. These primary causes were listed as:

(1) Poverty, since countries that depend almost entirely on agriculture, as do nearly all countries in the Middle East, are in general poorer than those that engage, even to a limited extent, in industry. Poverty prevents the majority of the population from securing an adequate diet and from obtaining expensive protective foods, when these are available.

(2) Pressure of population, which has increased without a parallel increase in the area under cultivation.

(3) The land tenure system prevailing, in which almost all land is owned by a small minority of absentee landlords whose primary interest is the production of cash crops.

(4) Unsatisfactory health conditions, including especially the prevalence of parasitic diseases, which pave the way for the occurrence of deficiency diseases.

(5) Ignorance and bad dietary habits, including poor weaning practices, the consumption of raw meat, with the consequent spread of certain parasitic infections, and the taboos against certain foods.

(6) The nomadic custom of the Arabs in various parts of the Middle East, since nomads must exist on a diet meagre in the extreme and lack food reserves to tide them over periods of shortages.[14]

SELECTED REFERENCES

1. Fisher, W. B. The Middle East. (3rd edit.) London, Methuen, 1956.
2. Adolph, W. H. Nutrition in the Near East. *Journal of the American Dietetic Association*, Vol. 30, No. 8, 1954, pp. 753-756.
3. Food and Agriculture Organization. *Monthly Bulletin of Agricultural Statistics*, January, 1956.
4. Worthington, E. G. Middle East Science. London, His Majesty's Stationery Office, 1946.
5. Abassy, M. A. Nutrition Problems in the Middle East. *Journal of the Royal Egyptian Medical Association*, Vol. 30, 1947, p. 502.
6. Food and Agriculture Organization. Problems of Food and Agricultural Expansion in the Near East. Rome, 1955.
7. Trowell, H. C. The World Distribution of Kwashiorkor. *Acta Union Internatl. Contra Cancrum 13*, No. 4-5, 1957.
8. Stephanides, C. S. Prospects for U. S. Dairy Exports to the Middle East. *Foreign Agriculture*, Vol. 19, No. 6, June, 1955, pp. 119-122.
9. Tannous, A. I. Food Production and Consumption in the Middle East. *Foreign Agriculture*, Vol. 7, No. 11, November, 1943, pp. 243-255.
10. Tannous, A. I. Agriculture and Democracy in the Middle East. *Foreign Agriculture*, Vol. 19, No. 1, January, 1955, pp. 13-17.
11. United States Department of Agriculture, Foreign Agriculture Service. The Problem of Agricultural Surpluses and Deficits in the Near East. March, 1959.
12. Food and Agriculture Organization, Nutrition Committee for the Middle East. Report of First Session of Joint FAO/WHO Committee, November, 1958. *F. A. O. Nutrition Meeting Report Series No. 24*, 1959.
13. *Middle East Economist*, November, 1959.
14. Food and Agriculture Organization. Note on Nutrition in the Middle East Prepared for the Standing Advisory Committee on Nutrition. Cairo, Food and Agriculture Organization Regional Conference for the Near East, 2 February 1948, Document No. 5.
15. United States Department of Agriculture, Foreign Agriculture Service. Indices of Agricultural Production in 13 Near East Countries. Mimeographed report. November, 1959.

Table 1

Indices of Agricultural and Food Production; Total and Per Capita in Selected Countries of the Near East
Average 1935–39, Annual 1957–58, 1958–59, and 1959–60

(1952–1954 equals 100)

Country	Total				Per Capita			
	Prewar 1935–39(a)	1957–58	1958–59	1959–60(b)	Prewar 1935–39(a)	1957–58	1958–59	1959–60(b)
AGRICULTURAL PRODUCTION								
Egypt	90	115	116	116	123	106	104	101
Iran	83	122	123	126	104	111	109	109
Iraq	72	125	111	106	111	116	101	94
Israel	70	168	201	216	117	144	166	171
Lebanon	78	102	100	96	115	94	90	85
Saudi Arabia		115	100	100		111	95	94
Syria	54	147	93	88	82	128	79	73
Turkey	66	109	108	102	90	97	94	86
Yemen		107	82	74		101	76	68
FOOD PRODUCTION								
Egypt	83	117	114	118	114	107	102	103
Iran	83	121	122	125	103	110	108	108
Iraq	72	123	109	104	111	114	99	92
Israel	70	165	196	211	117	141	162	167
Lebanon	79	101	98	93	116	93	88	82
Saudi Arabia		115	100	100		111	95	94
Syria	65	136	70	69	98	118	59	57
Turkey	68	111	110	103	93	99	96	87
Yemen		104	78	72		98	72	66
Near East Total	73	118	114	114	99	108	102	99

(a) Not available for some countries.   (b) Preliminary.

Source: Foreign Agriculture Service, U. S. Dept. of Agr. Indices of Agricultural Production in 13 Near East Countries, Washington, D.C., 1959.

Table 2

Supplies of Certain Foods Available for Human Consumption in Selected Countries

Country and Period	Cereals	Starchy Roots	Pulses	Sugar	Fats, oils	Fruit	Vege- tables	Meat	Eggs	Fish	Milk[a]
	Kilograms per caput per year at the retail level										
Iran 1953-55[b]	96	2	..	14	8	40	55	6	..	1	45
Iraq 1953-55[b]	119	3	13	23	5	58	55	10	2	1	83
Israel 1954-55	141	43	10	24	18	100	114	18	15	13	104
Lebanon 1953-55[b]	126	17	18	20	7	136	22	15	4	1	80
Turkey 1954/55[b]	195	32	12	12	6	86	76	16	2	3	55
United Arab Republic											
Egyptian Province 1955/56	186	6	12	18	4	66	65	13	1	6	59
Syrian Province 1953-55[b]	118	9	14	9	10	91	32	8	2	1	84

(a) Milk and milk products in terms of fresh milk.
(b) Provisional figures pending government approval.
Sources: Israeli data from: Statistical Abstract of Israel, 1958/59. Other data from: Joint F.A.O./W.H.O. Committee on Nutrition in the Near East. Report of First Meeting, 1958.

Table 3

Percentage Contribution of Various Food Groups to Total Calories and Protein

Country and Period	Percent of Calories From:						Percentage of Total Protein From:		
	Cereals	Pulses	Sugar	Fruits and Vegetables	Meat, Fish, Milk and Eggs	Fats and Oils	Cereals	Pulses	Meat, Fish, Milk and Eggs
Iraq 1953–55 [a]	56	6	12	11	9	6	56	13	23
Iran 1953–55 [a]	53	–	8	5	8	9	50	–	13
Israel 1954/55	47	4	9	6	14	14	51	7	33
United Arab Republic									
Egyptian Province 1955/56	67	4	7	6	9	4	66	9	19
Syrian Province 1953–55	56	6	5	11	11	11	57	14	23
Turkey 1954/55	71	5	4	6	6	6	71	8	14
Lebanon 1953–55 [a]	56	7	9	10	8	8	55	16	22

(a) Provisional.

Sources: Israeli data from Statistical Abstract of Israel, 1958/59. Other countries from: Joint F.A.O./W.H.O. Committee on Nutrition in the Near East. Report of First Meeting, 1958.

IRAN

I. GENERAL REMARKS

A. AGRICULTURE IN IRAN

Iran is a country approximately 1,625,000 square kilometers (628,000 square miles) in area, one fifth the size of the United States. The main geographical feature of Iran is a large central plateau ringed by the coastal plains of the Caspian Sea and the Persian Gulf. A large part of this central plateau is a practically uninhabitable region of desert and steppes, so that more than 65% of the total land area is considered unsuitable for agriculture. The remaining area includes forest lands, pastures, and arable land; this last category comprises slightly more than 10% of the total area. Of the arable land, only about one fourth is under cultivation in any one year, while the remainder is allowed to lie fallow.

This small percentage of arable land supports most of the population of Iran. The 1956 census, the first country-wide population count, showed that 75% of the 19.5 million inhabitants derive their livelihood from agricultural and pastoral pursuits, for the most part on a subsistence level. Although the over-all population density is low, the concentration of the population in the few arable regions makes for considerable population pressure in certain areas.

As elsewhere in the Near East, water is the principal determining factor in cultivation. There are few rivers and rain is abundant only near the Caspian Sea, so that water often is in short supply. A substantial and increasing portion of the land is cultivated by irrigation. Only 20% of the irrigated land area uses surface water; most of the remainder is irrigated from underground water supplies that are tapped by qantas, long, underwater channels that carry the water by gravity flow to the surface. A small number of wells also provide irrigation water and pumped water supplies are becoming increasingly available. About 10% of the total arable land is irrigated at present and this irrigated land grows 30% of all crops harvested in any one year. Dry farming is practiced in the Caspian littoral (except for rice), in considerable areas of Azerbaijan, and, to a limited extent, in Kurdistan, Fars, and Khorassan.

The most fertile and populous areas are the Caspian littoral, with a subtropical climate and abundant rainfall, northern Azerbaijan, Tehran and the surrounding plain, and the western part of the central plateau.

Although Iran is primarily an agricultural country, this is the area of the economy in which the least progress has been made.[10] Primitive methods of cultivation still are in general use and the light rainfall, the lack of good quality seeds, and the absence of other aids to agriculture result in poor yields. The poor quality of most soils and the inadequate water supplies make imperative the use of the fallow system. As a result, a large proportion of the agricultural land lies fallow each year. In some areas, where there is sufficient water, crop rotation systems are used so that a grain year may be followed by one in which melons or vegetables are grown.[9]

Fields are cultivated in small holdings of an average of 3 to 4 hectares in area. Cultivated areas are grouped around villages and separated from each other by semidesert or wild mountain country. There are an estimated 47,000 villages, containing 80 to 85% of the total population.

The traditional system of land ownership also retards the progress of agriculture. More than one half of the claimed land is owned by absentee landlords and the peasant cultivates it as a sharecropper. A large majority of the peasants are in this category. The harvest often is divided into five portions, with one portion each assigned to the provider of land, water, work animals, seed, and labor. Under this system the landowner, who may also provide seed, draft animals, and water, may be entitled to four fifths of the crop. Where land is owned by the cultivator, holdings tend to be small; some 63% of all farmers own less than $2\frac{1}{2}$ acres.

Attempts have been made to modify this absentee landlord system, primarily by distributing to landless peasants some of the extensive lands belonging to the Shah. The program was launched in 1951 and, as of 1959, some 201,990 hectares had been given to 20,608 peasants in 165 villages.

A Seven Year Plan for economic development was first formulated in 1949 and included recommendations for irrigation and drainage, for the introduction of farm machinery, for the construction of grain silos and sugar beet factories, and for other projects to be finances with oil revenues. Because of the unstable political situation this plan was more or less held in abeyance until after 1956, although a few of the recommended projects were carried out with funds provided by the International Cooperation Administration of the United States.

A second Seven Year Plan was approved in 1956 and is now in operation. Although results have not as yet been spectacular, production has increased. In addition to carrying out agricultural development projects, the Plan Organization cooperates in financing the technical aid projects of international organizations.

B. AGRICULTURAL REGIONS [4,6]

Because of climatic and topographic limitations, food production and agriculture in general are concentrated in certain limited localities. Since, in general, most crops are consumed where grown, areas with a more diversified and abundant production enjoy a more varied and satisfactory diet. Some surplus products are shipped to deficit producing areas of the country, such as the center and south, but this exchange is hampered by inadequate transportation facilities.

The most important agricultural area is in the north, and includes parts of Azerbaijan, the Caspian littoral, the Gorgan plains to the southeast of the Caspian and Khorassan in the northeast. This northern crop region includes only one fourth of the total area, but it produces about 60% of the wheat and barley, 70% of the cotton, 75% of the tobacco, 80% of the rice and dried fruits, and all of the tea, jute, and silk.

The Caspian Sea area includes the provinces of Mazandaran, Gilan, and Gorgan. It is characterized by subtropical vegetation and forests; rainfall is abundant, from 1,000 to 1,500 mm. a year, and the temperature is moderate. The main crop is rice, but other cereals, as well as tea and tobacco, are grown. Some cotton and flax are cultivated in the lowlands, especially in Gilan, where large areas have been reclaimed from the jungle. Large plantings of mulberry trees make this the silk center of Iran and the region also produces a large assortment of fruits and nuts.

The mountainous slopes of Azerbaijan, Kurdistan, Hamadan, and Luristan, extending down to Khuzistan, have rich pastures and fertile valleys. The climate in these regions is characterized by intensely cold winters and hot summers with little or no humidity. Rainfall in Azerbaijan and Kurdistan reaches 380 to 890 mm. a year.

The Khuzistan drainage basin, comprising much of the southwestern part of Iran, has a warm, semiarid climate. An elaborate development program, under the Plan Organization, has been set up for the area and it is hoped that extensive plantations of cotton and sugar cane, both of which are well adapted to the climate, will be successfully initiated once irrigation is available.

The Persian Gulf area is characterized by intense heat and high humidity during the summer months, but the climate is mild from November to March. Rainfall is scanty but the soil is rich and large streams allow intensive cultivation. Dates are the principal crop.

The central plateau is a great semiarid plain with two great salt deserts that include one fourth of the total area. Large fertile regions are found, usually along the periphery of the plateau; these include the plains of Hamadan, Tehran, and Khorassan and the great oasis of Ishfahan, which enjoys adequate rainfall and temperate weather.

Crops in the plateau area include wheat, tobacco, barley, sugar beets, cotton, fruits, and vegetables.

The distribution of crops in the important agricultural areas of Iran is shown in Map 1.

II. FOOD RESOURCES

A. GENERAL

Iran is generally self-sufficient in the production of foods, except for sugar, tea, and vegetable oils. Agricultural output has barely kept place with the increase in population and the increased consumption ascribable to higher incomes in certain sectors of the economy, as for example in the oil industry. Thus, although the total food production index rose 25% in 1958-1959 as compared to the 1952-1955 average, the percapita production of food increased by only 8%.[15]

The area under cultivation and the production of some of the principal crops in Iran are listed in Table 1. This table was drawn from two principal sources, the United States Department of Agriculture estimates, as drawn up by the Foreign Agriculture Service and from official reports of production contained in Food and Agriculture Organization publications.

Cereal crops usually are harvested from May to September, vegetables early in summer, and fruit from June to September, except for citrus fruits, which are gathered in November and December. Table 2 lists the harvest period of the most important crops as well as the months during which the bulk of the harvesting of each crop is carried out.

B. CEREALS

The staple cereals grown in Iran-wheat, barley, and rice-occupy nearly three fourths of the land under cultivation. Grain crops are under cultivation mainly in the north, northwest, and northeast, especially in the provinces of Azerbaijan and Khorassan, which are the granaries of Iran. The estimated cultivated land totals 2.6 million hectares. The distribution of wheat and barley production is shown in Map 2.

The methods used in cereal cultivation, as in all other agricultural pursuits, are for the most part those that have been practiced for thousands of years. Primitive agricultural implements in use include the wooden hook plow and the sickle, and both harvesting and sowing are done by hand.[7]

A large number of local varieties of different cereals are sown and these varieties, the result of adaptation to a particular environment, may differ markedly from those grown in neighboring regions. This is not surprising in view of the great diversity of climatic, topographic, and soil conditions[7] encountered.

Wheat is the most important of Iran's cereal crops from the standpoint both of area under cultivation and of contribution to gross agricultural income. In addition, it is the principal article of diet, contributing more than one half the caloric intake. Wheat is grown throughout the country, in the central plateau as a spring crop, under irrigation, and elsewhere as a winter crop. The most important area of cultivation is the province of Azerbaijan, where one third of the country's wheat is produced. Another important center is the province of Gorgan and the Turkmenian steppe. The best conditions for the expansion of wheat production are found in this area, which lends itself to mechanized farming.[7]

In other parts of the country, wheat is cultivated in widely scattered villages, usually only in land close to the settlements and with the help of irrigation. Large areas between villages are often not cultivated because of inadequate water supplies. Some wheat is grown without irrigation in these inter-village areas, but the yields are rather poor and crop failures frequent. Relatively favorable conditions for dry-farming of wheat exist in the huge plateau between Hamadan and Sanandaj.

Production of wheat from 1957 to 1960 is shown in Table 1. During 1952-1954 production was 2,284,000 tons. The amount increased to 3,100,000 tons in 1959-1960, but this increased production, already noted, was not enough to satisfy increased consumption.

Barley grown in the same locations as wheat but its area of cultivation is smaller.[7] An estimated one million tons were produced in 1959-1960, compared with an average of 828,000 tons during 1952-1954 and of 777,000 during 1935-1939.[13] The crop is grown primarily for livestock feed and is used for human consumption in only years during which there is a poor wheat crop.

Rice is the second most important food crop after wheat.[11] It is grown on the Caspian plains, which account for 75% of production, and in the lowland districts near Ishfahan. Total rice production is around 400,000 tons of milled rice; this is now a sufficient amount to allow an exportable surplus. In 1958 exports amounted to 1/8 of total production.

Rye and oats are present as weeds in wheat fields but are seldom cultivated, although a few fields of rye may be found in areas of Zerbaijan.[7] Some corn, millet, and grain sorghum also are produced; during 1956 the production of maize amounted to 14,000 tons, while the production of millet and sorghum in 1948-1952 amounted to 14,000 tons.[12]

C. OTHER EDIBLE CROPS

1. Vegetables and legumes. Some 940,000 tons of root and leafy vegetables were grown in 1959-1960. Vegetables grown included cucumbers, tomatoes, melons, and watermelons. Potatoes are grown only in small quantities. The average area planted to potatoes between 1948 and 1952 was only 4,000 hectares, and production was only 37,000 metric tons.

Legumes are an important article of diet, with beans, chick peas, and lentils the most important varieties grown and eaten. An estimated 148,000 tons of legumes were available for food out of an estimated supply of 155,000 tons in 1954-1955. Production in 1959-1960 was estimated to have risen approximately 15% from the 1954-1955 levels.

2. Fruit.[4] Fruit is of seasonal importance in the diet and is eaten fresh, dried, or preserved. Many varieties are grown and include, in addition to dates and citrus fruits, apricots, peaches, cherries, apples, pomegranates, plums, pears, figs, and grapes, as well as many kinds of nuts.

Dates are a staple crop along the Persian Gulf and in the southeast.[5] There are extensive groves in the southwest along the Shatt al Arab and the Karun Rivers. Production is reportedly more or less stabilized at approximately 120,000 tons per year.

Citrus fruits are grown in the Caspian Sea littoral and in a few areas in the south.[4] Production of oranges and tangerines was estimated at 40,000 tons in 1959-1960 and that of other citrus fruits at 63,000 metric tons.

Walnuts, figs, pomegranates, and almonds are among the fruits that grow abundantly in the valleys of the Caspian littoral.[5] Apricots, grapes, and other fruits are grown in many areas, especially in Ishfahan, Tabriz, and Shiraz. Dried fruits and nuts are important, not only for domestic consumption but also as an export item. For example, the total production of almonds in 1957-1958 was 28,000 metric tons and some 6,600 tons were exported.

Table 4 lists the net food supply in 1954-1955 of the most important fruits and nuts.

3. Sugar beets. The present production of sugar beets is not enough to satisfy domestic sugar requirements. The beets are grown under irrigation in the plateau area and are of importance not only as a source of sugar but also because beet sugar residues can provide an important silage for livestock. Sugar beets in 1957 were planted on 46,000 hectares and yielded 727,000 metric tons, enough to produce 93,000 tons of beet sugar. Production of refined sugar in 1959-1960 was expected to reach 115,000 metric tons.[6]

4. Tea. Tea is grown in the Caspian Sea littoral, but production is still considerably below domestic requirements despite Government support of production and marketing. Production in 1959-1960 was estimated at 7,000 tons, which constituted about one third of total consumption.

D. CASH CROPS

While the production of grain has not increased much in recent years, industrial crops such as cotton and tobacco have shown an appreciable increase both in acreage planted and in production.

Cotton is grown in many parts of the country.[5] The principal areas of production are the Gorgan and Mazandaran plains near the Caspian Sea, which together account for 50% of total production. Other cotton producing areas include the Khorassan area in northeastern Iran and the Veramin plains near Teheran. If the Khuzistan Development Plan is successful, a considerable portion of the developed area will be planted to cotton and acreage will correspondingly increase. Total production in 1959-1960 was estimated at 72,000 tons, of which approximately one half was destined for the export market. Of all the agricultural products, cotton is the largest export earner, but increased domestic consumption is reducing the amount available for export.

Tobacco production has not yet reached prewar averages and ranges between 12,000 and 14,000 tons a year. This crop is grown principally in the northeast on more than 20,200 hectares. A planned increase in acreage, combined with a program to improve the quality of the crop, is expected to result in greatly increased production.

E. ANIMAL PRODUCT RESOURCES

Animal husbandry is an ancient occupation in Iran. For centuries tribes of the central plateau have migrated with their flocks between the lowlands and the mountain slopes, and these tribes live almost exclusively on the products of their flocks. Throughout the agricultural economy livestock products are of importance, since they provide a substantial part of the farmer's income and contribute to the food supply.

Sheep are by far the commonest animals bred; they provide one half of the meat and at least 20% of the milk used as food, and they yield the wool used in making carpets, Iran's second most important source of foreign exchange. The number of sheep, as of March, 1958, was estimated at 27.2 million.

The next most commonly raised animal is the goat, estimated at 12.8 million head in 1958. Sheep and goat milk are the main sources of milk products in rural areas.

Cattle in Iran are used primarily as draft animals, and it is only in the vicinity of large cities that some are kept for dairying purposes. The total number is estimated at slightly more than 5 million. Smaller numbers of horses (452,000) and of mules and asses (1,620,000) are kept as beasts of burden, while buffaloes (182,000) and camels (440,000) are found in limited areas. Very few pigs are kept, and the average between 1947 and 1952 was estimated at not over 5,000 in the entire country.

Iran is not, by and large, a meat-eating country. For a vast majority of the population, meat is a luxury to be eaten at most only once a week and, in some poorer families, only on festive occasions.[13] Estimated production of meat in 1959-1960 was 320,000 metric tons, primarily lamb and mutton (50%), goat (25%), beef, veal, and buffalo (24%), and small amounts of pork. The production, net supply, and per capita consumption of each type was estimated in 1954-1955 as follows:[12]

	Production	Net Supply	Kg./capita/yr.
Mutton and goat	180,000	350,000	17.1
Beef	34,000	74,000	3.6
Poultry	17,000	37,000	1.8

Milk products are staple foods in the diet in most areas of Iran. However since they represent a source of cash for peasants, the rate of consumption generally is low in villages near urban centers. Cows' milk is produced on a small scale in the vicinity of larger cities but, as already mentioned, sheep and goat milk are more in use by the majority of the population, although these products do not constitute the bulk of the milk marketed. Estimated milk production in 1959-1960 was expected to total 1.5 million tons. Of this total, 60% was cow's milk, 20% sheep's milk, 15% goat's milk, and 5% buffalo milk. Fluid milk and fresh butter are not popular, chiefly because of the difficulty in preserving these products. Milk usually is converted to **mast,** a form of sour milk, or to buttermilk, cheese, and clarified butter. Production of butter was 40,000 metric tons and of cheese 2,000 tons during 1948 to 1952; later figures are not available.

Animals provide most of the fat content of the Iranian diet, either as clarified butter or as fat from fat-tailed sheep.

Poultry contribute an estimated 10% of the meat supply while consumption of eggs is at similar percapita levels. Estimated production of eggs in 1958-1959 was slightly lower than in 1954-1955, which means that consumption was substantially lower because of the increase in population.

Fishing always has been an important industry in Iran, but one that was principally conducted for the export trade. The bilateral agreement with the USSR for the exploitation of the Caspian Sea fisheries and the preparation of caviar came to an end in 1952, and the fishing

industry in Iran was nationalized. Operations were continued under a
new organization, the Iranian Shilat Corporation, with executive headquarters at Tehran and a main fishing center at Bandar Pahlevi. Four
fishing districts have been established with centers at Pahlevi, Hassan
Keyadeh, Babolsar, and Ashure Kuchek. The corporation owns eight
fishing units with a total capacity of 260 tons, plus a 30-ton fishing
boat used for follow-up fishing. The yearly products of the corporation during the last three months of 1958 and the first nine months of
1959 included 1,106 tons of cartilaginous fish, 2,295 tons of sclae fish,
and 145 tons of caviar. There was no indication as to how much of
this total catch was disposed of in domestic markets. The estimated
net food supply of fish of all kinds in 1954-1955 was 22,000 tons.

F. EXPORTS AND IMPORTS

Iran is largely self-sufficient in food production at a rather low
level of consumption. There are a few items the country does not
produce in sufficient quantities to meet domestic demands, and probably she will not be able to improve this situation in the foreseeable
future. These include tea, coffee, and some edible oils; Iran imports
about three fourths of the tea consumed.

Other items, such as wheat, are produced in quantities sufficient
to satisfy domestic demands in normal crop years and in exportable
surplus quantities in exceptionally good harvest, but they must be
imported in bad crop years when domestic production is not adequate
to meet demands. In recent years, wheat has become more and more
of an import item because domestic production is not able to keep up
with the increasing demands of a growing population and increasing
consumption. There are other items, now on the import list, in which
Iran hopes to become self-sufficient if present development plans are
carried out successfully; sugar is the most important of these. At
present approximately two thirds of sugar supplies are imported
yearly. Table 3 lists the quantity and value of the principal agricultural items imported and export during 1957-1958.

Agricultural products, raw or processed, are second in importance
only to oil as an export item. They account for 20.3% of the total export trade, including petroleum, and for 67% of exports excluding oil.
Principal exports include cotton, dried fruit, animal hair, hides and
skins, and nuts.

The amounts exported yearly of each of the principal crops produced is estimated as follows:

Rice	One eighth
Barley	One tenth
Almonds	Two thirds
Raisins	Three fifths

Apricots	One half
Dates	One fourth
Fish	One fourth

Cotton was shipped primarily to Europe, hair and hides to the United States, and legumes and fresh produce to the Persian Gulf states (see Table 3).

The Export-Import Bank has made loans to firms processing agricultural products primarily for export. The establishments aided, as of September, 1959, include a plant in Tehran that shells and cleans nuts and oilseeds and also provides cold storage facilities, as well as two raisin and dried fruit packing plants, one in Tehran and one in Tabriz.

G. INTERNATIONAL TECHNICAL AID

Numerous national and international agencies finance cooperative programs in agricultural development or nutrition. The Food and Agriculture Organization of the United Nations, for example, finances projects dealing with land and water use and the use of farm machinery, plant production, animal disease control, and forestry. The World Health Organization helps to finance the Nutrition Institute. UNICEF cooperates in a program of skim milk distribution that, in 1957, reached 149,000 children, and has also established milk conservation plants.

The United States Government, through the International Cooperation Administration and preceeding agencies, has financed economic aid programs in Iran since 1951. As of 1958 the mission operating in Iran carried out projects in livestock improvement, pest control and crop management, water resources management, and forestry. The mission carried out agricultural extension programs and helped to finance the Karaj Agricultural College. Private agencies in the United States that have financed programs in Iran include the Iran Foundation, which maintains a hospital and nursing school in Shiraz and has helped to purchase and distribute substantial amounts of surplus United States agricultural products, including powdered eggs, dried milk, and butter.

H. FOOD INDUSTRIES, STORAGE AND TECHNOLOGY

1. **Food processing.**[7] A total of 1,207 food processing establishments were in operation in 1958 and an additional 59 were engaged in the manufacture of alcoholic or carbonated beverages. These factories ranged in size from large modern establishments employing hundreds of workers to small, primitive, family-type companies with a

few employees and rudimentary or obsolete equipment. The majority of the factories were small establishments with less than 10 employees, whereas only two factories had more than 500 workers. The type and number of factories and the number of employees is shown in Table 5.

By far the largest number of food processing establishments were concerned with the processing of cereal products. Flour mills, which included 509 of the total listed, and of which there were 338, made up more than two thirds of the total number of factories. A great variety of foodstuffs was processed, as may be seen from Table 8, which details the kind and amount of foods processed in Tehran and each ostan. The largest concentration of factories was in Tehran, which provides the best market for manufactured products.

Most of the factories were privately owned enterprises but some of the government-owned establishments were among the largest and most modern in operation. Table 6 gives data on the number and production of government-owned factories, which include canneries, a pasteurization plant, some of the largest flour mills, and all the sugar mills now in operation.

As already mentioned above, by far the largest number of food processing establishments are flour mills. These are primarily small establishments: 90% of them have less than 10 employees, although there is one large flour mill that employs more than 1,000 people.

The number of small bakeries is not known but must run into the hundreds. There are four macaroni products factories and 12 biscuit-making plants.

All the rice fields are situated in the northern districts and it is here that all the threshing operations are carried out. There is a total of 338 factories, most of which are located in Ostans 1 and 2 (for distribution of Ostans see Map 3). These factories produced a total of 188,508 tons of rice, 5,890 tons of rice powder, and 26,940 tons of other products. A considerable portion of the production was exported.

There is a total of 51 fruit-drying plants, most of which are located in Ostans 3 and 4 in the northwest of the country. Of the 51 factories, 30 were in Azerbaijan. A total of 40,894 tons of dried fruit, mostly raisins, were produced and 85% of this total was exported, chiefly to Russia.

Most of the factories engaged in canning and compôte making are located in Khorassan, where there is an abundant supply of raw materials. Canning factories operated by the Plan Organization include one at Shahi and a fish canning factory at Bandar Abbas. Other canning factories have been established by the Plan Organization at Ishfahan, Meshed, and Azerbaijan, but they only started operations in 1959 and no production statistics are yet available. During 1958 the ten factories then in operation produced 2.43 million boxes of compôtes, 71,662 of conserves, and 310,739 of sardines. They also preserved cucumbers.

Sugar was produced in Iran in ancient times and in 1940 the government decided to revive the sugar cane industry in an effort to reduce sugar imports. The project was held in abeyance during the war years, but since 1949 the cultivation of sugar cane has been reintroduced in several localities with suitable climate. The first sugar factory was built at Kahrizak and since then twelve others have begun operations, as shown in Table 7.

With the encouragement of government loans, several private factories, including a sugar refinery at Ahwaz and a factory in Fariman, have been built; the first of these began operations in 1959. Production of sugar in 1958 was 133,579 tons as compared with 102,992 tons in 1956. The 1958 production figure amounted to approximately 34% of total sugar consumption, which was estimated at 383,128 tons.

The use of vegetable oils as a food is reportedly a recent development in Iran, and is ascribable partly to the high cost of ghee and partly to health education propaganda on the low cost and healthfulness of vegetable oils. A total of 39 vegetable oil extraction factories were in operation in 1958, most of them located in Tehran and in Ostans 1 and 2. Production of margarine was carried out only in Tehran and amounted to 13,731 tons.

There are only two milk pasteurization plants, both located in Tehran, the largest of which was completed in 1957 as a joint project of UNICEF, the Ministry of Health, and the plan Organization. The proposed maximum daily capacity of this plant is 16,000 gallons of pasteurized milk, 4 tons of butter, and 20 tons of yoghurt in addition to 4,000 pounds of ice cream; by the early spring of 1958, according to the Iran Review, the plant had reached a production of 10,000 gallons of milk per day. The 1958 production of the two factories included 1,402 tons of pasteurized milk, 44 tons of butter, and 813 tons of curd.

The climate of Lahyan is suitable for tea growing, and the planting and processing of tea has been rapidly increasing in importance in that area. Production in 1948 was 4,478 tons, of which 22 were exported; whereas in 1958 production was 8,018 tons, of which 249 were exported. Despite increases in production the amount of tea grown locally is not sufficient to satisfy demands, and it amounts to only about one fourth of domestic consumption.

There are a total of 32 soft drink factories of which 15 are located in Tehran and 11 in Ostan 9. These latter were small enterprises and only produced 23,000 bottles of drinks, whereas the 15 Tehran factories produced 121,193,000 bottles. There were, in addition, two plants bottling mineral waters, four breweries, and 21 distilleries making alcoholic beverages.

The traditional methods of preserving foods at home include drying,

smoking, and salting. Vegetables and fruits are dried in the sun and
then are stored for winter use. Sheep are fattened for winter slaughter
and their meat is pickled in brine. Fish is dried or smoked or preserved in large jars with salt packed between the layers of fish.[15]

2. Refrigeration facilities. Very little information is available on
the capacity and distribution of refrigeration facilities, but they are
known to be limited. Large towns have ice-making plants, but the ice
often is prepared from contaminated water and is sold in open carts
under unsanitary conditions.[1,17] Smaller towns and rural areas have
local ice houses in which ice made and collected in winter is stored
for the summer.[9] During 1957 there were 78 ice-making plants employing a total of 648 persons. Nearly one third of these, 23 factories
with 349 employees, were located in Tehran.

The fishing industry handles and prepares the catch in cold rooms,
of which the largest is located at Pahlevi and the next largest at
Hassan Keyadeh; two smaller establishments are located in the
Babolsar fishing district.

III. DIET TYPES

A. GENERAL REMARKS

The majority of the inhabitants of Iran consume a diet at bare subsistence level and sometimes below it. Among both rural and urban
low-income groups the major portion of the daily diet is made up of
cereals, usually in the form of bread, although rice may be used more
commonly in some areas of the country. In wheat-producing areas,
rice is a luxury, although in rice-producing areas wheat bread is
eaten more or less as a cake. Oats and barley are eaten in small
amounts. Cereals are supplemented by dairy products, by vegetables
and fruits in season, and by large quantities of sweetened tea. The
intake of fresh vegetables and fruits varies considerably with the season and agricultural region; in general they are eaten raw in summer
and preserved in winter. Meat is used rarely and the consumption of
other foods is low.

Three meals a day are usual. Breakfast generally consists of
sweetened tea and bread, occasionally supplemented with cheese,
rarely with butter, and very seldom with eggs or milk. Lunch and
dinner consist primarily of a soup or stew such as **ache** or **chourba**
(described below), accompanied by bread, cheese, and tea. Cheese
usually is present at one of the two main meals of the day.

Estimates of food supplies available for human consumption vary
widely, as is to be expected when accurate statistics of production
and consumption are not available. In the absence of accurate data,

all estimates are no better than informed guesses. The most detailed
current analysis of available food supplies is to be found in estimates
prepared for 1954-1955 by the foreign agricultural Service of the
United States Department of Agriculture, and these are presented in
Table 4.

These estimates differ in several significant respects from those
contained in data prepared by the Ministry of Agriculture of Iran for
1951 and in the 1953-1955 estimates presented to the Joint WHO/FAO
Nutrition Committee for the Near East in November, 1958. Consumption of each important category of food in these three sets of estimates
is compared in Table 9. Throughout the discussion of diets presented
in the following paragraphs, data contained in the United States Department of Agriculture estimates are used; where they are significantly different from the other estimates, these differences are mentioned.

Cereals supply about 69.0% of the caloric content of the diet. The
per capita annual consumption of wheat in 1954-1955, the latest year
for which food balances are available, was estimated at 114 kg., while
11.6 kg. of rice, 19.7 of barley, and 2.8 of other grains were used.
These supplied a daily total of 1,358 calories.[12] The Joint Nutrition
Committee estimates that cereals represented only two thirds of this
consumption, that is, 96 kg. per capita.

Cereals are most commonly eaten in breads. Although several
different types of bread are in use, two are particularly common.
Farmers, in general, favor a type of home-baked bread prepared
from wheat flour and called **lavache,** whereas urban dwellers usually
eat **sanguake,** a bread made of a mixture of wheat and barley. Both
types are thin, flat breads and, in both, yeast is used as a leavening.

Rice generally is eaten in the form of **pelow,** accompanied by different sauces of vegetables or meats if available.

The most commonly used food in winter among lower income
groups is **cholleh,** composed of a boiled semolina of wheat accompanied by onions and preserved meat.

Legumes are popular diet items and total consumption is estimated
at 7.2 kg. per capita per year. Beans and peas are prepared in soups
and stews, either with other vegetables, or with meat if this is available. The most commonly used dishes include a meat soup made with
chick peas and green vegetables, tomatoes, and eggplants; this is
known as **abgouchte.** A commonly used stew, called **ache,** includes
onions, cabbage, carrots, celery, or spinach, with added rice or chick
peas or different legumes, such as beans or lentils; this stew is
cooked with clarified butter, called **rogan.** Ache is the type of stew
served in army rations which, like most Iranian meals, are of the
one-pot type.

Other vegetables usually are eaten raw as accompaniment to meals
during the seasons when they are abundant. Common vegetables

include onions, tomatoes, cucumbers, and radishes. About 40 kg. of
root and leafy vegetables are consumed per capita per year.

A wide variety of fruits and nuts are popular, including citrus
fruits, melons, pistachios, almonds, dates, grapes, and figs, but fruit
as a whole only contributes 106 calories per day, or less than 10% of
the total caloric content, to the average diet. Fruits are largely limited in distribution to the producing areas. Thus grapes and apples
are luxuries in the Caspian, where oranges are grown, while oranges
are prized as medicine in Tabriz, where apples and grapes are abundant.

Meat is eaten regularly only by higher-income families. Lamb is
the most popular meat, with beef, veal, and poultry also available.
Estimates of consumption range from 6 kg. per year in the Joint
Nutrition Committee estimates to 20.7 kg. per capita, as estimated by
the United States Foreign Agriculture Service. Even the higher estimates of food consumption only amount to 92 calories per capita per
day, a very low consumption. Mutton and goat meat make up about
80% of the meat consumed, beef 15%, and poultry 5%. Pork is forbidden on religious grounds, while frogs, crabs, oysters, and hares also
are taboo. The consumption of fish is not over 1.2 kg. per capita and
fish is an article of diet only in coastal areas of the Caspian and Red
Seas.

Meat supplies usually are cooked and preserved in each family at
the beginning of winter, each housewife following her own traditional
recipe. This preserved meat is used for the preparation of the stews
and soups (**ache** and **abgouchte**) described above. Total consumption
of meat is variously estimated at 45 to 85 kg. per capita per year.

Milk rarely is consumed in the fresh state, primarily because of
the lack of facilities for preserving it. A survey of village families
near Tehran showed that only 17 of the 2,033 families queries used
fluid milk. Fluid milk is sometimes used in the spring in a soup made
with rice (**chire-berendye**) or with rice starch (**firni**).

The most commonly used milk product is **mast** (yogurt), a fermented
preparation made by boiling the milk to kill other organisms and then
seeding it with organisms from a previous batch of **mast. Mast** is
eaten alone, in combination with other dishes, or diluted in the form
of a cold soup called **d'abdough,** which is mixed with cucumbers and
seasoned with rose powder and dried raisins. This is a particularly
popular dish in summer.

The type of cheese most commonly used in Iran is a salted white
cheese clotted in a pouch made of dried sheep's stomach. Either cow
or sheep milk is used in its preparation. Butter, as already mentioned,
is rarely used fresh; it is almost always in the form of clarified butter. Milk and milk products in general are regarded as cash products
by the cultivators, especially near urban centers where demand is
great, so that consumption of milk among rural producers may be

particularly low. The following table shows the type of milk and milk product most commonly used among 2,033 village families in communities near Tehran:

Consumption of Dairy Products[8]
Rural Area of Iran

PRODUCT	FAMILIES WHO USED PRODUCT					
	Milk only	Cheese and mast	Cheese only	Mast only	Total	%
Boiled milk	16	453	11	30	510	25.1
Raw milk	1	63	1	3	68	3.3
No milk	--	742	47	179	968	47.6
No dairy products	--	- -	--	- -	487	24.0
	17	1,258	59	212	2,033	100.0

Tea is the national beverage and is consumed in large quantities at all economic levels. Since it is usually drunk heavily sweetened there is a corresponding increase in intake of sugar. Alcoholic beverages include cognac and beer, and large quantities of soft drinks, especially carbonated beverages, are used.

B. VARIATIONS IN DIET

1. **Urban and rural groups.** The diet of the peasants, as already mentioned, is composed primarily of cereals, which contribute over 70% of total calories and 66% of total proteins. These are supplemented by sweetened tea, and milk products, including especially **mast,** cheese, and clarified butter. Meat is eaten in very small quantities and contributes only about 2% of the calories and 6% of the proteins in the average rural diet. Onions are eaten frequently, as are cucumbers, radishes, melons, nuts, and other fruits and vegetables, when permitted by seasonal availability and family finances.

In the urban diet rice is the main course of many meals, alone or prepared with meat, vegetables, or spices. Fruit, especially melons, are eaten in season and vegetables and milk also are popular. A more varied diet is available to the townsman, but his choice is dictated by his finances.

Nomadic tribesmen make up a sizeable segment of the Iranian population, estimated at 2 million, or 10% of the total. These herdsmen accompany their flocks in seasonal migrations from mountains to plains. Their diet consists almost exclusively of the products of their herds, supplemented with cereals that they sow in the plains in the fall.

2. Variations due to differences in economic status. The differences between the diets of wealthy classes and the peasant cultivator are great, even by Middle Eastern standards. As stated by an observer recently, the majority of the Iranian population is traditionally accustomed to an alimentary regime that is at famine level.[1]

These differences in diets are emphasized by a recent survey comparing the diets of landowners with those of urban wage earners and peasant cultivators. The dietary habits of some 807 persons in 156 families were exhaustively studied. The consumption of the principal categories of foodstuff in each group is compared in Table 10, while Table 11 tabulates the caloric content and nutrient value of the diets of each group.

It was found that proprietors eat four times as much meat and eggs, seven times more fruit, more than twice the oils and fats, and three times as much sugar as peasant families, while the proprietors' consumption of cereals was only 88% and of vegetables only 66% of that of the rural group. Bread alone provided 71% of the calories and 61% of the proteins of agricultural workers, but only 34% of the calories and 35% of the protein intake of proprietors. Urban wage earners ate 29% more vegetables and 48% more meat and eggs than rural families, but their rate of consumption of other foods was more or less comparable.

The generally poor quality of Iranian diets is shown by the fact that even the diet of the landowners is shown to be quantitatively below the average food consumption in urban areas in France. The best diets in the Iranian survey contained 13% less calories, 28% less proteins, and 45% less proteins of animal origin than the urban diets of France. Comparison of the diets of French peasants with Iranian peasants showed even more striking differences. In the Iranian peasant's diet bread provided more than two thirds of the caloric and protein intake, whereas in the French diet only one third were from this source. Proteins of animal origins made up 53% of the total proteins in the French rural diet but only 18% of the Iranian. These rural and urban diets in France and Iran are contrasted in Table 12.

A tabulation of the intake of calories, animal proteins, total proteins, fats, calcium, and vitamin B_2 estimated for the average population of each of the three groups surveyed, as compared to recommended allowances established by the Institut National d'Hygiene of Paris, presented in Table 13, showed that even the best diet, that of the landowning group, was below recommended standards.

There is a very great variation in the percentage of the family budget that is spent on food in each of the three categories surveyed. The landowning class spent 38.1% of their total budget on food, the urban wage earners spent 74.2%, and the agricultural laborers spent 68.6%.

3. Seasonal variations in diets. There exists considerable seasonal variation in the diets of the peasant population; about 10% less calories and 22% less animal proteins are eaten in winter than the average for the entire year. Comparison of rural diets in the four seasons of the year is presented in Table 14, which shows the intake in grams per capita per day of the most important foodstuffs, as estimated for the average individual at each of the four seasons of the year.

4. Diets in the Iranian Army: At the request of the Imperial Army of Iran, the United States Interdepartmental Committee on Nutrition for National Defense (IDCNND) carried out a survey of the diets and nutritional status of members of the Iranian Army stationed in five different localities, which were chosen to represent a cross-section of the population. The results of the physical examinations and the evidence found of deficiency disease are discussed in section V: Diseases caused by Diets below. In general, diets were found to be adequate in calories and proteins as well as in the vitamin B complex, but low to marginal in riboflavin, in vitamins A and C, and in calcium. An analysis of the diets in the five areas is shown in Table 15.[14]

IV. ADEQUACY OF FOOD RESOURCES

In normal times Iran is generally self-sufficient in food at a low level of consumption. The only foods in general use that must be imported are tea and sugar, which are not yet produced in sufficient quantities. Wheat, which once was exported in good crop years, is now becoming a consistent import item since production has not been able to keep pace with increasing demand. Even in good irrigated soils, crop yields are low because of improper cultivation methods, ineffective control of insect pests, lack of fertilizers, inefficient use of water, and large harvest losses.

All these factors operate to an even greater degree in reducing the yield in years of drought, and Iran must then import even larger quantities of foodstuffs to fill minimum domestic demands. Despite imports, severe local shortages may develop because of poor methods of transportation, which impedes the transfer of supplies to deficit areas.[11]

Another factor affecting the adequacy of food supplies, in addition to the weather, is the fact that production is not evenly distributed throughout the country: some areas have to depend on the surplus production of others. When anything happens to impede this flow of goods, severe local shortages may develop. For example, when the Russians occupied part of the Iranian territory during World War II, the Soviet Union banned shipments of staple foods from Azerbaijan to other areas, and considerable shortages developed in the deficit food areas of the north and south.[15]

V. NUTRITIONAL DISEASE PATTERNS

No country-wide studies of nutritional status have been carried out, and only a few studies on selected groups are available. However, many indications of a low nutritional status are found; the evidence collected is summarized in the following paragraphs.

Undernutrition is general among persons in lower income groups, although the degree and incidence vary widely in different sections of the country.[11] One of the indications of a poor nutritional status can be found in the high infant mortality and stillbirth ratios, which are due, at least in part to faulty nutrition of the pregnant and lactating mother. Admittedly incomplete infant mortality rates are reported to be 216 per 1,000 live births in rural areas, while stillbirths are 86.5 per 1,000.[6] In 1955 it was reported that infant deaths were mainly due to inanition, ancylostomiasis, and chronic poisoning caused by the opium given by mothers to quiet the crying of hungry babies.[6]

Another indication of substandard food consumption may be seen in the below-average heights and weights of school children, as compared with children of the same age in France.[6] These data are presented in Table 16.

The few nutritional surveys that have been carried out indicate that a considerable proportion of the population show clinical signs and symptoms, ranging from mild to severe, of disturbances usually associated with poor nutrition. One such study carried out on the children in the region of Tehran showed that 60% presented some clinical sign of a nutritional deficiency, as shown below:

Clinical Signs Observed in Children in Tehran

Clinical sign	Present % of total
Xerosis of body, face, or limbs	94.8
Conjunctivitis	85.7
Parotid hypertrophy	70.7
Cheiloses	67.4
Perifolliculitis and keratoses	63.8
Papillar hypertrophy of tongue	48.8
Redness of mucosa	48.8
Hyperkeratoses	37.9
Pigmentation	28.3
Papillary atrophy	28.1

An assessment of the nutritional status of school children in seven areas of the country showed that signs of protein deficiencies were common in children from the Caspian littoral and around Shiraz and Tabriz.[11]

Vitamin deficiencies are reportedly widespread.[11] The same group of children in seven areas, mentioned above, showed obvious symptoms of deficiency of vitamins A and C and of ariboflavinosis. These symptoms were most common in children from Bushire, Abadeh, Shiras, Ishfahan, Tehran, Tabriz, and Risht. Rickets is reportedly common, especially in urban areas, whereas night blindness is prevalent in the adult population and osteomalacia is reportedly common in the southeast. Pellagra is reported to occur in many areas.[11]

The only complete nutritional survey of a large group that is available is the survey of the nutritional status of the armed forces of Iran carried out by the Interdepartmental Committee for Nutrition in National Defense of the United States at the request of the Government of Iran. This survey is discussed at some length because it is the only modern and complete one available, including as it does not only physical but also biochemical determinations, and in addition because the group surveyed may be taken to represent the very best state of nutrition available in Iran, a group of healthy young adults receiving an adequate diet.[14]

A sample of troops in each of five areas was chosen to represent a cross-section of the Army and to include the major geographical sections of the country. Dietary surveys were carried out and a general physical examination was performed on a total of 1,730 officers and men.

No advanced nutritional deficiency disease was found, nor was there any evidence of caloric or protein deficiency. However, an appreciable number of troops showed physical findings associated with less than optimum intakes of certain vitamins. For example, 30% showed follicular dermatitis, associated with vitamin A deficiency; 15% showed angular mouth lesions characteristic of vitamin C deficiency; and 14 to 22% showed abnormalities of the gums, although not of the typical scorbutic type. No severe lesions of low vitamin A intake, such as xeroses, were seen and advanced lesions, such as of perifolliculosis, were rare. There was variation among the troops from different areas: those from Rasht in the Caspian Sea area had the fewest physical signs of deficiency diseases while the troops in Tehran, in the north central area, and in Mahabad in the northwest were in the poorest physical condition. Follicular keratosis was noted in 50% of troops in Mahabad, while 40% of troops in Tehran showed signs of subclinical vitamin C deficiency. The results of the clinical examination and the number and type of lesions found, distributed in accordance with the locality of the troops, are shown in Table 17.[14]

VI. CONCLUSIONS

Iran is a country largely self-sufficient in food supplies, but at a very low level of consumption.

Until very recently Iran has produced enough of most types of food to supply domestic requirements and has needed to import only a few items, such as tea and sugar, which were not produced at all or were produced in insufficient quantities to satisfy domestic requirements. Recently, with increased consumption due to the increase in population and the increase in purchasing power attributable to oil revenues, Iran has become an importer of such items as wheat, especially in poor crop years. If the Plan Organization's agricultural development schemes are successful this situation may be reversed. However, progress has to date been slow on most development projects and it is doubtful if the situation will change greatly in the next few years, except perhaps in the Khuzistan Development Project areas. For the country as a whole, unfavorable climatic and geographical features combine with poor agricultural practices, absentee land ownership, and other social and political factors to retard the development of food supplies adequate to maintain an optimum level of nutrition.

SELECTED REFERENCES

1. Bahadori, A., and Claudian, J. Enquete sur l'alimentation et les budgets familiaux dans deux regions de l'Iran. *Bulletin de l'Institut National Hygiène,* 1957, pp. 593-631.
2. Food and Agriculture Organization. Yearbook of Production, Vol. 12, 1958.
3. Fisher, W. B. The Middle East. (3rd edit.) London, Methuen, 1956.
4. Iran, Ministry of Industry and Mines. Industrial and Mining Statistical Yearbook for 1958-59. Tehran, 1959.
5. Iran Information Office. Iran. Washington, D. C., 1959.
6. Jager, O. Health Conditions in Northern Iran and the First Results of Statistical Inquiry into the Incidence of Disease. *Zeitschrift für Tropenmedizin und Parasitologie,* 1955. (Abstract in Bulletin of Hygiene, 1956.)
7. Kuckuck, H. Report to the Government of Iran on the Distribution and Variation of Cereals in Iran. *F. A. O. ETAP No. 517,* 1956.
8. Mashayeki, M. D., and Hayes, G. S. Some Demographic and Health Characteristics of 173 Villages in a Rural Area of Iran. Mimeographed report.
9. Nichols, A. J. Development of Iran's Agricultural Extension Service, 1957.
10. Sharabi, H. B. A Handbook of the Contemporary Middle East. Washington, D. C., Georgetown University, 1956.
11. Simmons, J. S., *et al.* Global Epidemiology: Vol. 3, The Near and Middle East. Philadelphia, Lippincott, 1954.
12. United States Department of Agriculture, Foreign Agriculture Service. Food Balance Sheet: Iran, 1954/55.
13. United States Department of Agriculture, Foreign Agriculture Service. Indices of Agricultural Production in 13 Near East Countries. Mimeographed report. November, 1959.
14. United States, Inter-Departmental Committee on Nutrition for National Defense. Iran: Nutrition Survey of the Armed Forces. August, 1956.

15. Yale University, Human Relations Area File. Country Survey Series: Iran. (H. H. Vreeland, edit.) 1957.
16. West, Q. M. Agricultural Development Programs of Iran, Iraq and Sudan. *United States Department of Agriculture, Foreign Agriculture Report No. 112,* 1958
17. Wilber, D. K. Iran: Past and Present. Princeton, Princeton University Press, 1955.

Table 1

Principal Crops: Acreage and Production

Commodity	F. A. O. Data[a]			U. S. D. A. Estimates[b]		
	Date	Acres	Production	Production		
		1000 Hec- tares	1000 Metric Tons	1957/58	1958/59	1959/60
				1000 Metric Tons		
Cereals						
Wheat	1956	2900	2700	2800	2700	3100
Barley	1959	757*	1000*	1000	950	1000
Rice	1959	259*	526*	340	320	400
Maize	1956	8	14			
Millet (av)	1948-52	11	17	61	62	68
Other grains						
Vegetables & Legumes						
Potatoes (av)	1948-52	4	37			
Sugar beets	1957	46	727			
Dry Beans (av)	1948-52	34	25			
Chick Peas	1948		20			
Lentils	1948		12			
Vegetables				910	920	940
Legumes				136	140	155
Fruit						
Oranges & Tangerines				44	45	40
Other Citrus				61	65	63
Apricots dried				13	12	14
Grapes				258	260	259
Dates				105	125	118
Other fruits fresh				950	1000	850
Raisins				65	63	63
Olives				8	9	13
Almonds unshelled				28	32	40
Pistachios unshelled				5	4	4
Walnuts "				6	6	7
Other nuts				21	22	22
Other Crops						
Cotton lint	19 1958	260*	72*	61	70	72
Cotton seed				125	140	145
Sesame				10	10	12
Flax seed				11	12	14
Vegetable oils				30	24	30
Tobacco	1958	21*	127*	14	13	12
Tea				7	7	7
Sugar, refined				98	107	115
Sugar beets	1958	68*	730*			
Animal Products						
Meat				320	330	320
Milk				1550	1555	1500
Eggs				32	32	36

*Unofficial data

Sources: (a) Food and Agriculture Organization Yearbook 1958 and Monthly Bulletin of Agricultural Statistics 1960, Jan.-March.

(b) United States Department of Agriculture Foreign Agriculture Service: Indices of Agricultural Production in 13 Near East Countries, 1959.

Table 2

Harvest Calendar of Principal Crops

Crops	Harvest Period	Bulk of Harvest
Wheat	May-Sept.	May-Aug.
Barley	Apr.-Aug.	May-July
Maize	July-Aug.	Aug.
Millet	July-Oct.	Aug.-Sept.
Rice	Aug.-Nov.	Sept.-Oct.
Sugar beets	Sept.-Nov.	Oct.
Sugar	Campaign starting in November	
Potatoes	Oct.-Nov.	Oct.
Onions	Aug.-Nov.	Sept.-Oct.
Tomatoes	June-Nov.	Aug.-Sept.
Green peas	May-Sept.	July-Aug.
Broad beans (fresh)	May-Aug.	June-July
Dry beans	July-Sept.	July-Aug.
Broad beans	Mar.-July	May-June
Chick peas	June-Sept.	June-July
Lentils	June-Aug.	June-July
Apples	June-Oct.	July-Sept.
Pears	June-Oct.	July-Sept.
Grapes	June-Sept.	Aug.-Sept.
Apricots	Mar.-Aug.	July-Aug.
Oranges	Oct.-Jan.	Nov.-Dec.
Lemons	Sept.-Dec.	Nov.-Dec.
Dates	Sept.-Oct.	Oct.
Figs	Aug.-Oct.	Sept.-Oct.
Olives	Oct.-Dec.	Nov.
Cottonseed	Sept.-Dec.	Sept.
Linseed	July-Sept.	Aug.
Sesame	July-Oct.	July-Aug.
Tobacco	Aug.-Sept.	...
Cotton	Aug.-Oct.	Sept.
Jute	Aug.	...

Source: F.A.O., World Crop Harvest Calendar, Rome, 1959.

Table 3

Imports and Exports of Agricultural Products, 1957/58

Commodity	Quantity 1000 Tons	Value 1000 Dollars	% of Total Value
	IMPORTS		
Sugar	222.3	28,566	8.6
Tea	13.3	21,826	6.6
Edible oils	12.4	4,395	1.3
Wheat and wheat flour	60.1	3,229	1.0
Hides and skins	2.1	1,406	.4
Dairy products	.9	1,040	.3
Spices	2.7	709	.2
Rubber	2.9	670	.2
Coffee	.1	139	.04
Other Agricultural Imports		1,739	.5
Total Agricultural Imports			19.1
	EXPORTS		
Cotton	44.2	25,113	6.9
Fruit, Dried	53.2	10,137	2.8
Wool	8.7	7,329	2.0
Tea	8.4	4,109	1.1
Almonds	6.6	3,999	1.1
Animal hair	3.3	3,934	1.1
Sheep and goat skins	9.3	3,834	1.1
Pistachios	2.5	2,531	.7
Seeds for food	9.5	2,526	.7
Sausage casings	.6	2,258	.6
Edible fruits, fresh	34.8	2,152	.6
Oilseeds	7.7	1,260	.3
Pulses, dried	11.5	1,148	.3
Walnuts	2.3	822	.2
Vegetables, fresh	17.5	790	.2
Cereals, incl. rice	5.9	692	.2
Other Agricultural Exports		1,386	.4
Total Agricultural Exports			20.3

Source: United States Department of Agriculture Foreign Agriculture Service. Exports and Imports 1958. Agricultural Commodities by Principal Country of Destination. Washington, D. C., 1960.

Table 4

Iran: Food Balance 1954-55

Population: 20,500,000
January 1, 1955

Product	Domestic Supply		Net Trade Imports + Exports -	Total Supply	Non-Food Uses(a)	Domestic Disappearance Available for Food(b)			
						Total	Per Capita		
	Reported Production	Estimated Supply					Per Year	Per Day	
							Kilograms		Calories
	1,000 Metric Tons								
GRAINS									
Wheat	2,100	2,557	+ 40	2,597	260	2,337	114.0		1,040
Rice (milled	368	368	- 50	318	80	238	11.6		114
Barley	824	824	—	824	420	404	19.7		179
Other grains	60	60	—	60	2	58	2.8		25
Total									1,358
PULSES	135	155	—	155	7	148	7.2		67
SUGAR (centrifugal)	62	79	+206	285	—	285	13.9		147
OILS & FATS	15	45	+ 4	49	7	42	2.0		48

Oranges	49	49	—	49	5	46	2.2	2
Apricots (fresh)	80	80	- 35	45	—	45	2.2	3
Dates	140	140	- 33	107	—	107	5.2	40
Raisins	50	50	- 30	20	—	20	1.0	8
Grapes	250	250		250	100	150	7.3	13
Olives	11	11		11	—	11	0.5	2
Pistachios (unshelled)	6	6		6	—	6	0.3	3
Almonds (unshelled)	14	14	- 10	4	—	4	0.2	2
Other fruit	—	530		530	30	500	24.4	33
Total		530		530				106
MEAT								
Mutton and goat	180	350		350	—	350	17.1	67
Beef	34	74		74	—	74	3.6	16
Poultry	17	37		37	—	37	1.8	9
Total								92
FISH	30	30	- 8	22	—	22	1.1	3
MILK(c)	1,754	1,754		1,754	—	1,754	85.6	155
EGGS	37	37		37	6	31	1.5	6
Grand Total								2,001

Source: Foreign Agricultural Service, U. S. Department of Agriculture.

Table 5

Food Processing Industries: Type of Product
Number of Factories and Employees

Industrial Activity	Total Factories	Total Employees
Sausage making	6	83
Sausage casing processing	14	361
Food canning and preservation	1	55
Milk pasteurization	2	219
Fruit drying	51	3,172
Compotes	9	195
Flour milling	509	4,593
Rice threshing	338	1,213
Biscuit making	12	126
Sugar refining	13	3,668
Lump sugar production	97	691
Candy making	16	82
Chewing gums	4	81
Vegetable oil extraction	39	1,753
Macaroni making	4	67
Tea processing	94	1,132
Alcoholic beverages	21	604
Beer brewing	4	263
Mineral water bottling	2	23
Softdrinks	32	903

Source: Industrial and Mining Statistical Yearbook 1958/59.

Table 6

Government Owned Factories—1958

Type of Factory	No.	Employees	Product Manufactured	
			Type	Amount
Food canning and preservation	2	89	Compotes	42,000 boxes
			Conserves	71,662 "
			Sardines	310,739 "
			Fish Powder	15 tons
Milk pasteurization	1	177	Milk	1,402 tons
			Butter	39 "
			Curd	93 "
Flour mills	7	1551	Flour	180,882 tons
			Sift wheat	8,073 "
Rice Threshing and cleaning	5	57	Rice	6,612 tons
			Bran	2,110 "
Sugar refining	13	3180	Sugar	93,939 tons
			Granulated sugar	39,640 "
			Brown sugar	287 "
			Molasses	21,673 "
			Lime	479 "
			Beet wastes	154,922 "
Tea processing	5	79	Tea	307 tons

Source: Industrial and Mining Statistical Yearbook 1958/59.

Table 7

Sugar Factories in Operation: 1958

Location	Established Date	Capacity Tons/Day
Kahrizak	1932	170
Karadj	1932	400
Shahabad	1935	450
Marvdasht	1935	1000
Miandoab	1936	650
Adkuh	1936	650
Shahzand	1938	450
Rezaiyeh	1950	700
Torbat Heidariyeb	1951	700
Fasa	1954	350
Varamin Refinery	1954	90
Chenaran	1956	350
Bardsir	1956	350

Source: Industrial and Mining Statistical Yearbook 1958/59.

Table 8

Iran: Industrial Activities 1958 by Ostan(a)

Activity	Product	Unit	Tehran	Ostan 1	Ostan 2	Ostan 3	Ostan 4	Ostan 5	Ostan 6	Ostan 7	Ostan 8	Ostan 9	Ostan 10
Meat Products	Sausages	Tons	1486										
	Sardines	Boxes									310739		
Dairy Products	Pasteurized Milk	Tons	1402										
	Butter	"	44										
	Curd	"	813										
Food Canning & Preserving	Compotes	Boxes	1200000									1180000	50000
	Conserves	"									71662		
	Preserved Cucumbers	"		720									
Flour Milling	Flour	Tons	211659	33550	43106	138105	32236	53660	64620	37190	15235	242032	12540
Rice Cleaning & Threshing	Rice	"		56839	86822	857	180	2000	33790	6730			3290
Biscuit Making	Biscuits	"	911									22	
Sugar Refining	Sugar	"	28857	6110		3771	6373	7622		13602	2580	25024	
	Granulated Sugar	"	2272	36		3694	462	1020		15965	733	15458	
	Brown Sugar	"					25			19	231		
	Lump Sugar	"	227744	4058	12925	1535		111000		35	823		
	Molasses	"	1520	167		1618	2092	2664		6325	1135	6152	
Confectionary	Candies	"	6550	852		100							
Vegetable Oil	Margarine	"	13275							456			

Category		Unit	1	2	3	4	5	6	7	8	9	10
Extraction	Vegetable Oil	Tons	3889	75	10850	798		66			3048	
Macaroni Making	Macaroni	"	687			16					2900	
Fruit Drying	Dried Fruit											
	Raisins	"	2810			6191				21135		
	Apricots	"				558	3020					
Tea Processing	Tea	"		7397	621	7738						
Soft Drinks	Soft Drinks	Bottles	121193393	201500		698000	5000	486000	22620			
	Mineral Water	"	2900000			100000	1280000	750000	830000			
Alcoholic Beverages	Vodka	"	2829858	1020000	390443	604562	1235251	330680	500000			
	Cognac & Liquor	"					500					
	Beer	"	2896016	70000	5753	182850						
	Wine	"	4820880	90000	9625	9910	273041	32347	112000			

(a) Ostan 1 Rasht, Ghazvin, Zandjan, Lahidjan, Arak.
Ostan 2 Gorgan, Sari, Ghom, Shahi, Damghan, Babol, Kashan.
Ostan 3 Tabriz, Marand, Khalkhal, Ardabil, Sarab, Mianeh, Maragheh, Ahar, Meshgin, Shahr.
Ostan 4 Rezanjeh, Khoy, Mahabad, Maker.
Ostan 5 Kermanshah, Hamedan, Malayer, Tuyserkan, Nahavand, Sanandadj, Ghasre-Shirin.
Ostan 6 Abadan, Shwaz, Khoram-Shahr, Khoram, Abad, Brudjird.
Ostan 7 Shiraz, Kazerun, Marvdasht, Bandar-abas, Lar, Bushehr, Fasa.
Ostan 8 Kerman, Zahedan, Bam, Rafsandjan.
Ostan 9 Mashad, Neishabur, Shahrud, Torbat, Heidariyeh, Ghuchan, Bodynurd, Sabzevar.
Ostan 10 Esfahan, Shahreza, Nadjafabad, Charmahal, Yazd.
Source: Compiled from data in Industrial and Mining Statistical Yearbook 1958/59.

Table 9

Comparison of Available Food Supply Data

	Food Supply Available (Kg./capita/year)		
	1951[a]	1953/55[b]	1954/55[c]
Milk Products	77.8	45	85.6
Meat	9.4 ⎫		20.7
Poultry	0.8 ⎭	6	1.8
Fish	1.0	1	1.1
Eggs	1.9	...	1.5
Fats & oil	3.2	8	2.0
Cereals total	127.0	96	
Wheat	109.5		114.0
Barley	13.9		19.7
Rice	13.6		11.6
Pulses	6.7	...	7.2
Vegetables	33.3	57	35.1
Fruits & nuts	51.7	40	43.3
Sugar	10.0	14	13.9
Total calories		1730	2001
Total proteins		58	
Animal proteins		8	

Sources: [a] Ministry of Agriculture, Iran.
[b] Joint FAO/WHO Nutrition Committee.
[c] U.S. Department of Agriculture, Foreign Agriculture Service.

Table 10

Comparison of Food Consumption Among Peasants, Wage
Earners and Proprietors—Iran, 1957

Foodstuff	I Peasants Gm./capita	II Wage Earners Gm./cap./day	% of I	III Proprietors Gm./cap./day	% of I
			%		%
Bread Semolina Rice	544.7	577.6	106	478.9	88
Meat & Eggs	25.2	37.6	148	105.7	420
Milk Products	216.6	179.7	82	232.5	107
Oils & Butter	17.7	19.6	110	45.3	225
Vegetables	241.1	313.2	129	159.7	66
Fresh Fruit	7.8	12.5		59.8	
Sugar	30.9	32.2	104	95.5	308

Source: Bahadori et al.: Enquete sur l'alimentation et les budgets familiaux
dans deux regions de l'Iran. Bull. Inst. Nat. Hyg. Paris, 1957.

Table 11

Caloric Intake and Nutrient Value of Diets:
Peasants, Wage Earners, Proprietors

Nutrient	Unit	I Peasants Amts.	II Wage Earners		III Proprietors	
			Amts.	% of I	Amts.	% of I
Calories	#	1847	2123	114	2658	143
Animal proteins	Gm.	11.5	10.7	93	26.5	230
Vegetable proteins	Gm.	48.5	54.5	112	47.5	97
Fats & oils	Gm.	30.5	35.3	116	66.1	220
Calcium	Gm.	.432	0.3	78	0.5	121
Vitamin B_2	mg.	.55	0.7	120	0.8	141

Source: Bahadori et al. See Table 10.

Table 12

Comparison of Diets in Iran and France

Food	Iran Landowner		French Urban Dweller		Iran Peasant		French Peasant	
	Cal.*	Prtn.**	Cal.	Prtn.	Cal.	Prtn.	Cal.	Prtn.
Bread	34	34.6	28.9	24.0	71.0	60.0	35.6	30.0
Fats	14.5	—	15.4	—	8.7	—	11.4	—
Milk & Cheese	26	10.0	11.2	18.1	3.9	12.1	9.0	27.0
Meat	6.0	21.0	7.6	23.5	2.0	6.1	9.8	26.0
Sugar	14.0	—	8.1	—	6.8	—	5.0	—

*calories
**protein

Source: Bahadori et al. See Table 10.

Table 13

Actual and Recommended Intakes in Diets of Peasants,
Urban Wage Earners and Landowners

Landowners		Average Actual	Consumption Recommended	Difference in %
Calories	#	2658	2310	+15
Animal Proteins	(Gm.)	26.5	42.2	−38
Total Proteins	"	74	91	−19
Calcium	"	0.512	0.926	−45
Vitamin B_2	(mg.)	0.773	1.414	−45
Employees				
Calories	#	2132	2228	− 4
Animal Proteins	(Gm.)	10.7	41.8	−75
Total Proteins	"	65.2	89.5	−28
Calcium	"	0.330	0.909	−55
Vitamin B_2	(mg.)	0.659	1.449	−55
Peasants				
Calories	#	1847	2320	−20
Animal Proteins	(Gm.)	11.5	42.4	−73
Total Proteins	"	60	87.7	−32
Calcium	"	0.423	0.942	−56
Vitamin B_2	(mg.)	0.550	1.379	−60

Source: Bahadori et al. See Table 10.

Table 14

Seasonal Variations in Diets

Foods	3—10 May	3—10 Aug.	3—10 Oct.	3—10 Mar.
Breads	506	556	530	432
Cereals	21.6	17	19	25
Rice	18.6	18	19	20
Meat	24	20	22	17
Eggs	8	4	6	4
Milk	41	36	31	24
Yogurt	44	49	37	27
Cheese	31	23	27	17
Oils & fats	18	18	17.5	17
Potatoes	9	14	19	37
Dry vegetables	19	13	16	38
Fresh vegetables	210	220	209	57
Fresh fruits	—	15	10	5
Sugar	31	25	38	31
Calories	1816	1946	1849	1682
Glucides	312	390	324	306
Calcium (g)	0.482	0.441	0.420	0.349
Vitamin B_2 (mg)	0.623	0.604	0.608	0.366

Source: Bahadori et al. See Table 10.

Table 15

Summary Table of Nutritive Consumption at Five Places Surveyed
Per Man per Day

	Calories	Protein Gm.	Fat Gm.	Ca mg.	Fe mg.	Vitamin A I.U.	Thiamine mg.	Riboflavin mg.	Niacin mg.	Vitamin C mg.
Tehran	3694	135.1	69.0	352.9	26.5	4867	2.49	0.96	22.2	24.2
Ahwaz	3693	129.6	75.4	500.6	40.1	3943	2.72	1.21	36.1	18.4
Mashad	4072	145.2	74.4	642.0	40.5	7704	3.26	1.41	38.3	42.1
Mahabad	4018	143.0	82.1	398.3	36.0	405	3.07	1.24	39.2	10.4
Rasht	3852	133.2	70.4	397.0	33.1	1914	2.78	1.06	35.7	17.0

Note: Intakes of above nutrients considered "acceptable" for this population group:
Calcium   400-800 mgs/day
Iron   9-12   "   "
Vitamin A 3,500-5,000 I.U./day
Thiamine   0.3-0.5 mgs/1,000 calories/day
Riboflavin 1.2-1.5 mgs/day
Niacin   10-15 mgs/day
Vitamin C   30-50 mgs/day

Source: Inter Departmental Committee for Nutrition in National Defense, Iran, Nutrition Survey of the Armed Forces, 1956.

Table 16

Height and Weight of School Children
France and Iran

Age	Height (in cm.) France	Iran	Difference	Weight (in kg.) France	Iran	Difference (in kg.)
	BOYS					
5-6	107.9	100	7.9	18.44	12	6.4
6-7	113.6	105.82	7.8	20.40	18.12	2.3
7-8	117.7	113.81	3.9	22.23	20.28	2
8-9	121.8	119.23	2.6	24.26	22.03	2.2
9-10	127.9	122.62	5.3	27.03	23.68	3.4
10-11	132.9	126.72	6.2	29.68	25.17	4.5
11-12	137.8	130.97	6.9	32.61	27.95	4.7
12-13	142.5	135.45	7.1	35.97	30.15	5.8
	GIRLS					
5-6	106.9	100.17	6.8	17.81	14.33	3.5
6-7	112.6	111.33	1.3	19.52	18.33	1.2
7-8	116.4	114.67	1.8	21.20	18.82	2.4
8-9	122.3	120.56	1.8	23.99	21.09	2.9
9-10	127.7	125.96	1.8	26.76	23.03	3.7
10-11	133.9	129.19	4.7	30.24	24.69	5.5
11-12	138.6	133.66	5.0	33.88	27.44	6.4
12-13	145.6	137.92	7.7	39.02	29.29	10.7

Source: Bahadori et al. See Table 10.

Table 17

Iran: Clinical Summary by Location

	Tehran	Ahwaz	Mahabad	Rasht	Mashad	Total
No. Examined	506	308	307	292	317	1730
	%	%	%	%	%	%
APPEARANCE						
Good	40.9	50.0	47.9	64.4	47.0	48.8
Fair	54.2	47.7	45.3	34.2	47.6	46.9
Poor	4.9	2.3	5.8	1.4	5.4	4.1
Cachexic	0	0	1.0	0	0	0.2
SKIN						
Nasolabial Seborrhea	4.5	3.6	1.0	0.3	1.6	2.5
Follicular Keratosis	21.5	21.4	49.5	43.1	30.3	29.8
Perifolliculosis	0.6	0	0	0	0	0.2
Acneform Eruption	24.3	26.9	20.8	19.2	19.6	22.4
Bluish Cold Extremities	90.9	26.6	88.6	84.6	71.6	74.5
Xerosis	0.2	0	0.3	0	0	0.1
Crackled Skin	2.0	0	0.3	0	0	0.6
EYES						
Thickened Conjunctiva	7.1	7.1	7.2	8.6	15.5	9.1
Conjunctival Injection	12.5	3.9	7.5	7.9	6.9	8.5
Blepharitis	1.8	0	0.7	0.7	0.6	0.9
MOUTH						
Angular Lesions	19.0	7.5	18.9	10.6	13.9	14.6
Angular Scars	20.0	18.2	19.9	29.8	17.0	20.8
Angular Scars & Lesions	16.0	1.6	4.2	5.1	2.5	7.1
LIPS						
Cheilosis	6.5	1.3	2.6	3.1	1.4	3.4
TONGUE						
Filiform Atrophy						
(slight not included)	9.5	2.3	6.5	9.2	5.4	6.9
Fungiform Pap. Atrophy	18.8	7.1	23.1	22.3	17.4	17.8
Papillary Hypertrophy	10.1	5.2	15.0	4.1	9.5	9.0
Geographic Tongue	0.4	0.6	8.5	7.9	3.8	3.8
Fissures and Furrows	10.1	1.6	0.7	0.7	1.6	3.8
TEETH						
Caries	55.7	39.6	29.3	53.4	36.6	44.4
Worn Teeth	60.9	17.5	52.4	26.7	56.5	45.1
Fluorosis	1.6	2.6	1.6	0.7	1.3	1.6
GUMS						
Recession	72.7	51.9	39.1	46.2	50.5	54.5
Bleeding	20.6	12.7	7.5	5.5	13.2	12.9
Scorbutic Type	3.4	0	1.3	0.3	1.6	1.6
Marginal Redness	24.7	12.3	7.8	6.5	9.8	13.7
Marginal Swelling	38.5	18.5	13.7	5.1	22.1	21.9
Atrophy of Papillae	14.2	4.2	1.0	1.0	5.4	6.2
OTHER						
Hepatomegaly	0.4	0.6	0.3	0.3	0	0.3
Splenomegaly	0.2	6.2	2.9	0.7	0	1.8
Edema of Legs	1.4	0.6	0	0.3	0	0.6
Loss of Ankle Jerks	1.5	3.5	0	0.6	0.6	1.3

Source: I.C.N.N.D., Iran, Nutrition Survey of the Armed Forces, 1956.

Map 1

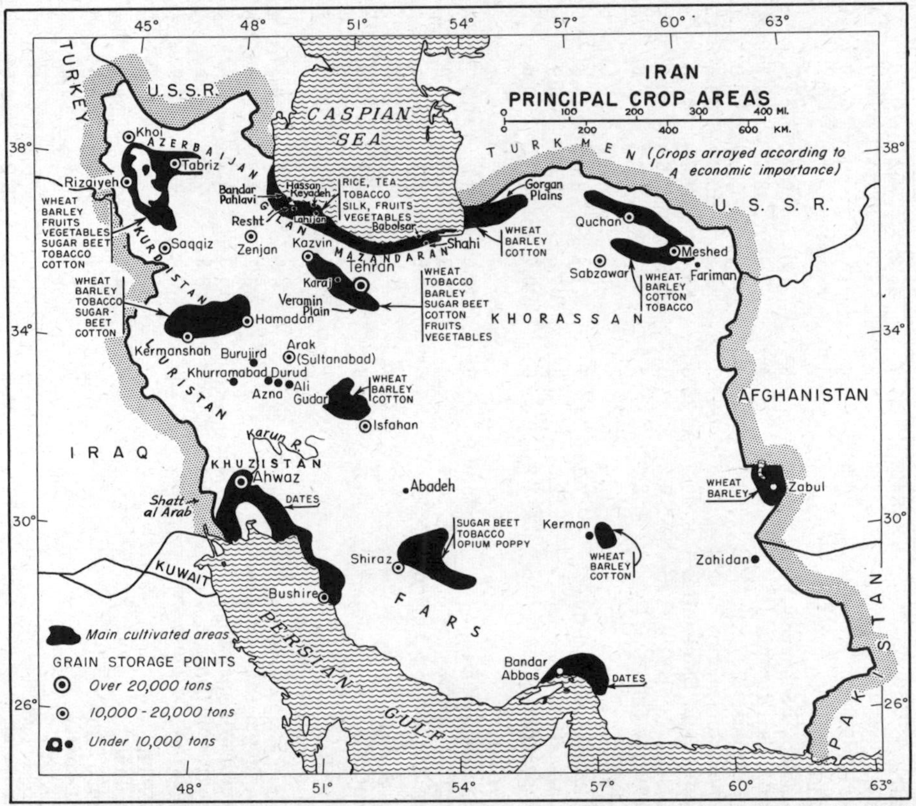

IRAN

PRINCIPAL CROP AREAS

(Crops arrayed according to
economic importance)

100 200 300 400 ML.
100 200 300 400 600 KM.

TURKEY

U.S.S.R.

CASPIAN SEA

TURKMEN

U.S.S.R.

AFGHANISTAN

Khoi

Rizaiyeh

Tabriz

AZERBAIJAN

WHEAT
BARLEY
FRUITS
VEGETABLES
SUGAR BEET
TOBACCO
COTTON

Saqqiz

KURDISTAN

Zenjan

Bandar
Pahlavi

Resht

GILAN

RICE, TEA
TOBACCO
SILK, FRUITS
VEGETABLES

Hasan
Kiadeh

Kazvin

Karaj

Bobolser

Shahi

MAZANDARAN

WHEAT
BARLEY
COTTON

Gorgan
Plains

Quchan

Sabzowar

Meshed

Feriman

WHEAT
BARLEY
COTTON
TOBACCO

KHORASSAN

Tehran

WHEAT
TOBACCO
BARLEY
SUGAR BEET
COTTON
FRUITS
VEGETABLES

Veramin
Plain

Kermanshah

Durud

Arak
(Sultanabad)

Khurramabad

Burujird

Hamadan

Azna

Ali
Gudarz

WHEAT
BARLEY
COTTON

Isfahan

Abadeh

Kerman

WHEAT
BARLEY
COTTON

Zabul

Zahidan

AFGHANISTAN

PAKISTAN

WHEAT
BARLEY

LURISTAN

KHUZISTAN

DATES

Ahwaz

Karun

Shatt
al Arab

IRAQ

KUWAIT

SUGAR BEET
TOBACCO
OPIUM POPPY

Shiraz

FARS

Bushire

Bandar
Abbas

DATES

PERSIAN GULF

GRAIN STORAGE POINTS

Main cultivated areas

◉ Over 20,000 tons

◎ 10,000 - 20,000 tons

◌ Under 10,000 tons

U. S. DEPARTMENT OF AGRICULTURE   NEG. 1453   OFFICE OF FOREIGN AGRICULTURAL RELATIONS

Map 2

IRAN: DISTRIBUTION OF WHEAT AND BARLEY PRODUCTION

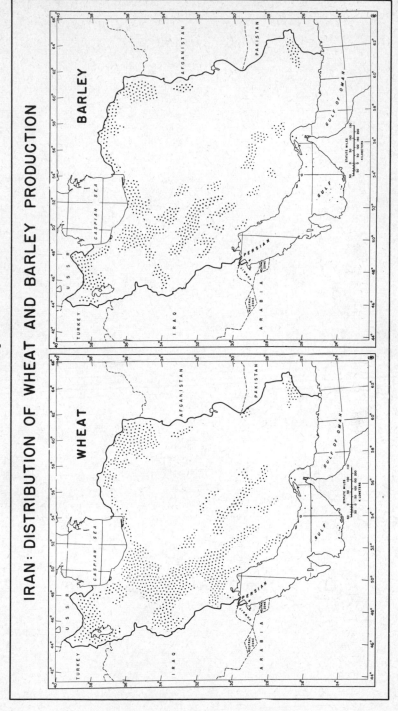

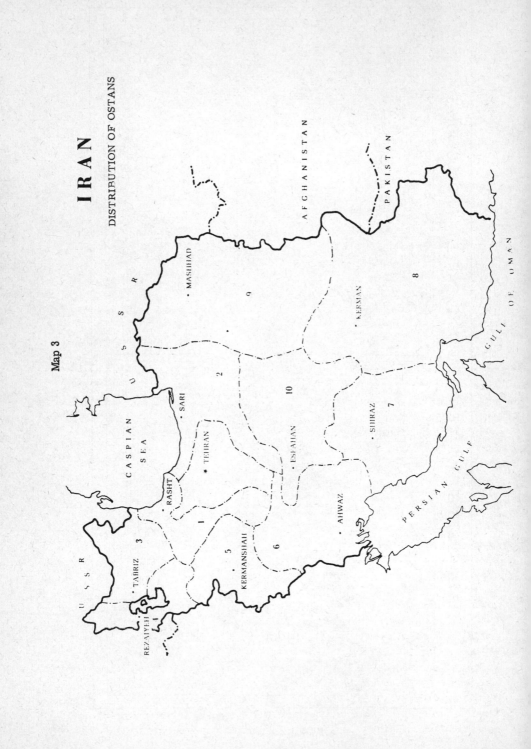

Map 3

IRAN

DISTRIBUTION OF OSTANS

IRAQ

I. GENERAL REMARKS

A. AGRICULTURE IN GENERAL

Iraq is predominantly an agricultural country. Three fourths of the population derive their livelihood from agriculture and animal husbandry. Unlike some other Middle Eastern countries, Iraq has a low population density, considerable undeveloped land surface, and is in the favorable position of being able to finance development of natural resources with income from oil royalties. The population, according to the 1957 census, totaled 6,538,000 on a total land area of 44,389,000 hectares (109,712,000 acres), of which only 12.3% was actually cultivated; an additional 27.2% was unused but potentially cultivable. Iraq is therefore sparsely populated and not subject to the population pressures that constitute such a grave problem in other countries, for example in Egypt. Despite these favorable factors, agricultural output is low, the standard of living of the peasants wretched, and methods of agricultural production still largely at primitive levels.

As elsewhere in the Middle East, the amount and management of water supplies available are the critical factors in agriculture. Only the north and northeast of the country receive enough rainfall to allow dry-farming; elsewhere agriculture depends on irrigation based on the water supplied by the Tigris, Euphrates, and Diyala rivers, wells, and springs. The methods of irrigation employed in each **liwa** and the amount of land cultivated by each method are shown in Table 1.

Periodic flooding of the Tigris and Euphrates used to devastate this area. These floods were particularly destructive, since they occurred when crops were already half grown instead of before they were planted, as is the case with the flooding of the Nile. The Tigris and Euphrates rivers, when at flood from March to May, may carry as much as 40 times the amount of water they contain at low water, in September and October.

Approximately 30% of the budget of the Iraqi Development Board, financed with oil revenues, is devoted to irrigation, flood control, and drainage projects. The overall, long-range plan aims at preventing floods and providing water for additional cultivation. Proposed projects will increase the water supply to land now under partial irrigation and eventually will irrigate 2.3 million hectares of new government owned land. This would constitute a 65% increase in cultivated area and would greatly increase the production of summer crops. The new projects include adequate measures for drainage and some old irrigated areas, such as the Dujaila, Saqlawiyah, and Abu Ghuraib, are being provided with drains.

The antiquated system of land ownership is another factor in retarding the economic development of the country and delaying any improvement in the standard of living of the peasants. The system of land tenure is even more complicated and confusing than in neighboring countries and the State retains the ultimate legal title to almost all the land. A few peasants in the northeast own their land, but the small size of holdings, the primitive methods, and the consequent low yields make these proprietors only a little better off than the tenant farmers and landless majority. The largest proportion of Iraqui peasants are sharecroppers, although smaller groups may be tenants or hired labor. Landlords receive as much as half the crop while taxes and other expenses take an additional share. In some areas of southern Iraq the cultivator's share may be as low as 20 to 40% of the crop, while in dry-farming areas of the northeast tenants may retain as much as 80 to 90% of the non-irrigated winter crops produced. A land reform program designed to correct such abuses was inaugurated recently (Miri Serf Land Distribution), but its implementation has encountered serious difficulty; as of December, 1959, only 60,000 acres had been distributed "provisionally". The resulting confusion among landlords and peasants as to ownership of lands and crops has been a factor in the recent decline of agricultural production.

B. AGRICULTURAL REGIONS

The country may be divided into three large zones on the basis of topography and climate: the desert zone, the zone of rain-fed agriculture, and the zone of irrigated crops.

The Iraqi desert area lies to the south and southwest of the country and includes approximately 40% of total land area. It consists in great part of wide, stony plains intersected by **wadis,** of which the best known is the Hauran. Along the dry watercourses of these wadis there usually lie a string of wells that provide water for the flocks of the Bedouin tribesmen, who are almost the sole inhabitants of this region. All the food supply of the desert zone of the south and southwest is derived from the flocks tended by nomadic tribesmen. These foods include milk, butter, and cheese, while cereals and dates are obtained by barter of the wool, hair, skins, and hides.

The rain-fed zone of the north itself can be divided into the plains region and the highlands, both of which have sufficient rainfall to

permit the growing of winter crops, of which the most important are
wheat and barley. The amount of rain, which averages about 380 mm,
per year, is not enough to allow the planting of summer crops, and these
are grown only where streams or springs provide additional water. The
high mountains of this area are covered with grazing lands used by the
Kurdish shepherds; the raising of livestock by these tribes is their
principal agricultural enterprise.

The main crops in the rain-fed zone of the north are wheat and barley, which are the principal winter crops, and cotton, rice, and tobacco, which are grown wherever there is sufficient water to permit
the cultivation of summer crops as well. A variety of fruits is grown
and orchards of apples and other fruits are scattered throughout the
zone. At higher altitudes of the northern areas, such as the mountains
of Kurdistan, livestock products derived from the herds of the Kurdish
shepherds are the most important item of food.

The irrigated crop area of Iraq includes the center and southeast of
the country. Rainfall is scanty and irregular, at most some 150 mm
a year, so that agriculture must depend on irrigation water supplied
by the large rivers that traverse the area. The central portion of
the irrigated zone, which includes the valleys of the Tigris and Euphrates and of the Diyala, is the most important from an agricultural
point of view since the northern zone (the northern Jezirah and the
land north of Baghdad and east of the Tigris) is either unsuited to agriculture or is still largely undeveloped. It is in the central region that
the majority of the inhabitants live and a major proportion of agricultural products are raised. Along the banks of the three rivers mentioned, pump irrigation predominates, while more remote areas are
supplied by canals from the Hindiya barrage on the Euphrates, the
Kut barrage on the Tigris, and the Diyala Weir. The alluvial soils of
the three valleys are very fertile but, because of lack of drainage,
much of the land has become saline. An estimated 20 to 30% of the irrigated land has been abandoned in recent years because of the increased salinity of the soil and it is estimated that adequate drainage
measures alone could increase the yield of cereals by 72%, rice by
36%, and citrus and dates by 60%. On these high salinity lands long
stretches of poor barley alternate with equally long stretches of camel
thorn, derelict salt encrusted land, and expanses of last year's flood
water.

The central and southern irrigated regions produce a variety of
crops. Barley is the most important winter crop in the central region,
followed by wheat, lentils, flax, and vetch. Rice and cotton are the
leading summer crops; others are sorghum, sesame, pulses, corn, and
millet. Dates are widely grown and citrus fruits are important in the
Diyala River valley. In the extreme southern region, rice is the
staple crop whereas dates are cultivated along both sides of the Shatt al
Arab.

II. FOOD RESOURCES

A. GENERAL

Low crop yields, lower than those of neighboring countries, are characteristic in Iraq in spite of the relative abundance of land and water. Some of the factors responsible include the primitive agricultural methods generally in use, the sharecropping system of land tenure, and the inadequate drainage of irrigated areas, discussed above.[1]

As of 1959, there was no typical farmer in Iraq. Rather there was an average farm laborer, working for a large landowner. Such a laborer would have to support a wife, several children, and also some relatives, such as a father or an orphan. This laborer would be responsible for about 9 hectares in a farm averaging 175 hectares. His duties would include tending a grove of 140 date palms from which he would get 20% of the profit, as calculated by the landlord. He also received 20% of the small-grain crop raised. He was entitled to keep all the vegetables he could produce by intercropping in the date groves but, since all crops have to be irrigated with water raised from a canal, often by hand, he could only raise a small crop of vegetables. The farmer is generally idle seven months of the year, and during this time he is able to grow vegetables and a few fruits that he can sell or keep for the use of his family. On this basis, such a farmer realizes a total gross cash income of $110 per year, including $15 from the sale of his vegetables, $55 from his share of the dates, and $40 from his share of barley and wheat. After repaying his debts, he has $26 for household expenses at the end of the year.

Cereals generally are harvested from May to September, some legumes ripen earlier, in March to April; most fruits are gathered from June to October. The harvest period for the principal crops, as well as the months when the bulk of the cereal and date crops are gathered, are listed in Table 2.

Latest available data on area and production of the principal crops grown is presented in Table 3. A brief discussion of the most important aspects of agricultural and especially food production is presented below.

B. CEREALS [1,2]

Cereals are the most important crop and the basis of the diet, contributing more than half of the total caloric intake. Almost nine tenths of the cultivated area is sown to barley and wheat, which are grown both in rain-fed and irrigated zones, with wheat more commonly grown in dry-farming areas. The overwhelming importance of cereals to the agricultural economy of Iraq may be seen in the following listing

of agricultural receipts, in Iraqi dinars, for the principal crops grown
in 1957-58:

Summer and winter crops (mostly grains)	1,845,558
Vegetables	18,391
Fruits	2,258
Palm trees	365,849
Tobacco	123,234
Others	475

The principal wheat-producing areas arc in the dry-farming lands
of Mosul, Kirkuk, Arbil, and Sulaimaniya, although some wheat is
planted in most areas of the center and south. The distribution of
wheat production is shown in Map 1. The area planted to wheat has
increased by two thirds between 1948-49 and 1956-57. Most of this
increase occurred in the northern dry-farming area, where large
tracts of marginal steppe bordering the desert were brought under
cultivation with mechanized means. This expansion has resulted in a
great yearly variation of the total crop of grain, since yield are determined by the amount of rainfall in any particular year. The production area and yield of wheat in both northern Iraq and the central and
southern areas is shown in Table 4.[2] Between 1956 and 1959 an average of 1,456,000 hectares were planted to wheat and production
amounted to 1,118,000 tons. All of the wheat produced is used locally
and, unlike barley, there are no exportable surpluses.

The bad drought of 1958 greatly reduced the amount of wheat produced, although acreage planted increased. Thus, in 1958 only
754,000 tons were produced on 1,532,000 hectares, while unofficial
data for 1959 estimated production at only 653,000 tons.

Barley is the principal crop of Iraq. More barley than wheat is
grown because of its greater resistance to the arid climate and poor
soil and because barley yields about twice as much grain per acre as
wheat. Production is such that all domestic needs are satisfied and
large surpluses are available for export.[1]

Large areas in the dry-farming region of the north are devoted to
barley production but, unlike wheat, barley also is grown rather extensively in the center and south because of its greater relative resistance to salinity in soils. The distribution of barley production in
Iraq is shown in Map 2. The total acreage devoted to barley in central
and southern Iraq remained more or less stable between 1948 and
1957, as shown in Table 4, but the area planted in the north nearly
doubled and so did production. Total acreage reached 1,239,000 hectares and production amounted to 1,305,000 tons in 1956-57. With increases in production, exportable surpluses have correspondingly increased but, unfortunately, this has happened at a time when the world
market demand for barley has been at a very low level and it has been
difficult to dispose of the surplus.

The unfavorable weather of 1958-59 reduced production of barley also but, because of its greater resistance to semiarid conditions, the reduction was not as great proportionately. Thus, 953,000 tons were grown in 1958 and an estimated 764,000 tons in 1959.

Rice is the only important summer crop and is grown throughout Iraq, but especially in the marsh land at the confluence of the Tigris and Euphrates. The cultivation of rice is controlled by the government, which specifies where it may be grown and issues special licenses authorizing its cultivation. The acreage planted to rice, and consequently, the total production decreased sharply after 1951 and remained at approximately one half of the previous levels (see Table 4). This decrease has been most pronounced in Amara and Duvaniya, formerly the most important rice-growing areas. The area planted in 1958 amounted to 89,000 hectares and production totaled 1,370,000 tons.

New developments in expanded irrigation and improved drainage practices should result in increased planting of rice. Although rice is a favorite food, a large proportion of the inhabitants cannot afford to purchase it, and it is estimated that one third of the inhabitants consume about nine tenths of the rice used for food.

Maize is grown in Baghdad, Ramadi, Diala, and Kut. Production amounts to 5,000 tons a year grown on approximately 6,000 hectares. Giant millet is grown in Amara, Nasiriya, and Diwaniya, while millet is grown in the same liwas as well as in Baghdad, Kut, and Ramadi. Production of giant millet in 1958 amounted to 9,200 tons and of millet to 4,500 tons.

C. OTHER EDIBLE CROPS

Vegetables and legumes. Many kinds of vegetables are grown near urban areas for sale in local markets, but they are not important as a staple of diet in rural communities. The most extensive vegetable plantings are near Baghdad. The area under cultivation of the principal vegetables is very limited and amounts to less than 25,000 hectares, as can be seen from Table 5, which lists the acreage planted to the most commonly grown vegetables as of 1953.

Several varieties of legumes are grown, both for green fodder and for food, and the total production of dry beans and peas amounted to 48,000 tons a year. Lentils are grown in the northern plains and mountains where the climate is well adapted to their cultivation, although they also are grown to a lesser extent on the coastal plains. About 13,000 hectares are planted to lentils but production in 1958 was only 3,000 tons compared to 8,000 tons on the same acreage in 1957. The principal producing areas include Mosul, Kirkuk, Sulaimaniya, and Arbil. Lubia or cowpeas, are widely planted for use as food and sometimes for forage. Broad beans grow as a winter crop, usually under irrigation; during 1957 the 9,000 hectares planted produced 8,000 tons. Chick peas are planted as a winter lugume to a somewhat limited extent in northern Iraq; production in 1957 amounted to 1,000 tons.[3]

Fruits.[2,7] Iraq is the world's largest producer of dates; they are one of the staple foods in Iraq and one of the most important agricultural export items. The principal date-growing area is along the Shatt al Arab in the south, the river formed by the confluence of the Tigris and Euphrates. The area on both sides of this river, which flows into the Gulf of Basra, is the world's largest date palm belt. During 1952-53 there were an estimated 18 million trees of fruit-bearing age in this region. Low quality dates, or dates left over from previous crops, are used by distillers to make alcohol and efforts are also under way to convert these unmarketable dates into fodder to improve the low level of animal nutrition. During 1958-59 an estimated 470,000 tons of dates were harvested but estimates of the 1959-60 crop predicted only 330,000 tons. Of this crop, only 60,000 tons were expected to be high quality dates, as compared with 110,000 tons the previous year.

Citrus is grown in the Diyala River valley, while a variety of fruits is cultivated in the mountain regions of the north. Small vineyards are found throughout the irrigated central plains but the largest grape growing area is in Sulaimaniya. All fruit produced is consumed locally.

Both watermelons and other types of melons are popular; in 1953 there were 12,620 hectares planted to watermelons and 5,362 to other types of melons.

The number of fruit-bearing trees of the most important varieties grown, as tabulated in the agricultural census of 1952-53, is listed in Table 6.

Sesame. These oil-bearing seeds constitute an important summer crop, being grown throughout Iraq. Area sown in 1958 totaled 21,410 hectares (52,920 acres) and production amounted to 14,300 tons.

D. CASH CROPS[2]

The growing of cotton is at present confined to central Iraq, and production is low. Baghdad, Kut, Diala, and Ramadi are the principal producing areas. The area cultivated increased from an average of 21,040 hectares (52,000 acres) pre-war to 63,120 hectares (156,000 acres) in 1957, and cotton is the crop that has shown the greatest expansion relative to its original acreage. Production in 1957 reached 14,000 metric tons, but it was estimated at only 9,000 tons in 1959-60. Most of the cotton produced formerly was exported since domestic cotton mills could not handle total production, but a new cotton textile fac-

tory built at Mosul will produce one third of the domestic consumption
of textile goods and can process 4,000 metric tons of cotton, more than
Iraq is now exporting. As more water becomes available for irrigation,
the acreage of cotton planted should expand rapidly.

Small quantities of tobacco are grown in Sulaimaniya and Arbil.
This is the main cash crop of the mountain region. Acreage amounted
to 8,000 hectares in 1958 and production was estimated at 5,300 tons.

E. ANIMAL PRODUCT RESOURCES

Iraqi peasants generally raise either crops or livestock, but not both,
so that many do not own livestock except for a draft animal, an ox,
donkey, or mule, to help in working the farm.

Unofficial estimates of the number of livestock in Iraq between
1935-1939 (averages) and 1957 gave the following totals:[2]

Livestock	Average 1935-39	1950	1955	1956	1957
		(000 deleted)			
Sheep	7,090	7,490	9,000	8,500	9,221
Goats	2,224	1,754	2,250	2,500	2,500
Cattle	374	1,035	1,720	1,910	1,900
Camels	(1)	279	(1)	(1)	(1)
Buffalo	(1)	200	(1)	(1)	(1)
Horses	(1)	184	(1)	(1)	(1)
Donkeys	(1)	326	(1)	(1)	(1)
Poultry	(1)	6,000	(1)	(1)	(1)

(a) Not available.

1950 data, The Economic Development of Iraq, International Bank for
Reconstruction and Development, 1952. Other years from U.S. Dept. of
Agriculture.

Approximately half of the sheep and goats are on agricultural holdings and the remainder are herded by nomads. Much of the land has
been overgrazed, and a considerable part of former grazing land has
been converted to mechanized agriculture, so that livestock nutrition
is at a low level. Losses from malnutrition may be as high as 20 to
30% in severe winters. Prevalent animal diseases also decimate the
badly nourished livestock and, in some outbreaks, mortality rates as
high as 50% have been reported.

As may be noted from the above tabulation, sheep and goats are the
predominant species, constituting three fourths of all livestock, excluding poultry. Sheep are all of the fat-tailed variety, with **Karradi**
sheep more common in the northern mountains, **Awassi** in the northwest and central regions, and **Arabi** or **Shevali** sheep, the hardiest of

the three breeds, predominating in the south. Cattle are important in
the northern and central parts of the country. Humpback cattle are com-
moner in the south and the straight-back variety prevail in the north.

The water buffalo is common in the plains and especially so in the
marshy areas of the south.

Camels are herded by the Bedouins, along with sheep and goats and
a number of horses.[1] Two varieties of camels are common, the Kha-
war and the Joudi.

Annual meat production is low, estimated at about 70,000 tons
per year, equivalent to a meat consumption of about 12 kg. per capita per year. This is one eighth of United States meat consumption, in
spite of the fact that Iraq has a higher animal population per inhabitant
than the United States. All meat produced is consumed in the country
and, in addition, a varying number of live animals are exported to
neighboring countries.[2]

The total annual slaughter in government-controlled slaughterhouses
in 1957 and 1958 was as follows:

Liwa	Sheep	Goats	Cattle	Buffalo	Camels
Baghdad	715,792	191,796	57,142	6,403	1,143
Mosul	187,928	92,195	15,137	143	24
Basra	98,931	2,292	22,750	3,017	155
Others	546,659	334,089	111,334	3,409	3,106
Total 1957	1,549,310	620,372	206,363	12,972	4,428
Total 1958	171,994	531,652	200,024	13,271	5,477

This represents about two thirds or more of the total estimated
slaughter. The remaining animals are slaughtered by individual
farmers.

No accurate data are available on the production and consumption of
milk and milk products in Iraq. Estimates of milk production range
from 800,000 to 1,200,000 metric tons per year. Reports indicate that
such milk and milk products as are available generally are of poor
quality and, in urban areas, are high in price. Deficits in the supply of
dairy goods in urban areas are made up by the importation of considerable quantities of powdered and condensed milk and other dairy
products.

Production of butter was estimated at an average of 24,000 metric
tons yearly between 1948 to 1952, whereas 10,000 metric tons of sheep
and goat milk cheese and 4,000 tons of cow and buffalo milk cheese
were produced in those years. Later estimates are not available, but
quantities must have increased if the estimated increase in milk
production is accurate.

Fresh-water fish are scarce in Iraq despite the large rivers and the
considerable number of lakes. The annual catch of fresh-water fish

probably does not exceed 10,000 tons and, since local demand is high, all supplies are marketed readily in the producing area. The only section of Iraq where fish is a staple of diet is reportedly among the marsh-dwelling Arabs of the south.

Commercial sea fisheries are undeveloped and the industry is of minor importance in producing food. Production is reportedly about 300 tons a year.

F. EXPORTS AND IMPORTS [2]

Iraq exports approximately 15% of its total agricultural and livestock production and such trade constitutes 85 to 90% of the total value of exports, excluding oil. Barley and dates are the two most important agricultural exports, while small quantities of wheat may be exported in good crop years. Some millet, rice, corn, and legumes also are shipped. Livestock products exported include wool, live animals, and hides.

The value of barley and date exports has declined sharply in recent years. Export trade in barley in 1952 was valued at 8,957,000 dinars, while in 1957 it was only 2,951,000 and in 1958 amounted to 4,760,000 dinars. The decrease in exports of barley is attributed to the drop in the world demand. Similarly, Iraq exported 4,652,000 dinars' worth of dates in 1952 but only 2,858,000 in 1958. The exports of other agricultural products also have declined: 693,000 dinars worth of pulses and flour were exported in 1952 and only 137,000 in 1957. These and other export values for 1952-1957 are presented in Table 7.

The decrease in exports of agricultural products is due to a combination of factors, including low demand and low prices for barley on the world market, the deterioration in the quality of Iraqi dates, and the increased domestic consumption of foodstuffs as a result of the increased personal incomes associated with the oil industry.

Imports of agricultural products are large and increasing steadily, with an increased demand for consumer goods stimulated by large oil revenues. During 1958 Iraq imported large quantities of sugar, tea, fats and oils, vegetables, oilseeds, fresh fruits, dairy products, rice, coffee, and other items. Agricultural imports accounted for 17% of all imports. Table 8 shows the quantity, value, and share of total value of the principal food exports and imports in 1958.

G. INTERNATIONAL PROGRAMS IN AGRICULTURE AND NUTRITION

Several international agencies carry out programs in agricultural development and nutrition. UNICEF, for example, has helped set up school feeding programs which, as of 1958-59, provided skim milk for

265,000 children in 1,745 schools. Some 91,000 of these children also receive a complete meal and the remainder get a vitamin oil capsule. The Food and Agriculture Organization supported projects on plant protection, control of animal diseases, forestry, and agricultural economics. The United States International Cooperation Administration has provided technical aid in several agricultural fields including, especially, forage problems. The USSR also has offered technical aid in agricultural fields; in 1960 a new training center in agriculture was to be set up, staffed by Russian technicians.

H. FOOD INDUSTRIES, STORAGE AND TECHNOLOGY

Food processing. The processing of agricultural products generally is on a small scale and is carried out by primitive methods.[4] The 1954 industrial census reported a total of 3,100 food processing establishments employing some 19,827 persons. These factories included 9 slaughterhouses, 127 dairies, 96 fruit preserving and date packing establishments, 960 grain mills, 1,563 bakeries, 171 confectioneries, and 122 factories processing other foods. Arak and beer were made by seven distilleries and breweries, while there were 45 soft drink and carbonated beverage plants. The distribution by liwa of these factories, according to the census findings is presented in Table 9.[5]

Development programs now in operation have expanded or modernized several factories processing agricultural products. A new cotton textile factory at Mosul is expected to supply an estimated third of the domestic consumption of cotton goods and process cotton now exported. A sugar plant at Mosul is to use both imported raw cane sugar and locally grown sugar beets, when this crop is planted on a commercial scale. A second plant in Karbela will produce 8,000 tons of liquid sugar and 9,000 tons of date syrup, while a third plant is being considered for Sulaimaniya, where sugar beet production is slated to expand. Modern dairying plants are being constructed in Basra and Karbela but, as far as is known, are not yet in operation. A dairy processing plant was being constructed in 1958 at Abu Ghuraib, near Baghdad, which is to have a capacity of 40,000 quarts of milk and one ton of butter daily. Plans call for concentrating at this spot all herds of milking buffaloes and cattle presently scattered throughout Baghdad so that all the milk will be processed and distributed through this plant.[6]

Some small-scale home preserving of food reportedly is carried out. Freezing of agricultural produce, as far as could be ascertained, is not done.[4]

Storage and refrigeration. Lack of adequate marketing and storage facilities for crops hamper both domestic and export sales of farm

produce. Grain is stored in villages in containers made of bamboo
splits or straw, which are plastered with mud or cow dung. Barley and
other grains are often mixed, sometimes intentionally, with dust, sand,
stones, and other foreign matter, and there are no facilities for cleaning the grain before marketing.

Grain is assembled in special locations known as **alwas** where it is
sold to retailers, bakeries, and grain dealers, or directly to consumers.
There were 2,298 of these **alwas** in 1958 and their distribution by
province is shown in Table 10. Dealers transfer their grain purchases
to **khans** or ship them to other markets. **Alwas** are improperly constructed and lack facilities for storing and grading; charges for marketing the grain vary, but generally they are high.

Some storage silos have been built at a few marketing centers by
the Grain Board, but their capacity is inadequate. These include the
following:[2]

Steel silo at Baghdad	Capacity 11,000 tons	
Concrete silo at Baghdad	" 5,000	"
Silo at Mosul	" 12,300	"
" " Arbil	" 8,300	"
" " Hilla	" 8,000	"
" " Basra	" 65,000	"

Vegetables and fruits are brought to special **alwas** where they are
sold at auction but, as in the case of grains, adequate marketing facilities are lacking. The marketing of dates is the one exception and then
only where the sale is controlled by the Date Association, which enjoys a monopoly of exports. The Association owns modern facilities
for cleaning, grading, and packing, while the export sale itself is highly
organized.[4]

Food supplies in general, and particularly in rural areas and small
towns, are not stored or marketed under conditions that will insure
their preservation or sanitation.[4]

III. DIET TYPES

A. GENERAL

The diet patterns of the various regions, of different economic
groups, and of the urban and rural population differ in many important
respects; some of the more important of these variations are discussed in some detail in B, Variations in Diets, below. Despite these
differences, however, some generalizations can be made that will apply to the diet of the large majority of the population.

A large proportion of the inhabitants of Iraq subsist on diets inadequate in quantity and quality, including especially the urban dwellers of lower economic status and the large majority of the rural population.[10] The staples of diet in all population groups include cereals, dates, and onions with sweetened tea or coffee. All diets are reportedly low in meat, fish and eggs and in fresh vegetables and fruits.[9] Estimates of the components of Iraqi diets vary considerably. The only food balance sheet available at the time of writing this report is presented in Table 11. The estimated supplies of cereals and milk on a per capita basis in this table are considerably higher than estimated consumption in provisional figures for 1953-55 presented to the Joint WHO-FAO Committee on Nutrition in the Middle East in 1959. These two estimates, for the same dates are compared below:

Comparison of Food Supply Estimates: Iraq

	(a)	(b)
Cereals	119	146.4
Starchy roots	3	1.7
Pulses	13	13.2
Sugar	23	20.1
Fats and oils	5	4.0
Fruits	58	35.0
Vegetables	55	60.3
Meat	10	9.9
Eggs	2	2.2
Fish	1	3.3
Milk	83	154.8
Total calories	2,070	2,338
Total proteins	59	
Animal proteins	14	

(a) Joint FAO/WHO Nutrition Committee for the Middle East.
(b) U.S. Dept. of Agriculture, Foreign Agricultural Service.

Cereals provide the major portion of the calories and proteins in the average diet, supplying 56% of total caloric intake and the same percentage of proteins. Staple cereals include wheat and barley, which are especially common in the north. Rice is cultivated in the irrigated and marshy riverine areas of the south; millet and maize also are grown and consumed, although in limited quantities.

Wheat and barley usually are eaten in the form of bread. The majority of urban dwellers eat bread made with high-extraction wheat flour while the poorer townsmen, the fellaheen and nomads use bread made of whole wheat or barley flour. In the south, bread may be made of barley or of millet and rice flours, a type which is called tabag. The bread is unleavened and made in large, thin pliable discs that serve the majority of the population as eating utensils. Wheat also is prepared as parboiled wheat or burghul in the north. Maize and millet,

which are especially popular in the center and south, also are made
into soups, in addition to being used in bread making. Total cereal
consumption probably amounts to about 120 kg. per capita per year,
with wheat accounting for two thirds of the total.

Meat is too costly for the average family and is eaten only at irregular intervals.[9] Sheep and goats, which are raised in large numbers
by both settled farmers and nomads, are the principal sources of meat.
The estimated consumption of meat in 1954-55 amounted to only 9.9
kg. per capita, an extremely low level. The low consumption of meat
is due primarily to the poor economic status of the majority of the
population and not to choice, since meat is an item of diet that is
greatly relished and that forms an important part of the diet of the
wealthier classes. An estimated one fourth of the inhabitants consume three fourths of the meat, an average of 30 kg. per capita per
year, instead of the national average of 12.

Poultry and eggs are produced in rural villages but are rarely consumed by farmers, who market these products in nearby towns, so that
they serve primarily as a cash crop for the peasant and not as an article of rural diet.[9] Consumption of eggs per capita in 1954-55 was
estimated at only 2.2 kg. per capita per year.

Milk and milk products are popular but are often in short supply[1] in
towns and, therefore, are too expensive for the poorer inhabitants; adulteration of milk is reportedly a common practice.[12] Sheep and goat
milk are the most widely used, rarely as fluid milk, but usually in some
fermented product such as **leban**. Cheese also is made but it does not
seem to be as popular as in other Arab countries.[9] Estimates of milk
consumption vary widely, but per capita intake probably is below 100
kg. a year.

Fish is available in riverine areas and along the coast but does not
constitute an important article of diet. Total consumption in 1954-55
was estimated at only 3.3 kg. per capita per year and may be lower.

As may be noted from the above figures, the intakes of foods of animal origin is low. They provide only 9% of the calories and 23% of
the protein supply of the average diet.

Peas, beans, and lentils usually are eaten throughout the year. Potatoes, French beans, turnips, beetroot, cauliflower, marrows, spinach,
broad beans, carrots, and lettuce are available primarily during the
winter season. A survey of the frequency with which certain vegetables
were used showed that tomatoes, okra, egg plant, pumpkins, runner beans,
potatoes, cauliflower, and French beans were available for only six
months in the year, during which time tomatoes were purchased daily,
okra and eggplant two or three times a week, and the other vegetables
only four months in the year, but it is then purchased on an average of
four times a week.[9] The supply of vegetables is limited and per capita
consumption is low. During 1954-55 vegetable intake was estimated at

only 60.3 kg. per capita per year, while consumption of legumes was
13.2 kg. per capita. Legumes provide 6% of calories and 13% of the
proteins in the diet.

Dates are the most important fruit, since Iraq is the world's largest
producer and exporter. They are a staple of diet, particularly in the
south and consumption is estimated at 19 kg. per capita per year.[12]
Other fruits are available only on a seasonal basis: oranges, lemons,
melons and watermelons, and bananas are available for general use
about five months of the year, while apples, apricots, pears, and
peaches are marketed only two months in the year. Consumption of
these fruits is estimated at 15.1 kg. per capita which, together with
the consumption of dates, gives a total average consumption of fruit
of 34.2 kg. per capita.

The traditional drinks are tea and coffee, both of which are popular
in towns. The rural inhabitants, as a general rule, drink tea and the
nomadic tribes prefer coffee.[1] A large proportion of the family food
budget is expended on these two items, both of which are imported, and
on the sugar to sweeten them. Sour milk, cinnamon and lime tea, fruit
juices and date **arak** also are popular beverages. Wine is used by the
Christian communities in northern areas but is not generally consumed.
American-style carbonated beverages such as Coca Cola are becoming
popular and beer of excellent quality is produced. Whiskey is in increasing use among the wealthier classes.[13]

B. VARIATIONS IN DIETS

(1) **Differences in urban and rural diets.** The diet pattern of the
townsman varies with his economic status, as is discussed in (3)
below. The more educated classes have adopted Western utensils and
table habits, but the dietary pattern remains the same.

There are usually, among the wealthier classes, three meals a day.
Breakfast consists of tea with bread, in some cases with the addition
of cheese or cream. The other two meals include rice or a vegetable
stew, with or without meat; this is accompanied by bread, fruit, and
tea. Alternatively, a snack of bread, cheese, or cucumbers is served
with kebabs or various preparations of crushed wheat.[12]

The poorer sections of the urban population eat a diet consisting
primarily of bread, tea, and dates. Vegetables and fruits are eaten in
season and meat and milk products as allowed by the earnings of the
family.

People in rural areas, for the most part, live on the food they produce themselves. Their diet consists mainly of cereals and starchy
foods, yet the total intake is so low that total caloric intake may be
below requirements. The diet as a whole is low in protective foods,
including vitamins, minerals, and, especially, good quality proteins.[4]

Bread and tea are the chief constituents of one, or often among the
poorer peasants two, of the daily meals, while the third may be supplemented by vegetables. Fruits are a luxury except in producing areas
such as the date groves of the south and the fruit growing areas of the
north. Meat and poultry rarely are eaten, at the most two or three
times a month, but many peasants can afford meat only on special occasions. Milk and milk products are available to those owning livestock, but a large proportion of cultivators do not raise or own livestock with the exception of a draft animal for farm work. Animal
proteins are therefore often absent from rural diets, fats are rarely
eaten, and consumption of vegetable oils is practically nil.[12]

Most of the money spent on food by the peasant is used for the purchase of tea and sugar; tea has no nutritive value and sugar is important only as a source of calories. It is unfortunate that this money
could not be used to purchase items that would fortify the deficient
diet.[12]

(2) **Regional variations.** Considerable differences in diet are observable in the various regions because of the variation in climate,
agricultural production, and wealth. Thus, in the dry-farming areas
of the north where grains and fruit are readily available, the diet contains a large proportion of wheat and barley. Fruit, either fresh or
dried, is a staple in the fruit-producing mountain areas, whereas fruit
is replaced in the diet by green vegetables, especially onions, or dried
dates in the northern plains. Wheat usually is eaten in the form of
bread, with burghul a close second in popularity.[12]

Rice, rather than barley, is second in importance to wheat in the
central and southern regions of the country and may be the most important cereal among the marsh-dwelling tribes. Fish, maize, and
millet supplement the diet in the central region while dates are staples
in the south. Where the farmer keeps livestock, milk and milk products
are available.[12]

The least diversified diet is that of the nomadic tribes of the western
desert, who subsist on the products of their herds supplemented by
wheat or barley breads. The bedouins depend on camel's milk, while
the tribal Arabs of the southern marshes subsist on water buffalo milk,
fish, and wild fowl.

(3) **Variations caused by differences in economic status.**[12] The low
quality of the diets among the poorer classes of the population has already been mentioned above in the discussion of rural and urban diets.
These differences were strikingly brought out in a survey of diets in
varying economic groups; the results are presented in Table 12. Although this survey is somewhat old, dietary patterns have not improved
to such an extent as to render the results invalid; this is especially
true with regard to the diets of the lowest economic groups, the poor
urban worker and the fellaheen.

Diets of wealthy landowners and high wage earners (groups I and II in the table) were found to contain adequate amounts of calories, fats, animal and vegetable proteins, and vitamins A, B, niacin, and riboflavin. The diets were generally low in calcium because of the relatively low consumption of milk and milk products.

The urban worker of intermediate economic class (III) consumed a diet containing adequate amounts of calories, iron, vitamin A, niacin, and vegetable proteins. The consumption of animal proteins, however, was low, as was the amount of fat, calcium, and thiamine in the diet.

The diet of the poor city worker was deficient in calcium and animal proteins and their caloric intake was low in relation to the heavy work these people performed. The amount of animal fats consumed was very low:

The diet of the fellaheen was deficient in almost every respect: the caloric intake was low, as was consumption of fats, iron, calcium, niacin, and vitamin A. Intake of animal proteins was especially low.

The poorer the economic status, the larger the proportion of the family budget that is spent on food. A survey of household budgets in the city of Baghdad in 1954 showed that 57.4% of the budget was spent on food by the inhabitants of built-up areas, but 65.6% was spent by dwellers in a Serifa camp on the outskirts of the city.

IV. ADEQUACY OF FOOD RESOURCES

Iraq produces enough of most foods to maintain a rather low level of subsistence for the majority of the population. Some foodstuffs, especially barley and dates, are produced in exportable amounts. Production of others, for example wheat, satisfies local markets without leaving any for export. Still others, such as sugar and tea, either are not produced at all or are produced in amounts insufficient to satisfy domestic demands, and additional supplies, therefore, must be imported.

The economic stimulus provided by large oil revenues has encouraged the importation of increasing quantities of food. In addition these revenues are being used to finance development programs aimed at increasing acreage under cultivation, at decontrolling water resources, and at improving agricultural practices. If these development programs are successfully carried out, they may raise food production and standards of living from their present low levels.

On the other hand, numerous factors, both climatic and man made, may seriously affect the adequacy of food supplies. The influence of the scanty and irregular rainfall on grain harvests in the north and the devastating effects of floods of the Tigris and Euphrates already have been touched upon in the text. The effect on the Iraqi economy of low world prices for exportable surplus crops can adversely affect food supplies. Political disturbances, such as the 1958 revolution, disrupt

development programs, while the renewal of the Israeli-Arab war
would seriously affect food supplies.

V. NUTRITIONAL DISEASE PATTERNS

Malnutrition is considered one of the major health problems of Iraq.
Actual starvation is rare, but the majority of the inhabitants subsist on
a diet grossly deficient in caloric content and nutritional balance.[1]
Undernutrition, anemia, and avitaminosis are prevalent, especially
among low-salaried town dwellers and the poorer peasants.

Although there is a deficiency of good quality proteins, actual protein edema is reportedly rare.[9,11] Subclinical signs of the various
vitamin deficiency diseases are frequently observed; for example,
clinical manifestations of vitamin A deficiency reportedly are widespread, with keratosis a common finding on clinical examination.[9,11]
Deficiencies due to low intake of the various vitamin B compounds are
rare; pellagra is almost completely absent and beriberi is sporadic
but rare, occurring most often as infantile beriberi, probably as a result of prolonged breast feeding and poor nutrition of the infants and
younger children.[9,10] Clinical signs of vitamin C deficiency are commonly observed and cases of scurvy reportedly are numerous.[9] It is
estimated that vitamin C is absent from the diet for as much as three
months of the year.[10] Recent data shows that scurvy and subclinical
vitamin C deficiencies may cease to be a problem if the consumption
of an herb called khoubbaz (**Malus rotundifolia**) can be increased. This
herb, which is eaten raw by both rural and nomadic peoples, has been
found to have a high content of ascorbic acid, 118 mg./100 gm.
Deficiencies in intake of calcium and vitamin D are seen in the numerous cases of osteomalacia and rickets, which is reportedly as common
as in Egypt.[9,10] Minor symptoms of ariboflavinosis frequently are
observed.[9]

As may be seen from the above listing of observed deficiency diseases,
the diet appears to be poorest in the protective foods, thus supplying
inadequate amounts of vitamins and minerals. Studies on special population groups bear out these observations. For example, a survey
was made of the diets and nutritional status of police and soldiers
stationed in Baghdad.[8] Both dietary surveys and physical examinations
were carried out. The diets of both groups were analyzed for nutrients, with the results shown in Table 13. As may be seen, diets were
adequate in caloric content, proteins, and the vitamin B complex in
general, but were found to be low in calcium, in certain other vitamins,
and in foods of animal origin. Clinical and laboratory examinations
showed that a large percentage of those examined were underweight
for their height, while hemoglobin determinations for the groups indi-

cated that 60% of those examined had hemoglobin contents less than 80% of normal.

The poor nutrition of Iraqi mothers is reflected in the low growth curves of lactating infants as compared to French children of similar ages. Thus, a study of 1,800 infants aged 1 month to 18 months, carried out in Baghdad showed that, up to the age of 2 months, there was no difference in the average weights of French and Iraqi children but that after the third month Iraqi infants were underweight in comparison with French children of similar age, and that this difference increased progressively. Thus, at 7 months Iraqi infants weighed 400 gm. less than the average French child, at 9 months the difference had risen to 1 kg. at one year it amounted to 1,300 gm. and at 18 months of age the average Iraqi child weighed 2 kg. less than the average French child.

Signs of frank and subclinical vitamin and protein deficiencies have been frequently observed in studies of Iraqi children. For example, of a group of 66 children 10 years of age examined in Sulaimaniya, a majority showed dry skin, cheilosis with mosaic skin, poor gums, and myoedema, all indicative of poor nutrition. Two thirds of children 10 years of age had a height found only in 10% of French children of the same age (124 cm.), while 32.4% weighed less than 24.1 kg., the weight of only 10% of French children. Among 12-year olds the same differences were encountered: 81% of the children weighed less than 28.3 kg. and 90% had a height below 132.8 cm., measurements found only in 10% of French children of the same age.

Poor nutrition was also observable in adolescent children. Numerous cases of keratosis were found in 14 to 16-year olds examined in Mosul, although in other respects their nutrition appeared to be generally good. Similarly, in a secondary school in Basra, 25 of 40 children between the ages of 15 and 19 showed inflammation of the gums, apparently associated with low vitamin C intake. Among 100 students 18 to 27 years of age, examined in an agricultural school at Abu-Ghreb, 68% weighed 8 kg. or less than their expected weight and only 11% had weights within a normal range. Clinical examination showed gingivitis in 40% of the students in this group.

VI. CONCLUSIONS

Like its Middle Eastern neighbors, Iraq is predominantly an agricultural country, but it possesses certain advantages over other countries in the region. Iraq has a low population density and considerable undeveloped land, and is able to finance the development of its agricultural resources with the income from oil revenues. Despite these favorable factors, agricultural output is low, the standard of living of the peasants is poor, and agricultural techniques still largely at primitive levels.

Cereals are the most important crop; vegetables are grown primarily for local consumption, and are available mostly on a seasonal basis. Iraq is the world's largest grower of dates. They are important agricultural export items and a staple in the diet of the rural and nomadic population. Livestock holdings are large; approximately one half of the herds are tended by nomads.

Imports of agricultural produce are large and are increasing steadily, concurrently with increased demand for consumer goods stimulated by high oil revenues. Agricultural exports, mostly barley and dates, constitute 85 to 90% of all exports, excluding oil.

A large proportion of the inhabitants of Iraq subsist on diets inadequate in quantity and quality, including especially poorer urban dwellers and the large majority of the rural population. Staples of diet in all population groups include cereals, dates, onions, milk products, sweetened tea, and coffee. All diets are reportedly low in meat, fish, and eggs, and in fresh vegetables and fruit.

Malnutrition is considered a major problem, with the majority of the inhabitants subsisting on a diet grossly deficient in nutritive value. Undernutrition, anemia, and avitaminoses are prevalent.

SELECTED REFERENCES

1. Yale University, Human Relations Area Files. Country Survey Series: Iraq. New York, Columbia University Press, 1956.
2. Food and Agriculture Organization, Mediterranean Development Project. Country Studies: Iraq. 1959.
3. International Cooperation Administration. Forage Problems and Resources of Iraq. Washington, D. C., 1957.
4. Ali, H. M. Land Reclamation and Settlement in Iraq. Baghdad, 1955.
5. Iraq, Ministry of Economics, Principal Bureau of Statistics. The Industrial Census of Iraq, 1954. Baghdad, 1956.
6. West, Q. M. Agricultural Development Programs of Iran, Iraq, and Sudan. *Foreign Agriculture Report No. 112* (United States Department of Agriculture), 1958.
7. Salter, Sir J. The Development of Iraq. London, Caxton Press, 1955.
8. Gounelle, H., *et al*. Enquete de nutrition en Moyen-Orient sur des jeunes adultes. *Bulletin Société Scientifique Hygiène et Alimentation*, 1956.
9. Simmons, J. S., *et al*. Global Epidemiology: Vol. 3, The Near and Middle East. Philadelphia, Lippincott, 1954.
10. Worthington, E. B. Middle East Science. London, His Majesty's Stationery Office, 1946.
11. Gounelle, H. Deficits nutritionelles en Moyen-Orient. *Bulletin Académie National Medicale*, 1956, pp. 79-82.
12. Jalili, M. A., *et al*. The State of Nutrition in Iraq. *Journal Faculty of Medicine* (Baghdad), May-July, 1950.
13. Longrigg, S. H., and Stoakes, F. Iraq. London, E. Benn, 1958.
14. Iraq, Ministry of Economics. Report on Household Budgets Enquiry in the City of Baghdad and Environs. 1954.
15. Iraq, Ministry of Economics, Principal Bureau of Statistics. Statistical Abstract, 1958. Baghdad, 1959.

Table 1

Methods of Irrigation Employed in Iraq
(in 1000 mesharas)[a]

Liwa	Area Irrigated by Flow	Area Irrigated by Pumps	Area Irrigated by Waterwheels	Area Irrigated by Other Means	All Irrigated Areas	Rainfed Area	Total Cultivated Area
Baghdad	352	982	3	2	1339	3	1342
Mosul	46	13	2	—	61	3857	3918
Basra	11	84	3	174	272	11	283
Kirkuk	511	10	2	19	542	2718	3260
Sulaimaniya	151	1	1	—	153	907	1060
Arbil	62	—	1	—	63	1882	1945
Diala	957	134	6	—	1097	742	1839
Dulaim	126	280	25	3	437	4	438
Kut	651	782	—	5	1438	6	1444
Hilla	942	111	46	1	1100	5	1105
Kerbela	208	8	7	—	223	2	225
Diwaniya	914	871	69	—	1854	2	1856
Muutafiq	1124	251	34	—	1409	52	1461
Amara	560[b]	951	25	1	1537	831[b]	2368
Total	6615	4478	224	205	11522	11022	22544

(Data taken from the 1952–1953 Agricultural and Livestock Census Report)

[a] Meshara = 0.25 ha.
[b] Area of 831,000 mesharas given as rainfed is actually irrigated by flood. The figure must be added to the 560,000 mesharas irrigated by flow. This will change the total area irrigated by flow to 7,446 and All Irrigated Land total to 12,353. There is some discrepancy between this figure and the total irrigated area in Table III-1, but it is only 5 percent and refers to the gross irrigated area. It is likely that part of the waste land under the canals has been excluded from the Census enumeration.

Source: F.A.O. Country Study, 1959.

Table 2

Harvest Calendar for the Principal Crops Grown

Crop	Harvest Period	Bulk of Harvest
Wheat	Mid May-Mid July	Mid May-Mid June
Barley	Early Apr.-June	Early Apr.-May
Maize	Early July-Aug.	Mid July-End July
Rice	Late Aug.-Mid Nov.	Beg. Oct.-End Oct.
Millet	Mid July-Early Sept.	...
Potatoes	Mid June-Early Oct.	...
Onions	May-July	...
Tomatoes	May-July	...
Green peas	Nov.	...
Green beans	Mar.	...
Dry beans	Oct.-Nov.	...
Broad beans	Mid Mar.-Mid Apr.	...
Chick-peas	Late Mar.-Mid Apr.	...
Lentils	Mid Apr.-May	...
Apples	June-Sept.	...
Pears	Mid June-Oct.	...
Grapes	June-Nov.	...
Oranges	Dec.-Mar.	...
Lemons	Sept.	...
Raisins	Mid Sept.-Oct.	...
Apricots	Mid Apr.-June	...
Dates	Aug.-Oct	Sept.-Oct.
Olives	Aug.	...
Sesame seed	Sept.-Oct.	...
Cotton	Aug.-Dec.	Mid Aug.-Nov.
Tobacco	Mid Aug.-Mid Oct.	Sept.

Source: F.A.O., World Crop Harvest Calendar, Rome 1959.

Table 3

Cultivated Area and Production of Principal Crops

		Area (in 1000 hectares)	Production (in tons)
Wheat	1959	—	653[a]
	1958	1,532	754
Rice (paddy)	1958	89	137
Barley	1958	1,157	953
	1959	1,165[a]	764
Cotton (lint)	1957	56	7
(seeds)	1957	—	14
Sesame	1957	24	154
Dates	1957	—	323
Tobacco	1958	8[a]	5.3[a]
	1957	8	4.9
Lentils	1958	13	3
	1957	13	8
Millet	1957	10	7
Maize	1957	6	5
Potatoes	2 year av. 1948–52	2	12
Dry Beans	1956	14	10
Broad Beans	1957	9	8
Chick Peas	1958	5	1.2
Sesame		88.2 } 1,000 donums	14.3
Cow peas		14.4 "	2.1

[a] Estimated.

Source: FAO Production Yearbook 1958, Monthly Bulletin of Agricultural Statistics. Iraq: Statistical Abstract, 1958.

Table 4

Production, Area and Yield of Principal Cereals

	Wheat			Barley			Rice		
	1948/49	1952/53	1956/59	1948/49	1952/53	1956/57	1950	1953	1957
Area (thousand mesharas)(a)									
Northern Iraq	1,839	3,147	4,093	1,156	1,299	2,140	38	35	51
Centre and South	1,654	1,643	1,732	2,658	3,086	2,819	832	343	313
Total	3,493	4,790	5,825	3,814	4,385	4,959	870	378	364
Production (thousand tons)									
Northern Iraq	166	442	773	176	402	627	26	21	26
Centre and South	284	320	345	574	709	678	215	142	121
Total	450	762	1,118	750	1,111	1,305	241	163	147
Yields (kilos per meshara)									
Northern Iraq	90	140	189	152	309	293	684	600	510
Centre and South	172	195	199	216	230	241	258	385	387
All Iraq	129	159	191	197	253	263	277	432	404

(a) 1 meshara = 0.25 ha.
Source: Statistical Abstracts of Iraq, 1952–1957.

Table 5

Area of Vegetable Planting According to Agricultural Census: 1953

Vegetable	Hectares
Tomatoes	11,332
Cucumbers	5,085
Egg Plant	4,164
Turnips	1,399
Spinach	1,110
Lettuce	514
Carrots	410
Cabbage	168
Potatoes	160
Cauliflower	72

Source: Salter, Sir J.: The Development of Iraq, 1955.

Table 6

Fruit Bearing Trees According to Agricultural Census: 1953

Species of Tree	Number of Bearing Trees
Pomegranate	2,000,229
Orange	1,293,592
Apple	763,982
Apricot	565,171
Sweet Lemon	332,636
Sour Lemon	181,752
Peach	178,099
Pear	103,203
Walnut	104,855
Almond	34,733
Olive	30,534
Pistachio	9,046

Source: Salter. Sir J.: The Development of Iraq, 1955.

Table 7

Value of Principal Exports
(in thousands of dinars)(a)

	1951	1952	1953	1954	1955	1956	1957
I Foodstuffs							
Dates	5,598	4,652	4,228	3,526	2,847	2,483	3,446
Barley		8,957	8,567	8,824	5,951	4,985	2,951
Wheat			39	453	1,686	—	96
Grand Millet	15,526	558	338	174	236	81	30
Other Grains	1		106	310	173	99	140
Pulses and Flour			693	276	593	315	137
Total Foodstuffs:	21,125	14,167	13,971	13,563	11,486	7,963	6,800
II Raw Materials							
Raw Cotton	1,805	1,125	409	279	649	758	959
Raw Wool	1,701	1,097	1,042	941	1,443	1,575	1,487
Hides and Skins	318	236	323	272	240	327	357
Seeds	649	330	573	335	482	364	313
Casings	335	149	100	149	211	280	290
Total Raw Materials:	4,808	2,937	2,447	1,976	3,025	3,304	3,406
III Live Animals	528	880	1,583	1,563	420	430	416
IV Other Commodities	796	792	1,068	874	987	1,504	2,289
Total	27,257	18,776	19,069	17,976	15,918	13,201	12,911
V Oil Exported	35,671	79,601	120,069	155,959	168,126	156,639	113,155
GRAND TOTAL	62,758	98,377	139,138	173,935	184,044	169,840	126,066

(a) 1 dinar =
Source: Statistical Abstract, 1954–57.

Table 8

Principal Food Exports

1958

Commodity	Quantity	Value	Share of Total Value
	1,000 Metric Tons	$1,000	%
Barley	313.8	13,327	33.4
Dates	239.3	8,003	20.1
Livestock (1,000 head)	210	1,784	4.5
Oilseeds	7.3	843	2.1
Other grains	8.9	601	1.5
Wheat	8.8	554	1.4

Principal Food Imports

1958

Sugar	174.5	22,190	7.2
Tea	15.8	16,003	5.2
Fats & Oils	17.1	3,519	1.1
Vegetables (fresh & frozen)	26.8	2,602	.8
Oilseeds	11.0	2,268	.7
Edible Fruits	11.4	1,620	.5
Dairy Products	1.9	1,033	.3
Rice	4.0	639	.2
Coffee	.4	445	.1
Other Agr. Imports	—	1,521	.5
Total Agr. Imports			16.9

Source: Foreign Agriculture Service, U. S. Dept. of Agriculture, Exports and Imports of Agricultural Commodities by Countries of Destination, 1958, Washington, 1960.

Table 9

Iraq: Food Processing Establishments, Type and Distribution

Type of

		Slaughter-houses	Dairies	Fruit Preserving & Date Packing	Grain Milling
Greater	#	5	10		32
Baghdad	E				196
Baghdad	#				17
Liwa	E				48
Basra	#			21	5
Center	E			5798	115
Basra	#			8	5
Liwa	E			1798	86
Kirkuk	#				203
Liwa	E				618
Arbil	#				272
Liwa	E				389
Sulaimaniya	#				11
	E				36
Daila	#				40
	E				156
Monsul	#	1	5	2	22
City	E		8		106
Mosul	#				23
Liwa	E				110
Dulcim	#		5		82
Liwa	E		14		187
Kut	#				78
Liwa	E				288
Hilla	#		89	35	42
Liwa	E		389	339	357
Karbela	#				16
Liwa	E				136
Muntafia	#	3	18		23
Liwa	E	8	24		146
Duvaniya	#			30	49
	E			247	235
Amara	#				36
	E				501
Total	#	9	127	96	960
	E				

#—Number   E—Employees
    Source: Iraq, Ministry of Economics, Principal Bureau of Statistics; The Industrial Census of Iraq, 1954; Baghdad, 1956.

Table 9

as Shown by Industrial Census of 1954

Factory

Bakeries	Confection-eries	Other Foods	Arak & Beer Manufacturing	Soft & Car-bonated Beverages	Total
291	64	6	4	9	151
1335	491	38	282	24	
4					21
7					
88	12			10	136
489	62			167	
24				4	41
98				16	
66	6			3	278
333	11			8	
34					306
140					
42	4			3	63
166	8			17	
170					210
353					
211	29		3	4	277
876	78		22	15	
10		18(a)			51
23		44			
53		6(b)			146
124		21			
116	3	3(b)			200
147	8	6			
139	11	48(a)(b)		3	367
281	21	135		13	
142	18	34(b)		5	215
534	39	129		18	
12	5			4	66
57	20			12	
9	5	7(b)			100
31	19	20			
152	14		•		202
205	39				
1563	171	122	7	45	

(a) Sesame products.
(b) Date juice.

Table 10

Distribution of Grain Stores (alwas)

1957-58	
Mosul	274
Arbil	16
Sulaimaniya	56
Kirkuk	76
Baghdad	367
Diala	96
Ramadi	137
Karbela	118
Kut	185
Amara	63
Hilla	293
Diwaniya	324
Nasiriya	134
Basra	159
Total	2,298

Source: Statistical Abstract 1958.

Table 11

Iraq: Food Balance 1954-55

Population: 5,975,000
January 1, 1955

Product	Domestic Supply		Net Trade Imports + Exports -	Total Supply	Non-Food Uses(a)	Domestic Disappearance		
	Reported Production	Estimated Supply				Available for Food(b)	Per Capita	
						Total	Per Year Kilograms	Per Day Calories
	1,000 Metric Tons							
GRAINS								
Wheat	734	734	-100	634	76	558	93.4	852
Rice (milled)	238	238	- 6	232	28	204	34.1	336
Barley	750	750	-490	260	156	104	17.4	158
Corn	5	5	—	5	—	5	0.8	8
Millet	19	19	- 15	4	—	4	0.7	6
Total								1,360
PULSES	40	90	—	90	11	79	13.2	123
SUGAR (centrifugal)	—	—	+120	120	—	120	20.1	212
ROOTS, TUBERS & STARCHES	5	11	—	11	1	10	1.7	3
OILS AND FATS	8	28	—	28	4	24	4.0	97
VEGETABLES	—	400	—	400	40	360	60.3	33
FRUIT								
Dates	350	350	-221	129	15	114	19.1	147
Olives	10	10	—	10	5	5	0.8	3
Other	—	100	—	100	10	90	15.1	21
Total								171
MEAT								
Mutton and goat	27	27	—	27	—	27	4.5	18
Beef	32	32	—	32	—	32	5.4	24
Total								42
FISH	—	20	—	20	—	20	3.3	8
MILK(c)	—	925	—	925	—	925	154.8	280
EGGS	—	16	—	16	3	13	2.2	9
Grand Total								2,338

Source: Foreign Agricultural Service, U. S. Dept. of Agriculture

Table 12

Nutrient Values of Diets Consumed in Iraq: 1950

Mean consumption of the whole year in different classes
Per adult person per day.

	Supplied in Great Britain in 1944(a)	Class I.	Class II.	Class III.	Class IV.	Class V.	Subclass V.
No. of families	—	15	18	6	6	10	1461
Calories	2923	3098	3328	2897	2613	1813	6.75
Animal protein, gm.	—	47.8	40.5	27.4	24.0	21.9	35.25
Vegetable protein, gm.	—	63.8	91.5	81.26	80.3	38.9	42.0
Total protein, gm.	87.0	111.6	132.0	108.66	104.3	60.8	236.8
Carbohydrates, gm.	381.0	475.8	499.6	475.9	475.0	273.2	13.0
Fat, gm.	117.0	74.1	79.9	55.0	26.8	37.1	10.6
Iron, mgm.	16.0	18.28	24.1	20.85	17.96	10.72	411.7
Calcium, mgm.	1037	663.5	431.8	477.45	473.5	722.1	
Vitamin A, I.U.(b)	3773	6997	8689	6069.2	5340.7	1363.4	
Vitamin B₁, mgm.	2.0	1.55	1.72	0.81	1.53	0.84	
Riboflavin, mgm.	2.1	2.32	3.82	3.27	1.47	2.14	
Niacin, mgm.	19.7	23.06	25.04	21.28	22.84	9.35	
Ascorbic acid(c)	123	144.7	130.9	135.9	68.2	39.0	

(a) Platt (1947).
(b) Vitamin A is mainly in the form of B-carotene in Classes IV and V. Carotene is only about one-half or one-third utilized by the animal body compared with an equal amount of vitamin A.
(c) Not all this amount of vitamin C is really taken by the consumer, as certain proportion of it is destroyed in cooking.
Source: Jalili, M. A., et al. The State of Nutrition in Iraq, J. Fac. Med. Baghdad, 1950.

Table 13

Analysis of Diets of Soldiers and Police

Baghdad

(Intake per capita per day)

	Soldiers	Police
Calories	3,516	3,934
Proteins	105 Gm.	116 Gm.
Fats	62 Gm.	88 Gm.
Calcium	327 mg.	407 mg.
Phosphorus	2,007 mg.	1,510 mg.
Iron	33.3 mg.	20 mg.
Vitamin A	2,769 I. U.	1,620 I. U.
Thiamine	2.3 mg.	1.6 mg.
B_2	1.2 mg.	1.6 mg.
Niacin	22.7 mg.	24.6 mg.
Ascorbic acid	56.2 mg.	129.4 mg.

Source: Gounelle, H. et al.: Enquete de Nutrition en Moyen-Orient sur des Jeunes Adultes. Bull. Soc. Sci. Hyg. et Aliment., 1956.

Map 1

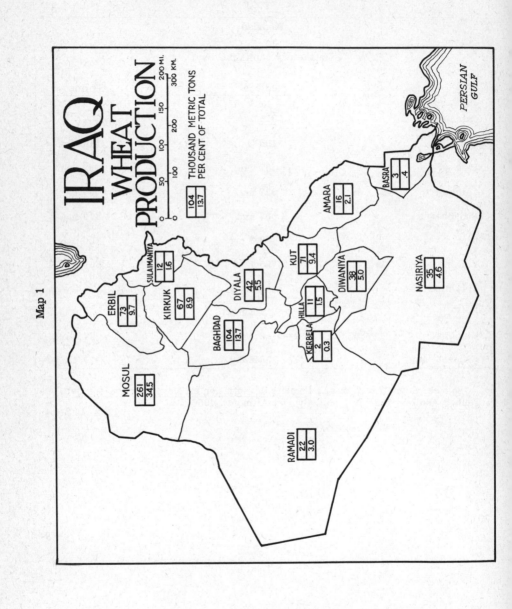

Map 2

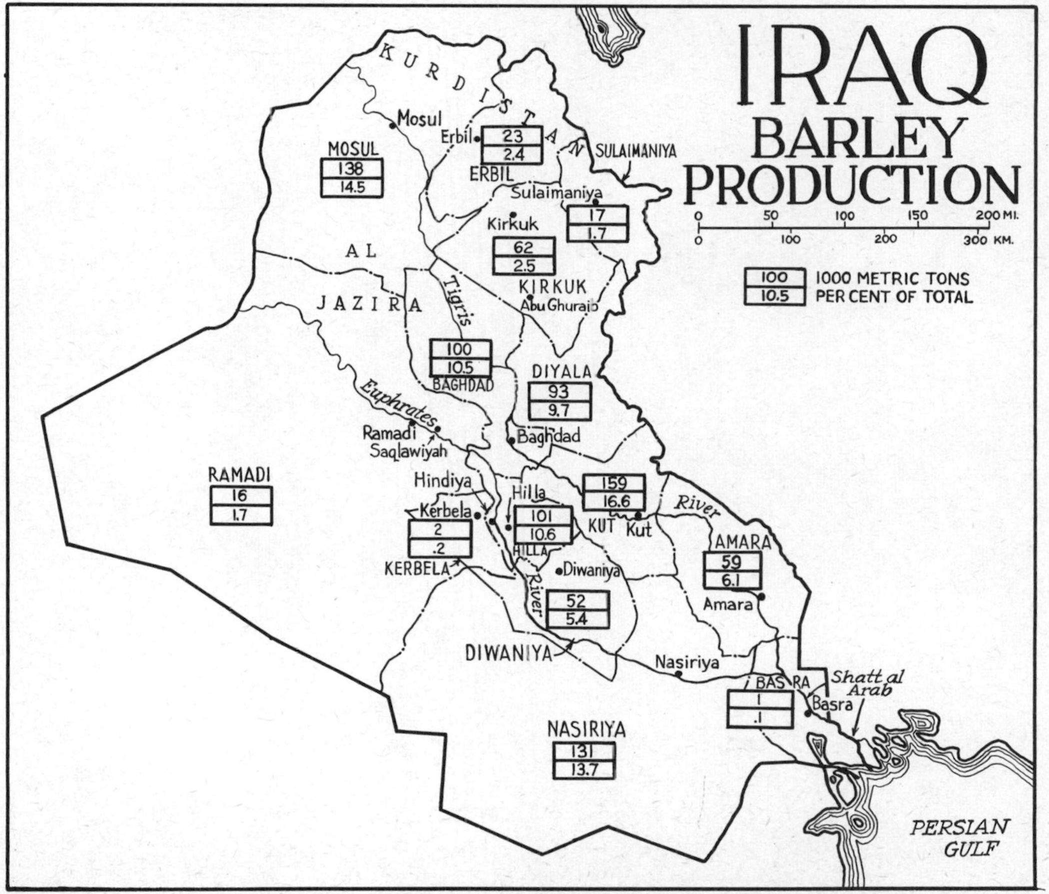

IRAQ

BARLEY PRODUCTION

0 50 100 150 200 MI.

0 100 200 300 KM.

| 100 | 1000 METRIC TONS |
| 10.5 | PER CENT OF TOTAL |

PERSIAN GULF

KURDISTAN

AL JAZIRA

SULAIMANIYA

KIRKUK

ERBIL

DIYALA

BAGHDAD

KUT

AMARA

BASRA

KERBELA

DIWANIYA

NASIRIYA

RAMADI

Mosul

Erbil

Sulaimaniya

Kirkuk

Abu Ghuraib

Baghdad

Hilla

Kut

Amara

Basra

Nasiriya

Diwaniya

Kerbela

Hindiya

Ramadi

Saqlawiyah

Tigris

Euphrates

River

River

Shatt al Arab

MOSUL	138	14.5
SULAIMANIYA	17	1.7
ERBIL	23	2.4
KIRKUK	62	2.5
DIYALA	93	9.7
BAGHDAD	100	10.5
KUT	159	16.6
HILLA	101	10.6
AMARA	59	6.1
KERBELA	2	.2
DIWANIYA	52	5.4
NASIRIYA	131	13.7
BASRA	1	.1
RAMADI	16	1.7

SAUDI ARABIA AND
THE ARABIAN PENINSULA

I. GENERAL REMARKS

A. AGRICULTURE IN THE ARABIAN PENINSULA

The Arabian Peninsula is the largest geographical unit in the Middle East. Bounded on the north by the curve of the Fertile Crescent, on the west by the Red Sea, on the south by the Arabian Sea, and on the east by the Persian Gulf, it is roughly rectangular in shape with an average breadth of 1125 kilometers (700 miles) and an average length of 1930 kilometers (1,200 miles).

A major portion of the peninsula is arid. There are both true deserts, with either rocky land or sand dunes and virtually no vegetation, and steppe deserts, with occasional water holes and a scanty vegetation. The sparse growth of thorned shrubs, bushes, and short grasses that cover much of these steppe deserts is converted into meat and milk by the camels, sheep, and goats of the Bedouin tribesmen. Rainfall is limited and uncertain. Northern areas usually get a few inches of rain in winter, although periods of drought may last several years. A fair amount of rain falls on the highlands of the western perimeter and on limited coastal areas in the south, but much of the interior is almost completely without rainfall so that the amount of rain for any one section may vary from an average of 12 to 20 inches a year in the high lands of Asir and Yemen to the almost total lack of rain in the drought-ridden Empty Quarter, where it may not rain for ten years.

Ground water supplies are equally scarce. Arabia has no perennial rivers; instead, a series of intermittent water courses, called "wadis", are a feature of the landscape. These are scoured out by floodwaters of occasional flash rains. Such subsoil water as may be available usually is found along the course of these wadis, and this is especially true in the interior of the peninsula.

Extremely high temperatures, 37.8° to 48.9° C in many areas in summer, make for high soil temperatures, in some cases higher than will support plant life. The salt content of the soil is high. Moreover, unwise irrigation practices increase the salinity of cultivated land to the point where it must often be abandoned after being reclaimed. Less than one fourth of the total land area is arable and probably not more than

one half the arable land is under cultivation. Most of this arable land
is either in oases, which are most frequent in the central portion of
the Peninsula, or in a ring of arable lands situated along the perimeter.
The highlands of Yemen and of Asir in Saudi Arabia are the most important of these fertile areas. Other pockets of arable land are found
in various localities, including the Hadramaut Valley of Aden, the Hejaz
and Hasa in Saudi Arabia, and in portions of Oman on the Persian Gulf.

Some of the countries of the Arabian peninsula, such as, Yemen,
the Aden Protectorate, and Muscat and Oman, follow the traditional
Middle Eastern economic pattern in which agriculture and animal husbandry are the chief contributors to the national income. This does not
hold true for the oil-producing countries, Saudi Arabia, Bahrein, and
Kuwait.

Agriculture, principally food production, contributes only a small
proportion of the national income of Saudi Arabia. More than one half of
the total is provided by oil; most of the remainder is derived from
pilgrims visiting the holy cities of Mecca and Medina. Of the estimated
15% of national income contributed by agriculture, livestock raising
represents the main part, with dates second in importance.

Despite the limited agricultural potential of Arabia, a majority of
its inhabitants derive their livelihood from the land. An estimated 70%
of the population is engaged in agricultural and pastoral pursuits, 20%
are nomadic Bedouins, and 10% derive their livelihood from the sea.
Less than 10% of the population live and work in towns.[14] The population density is low in terms of total area, but the inhabitants must concentrate in the few habitable and cultivable areas, where, population
density may be very high. The agricultural resources of these regions
cannot provide sufficient food.

Food supplies in the Arabian peninsula being limited, a chronic
shortage of food for the majority of people is usual. With the possible
exception of Yemen, none of the countries and territories located on
the peninsula are self-sufficient with regard to food supplies.

Both geographical and human factors limit food production. The most
significant geographical factors include scarcity of water, extremes of
climate, and salinity of soil, all of which have been touched upon above.
Of these, the most important limiting factor is the lack of adequate
water supplies.

Human factors that limit food production include primitive methods
of planting, spacing, and harvesting and other bad agricultural practices
still in general use. Little investment is made in improving the land or
in buying fertilizer or seed, or tools, or in preventing soil erosion.
Where water is available, irrigation may be excessive on the principle
that if a little water is good a lot of water is better; this leads to eventual waterlogging of the soil. The maintenance of irrigation networks,
on which almost all agriculture depends, is carried out in a haphazard
manner. Such networks are rarely extended or improved or even ade-

quately repaired. The lack of adequate transportation is a serious deterrent to agricultural development and is in part responsible for the
frequent local shortage of food.

Agricultural holdings are generally small, since they are limited by the
labor capacity of the farmer and his family. Farms range in size from
0.8 hectares in oases to a maximum of 20 hectares in grain areas. The
majority of small holdings are owned by the peasants who work them,
primarily on a subsistence basis. In addition, a large quantity of top
quality land is owned by members of ruling families, merchants, and
government officials, and is cultivated by slaves and freemen on a subsistence basis, or by peasants on a share-cropping basis.

The inadequacy of food supplies on the Arabian Peninsula is evident.
However, data on the extent and characteristics of the shortage cannot
be given because statistics on production, import, and consumption are
almost entirely lacking for all the countries under discussion. Any
analysis of the food supply situation, therefore, must be confined to general terms. Such data as have been assembled consist for the most
part of estimates, hardly more than informed guesses. The difficulties
of analyzing the food supply situation in the Peninsula also are increased by the multiplicity of political subdivisions, which range in
size from Saudi Arabia, which occupies two thirds of the Peninsula, to
the tiny sheikhdoms of the Trucial Coast.

The following report attempts to present information in general
terms with detailed discussion, wherever data are available, of conditions in each of the four major subdivisions into which the Peninsula
has been divided for the purposes of this study: Saudi Arabia, Yemen,
Aden, and the Persian Gulf states, including Muscat and Oman. As already mentioned, official statistics are lacking from most of these
countries, except Aden, and the information presented has been col-
lated from a variety of sources. In preparing this outline, extensive
use has been made of unofficial sources, including the valuable studies
on Saudi Arabia, eastern Arabia and southern Arabia prepared by the
American Geographical Society for the Human Relations Area Files.
An excellent analysis of the food production activities of Aden is contained in the Colonial Reports and in the annual reports of the various
departments of the Colony and the Protectorate. In addition, valuable
material is contained in the reports of travelers and workers in the
Peninsula, including especially Twitchell and Sanger; the first hand
observations of these two authors to a large extent form the basis of
this report. These and other sources consulted are detailed in the
bibliography.

B. AGRICULTURAL REGIONS

Although, as mentioned, agricultural production in the Arabian Peninsula is limited, in each country there are one or more areas where conditions are particularly favorable to agriculture and these are, in most cases, the principal food-producing areas of the country. The following is a brief description of some of the important agricultural areas in each of the countries under discussion.

The agricultural areas of Saudi Arabia are delineated in Map 1. Agriculture is impossible in the Hejaz of Saudi Arabia, except in a few wadis where there is cultivation of dates, millet, wheat, barley, and fruits, and stock rearing in the outskirts of the settlement. Such an oasis is Medina, which has plentiful water supplies that permit the cultivation of abundant fruits and vegetables including more than thirty varieties of excellent dates. Total production exceeds local needs but inadequate transportation bars the extension of the present market for the surplus. El Taif, situated in the mountains, is an excellent fruit-growing region and produces an assortment of citrus fruits, pears, peaches, pomegranates, and others. Large fields of alfalfa and grains also are cultivated.

The Nejd is an area where there is cultivation of dates, wheat, barley, and limes and the raising of livestock in isolated agricultural communities. Buraida is the center for more than 50 villages and is one of the richest agricultural sections in central Arabia. It has many orchards and palm and tamarisk groves. Anaiza, 24 kilometers to the north of Buraida, has orchards stretching for two miles outside the city. Hail produces dates, pomegranates, citrus fruits, and vegetables; Riyadh is a fertile and prosperous valley and the seat of government for a major portion of the year.

The Hasa is a section of approximately 4050 hectares with many areas where the soil is good for wheat and rice, especially at Hofuf, which is one of the most important cultivation centers of the country.

The highlands of Asir are well suited to agriculture and produce a variety of crops similar to those of Yemen.

Qatif is the center of the most important agricultural area along the Persian Gulf, an area that extends from Khobar to Qatif and Sfwa. There are extensive date palm groves, and the other fruits grown include bananas, pomegranates, mulberries, grapes, and papayas. Small quantities of rice and large quantities of alfalfa also are grown.

No discussion of agricultural areas of Saudi Arabia would be complete without some mention of the region with the greatest present and potential productive capacity, namely, the experimental farm at Al Kharj. This was started as a demonstration project before World War II with the aid of Iraqi and Egyptian technicians. Shortly after the war started, American advice and technical aid was made available as a means of increasing food production of items then in short supply be-

cause of the shipping curtailment. Water for irrigation is pumped
from limestone pits and channeled into fields that now extend over
1215 hectares. The principal crops grown are wheat, maize, barley,
dates, alfalfa, millet, and a great variety of fruits and vegetables, including especially watermelons, tomatoes, carrots, radishes, cucumbers, cantaloupes, onions, squash, cabbage, cauliflower, eggplant,
okras, peas, peppers, and turnips. The production in 1946-48, the last
years for which data are available, of some of the principal crops was
as follows:

Crop	Unit	1946	1947	1948
Alfalfa	Tons	719	1,720	1,858
Vegetables	Lbs.	98,860	123,450	302,851
Melons	Lbs.	606,000	720,800	1,026,600
Wheat	Bushels	2,710	7,591	18,361

Over one half the available land is planted to grains, principally wheat,
barley, and maize. Familiar crops, such as dates, have greatly increased their yields with the introduction of new strains and growing
methods, while many experimental crops have been grown successfully.
Poultry raising and livestock herding also are carried out.

The project had to overcome numerous obstacles created by man
himself—lack of funds, apathy, resistance to change, religious prejudice. Natural phenomena have also played their part by contributing
devastating floods which ruined the first crop and destroyed the newly
built irrigation network, and a locust plague which wiped out the second
crop.

Al Kharj has been extremely successful in achieving some of its
goals, such as in proving that modern agricultural methods can
greatly improve crop yields, and it has become an excellent source of
fresh produce, meat, and milk for the royal household. However, it is
felt that the farms have not yet succeeded in their most important goal,
that of improving the agricultural practices of the Saudi farmers. Inno-
vations are adopted less by peasant cultivators, who could benefit most
from them, than by a few educated landowners who realize the financial
advantages of the new methods.

Food supplies in Yemen are more abundant and varied in the plateaus and mountain valleys of the interior than in the coastal or eastern plains. The different sections of the country raise a considerable
variety of agricultural products, as may be seen in Table 2, which lists
the various agricultural regions and the most important products of
each.

Yemen has three important agricultural zones. The coastal zone,
the Tihama, is a very hot and humid, sandy or semidesert plain 65 to
80 kilometers wide that is peopled primarily by seminomadic tribes.
Agriculture in this area is dependent on rainfall, which is not always

abundant. The coastal plains merge abruptly into a plateau that is the second region, occupying most of the country. The lower slopes of this plateau, near the coastal plains, support a seminomadic population, while the higher plateaus and mountain valleys are characterized by a settled agricultural population. This plateau area is the most productive agricultural region of the country and the best cultivated part of the Arabian Peninsula, producing an amazing variety of crops and supporting large numbers of livestock. Rainfall totals approximately 508 mm. annually in two rainy seasons, one between July and September and a shorter season in March. Even in these rain-fed hills irrigation is important, and an elaborate system of terracing, dating back many centuries, serves to retain the water and the scanty soil. On the eastern side of Yemen the mountains descend equally abruptly to the vast plains of central Arabia. The eastern foothills are well irrigated and permit the cultivation of fruits and cereals, but farther east the real desert begins, merging into the desolate expanse of the Rub al Khali, the Empty Quarter, where no cultivation is possible.

There are several important agricultural areas in the Western Aden Protectorate such as The Abyan Development, a large irrigation project where most of the cotton is grown, and Lahej, a fertile valley, where most of the vegetables for the Aden Colony are grown. The Eastern Aden Protectorate has only one very productive area and that is the Hadramaut Valley. Here the wadi floors are cultivated partly with flood water and partly with well water. Around each well there are about 50 date trees on about 0.8 hectares of land. Two crops of sorghum are planted per year, as well as numerous subsidiary crops, some interplanted with the sorghum.

The only region in Kuwait where agriculture is carried out to any considerable extent, and the only one virtually self-sufficient in food supplies, is the oasis of Al Jahra, where extensive irrigated cultivation is carried out.[3] The staple crops include wheat, barley, and alfalfa with approximately 4,500 kilos of wheat and 20,000 of barley grown per year. Part of this cereal crop is cut green and is used for fodder. There are more than 2,000 date trees in the oasis, with an estimated production of 21,800 kilos per year. Animal proteins at Al Jahra are supplied by sheep and goats and there are enough cattle to insure adequate supplies of milk. Poultry and eggs are available, but only in limited amounts. Enough muskmelons and watermelons are produced to satisfy local needs, while several vegetables, including pumpkins, onions, radishes, leeks, clover, cress, eggplants, okra, and tomatoes, are grown in sufficient quantities to permit a very limited surplus to be sent to market at Kuwait. The tomatoes grown at Jahra are especially prized. Beans and other pulses are grown only for local consumption.[3]

The food resources of Oman are concentrated in three areas: (1) The fertile plains of Dhufar, which receive the monsoon rains in sufficient amounts to permit the cultivation of many subtropical crops, including coconuts and sugar cane and the raising of cattle and other livestock; (2) the terraced seaward slopes of the Jebel Akhdar foothills, where numerous fruits, especially citrus fruits, grow well, and (3) the main crop area, the 150-mile-strip of the Batinah Plain, primarily a date-growing area but also producing subsistence crops of fruits and vegetables and fodder for livestock and poultry.

Outside of these main areas, small cultivated plots in oases inland provide subsistence crops of dates, limes, peaches, grapes, vegetables, and a little grain.

II. FOOD RESOURCES

A. GENERAL

The Kingdom of Saudi Arabia occupies the greater portion of the Arabian Peninsula. More than one half of its area falls into the category of waste land, and poor to fair quality pastures account for more than 30% of the total area. Nomadic conditions prevail on these grazing lands because of the light and irregular rainfall. Arable land constitutes less than 4% of the total area (some 200,000 hectares). Probably not more than 2% of the land is under cultivation at any one time, since it is the practice to allow one half to one third of the land to lie fallow during years when rains are insufficient and irrigation water supplies inadequate. The small proportion of arable land supports one half of the population outright and supplies dates and grains to the rest.

Most of the cultivable land in Saudi Arabia is concentrated in four main areas, the Hejaz, Nejd, Hasa, and Asir. The last-mentioned, in the southwest, is the most important single agricultural area of the kingdom. The entire highland region of Asir, the so-called "cloudy zone," is a continuation of the highlands of Yemen and receives relatively abundant rain. These highlands are intensively cultivated, supplying a wide variety of agricultural products. The coastal plain, the Tihama, lying west of the Asir mountains, is suitable for the dry farming of grains. Major agricultural areas of Saudi Arabia are outlined in Map 1.

All the geographical and human factors mentioned above as limiting food production in the Arabian Peninsula are in operation in Saudi Arabia. The development of agriculture does not appear to keep pace with natural increase in population. This is shown by comparing food production indices on a total and per capita basis, using as an index of 100 the period 1952-54:

	1957-58	1958-59	1959-60
Food production index	115	100	100
per capita	111	95	94

Yemen is the country with the best arable land on the peninsula and one in which agricultural and pastoral industries have been practiced extensively for thousands of years. Its wide range of climatic and topographical features afford it a variety of crops, from semiarid to well irrigated, and from tropical to temperate.

Agricultural methods in Yemen are invariably primitive, so that yields are low even though the soil is fertile and may produce two crops of cereal a year. In addition, although the small farms characteristic of the country are almost invariably owned by the tribesmen who work them, high taxes and arbitrary methods of collection have impoverished the farmer and removed all incentive to increased production, resulting in a serious deterioration of agricultural practices with very low crop yields in some regions. Debt often forces farmers to sell out or leave poor land and become hired laborers or sharecroppers on more productive land.

Other factors adversely affecting food production, in addition to the poor agricultural practices already mentioned, include the lowering of the water table consequent to deforestation and the practice of devoting an excessively large amount of land to the growing of qat, addiction to which is one of the major economic and social ills of the country.

For all these reasons, increases in agricultural productions, as in Saudi Arabia, do not seem to keep pace with the natural increase of population and in a severe drought year, such as 1958, production per capita may be very much below previous years. This is shown in the following comparison of total and per capita agricultural and food production indices, using as a basis of 100 production in 1952-54:

	1957-58	1958-59	1959-60
Agricultural production index	107	82	74
per capita	101	76	68
Food production index	104	78	72
per capita	98	72	66

The agricultural activities of Aden Colony are confined to market gardens in urban areas and to date groves in the oasis of Sheik Othman. Other food production activities include fishing and livestock raising, aspects of which are discussed under animal products, below.

Although only about 1% of the total area of the Aden Protectorate is arable, these lands include some of the best agricultural regions in Arabia. The Eastern Aden Protectorate (E.A.P.) and the Western Aden Protectorate (W.A.P.) differ in geographical features that affect the food producing resources of the areas. The E.A.P. consists of an immense plateau, deeply dissected by watercourses that are dry for most of the year but carry torrents during the rainy season; the most important of these is the Wadi Hadramaut. Vegetation is sparse and there is relatively little soil or water in the barren plateau. The characteristic pattern of settlements is one of towns strategically placed along the more fertile of the coast areas and interior valleys; all the intervening places are empty.

Although parts of the E.A.P. yield good crops, the agricultural potential is lower than in the W.A.P. and the former area never has been and probably never will be self-sufficient. It is estimated that it produces only enough food to feed adequately one quarter of the inhabitants.

The W.A.P. has fewer nomads and more tribesmen willing to till their land and appears to have a greater agricultural potential than the E.A.P. The W.A.P. is characterized by a continuation of the highlands typical of Yemen, with fertile mountain valleys and fertile oases that contain the most productive soils in the Protectorate, as at Lahj and Abyan. More shrubs and grasses are found, but there are few trees except in occasional pockets. The W.A.P. is a land of villages with no urban centers of importance.

The farming potential of the Protectorate is limited by the scarcity of rainfall, which is everywhere capricious in amount and distribution except in the west, and is almost everywhere insufficient for dryfarming unless supplemented by flood or well irrigation. A large proportion of the arable land therefore is irrigated; dryfarming is practiced only in areas where there is a low rainfall with some runoff of water, and where the land has been suitably terraced. Elaborate terracing and irrigation are particularly characteristic of the Hadramaut Valley in the E.A.P. A good deal of the mountainous terrain affords grazing ranges particularly suited to camels, sheep, and goats, but there are no permanent pastures as such.

The influence of rainfall and availability of water on agricultural yields is well illustrated by a comparison of cropped land and yields of the principal crops in two successive years 1955 and 1956; the first was a "dry" year and the second was an average year. More cotton and sorghum was grown in the wet year, more grain crops and dates in the dry.

	1955		1956	
	Hectares	Tons	Hectares	Tons
Sorghum	19,200	17,000	26,300	21,500
Bulrush millet	6,900	3,050	7,300	2,900
Wheat	2,800	4,700	2,800	3,500
Barley	2,400	4,200	2,800	4,000
Sesame	2,000	1,100	2,000	1,250
Dates	4,850	8,000	4,850	6,000
Seed cotton	14,660	21,700 bales*	13,750	33,100 bales

* 1 bale = 330 lbs. ginned cotton.

Land-holding policies differ in each state in the Protectorate, but the general policy is to reserve ownership for the tribe and to favor

individual ownership as against State. Payment of a fixed cash rent for
land is found only under very unusual circumstances. Fixed payment in
kind is practiced only where a high value is placed on land and water.
The principal system involves share tenancy; in fertile areas the tenant
pays one half of the crop, while in mountain areas one third is the usual
levy. In more arid regions as little as one tenth of the yield may be asked.

The Persian Gulf States include a number of independent sheikhdoms
and sultanates in treaty relations with Great Britain. Included are
Bahrein, Kuwait, Qatar, Muscat, and Oman as well as a group of minor
sheikhdoms collectively known as the Trucial Oman or the Trucial
States. The area is, for the most part, a barren wasteland with some of
the worst lands of Arabia, although ground water supplies produce islands of cultivation that may be extensive, as in the case of the Batinah plain. The discovery of large oil resources has completely altered
the economy of several of these states, especially Bahrein and Kuwait,
but until the discovery of oil, the only sources of livelihood were pearl
diving and fishing on the coast, meager cultivation, especially of date
groves, in the fertile pockets, and animal husbandry on the scanty
grazing lands.

Agricultural holdings in the area, as elsewhere in Arabia, are limited by the working capacity of the farmer and his family. There is
little investment in improving land, in seed or tools, or in preventing
soil erosion or exhaustion. Irrigation practices are primitive, with
flooding where climate and topography permit. The productivity of the
cultivated area is low and the tilled land area smaller than it need be.

Agriculture plays a very small part in the economy of Kuwait, food
production being limited to a few localities where topographical accidents bring ground water supplies near the surface. There is some
subsistence farming near the coast, where dates, cereals and vegetables are cultivated; there are also scattered oases in the interior
where limited amounts of dates and grains are grown.

Agriculture also plays a minor role in the economy of Bahrein,
where it is estimated that less than 4500 hectares out of a total of
60,700 are cultivated [16] Food production is limited to a few localities;
on the main island, for example, it is restricted to a well watered
narrow belt in the north extending for a few miles down the east and
west coasts. Here, as in some of the smaller islands such as Sitra,
date-growing is the most important agricultural pursuit. Dates, lucerne, and vegetables, together with a little other fruit, constitute the
entire agricultural production.[16]

In Bahrein, as elsewhere on the Peninsula, water, not land, is the
limiting factor in increasing agricultural production. All agriculture
in Bahrein depends on irrigation, which may be of three types, flow
irrigation from natural springs, lift irrigation from shallow wells, or
irrigation from artesian well water. Water from springs in the hills
is carried to local gardens by means of qanats, or underground water

channels. During the 1920's and 30's many arterial wells were drilled and the traditional patterns of irrigation were altered thereby. So many wells were tapped at that time that the ground-water level went down alarmingly and a water commission had to be set up to determine which wells were to be drilled and where.[1]

Food production is more highly developed in Muscat and Oman than in any of the other Persian Gulf states. Exportable surpluses of dates, limes, and pomegranates are grown. These exports, together with the income from fish exports and a small British subsidy, help to equalize the unfavorable balance of trade, since most other foods must be imported.

The Batinah District, a coastal plain 240 kilometers long in the Gulf, constitutes the richest agricultural area in the Sultanate. Other arable areas are found in the terraced seaward slopes of the Jebel al Akhdar foothills and in Dhufar. These areas receive adequate water supplies from nearby hills, the water being distributed by an intricate system of underground tunnels. Dhufar also forms an unusual[21] climatic pocket in that it is the only area receiving the monsoon rains. Elsewhere the land supports only nomadic or seminomadic inhabitants, who derive their livelihood from pastoral occupations. Little accurate information is available on the food resources and dietary patterns of the Trucial Coast sheikdoms, but conditions undoubtedly are similar to those prevailing elsewhere on the Persian Gulf coast of the Arabian Peninsula. In some respects, the Trucial Coast states are probably worse off than the nearby states, since they have much less agricultural potential than, for example, Muscat and Oman and they have not yet been enriched by the finding of oil in their territories, except for some preliminary strikes near Abu Dhabi.

As elsewhere along these barren lands, which are probably the worst in Arabia with the exception of the Rub al Khali desert, those areas not covered by sand dunes are barren and rocky and support little or no vegetation. Rainfall averages only about 127 mm. a year, less than one half the amount necessary to maintain permanent pasturage. Agriculture therefore is limited to a few localities where topographical accidents bring ground water supplies near the surface.

These conditions exist in a few areas near the end of the Trucial Coast, as far west as Abu Dhabi. Here, small amounts of millet, wheat, figs, dates, pomegranates, citrus fruits, and various vegetables are cultivated for local consumption. Cows are rather rare, but goats and sheep are kept by the villagers and the Bedouins raise camels, goats, and sheep.

B. CEREALS

Saudi Arabian agriculture is primarily devoted to subsistence crops; of these, grains are second in importance only to dates. Poor seed and lack of proper cultivation and fertilizer reduce the yield to only 3 to 6 bushels per hectare of such crops as wheat and barley. None of the cereal crops are planted in quantities sufficient to meet local requirements.

Several different varieties of brown and white grain sorghum (millets), of which the best type is durra, are found in almost every cultivable region and they constitute the principal cereal crop. Durra is grown from sea level to 2,750 meters altitude, but is especially suited to highland zones above 1,525 meters. Sorghum is adapted to thriving in shady areas of the wadis, where a dwarf type only one meter high contrasts with the sorghum grown in the flood plains of southern Hejaz, a variety that reaches a height of more than 5.2 meters. Because of its adaptability and hardiness, sorghum is a staple grain both of Bedouins and farmers. In addition to being a staple cereal food in Arabia, grain sorghums are utilized as fodder in several districts.

Wheat and barley are important cereal crops that grow chiefly in the highlands of Asir, southern Hejaz, and Nejd, taking the place of millet and sorghum above 1,220 meters in the Asir mountains and at lower levels farther north. Wheat was a major crop in the country and a staple of diet prior to 1925, when rice began to be imported in quantities and at a price that induced practically the entire population to substitute rice for wheat. Curtailed shipping in World War II brought a return to wheat, and planting was reintroduced. Innumerable small plots raise wheat, but aside from the experimental farm at Al Kharj, the largest amounts were grown on the terraced slopes of Asir and the Eastern Highlands towards Najran and in those parts of the north towards Taif. Rice is cultivated in limited quantities in Hasa oasis, where a large volume of water from seven springs makes possible the flooding required. Most of the paddies lie in the date groves and the entire crop is consumed locally. The red variety now predominates, but attempts are being made to introduce the better yielding whites.

Oats and corn are gaining in popularity but are still relatively rare; corn could be profitably grown more extensively. The total acreage planted, yields per acre, and total production during 1956 for the principal cereal crops are detailed in Table 1. These are all estimated amounts since no accurate statistics are available. Production in 1957-1960 decreased for wheat, barley, millet and sorghum, and rice and increased slightly for corn, the decreases being ascribable to the low rainfall of those years. Estimates for this period were as follows:

Crop	1956	1957-58	1958-59	1959-60
		(in 1,000 metric tons)		
Wheat	37	33	25	27
Barley	23	21	20	20
Millet and sorghum	82	84	70	72
Rice	4	3	2	2
Corn	21	32	30	33

In Yemen, also, the traditional cereal crops are millet, maize, sorghum, and oats; the last named mainly in coastal areas, but some maize and bulrush millet also are found in the coast. Cereal crops are planted wherever there is sufficient soil or where terraces can be cut, and these crops are found not only in the fertile plateau region but anywhere along the coast where there is sufficient water available. In these coastal zones, planting may be limited because ground water in this area tends to be salty and because rainfall may be scarce in some years. Along the valleys and in irrigated lands, sorghum and maize, the main cereals, are grown alongside the coffee trees.

The principal cereal crop includes a variety of grain sorghums (millet). About 65,000 tons of sorghum are grown in good years, and this amount is sufficient to satisfy domestic demand and to provide an estimated 10,000 to 15,000 tons of surplus for export.

Barley, corn, and millet are grown in quantities sufficient for local consumption, but not enough wheat is grown to satisfy domestic needs and additional quantities must be imported. Production of the principal grain crops for the period 1957-1960 was estimated as follows:

Cereal	1957-58	1958-59	1959-60
	(in 1,000 metric tons)		
Wheat	20	10	10
Millet and sorghum	650	500	450
Corn	20	15	15
Barley	2	1	1

The principal cereal crop in the Aden Protectorate, as in the rest of the peninsula, is sorghum, which is grown largely on flood-irrigated land and to a lesser extent on lift-irrigated land. Where water supplies permit, as many as two crops a year may be raised. Wheat and barley are harvested from February to March, and sorghum and millet from November to January, as shown in Table 7. Varieties of millet, especially bulrush millet, are quite popular on poorer soils. Both sorghum and millet are grown throughout the Protectorate and provide the staple of diet for the inhabitants. The grain is ground into a coarse flour from which unleavened bread is made. During 1956 an estimated 21,500 tons of sorghum and 2,900 tons of bulrush millet were produced, while in 1958 an estimated 50,000 tons were harvested on 26,000 hectares.

Wheat and barley (temperate zone cultures) do well on land irrigated by wells. Production in 1956 totalled 3,500 and 4,000 tons respectively. Alfalfa for fodder is found on almost every farm.

Cereals also are grown to a limited extent in the other Arabian states. They are especially common in Muscat and Oman, where they are grown in inland oases but only for local consumption. Millet is an important crop in Dhufar, but no data on amounts produced were obtainable. No cereals are grown on Bahrein except on an experimental basis on the research farm at Budeeya.[17]

C. OTHER EDIBLE CROPS

Fruits and vegetables. Dates are the most important single crop in Saudi Arabia and no other native culture furnishes more food per acre. Except in the coastal areas where grain sorghum predominates, as much as 90% of the cultivable land up to 600 meters and a considerable proportion between 600 and 1375 meters is planted primarily to dates. Dates are found in all but the highest altitudes and wherever the soil is at all suitable and there is a permanent supply of nonstagnant underground water that is not too saline. Since they grow well in relatively saline soil, dates can be cultivated in otherwise unusable parts of the Tihama and the eastern province, but the best dates are grown in the Hasa Oasis and around Qatif. Dates are a staple of diet for nomads and agriculturists, but in urban areas the importance of dates as a diet item has been steadily decreasing.

In an average year, production amounts to about 200,000 tons, most of which is eaten locally or used with ground date seeds for livestock feed. Production in 1958-59 was estimated at 175,000 tons and in 1959-60 at 172,000 tons. Exports of dates were prohibited from 1940 to 1951 to conserve local food supplies, and at present only small amounts of special varieties, such as the prized At Khilas, are exported. Imports of dates are several times greater than exports.

In the last few years, the Saudi Arabian government has begun to give special attention to the improvement and expansion of date cultivation and marketing in the hope of raising nutritional standards and of producing a surplus for export. In 1953, a modern date processing plant was established with FAO help at Hofuf, and another at Medina. The sweet syrup, dibs, which accumulates wherever dates are stored, is used as a sweetening or allowed to harden and is eaten as candy.

Bananas, apricots, pomegranates, figs, citrons, papayas, crabapples, and grapes are grown in various regions, but in small quantities and for local consumption only. Apples, pears, and peaches are grown to a small extent wherever the land is high enough or sufficiently far north for an occasional winter frost, while citrus fruits are grown to a small extent on lands irrigated from wells at all elevations below the line of occasional frosts. Fruits may be brought to market in nearby villages and towns if produced in surplus quantities, but their price is nearly always beyond the reach of the majority of the Bedouins who rarely are found near settled communities. The largest fruit production is reported from the experimental farm at Al Kharj, as detailed, but the yield is devoted to the royal household and is not available to the population in general.

Vegetables are becoming increasingly important in the irrigated districts, and are especially in demand by the townspeople. Those that have long been available in small quantities and have recently become more plentiful include potatoes, eggplants, okra, squash, radishes, onions, tomatoes, and beans, and a large number of other vegetables are being introduced on an experimental basis. The increase in the production of vegetables is evidenced in the recent (1959) agreement by the Arabian American Oil Company (Aramco) to buy 500 tons of fresh vegetables from local farmers.

A wide variety of excellent fruits and vegetables are grown in Yemen in areas surrounding large towns. They are used to supply domestic needs and, except for raisin grapes from the San'a region, are not available for export. Dates are a staple crop of the low lands and can be found up to altitudes of 1220 meters. Other fruits grown include grapes, of which 23 varieties are found in San'a, bananas, pawpaws, mangoes, and other tropical fruits that do well in the warm moist lowlands, and in the highlands quinces, plums, apricots, peaches, pears, plums, pomegranates, figs, tamarinds, sweet limes, and custard apples are grown. The most important fruit-growing region is the Wadi Dahr, which is especially famous for its lemons and grenadines: olives are important at Ibb and watermelons at Bait al Faqih. No data on quantities produced are available. Many vegetables are grown here, although not in large quantities, as the demand is small and all produce is consumed locally. Potatoes are a staple crop, and pulses, especially chick peas, are more than adequate for domestic needs. Production of potatoes and beans and peas amounts to 3,500 to 4,000 tons. Both vegetables and fruits are important as supplementary foods in season but are scarce between harvests.

In Aden dates are grown in the Sheikh Othman oasis in Aden Colony, and are the most important fruit and one of the most important food crops in the Protectorate, where they are harvested from June to September. Over half a million date palms have been planted during the last 15 years in the Hajr Valley, while the Hadramaut Valley is reported to have 1,600,000 bearing plants. During 1955, an estimated 8,000 tons of dates were produced, enough for local needs and a surplus for export to the Colony. Other important fruits include the 'ilb tree, which produces a green, cherry-like fruit second only to dates in importance. A steady increase in the production of citrus fruits has been noticeable in recent years. Of these, limes are the most commonly grown. Both melons and sweet melons are grown in the coastal areas at Abyan and

Lahej and find a ready outlet in Colony markets. Coconuts are grown in a few coastal areas. Other fruits, including deciduous types, are grown successfully in the Lahej and Mukeiras regions, but on a small scale and primarily for local consumption. Apricots, grapes, plums, apples, peaches, and walnuts are among the fruits that grow successfully in the Audhali Plateau and in other highland regions. Originally, these crops were introduced to provide supplies for the Colony markets and a good source of income for the Protectorate, but local consumption has kept pace with production as the local inhabitants have developed a taste for these fruits.

Numerous vegetables are grown, but in small quantities and for local use. Attempts to grow sufficient quantities to provide marketable surpluses are handicapped by inadequate means of transportation and marketing. Common vegetables include onions, carrots, tomatoes, potatoes and sweet potatoes, okra, eggplants, chilis, peppers, cucumbers, pumpkins, beetroot, radishes, and spinach. Some particularly fertile areas, such as Lahej and Mukeiras, grow enough to supply a surplus for Colony markets.

Throughout the Persian Gulf states, dates are the most important crop. This is especially true in Bahrein, where date cultivation at one time provided a livelihood for a considerable percentage of the population. Now many of the inhabitants work for the oil companies established at Bahrein and the labor shortage on the date plantations has resulted in a steady deterioration in quantity and quality of the crop.

Dates are also the principal crop of the Batinah coastal plain in the north of Oman, and their export constitutes an important source of revenue. The date gardens extend over an area 240 kilometers long and 30 to 50 kilometers wide. Batinah dates mature earlier than the Basra crops and are famous for their flavor. Date cultivation also has reached a high level in the valleys of the interior of Oman.[21] However, no data on amounts produced in any of the Persian Gulf states were available.

A variety of other fruits and many vegetables are produced in most areas on a subsistence basis. In Bahrein a wide variety of low quality fruits are grown, including citrus, tamarinds, pomegranates, figs, guavas, Indian almonds, mangoes, bananas, and grapes. All of these are of minor economic and dietary importance. During the winters, a large number of European and domestic vegetables are grown, including tomatoes, cucumbers, marrows, pumpkins, carrots, onions, cabbages, sweet potatoes, okra, eggplant, and garlic. Most of these are brought to the markets of Manamah for sale as cash crops and are not generally available in the diet of the rural inhabitants.

Vegetables and fruits are not produced in Kuwait except in Al Jahra and elsewhere where they form part of the diet only of those families whose economic status allows the purchase of imported supplies.[3]

Other fruit besides dates grown in Muscat and Oman include bananas, coconuts, citrus fruits, pomegranates, and other subtropical fruits. Oman, because of its temperate highland, is the best fruit growing area but is far from urban markets. Many fertile oases in the Oman hills produce subsistence crops of limes, peaches, grapes, and vegetables, and sometimes small surpluses are brought to coastal markets.

Other crops. Other food products include coffee, honey, and sesame.

Yemen is the biggest producer of coffee, the main source of export revenue. The coffee of Yemen, known as mocha coffee, has been famous for centuries. It is grown on the western highland slopes at altitudes between 1200 and 1500 meters. Coffee production for 1958 was reported to total 5,100 metric tons. There has been a serious decline both in quantity and quality of the coffee crop. Reportedly, coffee in Yemen is being replaced as a cash crop by qat **(Catha edulis)**, a shrub grown under the same topographical and climatic conditions as coffee and one that brings a greater cash return to the grower. The leaves of qat contain a stimulant, cathine (norisoephedrine) and are chewed fresh by the Yemeni or made into a tea if dry. The use of qat degenerates into an addiction, and apparently a large proportion of the population is so addicted. This is held responsible, to a considerable extent, for the poor general health of the population, first because of the direct effects of prolonged use of the drug and second because money that should be used to purchase foods is expended in the purchase of qat.

Coffee is grown in other areas of the Arabian Peninsula, such as the highlands of Asir, and in some limited areas of the Western Aden Protectorate where climatic and topographical conditions similar to those of the Yemeni highlands are found. All the product of these plantations is consumed locally.

Yemen is a big producer of honey and in 1944 it reportedly had 684,832 hives. All of the honey produced is used to supply domestic demand. Extensive honey production also is carried out in the Aden Colony and Protectorate and, to a much lesser extent, in Saudi Arabia.

Sesame is a common crop. The seeds are crushed to produce sesame oil, widely used in cooking and seasoning. Sesame is an important secondary crop both in Aden and Saudi Arabia; about 2,000 hectares are devoted to this crop in Aden and production amounts to about 1,100 tons. In Saudi Arabia some 485 hectares produce 200 tons of seed.

Sugar cane is raised on a small scale in many coastal areas but nowhere in sufficient quantities to satisfy the demand for sugar.

D. CASH CROPS

Cotton is an important cash crop in the Aden Protectorate. Most of it is grown in the Abyan project; in 1956 some 33,100 bales were produced on 13,750 hectares.

Alfalfa has become an extremely valuable fodder crop in many parts of Arabia. In several places it is grown in the date groves among the palms and is cut monthly.

E. ANIMAL PRODUCT RESOURCES

Animal husbandry is of greater importance than agriculture as a source of food in many areas of the Arabian peninsula, especially in the steppelike deserts in which livestock raising is the only type of food-producing activity possible. The amount and accessibility of water supplies to a large extent determines the type of animal herded. Where watering places are separated by several days' travel, only camels are owned, since they are the only animals capable of subsisting without water for that length of time. Goats are hardier than sheep and can travel greater distances between water holes. Sheep are herded on pastures relatively near wells; cattle require water and better fodder conditions than the other species mentioned.

Livestock is the greatest source of agricultural wealth and social prestige in Saudi Arabia, and persons engaged in pastoral occupations enjoy a higher social status than the settled folk who cultivate the land. Camels, sheep, and goats are important as supplies of food, and other species, including cattle and donkeys, are found in smaller numbers. Estimates of the number of livestock in 1958 included roughly 3,700,000 sheep, 2,000,000 goats, 300,000 camels, 60,000 cattle, 40,000 donkeys, and 3,000 horses, but of course no accurate census has ever been made.

Camels are by far the most important animals raised, although they are outnumbered by sheep and goats. They provide meat, milk, hair, and transportation, but their great importance in the economy lies in the fact that they are the only animals that can survive in some of the barren wastes that make up such a large proportion of the territory. They are the main source of wealth and livelihood of the Bedouins and it is estimated that at least 15% of the total population depend primarily on the camel. The value of the camel and its importance in recent years have been reduced by the extension of motor roads, but a diminution of its value as a beast of burden does not detract from its remarkable ability to convert the sparse vegetation of the desert into milk and meat products for its owners.

Sheep are raised in all parts of Arabia for milk as well as for meat and hair. They cannot go without water for the length of time that camels can and must, therefore, graze at much shorter distances from a water

supply. The bulk of meat eaten is mutton, and with increasing prosperity there is an increasing demand. The milk of sheep is curdled
into a yoghurt-like product called **laban**, and is also made into excellent cheese. The sheep raised in Arabia have broad tails where de-
posits of fat accumulate (which is why they are known as fat-tailed
sheep). The fat is an appreciable item of domestic commerce. It is
heated to form a kind of butter corresponding to lard, and known as
samm.

Goats are kept primarily for milk and are about one half as numerous and fully as ubiquitous as sheep. Goats are better adapted to dry
conditions than sheep and can survive on poorer pastures, but are very
destructive to vegetation. Sheep and goats are not kept by desert
Bedouins as much as by nomadic steppe and hill tribes and by seminomadic tribal and nontribal groups in flat country. In addition, flocks
of sheep and goats are kept by villagers.

Cattle are generally unsuited to the grazing conditions found and
are usually kept only near cities, such as Jidda, with a sizeable foreign
population. There are only two dairies, both on experimental farms.
There would be an ample market for cattle products if good transportation became available, since cattle milk is greatly esteemed for its
supposed medicinal properties. Cattle are used, together with donkeys
and mules, and in a few instances, camels, to draw water from wells
for irrigation.

Poultry raising is not yet a common occupation on a large scale, but
practically every farmer and Bedouin has from one dozen to five dozen
chickens; they are seldom fed but thrive on foraging. Both poultry and
eggs are small; egg production per hen averages 70 a year. The raising of poultry could bring a cash income to the farmer as well as provide additional proteins for the family diet.

Despite the need for animal proteins in the Saudi diet a vast potential source, namely, the Red Sea fisheries, are not developed to their
maximum capacity. The fishing grounds are well stocked but their
utilization is hampered by the insufficient coastal population, the inefficient traditional equipment and techniques, and the difficulty of access to remunerative markets. Storms and shoal water have contributed to making the exploitation of fisheries attractive only to the
coastal inhabitants. The rest of the population shows antipathy to fish,
partly grounded on religious taboos. The Persian Gulf fisheries are
even less developed than those of the Red Sea. Sharks are the chief
catch in the fisheries in the Red Sea, together with tunny and sardines
In the Persian Gulf sardines, groupers, mackerels, barracudas, and
tunny abound. Sharks are baited with large hooks, and the other species are caught with nets of various kinds.

Grazing land is extensive in Yemen and the raising of livestock of
considerable importance, although not as much as in other parts of Arabia.
Animals provide food, transportation, power and fuel, and also yield

hides for export. There are no Bedouin tribes in Yemen, and animal husbandry is carried out by settled or seminomadic peoples.

Sheep and goats are the predominant livestock, sheep are ubiquitous and in 1949-50 reportedly numbered 8,681,000. However, since this enumeration was for tax purposes, actual numbers may be much higher. Goats reportedly outnumber sheep, except in the coffee-producing districts. There is an abundance of camels, which in Yemen are used for plowing, and of donkeys, and there also are considerable quantities of humped, zebu-type cattle and horses. Tax enumeration in 1943-44 included 71,937 camels, 314,058 cattle, and 2,559 horses.

Sheep and goats are the principal sources of meat but the poorer inhabitants cannot afford meat, which remains a luxury item in the average diet. In San'a, about 200 to 300 sheep and goats are slaughtered daily, as well as some 29 to 30 cattle.

Milk is plentiful, but consumption appears to be limited; in general, animal proteins do not appear to be an important constituent of the Yemeni diet.

A large number of cows (estimated at 4,000 to 5,000 in 1955-56), and sheep and goats are kept in the municipal area of Aden Colony. Both public and private stables are grossly overcrowded and there are large numbers of cattle in the street. No pasteurization of milk is undertaken.

Although considerable livestock is raised in the Aden Protectorate, both by the settled cultivators and by the nomadic or seminomadic tribesmen, pastoral industries are not as important as in other parts of Arabia. Fodder and grazing lands are dependent on the very scanty rainfall and often may be in extremely short supply. For example, in Alwan, where the spring rains failed completely in 1955, the livestock population had been reduced by 50% as of December of that year. Similarly, range grazing was very scarce in the Bedouin areas of the E.A.P., where, as a result, animals were in poor nutritional condition; severe losses were suffered in the sheep, goat, and camel population. The latest available estimates for livestock in the Aden Protectorate for the years 1955-56 included: 7,000 asses, 80,000 camels (1956-57), 68,000 cattle, 855,000 goats, and 200,000 sheep.

Milk of sheep and goats and of camels is used extensively in the diet, but only the pastoral tribes have adequate supplies. Cow's milk is used in some inland districts, especially in the W.A.P. where grazing conditions are the most suitable for the raising of cows. Ghee is used as a source of fat among the wealthier classes, and a similar product, samn, made from the fat of the fat-tailed sheep, is used commonly in the colony and in the E.A.P., but is almost unknown in the W.A.P.

The Aden fisheries are among the richest in the Middle East and fishing is one of the principal occupations of the inhabitants. The drying and salting of fish and the manufacture of fish oils and fish meal for cattle fodder and for manure are valuable industries. The fisheries are marine and, in general, fishing is confined to inshore waters. Handling or trolling from small dugouts are the methods usually employed.

Fishermen are usually financed by salt- and dry-fish merchants, who have a lien on the catches. After local requirements have been met the surplus fish either is salted or dried for export to the Far East and Europe. There is considerable dried and smoked fish trade to the interior of the E.A.P., where fish is eaten by the poorer population or used for agricultural and fodder purposes.

In Aden Colony the fish catch is almost totally absorbed by the local population, being sold immediately in the five fish markets of the Colony. If there is any surplus of fish, it is either stored on ice or salted for export to the Far East. There are few cold storage facilities but iceboxes are in good supply at all markets and can hold several days' supply of fish. In 1956 there were 1,200 fishermen who accounted for a catch of 1,259.7 tons having a wholesale value of £63,702.

The inshore waters of the E.A.P. support a much greater fishing industry than those of the W.A.P., principally due to the concentration of sardines in the coastal waters east of Mujalla. The area also supports a highly productive fishery for kingfish (Scomberomorus commerson), sherwi (Euthymus affinis), and zainoob (Thunnus tonggol). In the W.A.P. there is a winter fishery for anchovy (Anchoviella heteroloba), and kingfish, zainoob, and sherwi are encountered in small localized concentrations. Shark fishing by harpoon or line is carried on at most fishing centers. Rock fish is encountered on most rough bottoms especially in the Bal-Haf-Bir Ali area. During 1955, a total of 2,427 tons of sardines (dry weight), 60,152 tons of tunny, and 131,923 of kingfish were landed in Protectorate fisheries.

Wild animals of various species used to be a supplementary source of animal proteins, but game of all kind is getting scarce. Locusts are considered a delicacy and are collected and eaten roasted or boiled.

Throughout the Persian Gulf states animal proteins in the diet are derived primarily from fish and only to a limited extent from livestock.

The camel is of as great economic importance on this coast, as in Saudi Arabia, and constitutes the basis of livestock holdings of a considerable proportion of the pastoral population. Desert Bedouins with camels and a few sheep and goats make up one half of the pastoral population of these eastern Arabian states. Camels are a particularly important source of animal proteins in the diet in Muscat and Oman. Their milk constitutes the basic ingredient of the diet of the nomadic and seminomadic peoples of the interior. Oman camels are a highly valued breed that has been raised in the sultanate for centuries.

When rains are adequate, inland desert areas of Kuwait afford good grazing for the herds belonging to nomad tribes.[17] A large number of goats, sheep, and camels are raised by the pastoral Bedouins but these animals provide food items for local consumption only. Many Kuwaiti urban and village dwellers own sheep or goats which are pastured daily

in common pastures by community shepherds.[15] The milk supplied by
these herds is an important item of local diet, although it is inadequate
in quantity and poor in quality.

Cattle and goats as well as camels are raised in Dhufar; elsewhere,
cattle are rare. The straight-backed cattle of Dhufar are fed partly on
sardines and dried fish. The cow calf is raised for milk production,
while the bull calf is killed and eaten except for a few kept for breeding
purposes. Cattle and poultry also are raised in the Batinah district,
and there is sufficient grass in the Javal Ashsham area to permit widespread grazing for sheep and other livestock.

Bahrein cows, of the humped variety, are fed on fish, dates and date
stones, and lucerne.[13] Cattle and sheep are kept in Bahrein primarily for
milk, wool, and hides; most of the meat eaten is imported from Iran
and is very expensive and of poor quality.

Fishing is an important industry throughout coastal Arabia, and fish
are everywhere a staple of diet. Most of the fish are caught in pali-
saded reed traps called **hadhra**. Fishing is especially important in
the economy of Muscat and Oman, where the sun-dried fish represent
an important item of revenue.[17] Sharks are considered a delicacy and
their flesh is salted and dried for local consumption. Crabs, crayfish,
and oysters reportedly are eaten, but not lobsters.[21] The potential production of the fisheries is high, but they are not exploited beyond a
fraction of their capabilities.

F. EXPORTS AND IMPORTS

Throughout most of the Arabian Peninsula food production is not
sufficient to satisfy the demands of the population, and large imports
of food are required. Available statistics are fragmentary but, except
for Yemen, a major portion of at least some of the staples of diet must
be imported. Imports of some of the most important foodstuffs are
listed in Table 3, as can be seen, probably the largest import item is
wheat, either as grain or as flour for bread making.

In Saudi Arabia large imports of bread grains, rice, and sugar are
necessary, as are smaller amounts of numerous other items, including
coffee, tea, dates, and spices. The amounts imported are not specified,
since no statistics of trade are kept, but it is estimated that as much
as two-thirds of basic food supplies are imported in some years. Detailed statistics are available only for 1949-50 (Table 4), but it is
known that imports of food items have increased many fold since that
date. For example, the table lists slightly over 65,000 tons of wheat
imported in that year, whereas wheat imports from the United States
alone amounted to 70,000 tons in 1957 and total imports of wheat and
wheat flour in grain equivalents totaled 104,100 tons.

Yemen is the most nearly self-sufficient of the Arabian countries with regard to food supplies and must import only sugar, rice, some wheat flour, and such luxury items as spices. Exports are limited to coffee, hides, and skins, which are sent to Western Europe, the United States, and Saudi Arabia, and to qat leaves, dhurra, and small quantities of fruits and vegetables, which are shipped to Aden.

Almost all the food supplies of the Aden Colony are imported. Fresh fruits and vegetables and animals for slaughter are brought in from the Protectorate, and other items from countries overseas. Foodstuffs imported, in addition to those already mentioned, include rice, beans, peas, lentils and other pulses, wheat flour, refined sugar, coffee, beer, and alcoholic beverages; the last two items are primarily for the consumption of the European population Import and export statistics available for 1958 are detailed in Table 5. In general, quantities of food available are inadequate and prices of imported foodstuffs high and rising.

The principal food imports of the Protectorate are grain flour, rice, dates, sugar, sesame oil, tea, and spices; exports include coffee, cattle, ghee, sheep, goats, and fish.

The Bahrein Islands are dependent on imports for a large but unspecified proportion of their food supply. The government regulates the importation and price of certain essential foodstuffs such as wheat, rice, and sugar. Most of the meat is imported from Iran and is of poor quality and expensive. Fresh fruit sold in the Manamah markets is usually imported, while vegetables available from local production in winter must be imported in summer.

A list of food imports in 1949 included 1932 tons of rice, 5,691 tons of wheat and wheat flour, and 2,894 tons of sugar, as well as 1675 head of cattle and 40,255 head of sheep and goats for slaughter.[16] With the increases in oil revenues in the past ten years these imports must have multiplied many times over.

Most of the food supply of Kuwait, including such basic items as wheat, barley, rice, fruits, vegetables, and sugar, must be imported. Supplies are brought in from England, India, Australia, and even the United States. Convoys of trucks used to bring fresh vegetables from Damascus, but supplies are now flown in from both Syria and Lebanon.[13] The inadequate supply and low quality of milk produced locally has created an increased demand for imported powdered milk.[15] The higher cost of this imported food formerly restricted its use to the wealthier classes, but the increased prosperity of the colony due to oil revenues may eventually bring a balanced diet within reach of the majority of the inhabitants.

The principal source of income for the inhabitants of Muscat and Oman remains the production and export of dates, limes, and pomegranates, and of fish, dried fish, and fish meal. A considerable proportion of all other foods must be imported, and the value of imports far exceeds that of exported food, as shown by the table on the following page.

	Imports (rupees)		Exports (rupees)
Rice	98,81,200	Dates	81,27,400
Coffee	30,04,100	Fish and fish products	57,47,300
Sugar	22,33,400	Pomegranates and limes	15,18,100
Wheat	5,78,100		
Flour	9,89,200		

G. INTERNATIONAL TECHNICAL AID IN AGRICULTURE

The Food and Agriculture Organization of the United Nations has cooperated with the government of Saudi Arabia in the establishment of an Agricultural Institute and helps to finance several research projects in agricultural development, fisheries research, irrigation control, and others. Date packing factories have been established.

The International Cooperation Administration of the United States, and the agencies which preceded it, have cooperated in the operation of the Al Kharj Demonstration Farm as well as in the establishment of eight smaller Demonstration Farms throughout the country.

The Soviet Union has recently signed an agreement with Yemen, under the terms of which the USSR will send a team of agricultural specialists to conduct a survey of the present situation in Yemen. This group will then make recommendations on the type and volume of economic and technical assistance to be rendered.

H. FOOD INDUSTRIES, STORAGE AND TECHNOLOGY

Food processing. Food processing is traditional in the area, but it is almost invariably carried out on a household or, at most, a small-scale basis; modern factories for processing food are almost nonexistent. Traditional food preserving includes the drying and salting of fish, the drying and packing of dates and date syrup, and the preparation of dairy products made with fermented milk, which has better keeping qualities than the fresh product.

Food-processing establishments in operation include fish drying and salting concerns in coastal areas and date-processing establishments in date growing regions. No data on production were available, but in most cases factories are small; generally, primitive facilities and nothing resembling a modern food processing industry may be said to exist on the Arabian Peninsula.

Fish salting and drying is carried out most extensively in Muscat and Oman, where a large amount is prepared for export, and to a lesser extent in Aden and other coastal areas. Date processing is carried out wherever dates are produced for more than strictly local consumption, as for example in the Batinah coast of Oman and in Bahrein. Some efforts are being made to establish modern date-processing factories in Saudi Arabia with a view to preparing dates for export.

Storage and refrigeration facilities. Public storage and refrigeration facilities are primitive or nonexistent. Refrigeration facilities adequate to store several days'catch of fish are in operation in Aden, and grain storage facilities have been set up in various towns in the Hadramaut Valley of the Protectorate as an aid in preventing the periodic famines that were characteristic of the area. Large food merchandising establishments in the largest cities throughout the Peninsula have frozen-food storage facilities, since there is a great and increasing demand for frozen meats and other frozen products imported from Europe, the United States, and Australia. Wealthy persons, such as the royal families of Saudi Arabia and the other oil kingdoms, have elaborate refrigeration and storage facilities installed in their palaces.

III. DIET TYPES

A. GENERAL

The diet of the majority of the inhabitants of the Arabian Peninsula is inadequate both in quality and in quantity. Most of the people exist at a low subsistence level, with relatively low consumption of animal proteins, fats, and protective foods. Meat rarely is eaten even among livestock herders, since to them animals represent capital and are therefore not expendable for food. The extent of dietary deficiencies cannot be estimated with any degree of accuracy because of the absence of reliable statistics and because of the considerable variations in diets among various population and economic groups.

Three basic types of diets may be recognized—the diet of the nomadic Bedouin herdsman, the diet of the settled agriculturists, and the more varied but in some respects still inadequate diet of townspeople, including the inhabitants of the fishing villages in coastal areas. In general, urban dwellers, especially in large towns, eat better than agricultural or pastoral workers, and the Bedouins have a better balanced diet nutritionally than the agriculturists, but one with a lower caloric intake. Protective foods have never been eaten in sufficient quantities by any population group, but are becoming increasingly available, especially to urban dwellers. Within each diet group, variations dictated by economic status or by the local customs of the country may occur.

A discussion of each of the three diet types mentioned, together with
some relevant local variations, follows.

B. VARIATIONS IN DIETS

Urban diets.   Townspeople, especially those living in a seaport or
in an oil community, have access to a more varied selection of food, and
the actual diet therefore depends primarily on economic status and local preferences and prejudices. The diet consists mainly of cereals,
more fresh fruits and vegetables than is common in other groups, milk
and milk products, some meat, generally mutton, and assorted condiments and sweet meats, with a plentiful supply of coffee and tea. Cereals include millet, corn, wheat, and barley, as well as rice, which is
imported in large quantities. The use of dates has been decreasing
among the urban population. Clarified butter or the fat made from fat-
tailed sheep (**samn**) are favorite animal fats, while sesame oil is the
commonest vegetable oil used.

Fish is available in coastal areas, and in some poor fishing villages
may be the main, or virtually the sole, article of diet. Inland, fish is
not very popular and some species are under religious tabus, which
also exclude pork and the flesh of donkeys and asses. Furthermore,
Islamic law also prohibits the flesh of any animal (except fish and
locusts) that has not been ritually slaughtered; this limits for the
Arab population the use of salted and preserved meats and canned meat
products, which are available to the European and non-Moslem population of the large cities.

Poultry and eggs are available to the townsmen, since most of the
production is sold by farmers as a cash crop in town markets, but
these foods are not generally consumed, although they are increasing
in popularity. Townsmen have more different foods at one meal than
other population groups.

The diet of people in the larger cities—for example, Ridayh, Manamah, and Aden Colony—is by far the best on the Peninsula, both in quality and in quantity, while Arabs in fishing or farming villages have a
more meager diet with a lower consumption of meat and cereals. The
city of Ridayh, the seat of government for Saudi Arabia for a large
portion of the year, is in part supplied with the produce of the experimental farms at Al Kharj, and a varied diet is available to a considerable portion of the people. Similarly, almost any kind of foodstuff is
available to those who can afford it in the shops of Manamah (Bahrein),
which stock all kinds of tinned food supplies and a great variety of
imported fresh meats and produce. The Colony of Aden is a particularly
cosmopolitan community with a variety of food habits. All food is imported except for fish, milk, and the limited output of market gardens.

Bedouin diet.   Bedouin diet is monotonous and scanty. The principal
component is milk and milk products. Milk is obtained from camels,

goats, or sheep, depending on the tribal livestock pattern, and the milk is either drunk fresh or in a curdled form, similar to yoghurt, called laban. Various kinds of cheese are made of which labne, a kind of cream cheese, is the most popular. Small amounts of dried fruits, usually dates, are eaten. Most tribes obtain these from settled culti- vators on an individual basis, so that consumption depends on the fam- ily's prosperity; normally, all but the very poor can afford some dried fruit, and for the wealthier Bedouins it is a staple of diet.

Wheat, barley, and, occasionally, a little rice are obtained by barter, blackmail, or brigandage from the agriculturists or else are grown sporadically by the nomads themselves. Patches of ground are roughly sown and later the tribesmen return to harvest the crop. In general, cereal products are a staple diet item for the prosperous and are avail- able seldom and in small quantities to the poor. Millet (durra and other sorghums) and wheat are the commonest cereal items, usually cooked in a gruel.

Meat is provided in the Bedouin diet only as a great luxury, since the animals themselves represent the capital of the tribesmen and they must live from the yield. Aside from festive occasions when special slaughtering is done, only those animals that die naturally arc eaten. Mutton is the most commonly used meat, while camel's flesh, espe- cially of a young animal, is highly esteemed.

Although numerous goats are kept, goat meat is not often eaten. The wild animals that were formerly hunted to supplement the larder are becoming scarce. Locusts are considered a delicacy. Fat for cooking usually is rendered from the fat of fat-tailed sheep; the resulting prod- uct, samn, resembles ghee in appearance and utility.

Vegetables and fresh fruits are seldom available to the Bedouins but are enjoyed when obtained. Coffee, brewed either from the berry or from the husks, is indispensable and is served on all occasions.

Agriculturists' diet.   The diet of the settled agriculturist is higher in calories than that of the Bedouin, but it is deficient in proteins and fats. The basic component of the diet is grain. Millet (durrha and other grain sorghums) is the most widespread cereal and is used for making the flat, unleavened bread that is the staple of diet. To this staple ce- real are added abundant dates, some mutton, milk and milk products, and a growing proportion of fresh fruits and vegetables, in season and according to the level of family earnings. Fish is a staple of diet in coastal areas but rarely is used inland. Milk and milk products are widely available from goats and sheep, but their consumption is much more limited than among the nomads. Meat among the less prosperous is still reserved for special occasions. Wild animals that once served as a supplementary source of animal proteins, are becoming scarce. Locusts are a delicacy and a good source of protein. Bees are kept extensively in Yemen and the Aden Protectorate but to a much lesser extent in other areas of the Peninsula.

Very few dietary surveys have been carried out in the Peninsula. The only studies reported are those of the Arabian American Oil Co. on its employees. Their surveys showed that the average diet had a protein deficiency of 29-30%, while fats were deficient by 72% and carbohydrates by 5% when compared to a standard 2,800 calorie diet regarded as adequate for a working man.

Diet of women and children.   The diet of women and children is markedly even less satisfactory than that of adult males. Everywhere in Arabia it is the universal custom for the father and older sons of the family to eat first and for the women and children to eat only what the men leave. This means in actual practice that the women and children may not be able to obtain any of the foods considered as delicacies, such as meat, fruits, and vegetables, and protective foods in general.

IV. ADEQUACY OF FOOD RESOURCES

Throughout the Arabian Peninsula, production of foodstuffs, even in good crop years, is not sufficient to supply the needs of the inhabitants and considerable quantities of various food items must be imported each year. The only country in which this does not hold true is Yemen, where in normal times a sufficient quantity and variety of foods is produced to supply domestic requirements. However, even here, local shortages are frequent, primarily because of inadequate storage and transportation, so that seasonal products, such as fruits and vegetables, are in short supply or are unobtainable between harvests.

Under emergency conditions, when average supplies have been curtailed by poor crop yields, lack of rain or grazing lands, or locust infestations, the gap between production and consumption is even greater and may result in food shortages that may in turn degenerate into famine conditions. The numerous factors that contribute to the inadequacy of food resources even in normal times are well illustrated in Saudi Arabia. Included among these factors is the abnormally rapid growth of the large towns, lack of adequate transportation between production and consumption areas, and the overgrazing and erosion of steppe pastures. The new prosperity arising from oil revenues and the increased employment opportunities directly or indirectly provided by the industry have attracted a great many people to the larger towns, where practically all the food supplies must be imported. The lack of transportation affects the transfer of surplus products from such regions as Asir to these new urban markets. The overgrazing and close cropping of the already poor pasture lands has led to their overgrowth with inedible weeds, which have crowded out forage plants and rendered pastures almost useless for grazing. In the Gizan Tihama, for example, patches of these weeds as much as ten kilometers long are reportedly found, particularly near villages.

Any emergency situation affects the scanty food supplies and further reduces available production. Thus, during the last war many items that had to be imported were unobtainable and special efforts had to be made to increase production and to store available supplies.

A further factor in future adequacy of resources is that present revenues from oil allow the purchase of sufficient food from overseas to make up food deficiencies but the time will inevitably come when oil reserves have been exhausted. No major long-range plan has been formulated to cope with this eventuality.

Local food shortages here and in other parts of Arabia are now often relieved by the government-subsidized importation of food that is sold at stabilized or reduced prices. This is done primarily in countries at which oil revenues have enriched the government to an extent where such subsidies are possible. For example, a widespread drought in 1958 resulted in a considerable increase in wheat and other imports by the government of Saudi Arabia.

It is doubtful whether the Arabian Peninsula, because of geographical limitations imposed by its poor land and water resources, can ever produce food supplies adequate to feed its growing population.

V. NUTRITIONAL DISEASE PATTERNS

The majority of the inhabitants of the Arabian Peninsula suffer from undernourishment, malnutrition, or, in times of scarcity, downright starvation. This is true even in Yemen, where despite the variety and abundance of foodstuffs produced, the majority of the people are undernourished.

Factors that result in this chronic malnourishment of the inhabitants of Arabia are many, and include poverty, geographical factors that limit the production of food, poor transportation facilities that prevent surpluses of food produced in one area from reaching another where they are in short supply, and many others. As already mentioned, almost no scientific studies of nutritional deficiencies in Arabia have been reported. However, in every country of the Peninsula, reports of travelers and persons engaged in scientific work mention the existence of numerous nutritional deficiency diseases. Table 6 lists for each country the type of deficiency diseases reportedly present. These include protein deficiencies, as well as numerous avitaminoses including rickets, night blindness, scurvy, and others.

VI. CONCLUSIONS

The Arabian Peninsula at present is far from self-sufficient in the production of food, and it is doubtful whether it can become so in the foreseeable future. These shortages in food supply are ascribable both to geographical limitations of soil, climate, and scanty water supply, and to human limitations, such as poor agricultural practices, poor transportation, and the other factors discussed in this report.

There is no doubt that increased yields could be obtained by modification of traditional farming practices. However, extensive social reforms, years of re-education, and many cultural changes must be effected before agricultural rehabilitation benefits the population as a whole. Until then, the expanded purchasing power provided by the huge oil revenues perhaps may be used to import food supplies sufficient to improve the nutritional standards of the people.

SELECTED REFERENCES

1. Belgrave, J. H. D. Welcome to Bahrein. Stourbridge, Mark & Moody, 1953.
2. Crary, D. D. Recent Agricultural Developments in Saudi Arabia. *Geographical Review,* Vol. 41, 1951, pp. 366-383.
3. Dickson, H. R. P. Kuwait and Her Neighbors. London, Allen & Unwin, 1956.
4. Faroughy, A. Introducing Yemen. New York, Orientalia Inc., 1947.
5. Food and Agriculture Organization. Yearbook of Production, Vol. 12, 1958.
6. Tothill, J. D. Report to the Government of Saudi Arabia on Agricultural Development. *F. A. O. Report No. 76,* 1953.
7. Fisher, W. B. The Middle East. (3rd edit.) London, Methuen, 1956.
8. Heyworthe-Dunne, G. E. Al Yemen: A General Social, Political and Economic Survey. Moslem World Series No. 5, 1952.
9. Hickinbotham, T. Aden. London, Constable, 1958.
10. Keen, B. A. The Agricultural Development of the Middle East. Middle East Supply Center, 1946.
11. Petrie, P. W. R. Some Experiences in South Arabia. *Journal of Tropical Medicine and Hygiene,* Vol. 42, 1939, p. 357.
12. Saudi Arabia, Royal Embassy. The Kingdom of Saudi Arabia. [No date.]
13. Sanger, R. H. The Arabian Peninsula. Ithaca, N. Y., Cornell University Press, 1954.
14. Sharabi, H. B. A Handbook of the Contemporary Middle East. Washington, D. C., Georgetown University, 1956.
15. Simmons, J. S., *et al.* Global Epidemiology: Vol. 3, The Near and Middle East. Philadelphia, Lippincott, 1954.
16. Stewart, Sir H. The Possibility of Agricultural Development in Bahrein. (In manuscript.) British Middle East Office, 1949.
17. Tweedy, M. Bahrein and the Persian Gulf. Ipswich, East Anglian Magazine, 1952.
18. Twitchell, K. S. Saudi Arabia. (3rd edit.) Princeton, Princeton University Press, 1958.
19. United Kingdom, Colonial Office. Aden Colony, Annual Reports.
20. Yale University, Human Relations Area File. Country Survey Series: Saudi Arabia. 1956.
21. Yale University, Human Relations Area File. Country Survey Series: Eastern Arabia. 1956.
22. Yale University, Human Relations Area File. Country Survey Series: Southern Arabia. 1956.

Table 1

Principal Crops of Saudi Arabia: Acreage, Yield and Production

Crop	Year	Area 1,000 Hectares	Production Kg./Hectare	Total 1,000 Tons
Wheat	1956	43	8.7	37
Barley	"	23	10.0	23
Maize	1948/52 (av)	15	13.8	21
Millet	1956	16	8.3	13
Sorghum	"	28	2.5	69
Rice (paddy)	"	4	11.9	4

Source: F.A.O. Production Yearbook, 1958.

Table 2

Agricultural Areas of Yemen

District	Population	Remarks
		Liwa of San'a
Bilad al Bustan	32,634	Cereals, Vegetables, Qat, Coffee, Fruit
Beni Hushaish	9,353	Cereals, Qat, Fruit. Very fertile area
Beni'l Harith	16,414	Cereals, Qat, Fruit. Fairly rich soil
Amran	235,558	Coffee, Qat, Corn, Vegetables, Fruit.
Thila	14,373	Coffee, Qat, Corn, Vegetables, Fruit.
Al Tawrlah	85,500	Coffee, Cereals, Vegetables, Fruit. Fair Water Supply. Fertile
Al Mahwit	93,450	Coffee, Cereals, Qat, Fruit, Cattle
Al Haimah	28,842	Coffee, Cereals, Qat, Fruit
Haraz	120,787	Coffee, Fruit, Durra. Best Coffee area, well watered
Bilad Anis	57,800	Coffee, Cereals, Qat, Vegetables, Fruit. Well watered. Cattle
Raimah	134,080	Coffee, Cereals, Vegetables. Well watered. Cattle
Utmah	49,960	Coffee, Cereals, Qat, Well watered
Reda	39,590	Cereals, Vegetables, Fruit. Large desert areas
Al Baida	49,816	Cereals, Vegetables, Fruit
		Liwa of Ibb
Ibb	107,458	Coffee, Qat, Corn, Durra
An Nadirah	62,379	Cereals, Qat, Vegetables, Fruit. Well watered
Najd al Juma'i	17,148	Coffee, Cereals, Qat, Fruit
Dhi'i Sifal	27,895	Coffee, Cereals, Qat, Fruit, Cattle
Al Udain	119,763	Coffee, Cereals, Qat, Vegetables, Fruit, Cattle
		Liwa of Ta'izz
Ta'izz	272,445	Coffee, Cereals, Qat, Vegetables, Fruit, Cattle
Al Makha	67,496	Coffee, Cereals, Qat, Vegetables, Fruit. Interior cultivated.
		Liwa of Al Hajjah
Al Hajjah	210,504	Coffee, Cereals, Qat, Vegetables, Fruit, Cattle
Ash Sharafain	89,812	Coffee, Cereals, Qat, Vegetables, Fruit, Cattle
Hajur	27,038	Coffee, Cereals, Qat, Vegetables, Fruit, Cattle
		Liwa of Al Hudaidah
Al Hudaidah	238,867	Coffee, Qat. Only Bura Cultivated
Az Zaidyah	96,720	Coffee, Cereals, Qat, Dates
Al Luhayyah	73,456	Corn, Dates, Durra
		Liwa of Sa'dah
Sa'dah	138,427	Cereals, Vegetables, Fruit, Cattle

Source: Adapted·from Heyworth-Dunne. Al Yemen, 1952.

Table 3

Arabian Peninsula Imports—1957

(in metric tons)

	Total Peninsula	Saudi Arabia	Other Areas of Peninsula
Wheat	39,200	20,800	18,400
Rice	142,100		
Barley		8,600	
Sorghums, millet, other cereals	21,400		
Wheat flour	109,600	60,000	49,600
Wheat and wheat flour in grain equivalents	191,400	104,100	87,300
Oranges and tangerines	6,600		
Aples	4,700		
Dates		13,100	
Pulses	5,300		
Raw sugar	83,000	55,800	27,200
Coffee		2,200 (1948/52)	
Tea	5,800		

Source: F.A.O. Trade Yearbook, Vol. 12, 1958.

Table 4

Imports of Food: 1949-50

Food	Amount Imported (tons)
Flour.	21,822
Wheat	42,797
Barley.	2,299
Dura.	5,282
Dukhir.	853
Rice.	29,246
Lentils	842
Sesame.	173
Dates.	3,524
Horsebeans.	1,251
Chickpeas.	255
Sugar.	21,439
Vegetables.	644
Fruits.	1,046
Nuts.	277
Coffee.	2,936
Various food stuffs	7,932
Ghee	627

Source: Food and Agriculture Organization: Report to the Govt. of Saudi Arabia on Agricultural Development. Adm. Rept. #76, J. D. Tothill, Rome, 1953.

Table 5

Aden Colony

Exports and Imports: 1958

	Quantity (1000 tons)	Value (1000 $)	% of Total
EXPORTS			
Coffee	5.3	5,162	2.9
Sugar, refined	31.2	3,750	2.1
Spices	6.3	3,063	1.7
Rice	14.8	2,073	1.2
Wheat & wheat flour	17.1	1,633	.9
Oilseeds	11.7	1,151	.6
Fruits, dried & preserved	9.0	988	.6
Tea	.8	988	.6
Animals for food (1000 head)	57.0	773	.4
Pulses	7.0	620	.3
IMPORTS			
Sugar, refined	42.6	4,730	2.4
Coffee, raw	5.0	4,427	2.2
Animals for food (1000 head)	34.4	2,951	1.5
Wheat & wheat flour	31.6	2,676	1.3
Vegetables, preparations	20.6	2,033	1.0
Rice	14.2	2,004	1.0
Oilseeds	7.1	1,488	.7
Fruits, dried & preserved	13.6	1,362	.7
Tea	138.9	1,313	.7
Dairy products	3.6	1,183	.6
Spices	3.2	1,088	.5
Ghee	3.1	1,105	.5
Fruits, fresh	9.1	1,039	.5
Pulses	10.5	903	.4
Cotton seed	10.3	683	.3

Source: Foreign Agriculture Service, U. S. Dept. of Agr. Exports and Imports Agricultural Commodities by Principal Countries of Destination. 1958. Washington, D. C., 1960.

Table 6

Arabian Peninsula

Deficiency Diseases: Summary of Reports of Occurrence

Country	General Undernourishement	Protein Deficiencies	Deficiency Diseases Present but Unspecified	Specific Vitamin & Mineral Deficiencies:								
				Night Blindness	Pellagra	Beri Beri	Subclinical Vitamin C Deficiency	Scurvy	Rickets	Osteomalacia	Ariboflavinosis	Nutritional Anemia
Saudi Arabia	F			P	S	R	P	P	P		P	P
Yemen	F		P	F	R	R	P	R	P	P		
Aden	P			P	S	R	F	P	P			
Bahrein	S						F	S	F			F
Kuwait	F		F									
Trucial States	P		P									
Muscat and Oman	P		P									

Key: F—Frequent   P—Prevalent   S—Sporadic   R—Rare

Source: Compilation by the author.

Table 7

Aden Protectorate: Harvest Calendar for Principal Crops

Crops	Harvest Period	Bulk of Harvest
Wheat	Feb.-Mar.	Mar.
Barley	Feb.-Mar.	...
Sorghum	Nov.-Jan.	...
Millet	Nov.-Jan.	...
Potatoes	Oct.-Dec.	...
Dates	June-Sept.	Aug.
Bananas	Year round	...
Sesame Seed	June-July & Oct.-Dec.	...
Cotton	Jan.-May	Feb.-Mar.

Source: World Crop Harvest Calendar. F.A.O. Rome, 1959.

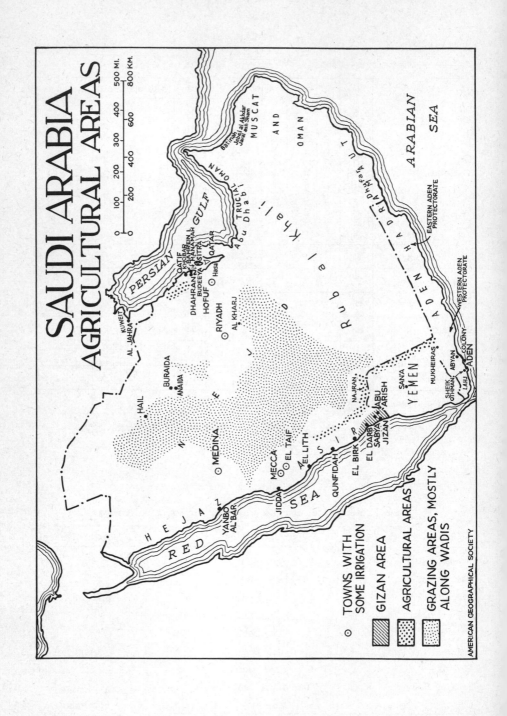

SAUDI ARABIA
AGRICULTURAL AREAS

500 MI.
800 KM.

600   400   200   0
400   300   200   100   0

PERSIAN GULF

KUWEIT
AL JAHRA

ARABIAN SEA

MUSCAT
AND OMAN

Jebel al Akhdar
Jaal ash Sham
Batinah

TRUCIAL OMAN

Abu Dhabi

QATIF
KHOBAR
DHAHRAN MANAMA
BUDEEYA SITRA
HOFUF   QATAR
         Hasa

RIYADH
AL KHARJ

Rub al Khali

BURAIDA
ANAIDA

HAIL

N E J D

MEDINA

MECCA
EL TAIF
EL LITH

HADRAMAUT
Dhufar

ADEN
EASTERN ADEN
PROTECTORATE

WESTERN ADEN
PROTECTORATE

MUKHEIRAS
ABYAN
ADEN COLONY
LAHJ
SHEIK
OTHMAN

NAJRAN
ABU ARISH
SABYA
EL DARB
JIZAN

SANA
YEMEN

A S I R

EL BIRK

QUNFIDAH

JIDDA
YANBO
AL BAR

H E J A Z

RED SEA

⊙ TOWNS WITH
  SOME IRRIGATION

  GIZAN AREA

  AGRICULTURAL AREAS

  GRAZING AREAS, MOSTLY
  ALONG WADIS

AMERICAN GEOGRAPHICAL SOCIETY

SYRIA

I. GENERAL REMARKS

A. AGRICULTURE IN SYRIA

Syria lies at the eastern end of the Mediterranean Sea on the southern border of Turkey. Since its union with Egypt in 1958, it constitutes the northern region, or province, of the United Arab Republic.

Although only about 11% of its 187,800 square kilometers (72,500 square miles) of land area is cultivated, Syria is predominantly an agricultural country. Of the total national income of 2,285 million Syrian pounds (1958) some 1,059 million were provided by agriculture, and agricultural products were the chief export earners, accounting for 65 to 85% of total value of exports.

The population of Syria, excluding Palestinian refugees, was estimated at 4,082,000 in 1957. The nomadic population is large and is estimated at between 200,000 and 320,000. These nomads may be classified into three groups: "bedouins of the camel," purely nomadic tribes that roam the more arid regions and rely almost entirely on camel products and dates for food; "bedouins of the sheep," less nomadic tribes that live near large market centers; and the settled tribes that cultivate land and move only within the limited radius of their holdings. Agriculture and animal husbandry provide a livelihood for about 75% of the total labor population. A large number of farmers plant crops entirely on a subsistence basis, and the same limitation applies to the nomadic herdsmen who live off the products of their herds but who contribute little food to local markets.

As in most other Middle East countries, agriculture is not diversified but rather depends on a few major crops, in Syria's case on cereals and cotton, to provide a major portion of agricultural income and most of the foreign exchange.

Scantiness and, especially, unreliability of rainfall is the greatest physical limitation to expansion of agriculture. Rainfall, besides being meager in quantity, is highly variable in amount; periodic droughts cause sharp drops in agricultural production every three or four years, as for example, in 1951, 1955, and 1958. These variations affect not only the growing of crops but also the yields obtained from livestock, since during a drought year spring pastures on which nomadic herdsmen graze their sheep and goats are scanty, burn out early in the spring, or fail to appear at all.

A major portion of Syrian territory is arid or semiarid and receives rainfall of less than 500 mm. per year. Most of the arid area is devoted to seasonal (spring) pastures, although cotton, sugar beets, and wheat may be grown under irrigation. The semiarid area is the one where the greatest expansion of grain crop acreage has occurred and where dry farming of barley, legumes, and sometimes even wheat is practiced, subject to fluctuations in rainfall. The humid coastal zone is the only area receiving over 800 mm. of rain per year, sufficient to allow planting of a variety of crops. The main production area of Syrian agriculture lies in the fertile crescent between this humid coastal zone and the arid and semiarid steppes. Some 85% of crops are grown on this rain-fed land, and as a result Syrian agriculture is even more susceptible to fluctuations in rainfall than are crops in other countries in the area. This has been especially true in recent years following expansion in the area under cultivation. Most of this expansion was in the semiarid zone on large marginal rainfall areas that fail to produce at all in years of drought. Expansion of irrigation would greatly increase the amount of land available for cropping and permit the cultivation of higher value crops than are presently possible with dry farming. As of 1958 the following government-financed irrigation projects had been completed:

Location	Source	Hectares irrigated
Homs-Hama)	Orontes River	22,000
Tell Maghass)	Khabour River	5,400
Sonn	Pumps	4,000
Matck	Kouck River	16,000
Mzerib	Springs	2,200
Cheikh Meskine	Den'enir River	400
		50,000

Much larger areas are at present irrigated by small, privately owned irrigation systems, mostly operating on the basis of water pumped from nearby streams. The total area irrigated in this manner has been estimated at 630,000 hectares.

The Syrian Government plans a considerable expansion in Government-financed irrigation schemes; projects now approved or under construction are expected to provide an additional 523,000 hectares of irrigated land by 1968. One of the more ambitious of the schemes is the Roston Dam on the Euphrates, which will irrigate a total of 800,000 hectares.

Most farming is carried out by primitive methods, with little application of modern techniques of farming, soil improvement, or seed
selection. However, in the last decade, a considerable amount of mechanization of farming techniques has been introduced, primarily in connection with the extension of grain acreage in such places as the Jerizeh,
where terrain is particularly suited to mechanized farming.

The antiquated system of share cropping and absentee ownership of
land has had a depressing effect on the agricultural economy of Syria,
as it has in most other countries of the Middle East. Tenant farmers
paid disproportionately high rents and share croppers received a very
small return for their labor, so that incentives for increased production were lacking. A law passed in 1958 fixed maximum rental charges
and wage scales and increased the duration of land rental contracts to
three years to ensure stability of tenancy. Later in the same year an
Agrarian Reform Law was approved, limiting the size of agricultural
holdings to a maximum of 460 hectares in rain-fed areas and 120 in
irrigated areas and providing for distribution of excess holdings to
landless cultivators. As of November, 1959, a total of 1,700,000 hectares had been distributed to 750,000 peasants and an additional 800,000
hectares of state land had been parceled out.

A Five Year Development Plan for agriculture was formulated in
1959 and was to include development of cotton plantings, improvement
in breeding strains of livestock, establishment of new industries processing agricultural products, and expansion of agricultural training
facilities.

B. AGRICULTURAL REGIONS[1,6,7]

Syria can be divided into seven or eight agricultural regions grouped
within three larger zones, which may be described as Western or Mediterranean Syria, the fertile crescent, and the steppes.

Western Syria consists chiefly of the mohafazat of Latakia, which
includes a coastal plain encircled by mountain ranges to the north and
east. The coastal plain has abundant rainfall and is well watered by
rivers, some of them permanent, and by springs or wells fed by rainfall on the hills. This region enjoys a Mediterranean type climate and
grows a variety of crops including, in order of importance, tobacco,
olives, figs, cereals, and citrus fruits. A variety of field crops as well
as legumes, vegetables, and cotton are grown in smaller amounts.

The fertile crescent area within Syria includes the Jezireh, Aleppo,
and Homs and Hama, as well as the Hauran region. These are, for the
most part, plains situated at altitudes of 400 to 800 meters above sea
level and with a continental climate. Rainfall ranges from 200 to 500
mm. per year, decreasing eastward from the coast and is characterized by a dry season, from June to October, and a wet season with 85%

of the rain falling from December to March. Most of the cultivated crops therefore are winter crops, since the amount of rainfall is too low to permit summer cultivation, except where irrigation is available.

The principal crops in the Jezireh are wheat, which covers 25% of the area, cotton, and rice. There is a small amount of barley, maize, and sesame grown. This is the area where the greatest expansion of grain acreage has occurred in recent years, largely on the basis of mechanized agriculture; about 40% of the wheat grown here is farmed by mechanized means.

In the province of Aleppo the agricultural region is divided between the northwest and the southeast. The northwest is characterized by mountains and valleys with a relatively high rainfall. Olives, figs, grapes, cotton, maize, sorghum, and some wheat are grown. The southeast of the province has a low rainfall but obtains irrigation water from the Euphrates. Crops here consist principally of wheat and barley. Between these two areas farming consists mostly of the growing of grapes, olives, and pistachios.

The region of Homs and Hama has a rainfall averaging 600 mm. per year and some irrigation, based mainly on the Lake of Homs. On irrigated land the main crops are cotton, sugar beets, and beans, with cereals, legumes, maize, and onions as minor rotation crops. Dry farming in this area includes the cultivation of wheat, barley, sorghum, some sugar beets, and fodder crops. Together with the Aleppo plains these areas produce about one third of the wheat, one half of the barley, and three fourths of the cotton grown.

The hauran, to the south of Damascus, is primarily a dry-farming area where wheat and grain sorghum are grown.

The Jebel Druze rises from the southern Syrian plain to a high plateau with many watercourses, some of which are permanent. Patches of fertile soils produce good crops of wheat and other crops with irrigation, as for example in the area south of Kanawat where there are many springs that water extensive vineyards and orchards.

The climate of the steppes has two distinct seasons, a very hot dry summer and a rather cold winter, when temperatures fall below freezing. Rain is scarce and seldom is above 100 mm., while absolute drought exists for six months of the year and grass for grazing is available only from December to June. This region is mainly inhabited by nomadic tribes, since permanent cultivation is possible only where there is a good supply of water, either along rivers, as in the valleys of the Khabour, Euphrates, and Barada Rivers, or in oases where there are abundant springs.

The most important of these zones of cultivation within the steppes is the Ghouta area, to the east and south of Damascus. Intensive mixed farming includes dairying as well as the growing of vegetables, fruits, cereal, and hemp. Irrigation in the Ghouta is by a system of canals, possibly pre-Roman in origin, which bring the waters of the Barada

River to the fields. Palmyra is the most important of the cultivated oases within the steppes, and extensive olive and date groves are planted in the surrounding area while other fruits and wheat also are grown.

II. FOOD RESOURCES[10,13,14]

A. GENERAL

The total area under cultivation, estimated at 1.52 million hectares in 1945, by 1957 had increased to 3.07 million hectares. This total does not include an additional 2 million hectares left fallow every year in dry-farming areas, so that total acreage devoted to cultivation is about 5 million hectares. The increase in area of some of the principal crops planted is shown below:

Area under various crops

(000 hectares)

	1945	1950	1954	1955	1956	1957	Increase (%)
Wheat	751	992	1347	1463	1537	1495	49
Barley	348	416	543	614	636	813	26.5
Rice	7.0	9.4	6.0	4.0	2.4	1.0	0.03
Maize	23.9	24.8	17.3	13.0	10.1	9.7	0.3
Cotton	17.5	78.0	187.3	248.8	272.2	258.3	8.4
Sugar beets	–	0.1	4.6	3.0	3.0	3.4	0.1
Tobacco	7.1	7.5	6.4	6.8	6.6	6.6	0.2
Sesame	6.8	10.9	22.6	20.9	22.6	6.9	0.2
Dry legumes	171	198	199	200	194	222	7.2
Vegetables	18	20	21	19	22	23	0.7
Fruits and nuts	170	192	209	217	227	228	7.4
	1520.3	1948.7	2563.2	2809.5	2932.9	3066.9	100

Harvesting of most field crops is carried out in May or June whereas fruits, for the most part, are harvested in late summer, except for oranges, gathered from December to May. Table 1 lists the harvest seasons for the principal crops as well as the month in which the bulk of the harvest is gathered.

A great variety of food crops is grown, while industrial crops are important as a source of foreign exchange and cash income to farmers. Large numbers of livestock are raised and contribute milk and milk products and some meat to the diet, as well as wool, hair, hides, and

skins for domestic use and export. Table 2 lists the estimated cultivated area and production of principal crops in 1958 and 1959, while
Tables 3 and 4 contain data on livestock and livestock products as of
1958.

B. CEREALS

Cereals, mainly wheat and barley, account for approximately one
half of total agricultural production. Between 1945 and 1957 an enormous expansion in the cultivation of grains took place and the total
area cropped nearly doubled in amount. A great deal of this expanded
area is cultivated by mechanical means and the number of agricultural
machines in the country doubled between 1952 and 1957.

Cereal production is not distributed evenly throughout the country.
Damascus and Latakia, for example, produce less grain than they consume, whereas the Jezireh, Aleppo, Deir-es-Zor, and Hauran are surplus producing areas. Cereals are grown without irrigation where
rainfall is in excess of 350 mm. per year and with irrigation if rain
falls below this amount.[13] The scantiness and unreliability of rainfall
is reflected in the fluctuations in cereal production. Droughts occur
on an average of every four to five years; in such years grain harvests
may be halved. For example, production of wheat amounted to 1,354,000
tons in 1957 and to 562,000 tons in 1958.

Although both soft and hard varieties of wheat are cultivated, most
of the wheat grown is hard wheat. Wheat yields are low, even for the
Middle East, and amount to only about one third of those in Egypt.[7]
During 1959 land planted to wheat amounted to 1.4 million hectares,
nearly one half of the total cultivated area, and production was estimated at 632,087 tons. Nearly one half (44%) of the wheat produced is
grown in the Jezireh, a region in the mohafazat of Hasakeh. Next in
importance as a wheat growing area is Aleppo, which produces about
one fifth of the crop, while lesser amounts are harvested in Deir-es-
Zor and Hama. Map 1 shows wheat production by mohafazat.

The type of barley grown in Syria is mostly Arab barley, a variety
relatively easy to mill, which grows in poor rain-fed land unsuited for
wheat. This type, known on the export market as Syrian barley, is
most commonly grown in the Hauran, Hama, and Aleppo areas. A second variety, which is grown west of Homs and also in Aleppo, requires
good soil and irrigation but produces higher yields.[13]

Some 727,466 hectares of land were devoted to the growing of barley in 1959 and production was estimated at 217,645 tons.[14] More than
one half of the crop is grown in Aleppo; thus, of 228,000 tons grown in
1958, some 128,000 were from this mohafazat.[10] Map 2 shows barley
production by mohafazat.

Maize is one of the chief food grains grown on irrigated land; about
one half of the total amount produced is grown in Damascus and nearly

one third in Latakia, with much smaller amounts farmed in other areas.
Total cultivated land in 1959 amounted to 8,535 hectares and production
to 12,434 tons. Corn is the staple of farmers in many villages, who prefer it to wheat.[3]

Another important food cereal is millet, which is often cultivated on
unirrigated lands not suited to maize. It is grown under irrigation in
the drier regions, for example, in the valley of the Euphrates.[3] Cultivated land in 1959 amounted to 57,706 hectares, with an estimated production of 41,651 tons.[14] The main producing areas are in Dir'a and
Deir-es-Zor, with substantial amounts also grown in Latakia.[10]

The cultivation of rice began during World War II along the banks
of the Jagh Jagh and Khabour Rivers and in most of the irrigated areas
of Aleppo, Latakia, and Hauran.[3] After the war, however, much of the
rice area was converted to cotton, which is a more profitable crop and
requires smaller amounts of water;[1] rice land decreased from 9,400
hectares in 1950 to 784 in 1959, and production amounted in the latter
year to about 1,682 tons.[14] Most of the rise grown is produced in
Homs, with smaller amounts in Damascus and Dir'a.[10]

Some 5,000 hectares of land are devoted to the growing of oats and
production totals between 4,000 and 6,000 tons a year. The largest
plantings are in the mohafazat of Latakia.

C. OTHER EDIBLE CROPS

1. **Vegetables**. A variety of vegetables is grown in many areas of
the country, as a rule on irrigated land. The most important vegetables grown include tomatoes, onions, egg plant, and potatoes. The
cultivated area and production of these and other vegetables is listed
in Table 2. Production is not sufficient to satisfy domestic demands
and considerable quantities must be imported.[10]

Tomatoes are an important crop in Latakia, Aleppo, and Homs;[10]
during 1959 a total of 11,345 hectares were planted and production
totaled 98,062 tons. More than one half of the onions produced are
grown in Homs and Latakia and each of these mohafazats produce
slightly more than one fourth of the total crop. Land planted amounted
to 3,671 hectares in 1959 and production was 28,435 tons. Egg plant,
a favorite vegetable, are grown throughout the country, especially in
Damascus, Aleppo, and Latakia, which together produce more than one
half the total crop. The area planted in 1959 amounted to 3,726 hectares and production reached 39,822 tons. Potatoes are grown at
higher altitudes in the Ghouta and two thirds of the total production
comes from this area in Damascus. Small amounts also are grown in
Latakia. Garlic is grown in substantial amounts both in Damascus and
in Latakia, with total acreage in 1959 amounting to 835 hectares and
production totaling 3,069 tons.

2. **Legumes**. Large quantities of legumes are grown both for feed, as green forage, and for food, as dry seeds. The most important varieties used for food include lentils, chick peas, broad beans, and fenugreek. Reportedly the quality of the crop is low, especially in the case of peas and beans.[4]

Lentils are an important crop on dry-farming land, with about two thirds of production concentrated in Aleppo and lesser amounts in Dir'a. Chick peas, also grown in Dir'a, are another important crop of dry-farming areas. Broad beans are grown under irrigation in Aleppo and Damascus, which produce most of the crop, as well as in Latakia, Hauran, and Hama. Haricot beans (dry beans) are grown in Aleppo and Homs, and small amounts of peas in Damascus. Other legumes, including flowering sern, rambling vetch, and bitter vetch, are primarily fodder crops.

3. **Fruits and nuts**. A large assortment of fruits are grown both on dry-farming and on irrigated land, and they are important items in the agricultural economy as sources of food, as raw materials for food processing industries, and as an export product. On the other hand, substantial amounts of certain types of fruit also are imported, since domestic production is not enough to satisfy demands. The most important fruits in this category are watermelons and citrus fruits.

Olives are the most valuable, useful, and widely planted fruit in Syria. Olive groves are common in Latakia, Aleppo, the Ghouta area of Damascus, and the Hauran, with Aleppo and Latakia being the main producing areas. Olives are cultivated on dry-farming land with scanty rainfall and grow well both on the plains and at higher altitudes.[13] Approximately 111,000 hectares were planted to olives in 1959 and production amounted to nearly 65,000 tons. The number of trees of bearing age was estimated at 8.2 million in 1958,[10] most of which were of the Al Dan type of olive, which is used primarily for oil.[13]

Vineyards are scattered throughout the farming areas and almost all villages have vineyards on the outskirts of the settlements. Important producing areas include Homs, Damascus, and Aleppo.[13] A total of 217,000 tons of grapes were produced in 1959 on 68,100 hectares.[14] Grapes are eaten fresh, dried as raisins, or are used to make molasses and alcoholic drinks.[13]

Figs are grown on dry-farming areas in Latakia, Aleppo, Homs, and Damascus, and under irrigation in the Ghouta and Deir-es-Zor.[13] About 18,000 hectares were devoted to this crop in 1959 and 39,600 tons of fruits were produced on some 3 million trees of bearing age.[10] Figs are eaten fresh, dried, or sliced and stewed with molasses or honey; they are also used for making date wine and arak.[13]

Apricots grow well with irrigation in almost all areas, but Damascus is the only important growing area and produces most of the annual crop. Apricots are the chief fruit crop of the fertile Ghouta region of Damascus, and this city is the center of trade for this fruit, selling it fresh in the local markets and exporting to other Arab countries large quantities of dried apricots and the "sheeted" apricot or apricot paste called **kamaradine**.[13] The area planted to apricots amounted to 7,800 hectares in 1959 and production was 25,700 tons, less than the 1958 production of 29,000 tons.[14]

Citrus fruits are not at present important crops; only about 800 hectares are devoted to their cultivation and production amounts to about 6,000 tons of oranges and lemons.

Apples and other pome fruits are important crops in the mountain areas, where they thrive in the mild, cool climate. The mountains of the Zebdani region and the Barada valley are important apple-producing areas, while pears are grown in the Ghouta. Peaches and quinces also are grown, primarily in the Ghouta, although quinces grow well almost everywhere in the territory. The cultivation of peaches is limited to a few areas where the climate is favorable. Pomegranates grow in all regions, but bear more fruit in the hotter areas; most of the production is in Aleppo. Pomegranates are grown either with or without irrigation, depending on the annual rainfall. These trees are used primarily as border trees in orchards and there are few groves devoted exclusively to pomegranates. Plums are grown in Damascus and cherries in Hasakeh.[13,10]

Many species of nut trees thrive. Almonds are grown in almost all areas, sometimes with irrigation, and the largest amounts are produced in Damascus, Hama, and Homs. Pistachios are grown both in Aleppo and in Damascus and the pistachios of Aleppo are particularly well known. Walnuts grow in almost all areas including the coast, the interior plains, and the mountains. They are next in importance to apricots as an export fruit crop.[13,10]

4. **Oil bearing crops.** Sesame is the most important crop grown primarily for oil, although large quantities of cottonseed are becoming available with the expansion of cotton planting. The cotton crop contributed some 27,000 tons of seed to the oil-extraction industry. Sesame is grown on some dry-farming lands west of Aleppo and on irrigated land in other areas, including especially in Deir-es-Zor. During 1959 some 11,600 hectares were planted with sesame and 7,000 tons of seeds were harvested. Sunflower is grown in the Homs area and is the source of a high-grade cooking oil. Peanuts are grown mostly in Latakia, and in 1959 acreage and production amounted to 2,900 hectares and 7,000 tons.

Total production of oil crops was insufficient to supply the needs of the extracting plants and additional quantities were imported.

5. **Sugar crops.** Sugar cane is grown in small quantities in coastal areas; cultivation is limited and growing areas are dispersed. A tenfold increase in planting and production occurred between 1958 and 1959. In the latter year cane plantings increased from 100 to 2,400 hectares, while production rose from 2,400 tons to 26,900 tons.

The cultivation of sugar beets was introduced in Syria about 1950 and both the area planted and production have undergone rapid expansion in the past decade. Homs and Damascus are the two most important beet-growing areas. Areas planted doubled between 1958 and 1959 and production more than tripled due to improved cultivation methods. Sugar beet production amounted to 91,600 tons in 1959.

D. CASH CROPS

The cultivation of cotton has expanded considerably in the post-war era and it now constitutes the main source of cash income for farmers of many areas. Cotton is grown primarily in Deir-es-Zor and Aleppo, with substantial amounts also produced in Hama and smaller quantities in other mohafazats. The area planted amounted to 227,200 hectares in 1959, and production totaled 264,900 tons.

Other fiber crops include flax and hemp. The latter is one of the most profitable crops grown in the Ghouta region, while small plantings of flax also may be found in Damascus.

Over 90% of the tobacco produced in Syria is grown in Latakia, mainly at higher altitudes on rather poor soil. Acreage planted in 1959 was 8,800 hectares, and production totaled 7,500 tons.

Alfalfa and fenugreek are cultivated around the big cities, especially near Damascus. In village areas other fodder crops are more common, including especially such pulses as rambling vetch and bitter vetch.

E. ANIMAL PRODUCT RESOURCES

Large numbers of livestock are kept and animal husbandry is an important occupation. Nevertheless, the value of livestock products amounts to only about one fifth of total agricultural value.[13] Many factors account for this low valuation, including inadequate nutrition, high incidence of disease and mortality among flocks, and poor breeding practices, all of which tend to depress livestock yields.[1]

The most important livestock area is in the northern part, especially in Aleppo, Hasakeh, and Deir-es-Zor. An estimated 5.9 million head of sheep and 1.6 million head of goats, as well as 298,000 head of cows, were owned in 1958, together with smaller numbers of asses, oxen, horses, mules, camels, and buffaloes and about 3 million head of poultry, mostly chickens. The increase in number of each of these species between 1946 and 1958, as well as the distribution by mohafazat in 1957 and 1958, is shown in Table 3.

Animal husbandry is carried out on a family or clan basis under traditional systems.[1] Steppe areas provide grazing grounds for about three million of the sheep and one million goats, which are herded by nomadic tribesmen, while in areas surrounding the steppe rural communities tend large numbers of cows. Most pastures are overgrazed so that the level of animal nutrition is low.

Table 4 lists the type and amounts of animal products obtained between 1946 and 1958, as well as the distribution of production, for each type, by mohafazats in 1957 and 1958.

Three kinds of cattle are common. The baladi, kept for milk production and as a draft animal, comprises about one tenth of the total cattle population; this is not a particularly hardy breed and requires good grazing and plentiful water. The Julani is an intermediate form, hardier than the Baladi but giving lower milk yields. The akshi cattle, the most common breed, makes up about 75% of the total cattle population; this is a small variety with low milk yields, but is a hardy breed that can survive severe climatic conditions and poor pastures.[13]

The majority of sheep are herded by bedouins on the desert steppes. Sheep are kept for wool, meat, and milk, while the rendered fat (**samneh**) of the fat-tailed sheep is an important by-product. The Awassi breed is the dominant one, being well adapted to the rigorous climatic conditions. It is estimated that 33% of the sheep are in the Aleppo area, 20% in the Euphrates area, and the remaining 47% equally distributed between the Jezireh, Hama, Homs, and Damascus areas.[6] The distribution of sheep by mohafazats is shown in Map 3.

Goats are of African stock and may be of two kinds, the Baladi, which is more common in the Damascus area, and the Jabali, which is a hardier variety commonly kept by villagers. This goat is particularly destructive to forests and pastures.[13] Camels are the mainstay of the desert Bedouins, and provide not only transportation, but also milk, hair, hides, and meat.

Poultry holdings have been of minor importance in the past and consisted almost exclusively of village or house flocks. However, since Syria is a grain surplus region, poultry production could be a profitable industry and could provide animal protein supplements to the diet and a welcome cash income to the farmer.[1] Egg production amounted to an estimated 138 million eggs in 1958,[1] equivalent to 9,200 tons.

Syria produces approximately 300,000 tons of milk a year, but production figures vary widely from year to year depending on whether adequate rainfall produces abundant pasturage. Thus, the 1958 production was estimated at only 256,000 tons, whereas production both in 1956 and 1957 amounted to more than 500,000 tons. About 40% of the milk is cow's milk and, of the remaining 60%, two thirds is sheep's milk. Part of the sheep and goat milk is consumed locally and part is exported in the form of white cheese, yoghurt, or other milk products. The cow's milk produced is all marketed in towns near the producing area. The milk sold locally often is handled with little regard to hygiene and sanitation and, in addition, may be skimmed or adulterated with water before selling.

There are few installations for the manufacture of cheese and butter and these products are processed, for the most part, by villagers in their homes. Estimated quantities of milk products processed in 1958 included 558 tons of butter and 11,058 tons of cheese.

The present production of meat is estimated at approximately 40,-000 tons annually, of which 5,000 tons are exported and 35,000 tons are used to supply domestic demand. An estimated 986,711 head of sheep, 165,746 goats, 21,251 head of cattle, 11,915 camels, and 177 buffaloes were slaughtered in 1958 at slaughtering and inspection centers.[10]

Fish is not an important item of diet and very little fish is caught, either in fresh water or sea fisheries. The total catch probably is less than 2,500 tons a year, of which about 50% are lake and river fish.[11]

F. EXPORTS AND IMPORTS

Both exports and imports are important in the Syrian economy. Agricultural exports earn the major portion of syrian foreign exchange, while imports of certain foods not grown in Syria, or grown in insufficient amounts, are necessary to supplement domestic supplies. Table 5 lists the most important exports and imports of agricultural products of Syria in 1957 and 1958.

Exports of agricultural products constitute the major portion of Syria's exports and account for 65 to 85% of the total value of earned foreign exchange.[1] The amount and value of agricultural exports varies with the size of harvests and the amount of yields from livestock; these variables, in turn, are dependent upon rainfall. The most important items in export trade include cotton, grains (principally wheat and barley), and animal products in general.

During 1957 cotton accounted for 34.4% of the total value of exports. Cotton fiber is exported to several countries, principally France and China, while cottonseed is processed in domestic oil extraction plants.

A considerable proportion, usually about 35% of grain produced in a good harvest year, is surplus grain available for export, and grain products may constitute as much as 30% of total export sales. Wheat is exported to Italy and Egypt and barley to Western Europe. In poor harvest years grain produced only is enough to satisfy domestic demands, and in some years imports may be necessary, as for example in 1960.

Animals and animal products are next in importance to cotton and grains as export items, and they average about 15% of total exports. Livestock and livestock products are exported principally to neighboring Arab countries. As may be seen from Table 5, the two most important categories are live animals, which are sent principally to Lebanon, and raw wool.[1]

A variety of food items are imported in small quantities, but these imports amount to less than 10% of total export trade. The only item imported in significant amounts is raw sugar, which is processed in the sugar factory at Homs. Next in value as an import item are fresh fruits and vegetables, including tomatoes, potatoes, legumes, cucumbers, and pumpkins, as well as dates, bananas, citrus fruits, apples, and melons. Several varieties of oil-bearing seeds are imported, since domestic production is not sufficient to supply oil extraction plants. Castor seeds, sesame, and cottonseed are among those imported. Tea, coffee, and such spices as are not grown locally also are imported to supply domestic markets.

The union of Syria and Egypt has resulted in increasing commerce between the two regions which, for the most part, have mutually complementary agricultures. During 1958 Syria imported rice, potatoes, and some vegetables from Egypt, while it exported various kinds of fruits and nuts as well as chick peas, lentils, and white flour. The most important items in this interchange of agricultural products in 1958 are listed in Table 6.

G. INTERNATIONAL TECHNICAL AID

Several agencies finance cooperative programs in agricultural development, including especially the Food and Agriculture Organization of the U.N., which has carried out projects and financed studies in forestry, pasture management, animal disease control, plant protection, development of water resources, and many others. The excellent country study in Syria prepared by Food and Agriculture Organization experts, in connection with the Mediterranean Development Program, was one of the most important sources used in preparing this report. The French Government maintains a cereal research station at Deir-el-Hajjar (Centre de Recherche d'Experimentation Agrico) that will eventually become a main government research station in all fields of agriculture.

The UNRWA maintains a forage trial station at Ramadan studying the best varieties of forage crops for irrigated and nonirrigated areas.

H. FOOD INDUSTRIES, STORAGE AND TECHNOLOGY

1. **Food processing.** Traditional food processing industries have been almost exclusively handcrafts, and include the production of sheeted apricots (**kamaradine**), the drying of fruits such as apricots and grapes, and the production of dibs (fruit molasses), oil, **samne**, cheese, arak, starch, and flour. These old industries are still an essential part of the economy of the country, but large modern factories are becoming more numerous and account for an ever more substantial

share of agricultural processing.[3] The distribution of food industries
in Syria is shown in Table 7, which lists the number of factories per
mohafazat for each of the more important types of food processing operations. A total of 6,037 establishments were reported, of which one
third, 2,216. were located in Aleppo, 1,409 in Latakia, and 875 in
Damascus.[10] During 1959 the establishment of numerous new food processing plants was authorized, but there were no details available on
type and planned location of these factories.

Although most of the food processing industries are traditional ones
that are, to some degree, undergoing modernization, some of the food
processing operations are of recent introduction. Margarine was not
produced until 1954, while the production of chocolates didn't reach
appreciable amounts until 1955. Output of selected food processing industries between 1950 and 1957 (with data for 1958 where available) is
presented in Table 8.[1]

The oil extraction industry has expanded rapidly in recent years.
The production of olive oil is an old, established industry, but many of
the old-fashioned presses are being modernized and new ones are being
built. An even more rapid expansion has taken place in the number and
production of cottonseed oil extraction plants, an expansion stimulated
by the increased cultivation of cotton and the concomitant increase in
the availability of cottonseeds. As of 1958 there were a total of 1,099
oil extraction plants, of which 807 were traditional animal-powered
presses and 292 were mechanized. The industry is concentrated
largely in Aleppo (509 plants) and in Latakia (504), except for 67 plants
that are located in Damascus. Production of olive oil amounted to 14,-
600 tons in 1958 and production of other vegetable oils increased from
7,000 tons in 1954 to 20,300 in 1957.

Several margarine factories are in operation, and production
amounted to 2,550 tons in 1957.

Grain mills constitute approximately one fourth (1,410) of all food
processing establishments, and they are to be found throughout the
country, with the largest number concentrated in Aleppo (284) and
Damascus (264). The power for grinding is supplied by water in 461
mills and by motors in 949. No figures were available on the amounts
and kinds of flour produced.

Fruit processing operations include the production of jams and jellies, dried fruits, fruit pastes, and fruit molasses. As mentioned
above, these are traditional crafts, centuries old. The first modern
factory for fruit preserves was established in Damascus in 1933. This
factory processed all kinds of jams from apricots, quinces, plums, and
other fruits. Other factories followed in 1940, 1949, and subsequent
years, and as of 1953 there were at least eight plants employing a total
of 570 persons. Production in 1957 amounted to 2,340 tons of fruit preserves.

The production of "sheeted apricot", **kamaradine,** is an old industrial specialty of Damascus. The sheets are made by boiling apricots
and sun-drying the resultant juice in flat pans. This paste is eaten dry
or soaked in water. Production totals about 9,000 tons per year and
large quantities of this product are exported yearly to other Arab countries. The whole fruit also is dried, as are grapes, figs, and other
fruits. Most of this sun-drying operation is carried out by villagers
in the fruit-producing areas.

Fruit molasses, called **dibs** or **dibis,** is made from dried or ripe
grapes, figs, or dates, and is an important food item of rural inhabitants. As of 1958, there were a total of 845 molasses-making plants
in operation, 542 of them in Aleppo and the rest in Damascus and Sweida.

A modern packing plant for packing fresh fruits and vegetables was
opened in 1958 in Damascus. This plant has a capacity of 5,000 tons
per year.

Some 140 factories produce an annual total of 5,000 tons of chocolates, candies, cocoa, and other sweets. The first of the modern plants
was established in 1949, although smaller plants had been in operation
before. The manufacture of **halvah,** a traditional and popular dessert,
is carried out in numerous small factories throughout Syria, but total
production cannot be estimated.

There were two sugar factories in operation as of 1958, a new one
at Adias with a capacity of 100 tons per day and an older one at Homs
with a capacity of 200 tons a day. The factory at Homs, which was established in 1946, produces not only sugar but also glucose, starch,
and alcohol. This factory was established with the primary aim of developing and encouraging the cultivation of sugar beets. Although the
production of this crop has increased considerably, the factories must
still depend on raw sugar imports of over 50,000 tons per year in order
to operate. Sugar production amounted to 56,000 tons in 1958, of which
approximately 3,000 tons were exported.

Milk products are popular and a number of processing plants are in
operation, ranging in size from small, primitive establishments at the
village level to large modern pasteurizing plants. In 1956 UNICEF provided funds for the establishment of two milk processing plants, one at
Damascus and one in Aleppo, which were to have a total daily capacity
of 30,000 liters each. Part of the milk produced was to be distributed
free to school children each year. Recently, mobile units, based on
towns in producing areas, were put into operation to follow herds of
nomads and to process the milk where it is produced. Each unit was
able to process from one to six tons of milk.

As of 1958 there were 22 plants making butter and 75 cheese-making
factories, mostly in Aleppo, Hama, and Damascus, while new units for
the production of cheese and leben were started in these cities recently.
During 1958 some 558 tons of butter, 11,058 tons of cheese, and 5,749

tons of **ghee** and **samneh** were produced. These amounts represented a
sharp drop in production over previous years, since 1958 was a drought
year when pastures were poor and livestock yields low.

Slaughterhouse facilities are grossly inadequate. Existing abbatoirs
are old, unsanitary, and wasteful, since they include no provisions for
processing the valuable by-products of slaughter.

Macaroni is made in a half dozen plants employing less than 100 persons; production in 1957 amounted to 1,620 tons.

Several large biscuit-making plants are in operation, including two
factories established in Aleppo in 1951 and two others started in
Damascus in 1952. There are, in addition, about half a dozen smaller
factories in other parts of the country. Total biscuit production averages about 500 tons a year.

Some canning operations are carried out and production amounted to
3,000 tons in 1957, but no details were obtainable on the number and location of plants or type of product manufactured; it is not known whether
these factories processed fruits, vegetables, or fish.

Both alcoholic beverages and soft drinks are popular. Production
in 1958 totaled 3,620 tons, mostly of arak, the national beverage, with
smaller quantities of wine, cognac, beer, and other alcoholic drinks.
There are a total of 77 distilleries, of which 35 are located in Aleppo
and 15 in Damascus.

As mentioned above, processing of food products is a traditional occupation and is carried out not only on a commercial scale but also
by individual families to preserve harvests for winter use or for times
of scarcity. The drying of fruits and the preparation of apricot paste,
already described, is done on a family scale in rural households. Most
of the dairy foods processed are prepared by villagers in the producing
area, primarily for local use. Other foods preserved include legumes,
which are sun-dried, and tomatoes, which are puréed into tomato sauce.

2. **Storage and refrigeration.** The lack of adequate marketing and
storage affects the availability of food resources and family incomes
in rural areas. For example, a considerable proportion of Syrian grain
crops, in some years as much as 35%, is exported, but lack of grading
and cleaning equipment and the high cost of transporting grain from
producing areas to export outlets adversely affect world demand for
Syrian grains. Likewise, farmers are forced to sell their products
cheaply immediately after harvests, since there are few storage facilities where crops can be held to wait for better prices.[1] Present grain
storage facilities include two warehouses at Derbassiye in the northern
region of Syria, with a capacity of 10,000 tons each, and a few smaller
storage buildings at different grain centers, as well as a newly built
export silo in Latakia. Most grain is stored in bags in the open air, or
in primitive private warehouses, subject to heavy losses from rodents,
insects, and weather. Map 2 details present and planned storage facilities in Syria.

There are three cold storage plants for the preservation of agricultural products, one in Aleppo, one in Damascus, and one in Hama, but information on capacity or operation is not available.

III. DIET TYPES

A. GENERAL

The diet of the population varies with the region, the population group, and the economic status of the family. Numerous factors, including lack of storage facilities and poor transportation methods, affect the regional availability of food so that, except for grains and dates, most food is consumed in or near the producing area. This contributes to the establishment of varied dietary patterns, but in spite of variations, several characteristics of diets are common to all groups.

The only available estimates of supplies of food for human consumption are the provisional ones (pending government approval) presented to the first meeting of the Joint WHO/FAO Committee on Nutrition in the Middle East. These estimates are presented in Table 9, while the more important features of the data are included in the discussion below.

For the vast majority of the population, cereals are the staple of diet. Per capita consumption was estimated at 118 kg. per year, which amounted to 56% of caloric intake and 57% of the protein content of the diet. Wheat breads are eaten in all parts of the country and barley, maize, and millet are combined with wheat to make regional varieties of bread. Rice is universally popular and large amounts usually are imported.

Milk products are widely used, although fresh milk itself is not popular. Consumption of milk products is high, an estimated 84 kg. per capita per year in fluid milk equivalent. The most commonly used diary product is leban, a type of sour milk, followed in popularity by cheese and clarified butter. In rural areas approximately 75% of the milk is converted into leban and 10% into clarified butter, ghee. The type of dairy product used varies with the locality and the economic status of the family.

Mutton is the most popular meat, although cattle, goat, and camel meat also are used. The meat consumption level is one of the lowest in the Middle East, amounting to only 8 kg. per capita per year, and it is especially low in rural areas, where meat may be available only on special occasions or when an animal dies of natural causes.

Fish is a valuable source of proteins to the inhabitants of the Euphrates and Khabour valleys and along the coast, but it is seldom eaten in other regions and is everywhere eaten in small amounts, with an annual per capita consumption of only 1 kg.

Animal products contribute only 11% of calories and 23% of proteins of the average diet. Milk and milk products make up more than 85% of the total annual consumption of animal products, with small amounts of meat, eggs, and fish making up the remainder.

Broad beans, chick peas, and lentils are basic food items and they contribute 6% of the calories and 14% of proteins in the diet, with a per capita consumption of 14 kg. per year. Vegetables eaten include onions, potatoes, beets, tomatoes, egg plant, and leafy vegetables such as spinach or lettuce. The amounts used depend on season and region. Vegetables are more common articles of diet in producing areas, such as near Damascus. Annual per capita consumption in 1953-1955 was estimated at 32 kg., a rather low figure.

A large variety of fruits is eaten in season and additional quantities are imported and consumed in the large cities, so that per capita consumption is relatively high, estimated at 91 kg. per year. Olives and olive oil are important in the diets of all population groups.

The annual consumption of fats and oils amounts to 10 kg. per capita, which represents 11% of total caloric intake. Fats used include clarified butter and the fat of fat-tailed sheep, while vegetable oils include cottonseed, sesame, and sunflower oils.

B. VARIATIONS IN DIETS

1. Urban and rural diets. Townsmen enjoy a more varied and generally better diet than inhabitants of rural areas, except for persons in the lowest economic categories. Bread, burghul, fruits in season, vegetables, dairy products, and meat all are available, and the diet varies in accordance with the economic status. A survey of food consumption among middle class families in Damascus showed that the daily per capita consumption amounted to 2,766 calories distributed as follows:[9]

Foods	calories
Cereals and cereal products	1,607
Fats	207
Eggs and milk	128
Meat and fish	299
Vegetables	99
Fruits	77
Sugar and jams	220
Other	129
	2,766[1]

In this income group about 50% of the total budget was devoted to the purchase of food. The proportion of the budget spent on food varied between 58% in the lowest income group surveyed to only 35% in the highest.[1]

Diets in rural areas generally are limited by the type of food produced in the region, while the state of nutrition of the inhabitants is directly dependent on their economic status and the success of the harvests. In poor villages, fellaheen may eat a diet composed almost exclusively of cheese and maize bread, with wheat eaten either as a component of the corn bread or as burghul. Vegetables may be included in the diet as rarely as once a month and meat only on special occasions.[16] The diet of villagers in wealthier agricultural regions may include fruit, sour milk, and stewed or raw vegetables, but among all classes meat is eaten rarely. Dibs, fruit molasses, is an important sweetener.

A survey of rural diets in Homs showed that bread was the staple of diet, with fruits and vegetables relished in season. In spring, when hens were laying best, the diet might be supplemented with one egg per week, but meat was eaten at most once or twice a year.[3] This survey also showed the seasonal variations in peasant diets: during winter the proportion of cereal to milk products was in the order of 90% burghul to 10% leben, while at other seasons it was 75% to 25%.[3]

2. Diet of nomads. As already discussed above, nomads constitute an important unit of population and include purely nomadic tribes as well as semisedentary and mostly sedentary ones. The more sedentary bedouins eat a diet similar to that of the majority of the rural population, while the other two groups eat a diet that consists almost exclusively of milk and milk products supplemented by cereals and dry bread. Two meals are eaten each day, with the main meal of the day the evening one. Bread is rarely baked and cereals are most often eaten in a porridge. Meat is a luxury and is partaken of only on special occasions or when an animal dies. Locusts and wild plants are delicacies that, to some measure, supplement the diet. When camping in the desert in winter, nomads live on dry dates and some boiled cereals, either burghul, rice, or sorghum. The fat content of the nomad diet is especially low. "Nomads of the camel," the purely nomadic tribes, do not use butter because camel's milk has a very low fat content; seminomads herding sheep and goats use samn made from the fat of fat-tailed sheep or clarified butter from sheep and goat milk. A diet such as this is well balanced in nutrients but is low in caloric content.

IV. ADEQUACY OF FOOD RESOURCES

Food supplies produced by Syria are in normal times sufficient to satisfy domestic needs at the present low level of consumption, except for a few items, such as tea, coffee, and raw sugar, which either are not grown in the country or are produced in inadequate amounts. The great expansion of agricultural acreage has insured a greater supply of cereal grains, but the production of fruits, vegetables, milk and milk products, and meat is low.

Furthermore, inadequate transportation hampers the free flow of agricultural produce from surplus producing to deficit areas, so that even in good harvest years shortages may occur in areas where there has been a poor harvest because of localized conditions.

The agriculture of Syria, being largely based on rain-fed, rather than on irrigated crops, is particularly susceptible to the ravages of droughts. Most of the expansion of grain acreage has been onto poor agricultural land on marginal rainfall areas. In a drought year, such as 1958, the harvest of wheat and barley, for example, was so poor that exports of these grains had to be prohibited. Production of each of these grains was about halved, and was barely enough to satisfy domestic needs. This is more clearly shown in the comparison below of agricultural production in 1957, a good year, and in 1958, a drought year, as compared to a base line of 100 in 1956:[10]

Products	1958	1957
Cereals	53	132
Dry legumes	51	107
Vegetables	82	106
Industrial crops	100	113
Fruit	99	95
Total crops	74	119
Milk products	55	88
Meat, viscera, and hides	123	105
Wool and hair	95	106
Others	93	96
Total animal products	78	95
Total agricultural products	76	107

Because of the numerous limiting factors touched upon in this report, agricultural and food production does not seem to have kept pace with increases in population. This is shown by the United States Department of Agriculture's estimates of agricultural production and food production indices, which are contrasted on the following page, both on a total and on a per capita basis. Average annual production from 1952-1954 is used as the base period of 100.

	Average 1935– 1939	Average 1952– 1954	1957– 1958	1958– 1959	1959– 1960
Agricultural production:					
Total	54	100	147	93	88
per capita	82	100	128	79	73
Food production:					
Total	65	100	136	70	69
per capita	98	100	118	59	57
Population index					
(1953 = 3,545,000)	66	100	115	118	121

V. NUTRITIONAL DISEASE PATTERNS

Few data are available on the nutritional state of the population and on the incidence and prevalence of deficiency diseases, but all reports state that undernutrition is a serious problem, especially in rural areas and among nomads. Frank clinical deficiency diseases do not appear to be frequent but subclinical signs and symptoms commonly are found. Thus, 33% of children in the 5- to 16-year group studied in one survey were found to show clinical signs of vitamin A deficiency.[3] The high consumption of whole wheat and other cereal products is responsible for the comparative absence of vitamin B complex deficiencies. Scurvy is rare, but subclinical vitamin C deficiency was found in 58% of the group of children mentioned above.[3] These signs of subclinical vitamin C deficiency appear to be more common in the grain-producing areas, where little fruit is grown. Ariboflavinosis is reportedly rare. Cases of rickets are common, especially in urban areas.[8] In Damascus, 14% of young children at maternal and child health centers, or admitted to hospitals, showed frank signs of rickets.[16] Iron deficiency anemias associated with poor nutrition, aggravated by hookworm, and, to a lesser extent, other diseases, was a common cause of admission to hospitals of young children.[12]

VI. CONCLUSIONS

Agriculture is the chief contributor to the Syrian national income and is the source of livelihood for a majority of its inhabitants. The scantiness and, especially, the unreliability of rainfall is the most important limiting factor in the development of agriculture. The fact that

85% of crops are grown on rain-fed land makes Syrian agriculture particularly susceptible to these fluctuations in rainfall.

A considerable expansion of cultivated land has occurred in the last decade; most of the new land is devoted to the planting of grain. In good rainfall years Syria produces exportable surpluses of grain; in drought years production is barely sufficient to satisfy domestic demands. Animal husbandry is an important occupation, but the low level of nutrition of herds depresses livestock yields.

Agricultural exports earn the major portion of Syrian foreign exchange, while imports of certain foods are required to supply deficits in production.

Cereals are the major article of diet, except among the nomadic population, and grains provide 56% of calories and 57% of the protein content of the diet. Milk products are widely used but consumption of animal products, especially meat, is at a rather low level. This is also true of consumption of protective foods in general.

Present food supplies are adequate to supply most domestic needs at a rather low level of consumption. Undernutrition reportedly is a serious problem, especially in rural areas and among nomads. Frank clinical disease is not frequent, but subclinical signs and symptons of deficiency disease often are observed.

SELECTED REFERENCES

1. Food and Agriculture Organization, Mediterranean Development Project. Country Studies: United Arab Republic, Syrian Region. Rome, 1959.
2. Food and Agriculture Organization, Nutrition Committee for the Middle East. Report of First Session of Joint FAO/WHO Committee, November, 1958. *F. A. O. Nutrition Meeting Report Series No. 24*, 1959.
3. Garnier, M. Les Produits laitieres du Liban et de la Syrie. Paris, 1957.
4. International Bank for Reconstruction and Development. The Economic Development of Syria. Baltimore, Johns Hopkins Press, 1955.
5. Mahhouk, A. Recent Agricultural Development and Bedouin Settlement in Syria. *Middle East Journal*, Vol. 10, No. 2, Spring, 1956, pp. 167-176.
6. Money-Kyrle, A. F. Agricultural Development and Research in Syria. *American University of Beirut, Faculty of Agricultural Science, Publ. No. 2*, 1956.
7. Patai, R., edit. The Republic of Syria. (2 vols.) New Haven, Human Relations Area File Press, 1956.
8. Simmons, J. S., *et al.* Global Epidemiology: Vol. 3, The Near and Middle East. Philadelphia, Lippincott, 1954.
9. Theimer, O. F. Report to the Government of the United Arab Republic (Syrian Province) on a Grain Storage Construction Plan. *F. A. O. Report No. 1054*, 1959.
10. United Arab Republic, Syrian Region. Statistical Abstract. Syria, 1958.
11. United Arab Republic, Syrian Region. Syria 1958 Yearbook.
12. United Arab Republic, Information Department. Yearbook 1959.
13. United Arab Republic, Syria Directorate General of Information. Syria: Vol. 2, Economy and Finance. Damascus, 1955.
14. United Arab Republic. Étude mensuelle de l'économie et la marche syrienne. November, 1959.
15. United Arab Republic, Syrian Region. Summary of Foreign Trade for the 4th Quarter and Year 1958.
16. United Nations Technical Assistance Administration. Syria. TAA/Syria. 1955.

Table 1

Harvest Calendar for Principal Crops

Crops	Harvest Period	Bulk of Harvest
Wheat	May–July	June
Barley	Apr.–June	May
Oats	Apr.–June	May
Maize	July–Sept.	Aug.
Millet	Aug.–Oct.	Sept.
Rice	Sept.–Oct.	Oct.
Sugar cane	Nov.	Nov.
Sugar beets	Nov.	Nov.
Potatoes	May–Oct.	Sept.
Onions	Sept.–Oct.	Oct.
Tomatoes	July–Nov.	Sept.
Cucumbers	May–Oct.	July
Pumpkins	May–Dec.	Aug.
Sweet melons	June–Aug.	July
Watermelons	June–Aug.	July
Cabbage	Nov.–Feb.	Jan.
Cauliflower	Nov.–Feb.	Jan.
Green peas and beans	May–Nov.	Aug.
Carrots	Sept.–Mar.	Feb.
Dry beans	Aug.–Sept.	Sept.
Dry peas	May–June	May
Broad beans	May–June	May
Chick-peas	June–July	June
Lentils	May–June	May
Vetch	May–June	May
Apples	June–Sept.	Aug.
Pears	June–Sept.	Aug.
Grapes	Aug.–Nov.	Oct.
Oranges	Dec.–May	Mar.
Lemons	Dec.–May	Mar.
Figs	Aug.–Oct.	Oct.
Grenades	Sept.–Oct.	Oct.
Almonds	Aug.	Aug.
Pistaches	Oct.	Oct.
Olives	Sept.–Dec.	Nov.–Dec.
Groundnuts	Sept.	Sept.
Cottonseed	Sept.–Nov.	Oct.
Linseed	June–July	June
Sesame seed	Aug.–Sept.	Sept.
Sunflower seed	Aug–Sept.	Sept.
Hempseed	Oct.–Nov.	Nov.
Castorseed	June–July	July
Tobacco	Aug.–Oct.	Sept.
Cotton	Sept.–Nov.	Oct.
Hemp fiber	Oct.–Nov.	Nov.

Source: F.A.O. World Crop Harvest Calendar, Rome, 1959.

Table 2

Area Planted and Production of Principal Crops, 1958 and 1959

	Area Planted (1000 Ha.)		Production (1000 T)	
	1958	1959	1958	1959
Cereals				
Barley	769	728	228	205
Wheat	1461	1422	562	632.1
Rice	0.4	0.8	0.7	1.7
Maize	8.5	8.5	9.6	12.4
Oats	5.2	5.4	7.0	3.9
Millet	57.4	57.7	50	41.6
Dry Legumes				
Chick Peas	35.5	28.6	7.0	5.9
Lentils	119.3	83.7	35.8	31.6
Rambling Vetch	62.2	42.5	21.8	21.6
Peas	0.2	0.2	0.2	0.2
Haricot beans	1.5	1.6	1.0	1.3
Broad beans	12.5	11.3	6.7	7.5
Flowering sern	9.3		2.1	
Bitter Vetch	28.6		7.7	
Other legumes		12.1		79.3
Vegetables				
Garlic	0.8	0.8	3.4	3.1
Potatoes	2.2	1.6	21.1	14.3
Onions	3.4	3.8	32.0	28.4
Tomatoes	10.3	11.3	71.1	98.1
Eggplant	3.6	3.7	37.2	39.8
Industrial Crops				
Sesame	9.1	11.6	4.0	7.0
Cotton	260.8	227.2	249.8	264.9
Tobacco	6.9	8.8	6.5	7.5
Sugar Cane	0.1	2.4	2.4	26.9
Linseed	0.2		0.1	
Tombac	0.2		0.2	
Sugar Beet	2.2	5.0	31.6	91.6
Hemp	3.4	2.3	2.1	2.3
Peanuts		2.9	6.0	7.0
Fruits				
Olives	111	110.8	65	64.7
Grapes	71	68.1	200	217.7
Apricots	12	7.8	29	25.7
Apples	4	4.5	8.1	7.5
Pears	2.0	2.0	2.2	2.4
Plums	1.2	1.3	2.8	3.1
Peaches	0.9	0.9	1.4	1.6
Nuts	6.8	6.7	3.4	3.6
Pomegranates	2.3	2.4	4.7	5.4
Figs	18	17.7	49	39.6
Almonds	2.0	2.0	1.6	2.2
Cherries	1.4	1.4	0.8	1.6
Quince	0.6	0.6	0.8	0.7
Pistachio of Aleppo	3.2	3.3	0.4	1.2
Melons		20.6		118.3
Lemons		0.2		1.2
Oranges		0.7		5.1
Watermelons		29.6		163.2

Source: United Arab Republic, Syrian Region – Statistical Abstract of Syria, 1958. Food and Agriculture Organization, Production Yearbook, 1958.

Table 3

Livestock & Poultry by Mohafazat, 1946-1958
(in thousands)

Years, and Mohafazat	Beehives	Buffalo	Camels	Goats	Sheep	Poultry
1946	40	6	57	1,330	3,592	2,029
1947	42	6	54	1,185	3,176	1,825
1948	48	7	70	1,220	2,935	2,235
1949	56	6	71	1,196	2,750	2,447
1950	53	7	78	1,230	2,930	2,483
1951	63	6	71	1,434	3,085	2,820
1952	54	6	97	1,572	3,560	2,918
1953	58	7	82	1,614	3,746	2,881
1954	64	6	106	1,652	3,955	3,147
1955	62	6	76	1,690	4,340	2,976
1956	72	5	83	1,741	4,703	2,770
1957	67	4	79	1,803	5,466	2,973
1958	74	4	63	1,645	5,912	2,821
1957						
Damascus	7	1	22	319	481	125
Homs	4	0	5	120	641	150
Hama	7	0	7	123	539	191
Latakia	19	1	1	148	80	622
Aleppo	28	1	8	355	1,410	662
Hasakeh	1	0	3	219	724	470
Deir-ez-Zor	—	—	25	253	1,332	315
Sweida	0	—	3	163	121	100
Dir'a	1	1	5	103	138	338
1958						
Damascus	7	1	11	284	474	129
Homs	4	0	4	102	702	170
Hama	6	1	5	113	638	190
Latakia	19	1	1	136	79	629
Aleppo	36	0	7	340	1,510	692
Hasakeh	1	0	1	210	801	183
Deir-ez-Zor	—	—	24	208	1,436	380
Sweida	0	—	3	148	128	90
Dir'a	1	1	7	104	144	358

Table 3 (Continued)

Years, and Mohafazat	Asses	Mules	Horses	Oxen	Cows
1946	232	49	111	149	371
1947	230	47	141	190	354
1948	245	57	108	168	369
1949	267	54	98	171	197
1950	271	58	97	198	232
1951	244	70	100	183	294
1952	250	74	101	190	252
1953	260	78	101	182	258
1954	271	84	103	196	279
1955	271	86	101	195	273
1956	223	88	103	206	280
1957	239	81	101	204	304
1958	227	77	97	200	298
1957					
Damascus	24	5	7	27	25
Homs	17	13	10	26	31
Hama	17	9	8	13	32
Latakia	36	3	3	46	52
Aleppo	65	27	35	30	68
Hasakeh	10	10	9	14	26
Deir-ez-Zor	39	10	20	8	13
Sweida	10	2	3	15	11
Dir'a	21	2	6	25	46
1958					
Damascus	24	5	7	27	25
Homs	17	13	10	27	34
Hama	16	8	8	13	31
Latakia	34	2	3	46	51
Aleppo	62	27	31	29	66
Hasakeh	10	11	9	13	28
Deir-ez-Zor	36	8	20	7	12
Sweida	8	1	3	12	5
Dir'a	20	2	6	26	46

Source: Agricultural Statistics Dept., Ministry of Agriculture, as quoted in Statistical Abstract of Syria, 1958.

Table 4

Animal Products in Syrian Region by Mohafazat, 1950 - 1958

Years and Mohafazat	Silk Cocoons Tons	Honey Tons	No. of Eggs 1000	Goat Hair Tons	Wool Washed Tons	Butter Tons	Cheese Tons	Ghee Samneh Tons	Milk 1000 Tons
1950	414	235	90,853	1,837	3,228	638	6,084	5,456	349
1951	316	242	143,650	1,762	2,839	626	12,985	5,576	274
1952	382	256	217,385	1,848	3,976	832	12,745	6,029	297
1953	395	246	216,687	1,301	3,999	1,668	18,253	10,727	327
1954	298	207	179,856	1,484	4,150	1,647	13,109	11,790	366
1955	285	278	156,785	1,497	4,563	1,945	11,211	9,574	341
1956	389	195	155,495	1,295	5,125	1,897	11,741	11,515	503
1957	424	211	146,348	1,514	5,238	856	14,867	8,716	501
1958	284	150	137,685	1,259	4,838	558	11,058	5,749	256
1957									
Damascus	—	35	6,490	299	456	101	1,210	431	27
Homs	21	13	3,250	109	568	16	203	990	25
Hama	101	11	11,950	57	409	116	2,328	411	86
Latakia	302	27	19,800	68	74	26	375	238	13
Aleppo	—	111	41,138	199	1,340	273	2,686	1,649	190
Hasakeh	—	7	33,500	460	1,100	300	2,000	2,025	35
Deir-ez-Zor	—	—	8,200	227	985	22	6,050	2,312	89
Sweida	—	—	5,320	74	126	2	11	349	11
Dir'a	—	7	16,700	21	180	—	4	311	25
1958									
Damascus	—	36	6,506	284	431	92	1,004	385	21
Homs	15	13	4,500	89	460	12	112	490	13
Hama	58	4	11,650		404	94	2,040	410	34
Latakia	211	28	21,200	68	52	22	388	243	14
Aleppo	—	61	46,063	211	1,510	173	2,036	1,240	63
Hasakeh	—	2	23,450	300	880	150	1,000	810	18
Deir-ez-Zor	—	—	5,060	200	875	15	4,470	1,770	68
Sweida	—	—	4,256	30	51	—	4	139	5
Dir'a	—	6	15,000	17	175	—	4	262	20

Source: Agricultural Statistics Dept., Ministry of Agriculture, as contained in Statistical Abstract of Syria, 1958.

Table 5

Trade in Agricultural Products: Exports and Imports, 1956 to 1958
(Quantities in tons and Value in £S 1,000)

Exports of Main Agricultural Products[a]

Commodity	1958		1957	
	Value[b]	Quantity	Value[b]	Quantity
Millet	2,906	20,156	2,680	13,131
Flour of hard wheat	1,518	5,854	1,762	5,958
Bran	2,006	20,916	3,145	23,382
Sesame seed	56	51	572	1,126
Cottonseed	9,691	41,824	14,430	55,860
Sowing seeds excluding oil seeds	—	—	2,125	4,113
Liquorice (roots, powder & essence)	205	584	735	1,754
Anseed	311	324	459	506
Straw of cereals	265	38	1,094	43,768
Cottonseed oil	1,290	1,143	1,830	1,534
Olive oil, for soap industry	2	1	66	55
Olive oil, edible	199	78	2,975	1,295
Apricot paste	1,011	881	2,038	1,586
Oil cakes and other residues from vegetable oils extraction	8,765	57,948	7,249	33,980
Tobacco leaves	621	303	880	402
Sheep hides	2,215	778	2,490	800
Goats hides	905	391	844	370
Other hides	3,090	1,019	562	244
Sheep and Goats skins, tanned or prepared	760	178	741	238
Wool, raw	26,340	6,583	29,891	6,504
Cotton, raw	170,630	78,066	188,585	81,559
Cows (000' heads)	4,041	48	4,330	53
Rams, ewes and wethers (000 heads)	8,094	200	963	25
Goats (000 heads)	39	0	306	9
Poultry	487	304	799	502
Ghee (Samneh)	4,657	777	7,636	1,481
White Cheese, soft	2,670	1,439	2,727	1,685
Eggs in shell	3,827	2,210	3,979	2,422
Guts, bladders and stomachs of animals	2,168	150	1,915	166
Tomatoes	949	3,481	514	2,400
Onions	1,020	7,105	704	4,969
Haricot beans, dried	218	386	148	374
Broad beans, dried	650	2,274	905	3,054
Peas, dried	32	96	71	245
Lentils	8,209	17,146	12,636	38,215
Flowering sern and bitter vetch	305	1,367	1,005	4,553
Chick-peas	1,618	4,528	1,922	5,722
Grapes, fresh	568	1,874	1,162	5,906
Pistachio, unshelled	59	14	263	127
Walnuts, shelled	336	140	372	167
Walnuts, unshelled	228	182	1,173	1,215
Water-melon	646	4,146	463	4,436
Wheat	44,749	177,834	88,624	352,807
Rice, husked	13	31	79	174
Barley	12,901	89,560	51,972	331,416

(a) Products which value of export exceeded 1/2 million £S in 1956 or in 1957.
(b) Values are computed on the basis of the free currency rates.

Table 5 (Continued)

Commodity	1958		1957	
	Value(b)	Quantity	Value(b)	Quantity
Rice, husked	4	3	10,133	23,158
Flour of hard wheat	581	2,505	119	282
Flour of soft wheat	623	2,568	24	50
Copra, Castor seed and linseed	1,640	2,710	3,217	5,086
Sesame seed	1,733	2,396	1,000	1,354
Cottonseed	832	800	1,037	1,059
Sowing seeds	—	—	1,688	2,157
Sugar beet, even cut or dried	51	1,009	134	2,052
Plants for tanning or dyeing except woods, barks and Henna	242	372	275	255
Olive oil, edible	379	208	1,445	763
Palm oil, acidity: less than 20%	901	848	966	893
Palm oil, acidity: 20% and more	2,478	2,958	2,112	2,491
Preserved fishes	1,034	568	1,637	923
Raw sugar	18,112	53,894	19,791	40,171
Date molasses	837	3,312	647	2,962
Sheep hides	1,850	1,600	1,103	1,084
Other animals hides	4,527	2,777	4,728	2,991
Fir wood, sawn	22,010	67,034	13,968	41,744
Beach wood, sawn	2,855	9,120	1,298	4,346
Wool, raw	436	325	657	389
Rams, ewes, and wethers (000' heads)	2,943	138	2,790	137
Goats (000' heads)	17	1	121	6
Milk powder, not for industrial purposes	1,1508	660	977	413
Cheese of all kinds, except gruyère, roquefort and kashkawal	205	93	568	229
Tomatoes	2,798	10,788	2,654	10,518
Potatoes	1,211	6,133	3,526	19,839
Haricot beans and broad beans, fresh	495	2,104	705	2,726
Cucumbers and pumpkins	1,315	5,120	905	3,364
Dates other than small tins	6,313	45,771	3,258	23,610
Bananas	3,835	9,536	2,583	6,315
Oranges and tangerines	7,483	30,304	6,905	29,728
Lemons	1,237	3,544	887	2,527
Apples	2,646	6,629	2,822	6,266
Plums	187	720	448	2,558
Water-melon	2,148	16,780	2,703	16,160
Coffee, not roasted	5,753	1,747	5,497	1,517
Tea	8,286	1,599	7,372	1,486
Pepper and all-spices	311	211	494	297
Wheat	13	20	1	1

Source: Statistical Abstract, 1958.

Table 6

Internal Trade

Principal Foodstuffs Imported from and Exported to Egypt
1958

	Quantity	Value ('00 £S)
From Egypt:		
Potatoes	11,881	2348
Asparagus and artichokes	135	52
Rice (husked)	25,832	8641
To Egypt:		
Lentils	876	470
Chick peas	600	290
Dried figs	377	237
Raisins	118	148
Shelled almonds	23	144
" pistachios	7	71
Unshelled pistachios	13	68
Shelled walnuts	55	248
Unshelled walnuts	217	347
Cherries	17	27
Dried fruits	321	457
White flour	1,283	683
Copra, castor oil and linseed	791	455
Liquorice	674	710
Seeds and Fruits	502	710
Apricot paste	843	1167

Source: U. A. R. Province of Syria, Summary of Trade, 1958.

Table 7

Food Processing Industries: Type and Distribution

	Dir'a	Sweida	Deir-ez-Zor	Hasakeh	Aleppo	Latakia	Hama	Homs	Damascus	Total
Mills Total	74	71	135	124	284	193	184	81	264	1410
Water	8	–	3	41	40	70	108	38	153	461
Motor	66	71	132	83	244	123	76	43	111	949
Oil Extraction Plants	5	–	–	–	509	504	1	13	67	1099
Animal	3	–	–	–	417	327	–	9	51	807
Motor	2	–	–	–	92	177	1	4	16	292
Butter	–	–	–	–	13	–	1	1	7	22
Cheese	–	–	–	–	30	–	31	–	14	75
Molasses	–	119	–	–	542	–	7	–	177	845
Alcohol dist.	–	–	–	–	35	15	4	8	15	77
Totals	158	261	270	248	2216	1409	413	197	875	6037

Table 8

Output of Selected Industries, 1950 - 1957

	Unit	1950	1951	1952	1953	1954	1955	1956	1957	1958
Sugar		8.2	10.0	19.2	29.6	36.3	45.2	50.4	44.60	56.7
Biscuits	tons	204	272	228	313	350	419	510	481	—
Margarine	000 tons	—	—	—	—	0.42	2.11	2.46	2.55	—
Conserves	"	1.66	1.19	1.25	1.34	1.66	2.97	2.60	2.34	—
Macaroni	"	0.64	0.80	0.98	1.10	1.15	1.20	1.49	1.62	—
Vegetable oil (excluding olive oil)	"	—	—	—	—	7.0	10.0	10.3	20.3	—
Olive Oil	"	—	—	—	—	—	—	12.4	7.4	14.6
Salt	"	—	—	—	—	—	14.0	32.7	33.8	—
Alcoholic drinks and liquids	"	—	0.87	1.82	1.59	1.39	1.55	1.75	3.26	3.62
Chocolates	tons	—	—	—	—	—	292	291	350	—

Source: F. A. O. Country Studies, United Arab Republic, Syrian Region, 1959.

Table 9

Supplies of Certain Foods Available for Human Consumption

Syria: 1953-1955 (Provisional figures pending government approval)

Food	Consumption Kg. per Capita Per Year	% of Total Calories	% of Total Proteins
Cereals	118	56	57
Starchy Roots	9		
Pulses	14	6	14
Sugar	9	5	
Fats, Oils	10	11	
Fruits	91		
Vegetables	32	11	
Meat	8		
Eggs	2		
Fish	1	11	23
Milk	84		

Total Calories (#) 2,100
Total Proteins (Gm.)   61
Animal   (Gm.)   14

Source: F. A. O./W. H. O. Joint Committee on Nutrition in the Near East, Report of First Session, 1958.

Map 1

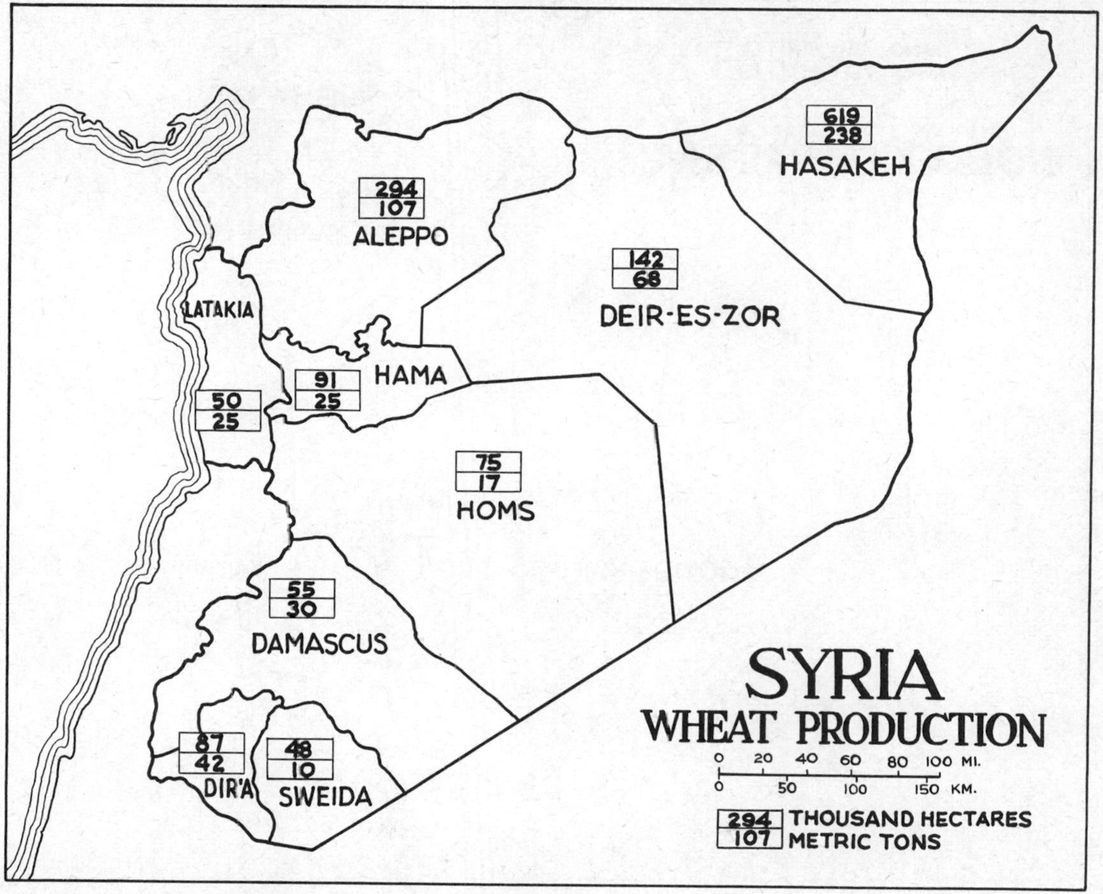

SYRIA
WHEAT PRODUCTION

| 294 | THOUSAND HECTARES |
| 107 | METRIC TONS |

HASAKEH
619
238

DEIR-ES-ZOR
142
68

HOMS
75
17

ALEPPO
294
107

HAMA
91
25

LATAKIA
50
25

DAMASCUS
55
30

SWEIDA
48
10

DIR'A
87
42

0 20 40 60 80 100 MI.

0 50 100 150 KM.

Map 2

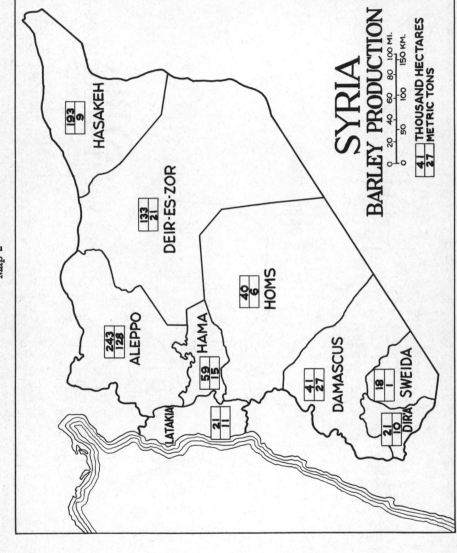

SYRIA
BARLEY PRODUCTION

| 41 | THOUSAND HECTARES |
| 27 | METRIC TONS |

0 20 40 60 80 100 MI.
0 50 100 150 KM.

HASAKEH
193
9

DEIR-ES-ZOR
133
21

ALEPPO
243
128

HAMA
59
15

HOMS
40
6

LATAKIA
21
11

DAMASCUS
41
27

DIRA
21
10

SWEIDA
18
1

Map 3

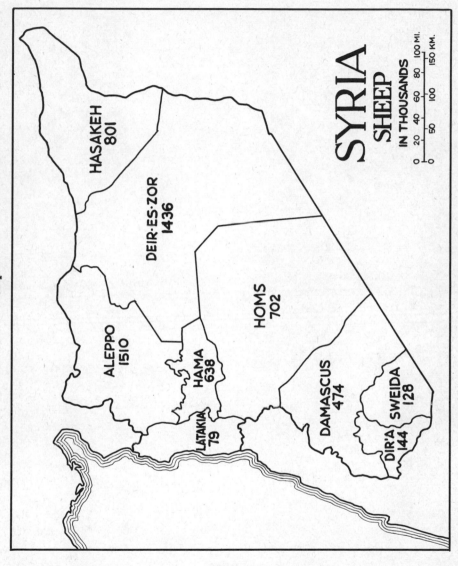

SYRIA
SHEEP
IN THOUSANDS

0	20 40 60	80	100 MI.
0	50	100	150 KM.

HASAKEH
801

DEIR-ES-ZOR
1436

ALEPPO
1510

HAMA
638

LATAKIA
79

HOMS
702

DAMASCUS
474

SWEIDA
128

DIR'A
144

LEBANON

I. GENERAL REMARKS

A. AGRICULTURE IN LEBANON

The topography of Lebanon is characterized by the presence of parallel ranges of mountains, the Lebanon and Anti-Lebanon ranges, separated by a high valley, the Beqaa, and ringed near the sea by a narrow coastal plain. The climate varies with the altitude and proximity to the sea; mountain areas generally have lower temperatures and more rainfall than the coast. Rain falls in the mountains just a few months of the year, necessitating the construction of elaborate terraces to conserve water and prevent the heavy rains from washing away the topsoil.[13]

The varying topography and climate allow the growing of a wide range of crops, from semitropical bananas and pineapples on the hot damp coastal plain to cereals, apricots, and peaches on middle slopes, and to apples and potatoes at higher altitudes.

The agriculture of Lebanon differs in certain important respects from that of neighboring Moslem countries of the Near East. Lebanon is one of the few countries in the area where agriculture is not the major contributor to the national product; in 1958 the net product amounted to £1,325 million to which agriculture contributed only £219 million. Although agriculture contributed only one fifth of the national income, it was of importance as a source of employment; it is estimated that one half of the inhabitants derive their livelihood from agricultural pursuits.

Another point of differences between Lebanon and other countries in that region is that in Lebanon production of cereals and grains accounts for only a small proportion of the total value of agricultural products, which is derived mostly from fruits, industrial crops, and vegetables, as tabulated below:

Value of Total (Gross) Agricultural Production for 1958 (1,000£)

		(%)
Cereals	18,690	8.2
Industrial crops	44,350	19.0
Fruit trees	93,910	40.7
Total carried forward	156,950	67.9

Value of Total Agricultural Production (Continued)

		(%)
Total brought forward	156,950	67.9
Legumes	8,945	3.9
Market-garden products	23,461	10.4
Meat, wool and by-products*	20,044	8.7
Milk and milk products, and eggs	20,600	9.1
Total	230,000	100.0

*Estimated

Agriculture in Lebanon also is characterized by a more advanced technology than is normally used in the region as a whole. There is a higher degree of specialization, with the greater part of the agricultural income arising from a limited number of crops that command higher prices than cereals but that require greater skill and capital.[1] A further indication of the more advanced state of agriculture in Lebanon lies in the fact that the postwar increases in agricultural production have been achieved primarily by improvements in soil management and farming methods rather than by any increase in acreage planted. Such improvements include increased use of fertilizers and improved terracing, on which most cultivation depends, as well as some expansion in irrigated areas. The importance of improved terracing can be appreciated if it is realized that fully half of the agricultural land in Lebanon is on sloping hills or on mountain land, which is farmed in terraces. Irrigated terrace land, 15% of the total, is used for fruit trees and vegetables, while of the unirrigated terraced land one third is planted to olives, figs, grapes, and tobacco and the remainder used for the cultivation of cereals, especially wheat and barley. If dry-farming terraced acreage can be irrigated, as is planned in water development schemes, it can be converted to such crops as fruits and vegetables, which yield a much higher cash return than cereals. Land irrigated in Lebanon is estimated at 88,000 hectares; this figure includes all irrigation, on the plains and in the mountains. A considerable part of this area is only partly irrigated. Existing and proposed development of irrigation is detailed in Table 1.

Another point of difference between the Lebanese agricultural economy and that of other Arab countries in the Near East is that there is no land-tenure problem in Lebanon caused by absentee ownership of land. Although there are large estates with tenant farmers, mostly in coastal areas, the predominant pattern of land ownership, especially in mountain areas, is that of the peasant cultivator who owns the land he farms.[1] The difference between Lebanon and neighboring Arab countries is further shown and, in part caused, by the considerable differences in the composition of the population. Lebanon is the only Arab country with a predominantly Christian population (52% of the total compared with 40% Moslem); it is perhaps due to this fact that Lebanon has always been the most "Westernized" of the Arab countries. The population totals about 1,500,000 and the population density is 375 per sq. mile, a high figure for the Middle East.

B. AGRICULTURAL REGIONS.[1]

Despite the limited extent of its territory, Lebanon displays a great variety of topographical and climatic conditions that, combined with variations in the character of soils and the availability of water, result in a number of well defined agricultural zones of varying character.[1] These zones include the coastal belt, the low altitude and high altitude zones and the Beqaa valley. The coastal belt has an average width of 2 kilometers in most places, widening out at various plains that are usually fertile if irrigation water is available. Winter in this area is mild and a rainfall amounting to 700-850 mm. falls, primarily from October to May.

Irrigated areas of the coastal plain are the most intensively farmed lands in Lebanon. Citrus and banana plantations are extensive and large areas in the vicinity of towns are devoted to vegetable gardening. Proposed irrigation projects, as shown in Table 1, will benefit this area, providing full irrigation for about 7,000 hectares of dry-farmed or partly irrigated land. One of the rather extensive plains of the coastal belt is in the north: the plains of Akkar at the mouth of the Nahr el Kebir. This is an important cereal-producing area and constitutes one of the granaries of Lebanon.

On the plains of Akkar cultivation is generally of the dry-farming type and irrigation is limited to about 2,000 hectares with an additional 5,000 hectares to be provided under proposed water-development schemes. The plains are exposed to rather strong winds and have lower temperatures than the rest of the coastal belt.

The lower slopes of the mountains are suited to the cultivation of olives and other warm climate trees, which are planted on terraced slopes with relatively good soils. Grain is grown on poorer soils or on inadequately terraced lands, but it is often responsible for erosion of the slopes.

The higher-altitude zones of the mountains are well suited to the growing of apples and other temperate zone fruits. The last orchards are found at approximately 1,000 meters altitude. Elaborate terracing of the slopes is required and the high cost of this terracing limits the extension of the growing area.

The Beqaa valley, lying between the Lebanon and Anti-Lebanon ranges, has an area of about 100,000 hectares and is the largest agricultural region in Lebanon. The climate is largely continental with severe winters and late frosts. Summers are dry and relatively hot. Rainfall decreases from north to south in a range of 600 to 200 mm. per year. Because of this variation in rainfall, agricultural conditions

are not uniform. At the northern end of the valley the low rainfall creates
a steppelike condition, which makes this area marginal for dry-farming.
The central area of the valley, although having scanty rainfall, is trav-
ersed by several large rivers and is intensively farmed with large agricultural centers at Zahle, Chtaura, and Baalbek. The total irrigated area
in the basins of the two principal rivers of the valley, the Litanin and
the Orontes, was estimated at 15,000 hectares in 1958 but is to be
doubled by proposed irrigation projects. Crops grown in the Beqaa
include fruits, potatoes, onions and other vegetables, and wheat.

In addition to the agricultural zones described above, Lebanon has
rather extensive areas of mountain lands not suitable for agriculture,
but capable of profitable development as forest or range land. Most of
these areas are in the Anti-Lebanon and on the highest slopes of the
Lebanon range.

II. FOOD RESOURCES

A. GENERAL

Lebanon is not self-sufficient in food supplies, and considerable
quantities of cereals, legumes, and livestock products must be imported yearly to supplement domestic production. Vegetables are, for
the most part, produced in amounts sufficient to meet local demands
and fruits are harvested in surplus quantities, constituting one of the
chief export items.

The bulk of the cereal harvests are collected from June to July,
while the peak harvesting season for fruits is in the late summer and the
early fall, except for oranges, most of which are picked from November
to April. The harvest season and the period when the bulk of the harvest is collected for each of the principal crops grown is shown in
Table 2.

Table 3 gives the area, yield, total production and value of crops
planted in 1958. The most important categories of food stuffs and industrial crops produced are discussed in the following paragraphs.

B. CEREALS

Grain crops were planted on approximately one half of the total crop
land in 1958 and included slightly less than 100,000 hectares in actual
production plus one half as much fallow land, a total of 150,000 hectares.
Despite the large acreage planted, the 84,500 tons produced in 1958 represented only 10% of the value of crops and 8% of the total agricultural
production including livestock and poultry. Local production of grains
fills about one third of domestic requirements and imports make up the
balance.[1]

Wheat is planted on an average of 65,000 hectares and production amounted to 58,000 tons in 1959. Cultivation is centered in the Beqaa valley, which contains about one half of the acreage planted and produces slightly more than one half of the total crop.

There has been a small but steady decrease in wheat acreage in the past decade (about 5%) but production has risen due to increased use of fertilizers and the extension of irrigation. This increased production has been more than offset by increased consumption and wheat imports have amounted to about 156,000 tons, more than three times the domestic production. As is obvious from these figures, Lebanon is far from self-sufficient in the production of wheat.[1]

Acreage planted to barley amounted to 19,000 hectares in 1958, less than 60% of the prewar acreage of 33,000 hectares. Production in 1958 amounted to 18,500 tons. Most barley is grown on rather poor land and the decrease in acreage may represent a trend toward discontinued plantings on poorly terraced lands.[1]

The acreage planted and the production of maize is more or less constant, with approximately 8,000 hectares in 1958, yielding 14,000 tons of corn.[1] Sorghum for grain production was planted in 1958 on only one third of the acreage devoted to this crop in 1950, i.e., on 3,500 hectares, but production has remained stable because of improved agricultural practices. The total amounts to about 3,500 tons per year.[1]

C. OTHER EDIBLE CROPS.

Vegetables and legumes. A large variety of vegetables is grown but, in general, they are not regarded by farmers as a major crop. Total acreage devoted to vegetables in 1958 was estimated at 18,800 hectares and production at 183,060 tons. Practically all vegetable growing is on irrigated land, and in many cases two crops are possible each year.

Potatoes are the most important vegetable grown, both in acreage (4,700 hectares) and in production (38,000 tons). Onions are a close second, being planted on 2,500 hectares and yielding a crop of 36,000 tons. Next in importance are tomatoes, with 28,000 tons produced on 2,300 hectares and watermelons with 26,000 tons on 2,800 hectares. These four vegetables account for 60% of the total production and of acreage devoted to vegetables. The acreage and production of all important vegetables grown in 1958 is listed in Table 3.[1]

Legumes or pulses are grown on approximately 15,000 hectares, of which only one fifth is irrigated. Irrigated land is used mostly for dry beans, while lentils, chick peas, broad beans, and vetches are grown on dry-farming land, usually as a rotation crop with grain. Production totaled an estimated 20,700 tons, as shown in Table 3, and included 4,800 tons of vetches, 4,800 tons of dried beans and 3,700 tons of broad beans.[1]

Fruits. Many kinds of fruit are grown in Lebanon on an estimated total of nearly 59,800 hectares of land and with a total annual production of 376,000 tons. The most important varieties include citrus fruits, bananas, apples, olives, and grapes and these crops are discussed in some detail below. Other important fruits grown include watermelons, with 28,000 tons grown on 2,800 hectares, figs, with a total acreage of 2,500 hectares and a production of 18,000 tons, peaches on 1,800 hectares, yielding 6,200 tons, and pears, grown on 1,800 hectares and producing 5,000 tons. Other fruits grown include plums, apricots, medlars, quinces, pomegranates, almonds, and walnuts. The acreage and production of each of these varieties are listed in Table 3.[1]

Citrus production is the most important agricultural undertaking. The area planted to citrus fruits in 1958 was 8,000 hectares and production totaled 131,000 tons. The industry has been expanding steadily since 1951 and most of the land that is to be brought under irrigation in the coastal zone is expected to be devoted to citrus plantings. Local consumption of citrus fruits in Lebanon is only about 50,000 tons, so more than half of the annual production must be exported.[1]

The area in bananas was estimated at 2,150 hectares and production at 27,500 tons. Bananas are grown on irrigated lands and plantings generally are limited to south Lebanon and to small valleys which are protected from cold winds. Bananas often are intercropped with young citrus trees until the latter reach the bearing stage.[1]

The production of apples has become a very important phase of Lebanese agriculture and an important component of its export trade. The growth of this industry in the past decade has been very rapid; during 1951 production of apples was estimated at 9,000 tons while the 1959 production has been estimated at 55,000 tons, a sixfold increase. During this interval acreage increased from 2,600 hectares in 1951 to 9,000 in 1958.

The climate in the mountains of Lebanon is ideally suited for apple growing, while neighboring countries have climatic and topographical conditions in general unsuited to the production of some fruits. A large quantity of apples are therefore exported, and a highly developed marketing system, which includes transportation facilities, cold storage and special handling facilities, has been developed in recent years.[1]

Olives have grown since ancient times in Lebanon and they occupy the largest area (22,500 hectares in 1958) of all crop trees. Olive trees usually bear fruit in alternate years so that production varies widely from year to year. A good crop year will produce 70,000 tons of olives; a poor crop year 15,000 tons. Average production between 1953 and 1958 amounted to 35,000 tons annually. Olive growing is well adapted to the conditions of the coastal area and may expand farther into the dry-farming area of this zone.[1]

Table olives account for almost one third of the total crop; about 10,000 tons are processed for this purpose and some 2,000 tons are exported. The remaining crop is used in the production of olive oil, which amounts to 6,000 to 7,000 tons per year. Most of the olive oil produced is consumed locally and only about 1,000 tons are exported in a good crop year. During poor crop years both olives and olive oil may be imported.

Vineyards occupy approximately the same acreage as olive groves, 22,500 hectares, and they yield from 70,000 to 100,000 tons of grapes per year. About 70% of the vineyards are in the Beqaa valley; the bulk of grapes produced are consumed as table grapes or for the production of alcohol and **arak,** while smaller quantities are dried, made into molasses, or fermented into wine.[1]

Sugar crops. Sugar cane is grown on 250 hectares, mostly in the northern coastal zone. Production totals about 8,000 tons, of which one third is used to produce 300 tons of sugar and the remainder is eaten fresh.[1]

Sugar beets are a recent introduction in the Beqaa valley, which has favorable conditions for growing this crop. Present acreage totaled 550 hectares in 1958, with a yield of 8,100 tons, but the extension of irrigation in the central valley should make it possible to plant an additional 4,000 hectares. Sugar beets are processed in a new refining plant in Beqaa that began operations in December, 1958. The plant has a potential annual capacity of 120,000 tons of beets, producing 20,000 tons of sugar; as may be seen from the production figures, however, present beet yields provide less than one tenth of this amount. An increase in the growing of sugar beets and the production of sugar would reduce the dependence on imported supplies, which at present amount to 30,000 tons annually.

Oil bearing seeds. Peanuts are grown on 1,400 hectares and yield a crop of 1,900 tons, while sesame is grown on 800 hectares and yields 850 tons of sesame seed. Both of these seeds are grown as "filler" crops on irrigated land.[1]

D. CASH CROPS

The growing and marketing of tobacco is under the control of a company that, under contract with the Government, enjoys a monopoly of the growing, manufacturing, and sale of the crop. Tobacco is a very profitable crop, especially for the dry and rather poor farm land it requires. Income from 1958 production averaged £2,500 per hectare in contrast with an income of only £200 per hectare for wheat, which is grown on the same type of land. A total of 3,250 hectares were planted in 1958, producing 2,800 tons of tobacco.[1]

A very limited area, ranging from 100 to 200 hectares, is planted to cotton, and it is probable that this crop will disappear entirely since it cannot compete in economic value to the farmer with citrus fruits, vegetables, and other crops that can be grown on irrigated land.

Sericulture is another declining industry that, in the past, provided employment to a considerable proportion of the agricultural population. The decline in the demand for silk in world markets has resulted in the virtual disappearance of the industry; only 140 tons of cocoons were produced in 1958 as compared with 850 tons in 1938.[1]

E. ANIMAL PRODUCT RESOURCES

Animal husbandry in Lebanon, unlike in other Arab countries, has always been of minor importance, since the country does not have extensive steppe pastures, which in other countries provide grazing land for the flocks of nomadic herdsmen. Grazing lands account for only 1% of total area and livestock raising must compete for the limited resources of land and capital with the much higher-income-producing fruit and vegetable crops.

Present livestock holdings include primarily native sheep, goats, and cattle, fed on natural pastures and on grain residues such as stubble and grain straw. The number of livestock in 1958 was estimated at 380,000 goats, 88,000 cows, 70,000 sheep, 5,500 pigs and 2 million poultry. Work animals included 10,000 horses and mules, 21,000 asses, and 10,000 dromedaries. The total value of livestock amounted to slightly over £33 million as detailed in Table 4. The poultry-raising industry has made great progress in 1954, aided by grants and the technical aid of the U.S.O.M. in Lebanon. Before 1954 poultry raising on a commercial scale was almost nonexistent and the fowls were to be found almost exclusively in small barnyard flocks of native stock, among which both meat and egg production were low. In 1953 there were an estimated million birds, egg production was about 40 million, and an additional 30 million eggs had to be imported from Syria. By 1958 commercial poultry raising appeared to be well established. There were about 50 poultry breeders specializing in egg production and 25 smaller projects for broiler production which marketed from 300 to 2,000 birds a week. Egg production in 1958 was estimated at 130 million,[8] of which about 50 million were marketed and the remainder used locally.[1] There is no accurate census of the poultry population, but it is known that chickens are by far the most popular kind. There is some interest in turkey raising and less in duck, but a considerable number of geese are raised in the good pastures of the Baqaa valley.[3]

Milk production was estimated in 1958 at 52,000 tons, of which 14,000 was used as fluid milk, 25,000 for cheese, 8,000 for curds and 4,000 for butter. These figures probably represent an overestimate but, even if they are accurate, total production is grossly inadequate and amounts to only 30 kg. per capita per year.[1] In order to meet the deficits created by this low domestic production about 7,500 tons of dairy products, including some condensed, evaporated, and powdered milk, are imported each year.

Because of the relatively low level of animal husbandry, only a small portion of Lebanon's meat requirements, about one fifth are supplied by domestic livestock. During 1954 the amount of animals, meat, and dairy products imported was greater than the total domestic production in each of these categories, as shown in Table 5, which contrasts the relative supplies of imported and domestic meats. Only 1,700 of 4,600 tons of the beef and veal, 400 of 8,000 tons of the mutton and lamb, 720 of 1,280 tons of the goat meat, and 64 of 80 tons of the pork consumed were produced locally. Import figures for 1958 are substantially in line with those for 1954 in Table 5, showing that the situation remains unchanged with regard to reliance on imported supplies of livestock products. As a matter of fact, imports have risen sharply as domestic consumption has increased; between 1950 and 1957 consumption of beef rose by 93%, mutton by 48%, and pork by 183%.

Fishing is carried out on a very small scale, largely on inland waters.[4] The annual catch is small and far from sufficient to satisfy local demands, so that fish products to the value of more than £1.5 million are imported yearly.[5]

F. EXPORTS AND IMPORTS

Despite a steady increase in agricultural output, Lebanon does not produce enough food to satisfy domestic requirements and additional quantities must be imported. This does not apply to fruits and some vegetables, which are in abundant supply and to some industrial crops, which are produced in quantities sufficient to meet local demands and also to provide profitable surpluses for export, but there are serious shortages of cereal crops and meat and milk products, as well as of minor crops such as tea, coffee, sugar and spices.

Exports of agricultural products, chiefly fruits, are of great importance in the Lebanese economy, since they provide a large share, nearly one half, of foreign exchange earnings. The relatively high prices of Lebanese fruit, as well as inferior and variable standards of grading and packing, have adversely affected the Lebanese exports of fruit in recent years. In an attempt to increase exports, the Lebanese Fruit Office was established in November, 1959, with the power to set up and enforce grading and packing standards.

Table 6 presents the quantity and value of the principal agricultural commodities exported and imported by Lebanon in 1958. Agricultural exports, which amounted to 49.1% of total export trade, included principally fruits (24.9% of total exports), fresh vegetables (5.2%) and dry legumes (4.6%).

Imports of agricultural products amounted to only 20.6% of total imports, but provided a major share of the domestic consumption of several food items. Included among important imports are livestock, dairy products, wheat and wheat flour, oilseeds, rice, coffee, barley, and wool. The wheat was imported from the United States, livestock and dairy products from Syria, together with some wheat and oilseeds, and the rice from Egypt. Sugar was imported from both Indonesia and Cuba. The share of imported animal products in total consumption is shown in Table 5.

G. INTERNATIONAL TECHNICAL AID

Several international organizations carry out aid and development programs in Lebanon with special emphasis on agriculture and food production. The Food and Agriculture Organization, for example, supports projects on animal disease control, agricultural economy, and on fisheries research. The United States Technical Aid (Point 4) Program maintained a mission in Lebanon that operated more than twelve separate agriculture development projects, including poultry raising, marketing, forestry, entomology, animal husbandry, and many others. The work of the U.S.O.M. in the country has been suspended since the recent change in government in Lebanon.

H. FOOD INDUSTRIES, STORAGE AND TECHNOLOGY

Food processing. The food processing industries of Lebanon employed more people than any other single branch of industry and, together with the beverage industry, accounted for 21% of total industrial employment at the time of the last census in 1955.[1] Food industries, however, are not well developed. Since the country does not produce enough of many foods to satisfy local demand, there are no large agricultural surpluses to process. In addition, although some of the newer factories are equipped with the latest and most modern machinery, a large proportion of the establishments are small and have old or obsolete equipment. Food processing, in many phases, is changing from hand crafted production to a fully machine-processed modern industry. Some of the more important types of food processing establishments are discussed below, based on data provided by the 1955 census:

There are 16 flour mills with 370 employees; 13 of these are located in Beirut and the Beirut metropolitan area. There are 452 bakeries throughout the country employing a total of 4,348 persons. More than one half of these, 253, are located in Beirut and an additional 86 in the Beirut metropolitan area. Included are three biscuit-making concerns producing some 1,500 tons a year, chiefly for the export trade.[8]

Some 31 factories are engaged in the production of cocoa, chocolate and similar confectionery products. Among the 21 located in the Beirut area are at least four with modern equipment. Twenty of the factories, making halave and tahine, are located throughout Lebanon and their products are sold both in local and export markets.[8]

The 20 factories processing meat and dairy products, which employ a total of 178 persons, include 2 small pasteurizing plants that process small amounts of milk, butter, and cheese. The dairy products industry is severely limited by the inadequate production of milk. The entire output of cheese, butter, and labné, as well as of pasteurized milk, is consumed locally.[8]

In 1950 there were a reported total of 18 factories in the suburbs of Beirut and Tripoli which produced both edible and nonedible vegetable oils for local consumption and export. Production in 1949 was reported to total 25,000 tons.[8]

The 1955 census listed 32 factories with 784 employees in the category of "preserving and canning vegetables and miscellaneous food products." This total includes two factories in the suburbs of Beirut that make jam and other fruit preserves, primarily for export.[8] Other factories in operation make vinegar, ice cream, starch and glucose, and macaroni products.

Many types of fermented, distilled and soft drinks are manufactured, including arak, which is distilled from grape alcohol, beer and carbonated beverages. The most important beverage industry is devoted to the manufacture of arak, more or less a national drink, which is produced in distilleries scattered all over Lebanon. Wine is made throughout the territory, while beer is made in breweries located in Beirut and its suburbs and in Bhamdoun. There are 15 carbonated-beverage plants listed in the 1955 census, with the main ones in operation in Beirut.

Table 7 shows the distribution throughout Lebanon of all food processing industries, as tabulated in the 1955 census. The total number probably is much greater since the census only included factories employing more than four persons and there are many small family establishments engaged in the production of such things as halvah, arak and other food products. Thus, although the census lists only 52 distilleries, a study of industries in Lebanon in 1950 counted 101 plants for making arak.

Storage and refrigeration. The refrigeration and packing industries of Lebanon have been established primarily for the handling and marketing of apples and oranges and, to a lesser extent, of bananas and other fruits which constitute so large a proportion of total export trade. The sharp rise in production of apples has led to expansion of cold-storage facilities which now include 38 cold stores with a total capacity of 2 million boxes of apples. Fruit can be stored at peak production and sold when supplies are low, therefore extending the marketing seasons and stabilizing prices.[6,9]

Information on facilities for the storage and handling of other foods, especially grain, is not available. It is known that there are at least 19 ice-making plants located in the cities and that the country imports

1,000 lbs. of frozen meats yearly; hence facilities for handling and marketing frozen foods must exist, at least in Beirut, but no further details were obtainable.

III. DIET TYPES

A. GENERAL

Staples of the Lebanese diet include the traditional flat, round bread called pita, together with olives and some garden vegetables, and sour milk, or leben. This basic diet is supplemented in accordance with the economic status of the family and the type of farm production common in the area.

The bread is made from wheat, barley, or millet in varying combinations and, together with burghul or parboiled wheat, constitutes the main cereal components of the diet. Rice is popular and large quantities are imported from Egypt to satisfy domestic demand.[10] Cereals of all kinds provide 126 kg. per capita per year. This represents 56% of the total caloric content and 55% of the protein intake of the average diet in 1953-55, the latest years for which data are available.

A large part of the meat supply has to be imported (Table 5), mostly from Syria and this imported livestock is the main meat supply of urban centers. Rural inhabitants eat meat not oftener than once a week, with mutton and beef as the two types most commonly eaten. Goat meat also is used and pork is used in Christian communities. Poultry and eggs are much more plentiful than formerly and are now being produced commercially in increasing quantities.[10] The national meat dish is kibbe, made with raw or cooked meat and burghul. Total meat consumption on a per capita basis is extremely low and amounts to only 15 kg. per capita per year.

Fresh milk rarely is used in the diet except in the larger cities where processing plants are now in operation. Most of the milk is consumed either in fermented products, such as leben, or as cheese. Sheep and goats are the main sources of meat in rural areas and, less frequently, cows.[10] Additional quantities of powdered and processed milk and other dairy products are imported to supplement domestic production. Consumption of milk and milk products in terms of fluid milk amounted to 80 kg. per capita per year, as of 1953-55.

As may be seen from the above figures for consumption of meat and milk, the Lebanese diet is low in proteins and especially in proteins of animal origin. Cereals and pulses provide over 70% of the total daily protein intake, while only 15 g., or 22% of the proteins in the daily diet, are contributed by meat, eggs, fish, or milk.

Legumes are an important source both of calories and of good quality vegetable proteins. Total annual supply amounts to 18 kg. per capita and this constitutes 7% of the total calories and 16% of total proteins in the diet.

Lebanon is an important producer of a wide variety of fruits and fruit consumption is relatively high, amounting to 136 kg. per capita per year. Potatoes, onions, tomatoes, and numerous other vegetables are produced and consumed in substantial quantities, but per capita consumption is relatively low, amounting to only 22 kg. per capita. Fruits and vegetables together contribute 10% of the total calories in the diet.

The primary sources of fats and oils in the diet are clarified butter (**ghee**) and olive oil. Per capita consumption amounts to a total of only 7 kg. per year and this represents only 8% of total caloric intake.

Table 8 shows the per capita supply of food in kilograms per year as well as the percentage of total caloric and protein intake that each group of foodstuffs contributes to the average diet. The figures, which are the latest available at the time of writing, are for 1953-55 and are provisional, pending the approval of the Lebanese government.[14]

B. VARIATIONS IN DIETS WITH ECONOMIC STATUS

Bread and burghul are important constituents of the diet in all economic groups while vegetables and fruits, in season, also form part of the diet of all but the poorest classes. The main variations occur in the consumption of meat and dairy products, both of which are in short supply. Thus, the population groups of lower income generally will consume little fresh milk, cheese or butter; large quantities of leben and labne will be consumed, while meat is rarely eaten more than once a week, if that often. Families in middle income groups show a variable consumption, usually moderate, of fresh milk, leben, labne and cheese but little butter, while the wealthier classes are important consumers of milk and milk products, meat, and fish.[12] The rise in price of some important staples of diet within the past few years have priced these items beyond the resources of lower income groups. For example, the price of meat rose by 60%, of **samneh** by 25%, and of cheese by 30% between 1955 and 1957.[1]

A survey of the diet of the middle class rural Lebanese families showed that the consumption of proteins, calcium and, perhaps, of riboflavin was low, and that the diet also was rather inadequate in calories.[1]

Calories, number	2140
Proteins, Gm.	56
Calcium, Gm.	0.4
Iron, mg.	12
Vitamin A, I.U.	4300
Thiamine, mg.	1.5

Riboflavin, mg.	1.0
Niacin, mg.	13
Ascorbic acid, mg.	79

IV. ADEQUACY OF FOOD RESOURCES

Although agricultural production and the production of food have increased in recent years, the rate of increase has been slower than the rate of population growth. This is shown in the following comparison of indices of agricultural and food production on a total and per capita basis:

Index	Average 1935-39	Average 1952-54	1957-58	1958-59	1959-60
Agricultural production, total	78	100	102	100	96
Agricultural per capita	115	100	94	90	85
Food production, total	79	100	101	98	93
Food production per capita	116	100	93	88	82
Population (1953 = 1,353,000)	68	100	109	111	113

That this has long been the case can be seen from Table 9, which lists the production, consumption, and deficit or surplus of the most important agricultural products in the diet in 1953. Only vegetables and fruits are produced in surplus quantities; all other foods are available in quantities insufficient to meet domestic demands.

In normal times the mercantile activities and tourist-trade income of Lebanon provide enough revenue to import sufficient food to offset production deficits. However, any stress situation that would adversely affect the foreign exchange earnings would also seriously affect food supply. A world depression, or the outbreak of war in the region, would promptly affect the availability of food supplies.

V. NUTRITIONAL DISEASE PATTERNS

The nutritional status of the population is reportedly adequate and undernutrition is prevalent only in congested areas and some poor rural communities. Although no country-wide survey of the nutritional status of the population has ever been carried out, the reported clinical impression of many observers is that frank deficiency diseases are relatively rare, although subclinical vitamin A, C, and D deficiencies are common among the poorer inhabitants. This is indicated by the following scattered observations reported from a variety of studies over a long period of years.[12]

Hyperkeratosis was found to be present in 16% of children 2 to 16 years of age and in 8% of adults examined in one survey. Subclinical vitamin C deficiency was especially common in interior areas that are not fruit-producing areas, but were rare on the coast where citrus plantations are extensive. In the Lebanon mountains 14% of children and 49% of the adults surveyed were found to have glossitis and mal-formations of the gums, which, however, were not always typical of vitamin C deficiency lesions. Rickets has been reported for the south of Lebanon, but vitamin C deficiencies, if at all present there, are ex-tremely rare.

VI. CONCLUSIONS

The agriculture of Lebanon differs in certain important respects from that of neighboring Moslem countries of the Near East. Lebanon is one of the few countries in the area where agriculture is not the major contributor to the national product. Agricultural methods in use are technically more advanced than in the region as a whole and, as a further point of contrast, the main agricultural income is derived from fruits instead of cereals, as is the case elsewhere in the Near East. Another point of difference is that there is no land tenure problem caused by absentee ownership of land, the predominant pattern of land ownership is that of a peasant cultivator owning the land he farms.

Lebanon is not self-sufficient in food supplies and imports consider-able quantities of cereals, legumes and livestock products to supple-ment domestic production. Vegetables are harvested in amounts suf-ficient to supply local markets and fruits are harvested in surplus quantities, constituting one of the chief export items.

Staples of the Lebanese diet include the traditional flat, round loaf called pita, together with olives and some garden vegetables and sour milk, or leben. This basic diet is supplemented in accordance with the economic status of the family and the type of farm production common in the area.

The nutritional status of the population is reportedly adequate, and undernutrition is prevalent only in congested areas and some poor rural communities. Although no country-wide survey of the nutritional status of the inhabitants has been carried out, the reported clinical impres-sion of many observers is that frank clinical deficiency disease is rare, although subclinical vitamin A, C, and D deficiencies are com-mon among the poorer inhabitants.

SELECTED REFERENCES

1. Food and Agriculture Organization, Mediterranean Development Project. Country Studies: Lebanon. Rome, 1959.
2. Abassy, M. A. Nutrition Problems in the Middle East. *Journal of the Royal Egyptian Medical Association,* Vol. 30, 1947.
3. United States Department of Agriculture, Foreign Agriculture Service. World Poultry Production. 1957.
4. Fisher, W. B. The Middle East. (3rd edit.) London, Methuen, 1956.
5. Food and Agriculture Organization. Mediterranean Development Project. Rome, 1959.
6. Persen, W. Lebanese Economic Development Since 1950. *Middle East Journal,* Vol. 12, No. 3, Summer, 1958, pp. 277-294.
7. United States Department of Agriculture, Foreign Agriculture Service. Indices of Agricultural Production in 13 Near East Countries. Mimeographed report. November, 1959.
8. Association of Lebanese Industrialists. Guide to Lebanon's Industries, 1949-50. Beirut, 1951.
9. Food and Agriculture Organization. Selected Problems of Production and Trade in the Near East. Rome, 1956.
10. Simmons, J. S., *et al.* Global Epidemiology: Vol. 3, The Near and Middle East. Philadelphia, Lippincott, 1954.
11. Adolph, W. H. Nutrition in the Near East. *Journal of the American Dietetic Association,* Vol. 30, No. 8, 1954, pp. 753-756.
12. Garnier, M. Les Produites laitieres du Liban et de la Syrie. Paris, 1957.
13. Yale University, Human Relations Area File. Country Survey Series: Lebanon. (R. Patai, edit.) 1956.
14. Food and Agriculture Organization, Nutrition Committee for the Middle East. Report of First Session of Joint FAO/WHO Committee, November, 1958. *F. A. O. Nutrition Meeting Report Series No. 24,* 1959.
15. United States Operations Mission to Lebanon. Report for 1957.
16. Ward, H. G. Poultry in Lebanon, 1959. United States Operations Mission, Lebanon.

Table 1

Irrigation—Existing and Proposed Development[a]

Basin	Annual Runoff Average Year (million m³)	Irrigation — Hectares		Total
		Existing[b]	Proposed	
Nahr Ostouene	74.7	2,000	5,200	7,200
Nahr Arka	76.3	2,400	1,000	3,400
Nahr El Bared	257.1	1,600	1,500	3,100
Nahr Abou Ali	399.2	1,600	3,000	4,600
Nahr Ibrahim	465	500	500	1,000
Nahr El Kelb	250	120	None	120
Nahr Beirut	122	1,100	None	1,100
Nahr Damour	167	400	(1,100)[c]	400
Nahr El Assi	459	5,000[d]	3,800	8,800
Nahr Litani	755	9,400[e]	19,600[f]	29,000
Totals	3,025.3	24,120	34,600	58,720

[a] Adapted from the "Water Resources Investigations Reports".
[b] Excluding irrigation in mountain areas.
[c] Nahr Damour water will be pumped into the Saida Beirut canal for serving the 1,100 hectares of land in the Nahr Beirut basin which is only partially irrigated at present.
[d] Including about 3,000 hectares outside the project area.
[e] Including the Kasmie and the old Amjar projects but not irrigation outside the project areas.
[f] Including 1,000 hectares that are to be irrigated from groundwater supply.
Source: Food and Agriculture Organization, Mediterranean Development Project. Country Study, Lebanon, Rome, 1959.

Table 2

Harvest Calendar for Principal Crops

Crops	Harvest Period	Bulk of Harvest
Wheat	June–Aug.	June–July
Barley	June–Aug.	June–July
Oats	June–Aug.	June–July
Maize	July–Oct.	Aug.–Oct.
Sorghum and Millet	Sept.–Oct.	Sept.–Oct.
Rice	Sept.–Oct.	Sept.–Oct.
Sugar beets	Sept.–Oct.	Sept.–Oct.
Sugar cane	Sept.–Dec.	Sept.–Nov.
Potatoes	Mar.–Oct.	June–Oct.
Onions	June–Oct.	July–Sept.
Tomatoes	May–Dec.	July–Nov.
Cucumbers	May–Dec.	June–Oct.
Pumpkins	Apr.–Dec.	May–Nov.
Sweet melons	June–Oct.	July–Sept.
Watermelons	July–Nov.	Aug.–Nov.
Cabbage	May–Feb.	May–Jan.
Green peas and beans	Apr.–Dec.	Apr.–Nov.
Carrots	Whole year round	Whole year round
Dry beans	Aug.–Oct.	Aug.–Oct.
Dry peas	June–Sept.	June–Sept.
Broad beans	Apr.–Jan.	May–Oct.
Chick-peas	June–Sept.	June–Aug.
Lentils	June–July	June–July
Vetch	June–July	June
Apples	June–Oct.	July–Sept.
Pears	June–Oct.	July–Sept.
Apricots	June–Aug.	June–July
Peaches	June–Sept.	June–Aug.
Plums	June–Sept.	June–July
Cherries	May–July	May–July
Grapes	June–Dec.	July–Nov.
Oranges	Oct.–June	Nov.–Apr.
Lemons	Sept.–July	Oct.–May
Figs	June–Oct.	July–Sept.
Bananas	Whole year round	Mar.–Dec.
Carobs	Oct.–Nov.	Oct.–Nov.
Almonds	July–Sept.	July–Sept.
Walnuts and hazelnuts	Aug.–Sept.	Aug.–Sept.
Olives	Oct.–Jan.	Nov.–Dec.
Groundnuts	Sept.–Oct.	Sept.–Oct.
Sesame seed	Sept.–Oct.	Sept.–Oct.
Sunflower seed	Aug.–Oct.	Aug.–Oct.
Tobacco	Aug.–Sept.	Aug.–Sept.
Cotton	Sept.–Oct.	Sept.–Oct.
Hemp	Sept.–Oct.	Sept.–Oct.

Source: F.A.O. World Crop Harvest Calendar, Rome, 1959.

Table 3

Acreage and Production of Principal Crops (1958)

Area, yield, total production and value of crops

Cereals	Area (hectares)	Production (tons)	Value Per Ton (L. L.)	Total Value (1,000 L. L.)
Wheat	68,000	48,000	250	12,000
Barley	19,000	18,500	180	3,330
Maize	8,000	14,000	200	2,800
Sorghum	3,500	3,500	160	560
Total	98,500	84,000		18,690
Industrial Crops				
Cotton	100	25	3,000	50
Cotton seed		50	200	10
Ground-nuts	1,400	1,900	800	1,525
Hemp	100	100	100	10
Sesame	800	850	750	638
Anise	50	50	800	40
Olives	22,500	9,000	800	7,200
Olive oil		10,300	2,000	20,600
Beet	550	8,100	80	648
Row cocoons		140	3,100	434
Sugar-cane	240	8,000	600	4,800
Tobacco	3,250	2,800	3,000	8,400
Total	28,990	41,315		44,350
Fruit Trees				
Oranges		93,000	250	23,250
Lemons	7,950	30,000	300	9,000
Other citrus fruit		8,000	250	2,000
Apples	9,000	43,000	320	13,400
Plums	1,200	5,500	150	825
Pears	1,850	5,000	650	3,250
Bananas	2,150	27,500	370	10,175
Peaches	1,800	6,200	300	1,860
Apricots	850	4,300	350	1,505
Medlars	500	4,500	500	2,250
Cherries	425	4,200	550	2,310
Quinces	180	1,650	200	330
Grapes	22,500	80,000	200	16,000
Pomegranates	1,530	14,000	230	3,220
Figs	2,500	18,000	150	2,700
Fresh almonds	1,200	2,550	600	1,530
Walnuts	250	750	250	188
Pine-seeds	3,000	220	350	77
Total	56,885	348,370		93,910

Table 3 (continued)

Legumes	Area (hectares)	Production (tons)	Value Per Ton (L. L.)	Total Value (1,000 L. L.)
Vetches	6,100	4,800	440	1,056
Lentils	2,300	2,500	600	1,500
Chick-peas	2,000	2,200	370	814
Broadbeans	2,000	3,700	550	2,035
Dried beans	2,400	4,800	600	2,880
Lupins	50	50	200	10
Lucerns	100	2,100	100	210
Peas	350	550	800	440
Total	15,300	20,700		8,945
Market-Garden Products				
Onions	2,500	36,000	75	2,700
Garlic	50	500	800	400
Tomatoes	2,300	28,000	100	2,800
Egg-plants	700	4,000	75	300
Potatoes	4,700	38,000	120	4,560
Water-melons	2,800	26,000	80	2,080
Melons	200	2,700	100	270
Cucumbers	1,800	18,000	150	2,700
French beans	1,500	8,100	170	1,377
Okra	350	700	400	280
Green broadbeans	1,200	7,500	80	600
Artichokes	90	3,000	500	1,500
Strawberries	50	210	1,000	210
Carrots	380	5,500	150	825
Cabbages	700	9,000	50	450
Cauliflowers	270	3,800	90	742
Beet	280	4,000	70	280
Lettuce	450	8,200	150	1,230
Radishes	220	1,800	100	180
Jerusalem artichokes	80	1,050	130	127
Spinach	180	3,000	80	140
Total	20,800	209,060		23,461

Source: F.A.O. Mediterranean Development Project, Country Study, Lebanon, 1959.

Table 4

Livestock Population: Quantity and Value

Livestock Population	Number	Value Per Unit (L. L.)	Total Value (1,000 L. L)
Horses and mules	10,000	250	2,500
Asses	21,000	25	525
Dromedaries	2,000	275	550
Cows	88,000	150	13,200
Sheep	70,000	40	2,800
Goats	380,000	25	9,500
Pigs	5,500	40	220
Poultry	2,000,000	2	4,000
Total			33,295

Source: F.A.O. Mediterranean Development Project, Country Study, Lebanon, 1959.

Table 5

Meat Consumption—Imports and Local Production

(Year 1954)[a]

Kind of Animals	Animals Slaughtered (head)		Carcass Weight Kg.	Imported Animals (head)[b].	Meat Produced (tons)		Total Meat (tons)
	In Government Slaughter Houses	Total			Imported Animals	Local	
Cattle	35,700	40,000	115	25,300	2,900	1,700	4,600
Sheep	285,300	400,000	20	379,300	7,600	400	8,000
Goats	61,100	80,000	16	35,100	560	720	1,280
Hogs	2,000	2,000	40	400	16	64	80
		522,00		440,100	11,076	2,884	13,960[c]

[a] The above figures are taken from a special study conducted by the United States International Cooperation Administration, Mission to Lebanon, Beirut, 1956. For the year 1953-1956 the FAO Production Yearbook gives higher figures for animals slaughtered which with the above carcass weights give a total supply of meat from locally slaughtered animals of 18,300 tons.

[b] Imports for the year 1957 as given in the Bulletin Statistique of the Ministry of National Economy are considerably lower than the above figures. The 1958 figures of the same source are in line with the 1954 figures. Imports in 1958 were mostly through the ports and were better recorded. It is quite likely that a large percentage of the imports during 1957 when the frontiers with Syria were open did not follow the regular commercial routes.

[c] In addition to live animals, imports include frozen meat (not included above) in the order of 1,000 tons annually—811 tons in 1957.

Source: F.A.O. Country Study, Lebanon, 1959.

Table 6

Exports and Imports of Foodstuffs

1958

Commodity	Quantity 1,000 Metric Tons	Value 1,000 Dollars	Share of Total Value %
	EXPORTS		
Fruits, fresh	93.6	8,816	24.9
Vegetables, fresh	36.9	1,852	5.2
Dry legumes	13.4	1,625	4.6
Millet	4.0	249	.7
	IMPORTS		
Livestock (1,000 head)	394	6,011	3.6
Dairy products	8	5,139	3.1
Wheat	68.9	4,382	2.6
Wheat flour	79.1	3,596	2.2
Sugar	25.7	1,916	1.2
Cottonseed	26.5	1,892	1.1
Other oilseeds[a]	9.8	1,529	.9
Rice	12.6	1,349	.8
Coffee	1.8	1,126	.7
Barley	18.0	805	.5

[a] Sesame, copra and peanuts.
Source: U. S. Dept. of Agriculture Foreign Agricultural Service.

Table 7

Food Processing Establishments—1955

	Meat & Meat Prods. Dairy Prod.			Preserv. & Canning of Veg. & Misc. Food Prep.			Grain Mill Products			Bakery Products			Sugar Factories & Refineries		
	[1]	[2]	[3]	[1]	[2]	[3]	[1]	[2]	[3]	[1]	[2]	[3]	[1]	[2]	[3]
All Districts	20	178(a)	964	32	784(b)	5876	16	370	2517	452	4348	15156	3	358	9729
Beirut	11	117	704	11	239	1298	8	247	1281	253	2411	8893	—	—	—
Mount Lebanon	2	22	133	7	264	1316	1	17	157	17	174	741	—	—	—
North Lebanon	1	4	11	6	64	278	1	11	19	84	764	1932	2	238	9650
South Lebanon	2	10	20	3	42	215	—	—	—	12	90	176	—	—	—
Bekaa	2	12	18	—	—	—	1	5	6	—	—	—	—	—	—
Beirut Metrop. Area.	2	13	78	5	175	2769	5	90	1054	86	909	3414	1	120	79

	Cocoa, Choc., & Asst. Prod.			Dist. Rectifying & Blending Spirits			Breweries Malt & Wine			Soft Drinks & Carbonated Water		
	[1]	[2]	[3]	[1]	[2]	[3]	[1]	[2]	[3]	[1]	[2]	[3]
All Districts	31	430	2029	52	1657	390	7	212	2548	15	438	3820
Beirut	21	286	1114	13	697	122	2	72	1488	5	202	1810
Mount Lebanon	1	50	674	7	208	59	1	110	961	2	67	346
North Lebanon	6	57	68	2	42	19	—	—	—	2	23	187
South Lebanon	1	14	80	1	47	10	—	—	—	3	12	19
Bekaa	2	23	93	24	385	130	4	30	99	1	10	34
Beirut Metrop. Area	—	—	—	5	278	50	—	—	—	2	124	1424

[1]—No. of plants
[2]—Employees
[3]—Production (in 000Lf)

(a) Meat, meat products, dairy products.
(b) Preserving and Canning of Vegetables and Miscellaneous Food Preparations.
Source: American University of Beirut. The Industrial Census of Lebanon, 1955.

Table 8

Lebanon: 1953-1955

Supplies of Certain Foods Available

Foodstuff	Annual Consumption	Share of Total Intake:	
	Kg. per Capita	Calories %	Proteins %
Cereals	126	56	55
Starchy roots	17		
Pulses	18	7	16
Sugar	20	9	
Fats and oils	7	8	
Fruits	136 ⎫	10	
Vegetables	22 ⎭		
Meat	15 ⎫		
Eggs	4 ⎪	8	22
Fish	1 ⎬		
Milk(a)	80 ⎭		
Total calories (number)	2,240		
Total proteins: Total	66		
Animal	15		

(a) In terms of fluid milk.
Source: Joint FAO/WHO Nutrition Committee for the Near East, Report of First Session, 1958.

Table 9

Production and Consumption of Foodstuffs

Lebanon 1953

Foodstuff	Consumption		Deficit	Surplus
	Production			
	------------------in 1,000 metric tons------------------			
Cereals	101.8	277.0	175.2	
Legumes	31.7	43.3	11.7	
Vegetables	207.8	169.7	5.2	43.3
Fruit	240.5	154.5	0.6	86.6
Meat	5.3	21.7	16.4	
Milk Prod.	34.6	74.6	40.0	
Eggs	1.5	2.1	0.6	
Fish	3.0	3.5	0.5	

Source: F.A.O. Mediterranean Development Project, Country Study, Lebanon.

THE REPUBLIC OF ISRAEL

I. GENERAL REMARKS

The Republic of Israel was proclaimed in May, 1948, upon termination of the British mandate over Palestine. It lies at the eastern end of the Mediterranean Sea and is bordered by Egypt in the south, Syria and Jordan in the east, and Lebanon in the north. The total area amounts to 20,700 square kilometers (7,992 square miles), about three fourths of the area of the mandate.

The population of the state when it was established was estimated at 655,000. Unlimited immigration, amounting to an influx of Jews from all over the world, has increased this to over 2 million. Integration of this large number of immigrants into the economic life of the nation has presented serious financial, social, and political problems.

Of the total area of Israel, which amounts to 20,700,000 dunams,* only 4 million dunams were under cultivation as of 1958, including 1,290,000 dunams of irrigated land. Field crops occupied the largest area, 2,365,000 dunams of nonirrigated and 465,000 of irrigated land, while vegetables, potatoes, and ground nuts were grown on 285,000 dunams; an additional 680,000 dunams were devoted to fruit planting. The remaining land was put to miscellaneous uses, including fish ponds, nurseries, flower cultivation, and others, as detailed in Table 1.

Most of Israel is semiarid, with scanty rain that falls during the winter months only. Rainfall is highest in the northwest, and decreases towards the southeast; the amounts range from zero to 635 mm. (0 to 25 inches) a year.[19]

The coastal plains, the most productive area, differ in character and are put to different uses; citrus is grown on light soils and vegetable and fodder on heavy soils. A coastal fringe of shifting sand dunes sometimes buries the fertile soils bordering them. Sand also has blocked the mouths of streams and created marshes, which are now being reclaimed by the government and which are developing into some of the most productive areas.

Agricultural production has increased at a very rapid rate since the creation of the state; between 1948-1949 and 1956-1957 agricultural production tripled, with an average annual rate of growth of 17%. The cultivated area increased in this interval by 132% and the

*One dunam equals one quarter of an acre or 0.1 hectare.

acreage of irrigated land by 279%. The same rapid rate of growth was maintained up to 1958-1959, the last year for which data are available. Increased production has enabled the country to become self-sufficient in many food items and to close the gap between production and consumption with regard to many others.

The problems created by share-cropping and by absentee land ownership in other Near Eastern countries do not exist in Israel. Jewish farms, which are in the majority, comprise 3,345,000 dunams of the total cultivated land; they range in type of ownership from individual farms, owned by the cultivator, to communally owned farms on which there is no private ownership of land or of the products of the land. Private ownership is characteristic of Arab farms, which comprise 695,000 dunams of the total land farmed.

The scarcity of water is one of the most difficult problems with which the nation has to deal, as is the case elsewhere in the Middle East. The quantity of water available appears to be the limiting factor in continued agricultural progress, so that planning of cultivation is determined by the largest net production of crops per cubic meter of water, rather than production by unit of land, of capital, or of labor invested.[6]

The main sources of water supply are three: flowing water in rivers and springs, which tends to be highly variable in amount, floodwater during or after heavy rains, and underground sources. There are no large rivers comparable in supply to the Euphrates, Tigris, or Nile, and use of the River Jordan is in dispute with neighboring Arab countries.[1]

A possible solution to the water shortage problem may lie in the success of a new desalinization process for obtaining fresh water from sea water. This process, which has already proved successful in laboratory and pilot plant tests, involves freezing sea water in a vacuum, thus forming ice crystals of pure water while the salt drains off in brine; the crystals are then melted to produce fresh water. The first large-scale plant, expected to produce 250,000 gallons of fresh water daily, was scheduled to begin operation in 1960.

Present agricultural policy, governed primarily by the availability of water, tends to emphasize high-quality, high-value crops as embodying the most profitable and productive use of water resources. These high-value crops are then exported, and the foreign exchange thus obtained is used to purchase cheap agricultural commodities for domestic use.

II. FOOD RESOURCES

A. GENERAL

Israel's food supply pattern has been transformed within the past
few years from one of scarcity to one of relative abundance, especially
with regard to milk and milk products, vegetables, and fruits. During
the first years of its existence as an independent state, Israel suffered
from severe shortages due both to the low level of production and to
the increased demands of an expanding immigration. Severe rationing,
price control, and control of importation of foodstuffs were instituted;
most of these restrictions have now been lifted. The Government retains a monopoly of wheat importation and marketing, but there are no
food items rationed and price supports have been discontinued.

Table 2, which details the area of land in agricultural use, gives
(1) the cultivated area of field crops from 1948-1949 to 1957-1958, on
both irrigated and unirrigated land; (2) the acreage planted to vegetables, potatoes, and peanuts; and (3) the area devoted to fruit crops,
according to a census of fruit plantation carried out in 1955-1956.
Nearly one third of the field crops of nonirrigated land were grown on
Arab farms, but less than a 0.1% of irrigated field crops were Arab-
grown. Vegetables and fruit cultivation also was carried out primarily
in Jewish farming communities. Arabs raised nearly all the tobacco,
watermelons, and sesame grown, as well as substantial proportions of
the barley, wheat, pulses, and sugar melons.

Table 3 presents the total agricultural production of Israel between
1953-1954 and 1957-1958. Data include not only the amounts of field
crops, vegetables, and fruits produced, but also the production of milk,
eggs, meat, fish, and all other products used as food. The table also
compares amounts produced on Jewish and Arab farms.

Israel still is not self-sufficient in the supply of food, and probably
never will be with regard to items such as grains, and also possibly
sugar. However, the share of local agriculture in the supply of local
food consumption has been steadily increasing. Comparison between
the share of local agriculture in the total food supply in 1956 and 1957
shows this improvement, and increases in agricultural production reported in 1958 and 1959 must have closed the gap still further:

Share of local agriculture in total food supplies

	1956		1957	
	No.	%	No.	%
Calories	889	31.1	1077	37.4
Animal proteins	20.4	68.2	22.4	73.4
Vegetable proteins	16.9	28.7	19.8	33.6
Fats	33.6	40.9	33.5	

The harvest seasons of the various crops vary considerably: in general, cereals and legumes are harvested in May and June and fruits from November to April, while other field crops are harvested from July to September. Table 4 gives the harvest seasons of the more important crops as well as the months during which the bulk of the harvest is gathered.

B. CEREALS

Annual cereal consumption amounts to approximately 250,000 tons. A large part of this total must be imported since sufficient land is not available in Israel to produce this amount of grain. An estimated 6 million dunams of irrigated land would be required to produce all the cereals consumed in Israel, and the total cultivated area at present is less than this amount. Proposals have been advanced for increasing the grain supply by introducing wheat as a nonirrigated crop into an irrigated crop rotation system, but these plans have not yet been put into effect and, in any case, production would still fall short of supplying local demands.

Wheat and barley are the two main cereals grown, and together they account for nearly one half of all the area devoted to field crops. Wheat is by far the most important food cereal in Israel; crop area in 1957–1958 amounted to 592,711 dunams, most of which was planted in Acre and Yizre'el in the north and in Beersheba in the south. Wheat is grown as a winter crop on nonirrigated land and is more commonly grown in Jewish farms, which contain 420,937 dunams of the total cultivated area. Production in 1957–1958 totaled 62,500 tons, about one fourth of the amount consumed. Barley also is predominantly a winter crop that grows well on poor soils and under semiarid conditions, even on the area bordering the Negev desert. Local varieties grown produce only moderate yields but are well adapted to the rigorous climatic conditions. Acreage planted to barley nearly equals that of wheat, amounting to 582,747 dunams in 1957–1958; barley is grown in the same areas as wheat: Acre, Yizre'el, and Beersheba. Unlike wheat, barley is more common on Arab farms, which accounted for two thirds of the total acreage. Since barley is planted primarily as fodder, only about 126 tons were used for food in 1957–1958.

The cultivated area and production of sorghum and maize have increased in recent years, but these crops are also primarily fodder crops. Maize is grown in the Kinreret subdistrict in the north and millet is grown in Acre and Yizre'el. The rate of consumption of these foods is so low that they do not appear on food balance sheets, and therefore it is not known how much of the total production is used as food.

Rice is being planted on an experimental basis in the reclaimed area of the Huleh and in various other regions. Certain fast-growing

varietіеs of rice are now being tested; these require only limited
amounts of water and it is possible that they may prove economically
feasible. However, it is doubtful whether Israel can ever grow enough
rice to satisfy domestic demands in view of the severe water shortage
problems discussed above.

C. OTHER EDIBLE CROPS

1. **Vegetables and potatoes.** Vegetables and potatoes are popular
items in Israeli diets and large quantities are produced. Formerly,
some potatoes and onions had to be imported during months when they
were in short supply locally, but at present all domestic needs are
met from local production and there is a surplus for canning and processing and for export. However, sharp seasonal fluctuations in the
availability of different vegetables in the market still occur, and the
Vegetable Growers Association reached a two-year agreement with
the Ministries of Agriculture and of Commerce and Industry guaranteeing minimum prices regardless of season. Surplus quantities of
vegetables purchased are kept in cold storage to await a favorable
market. In connection with this agreement the Association will regulate the cultivation of tomatoes, peppers, egg plant, carrots, cabbages,
cauliflowers, cucumbers, and onions to ensure more uniform marketing of these crops.

Total vegetable production amounted to 363,000 tons in 1957-1958
(Table 3), and the area devoted to major vegetable crops, both in
Jewish and Arab farms, totaled 223,920 dunams, as listed in Table 2.
The main vegetable-growing area is along the coastal plain. Potatoes
are grown mainly in Acre, Haifa, Yizre'el, and the Central district,
while tomatoes and onions are cultivated in the Central district, prin-
cipally in Sharon but with smaller quantities planted in Yizre'el and
Acre. The largest cucumber plantings are in Sharon.

Tomatoes are Israel's major vegetable crops and represent 30% of
total vegetable production. During 1957-1958 some 75,361 tons were
marketed, more than one fourth of all vegetables sold.

Potatoes yield two crops a year with the highest production in the
spring crop. Total production in 1957-1958 was 98,000 tons and land
planted amounted to 50,095 dunams. Only 78,000 tons of the potatoes
produced were available for human use, providing a per capita consumption of 39.6 kg. Local demands are fully satisfied by domestic
production and small amounts are exported.

Onions are of recent introduction in Israeli agriculture, but expansion of cultivation has been rapid and in 1957-1958 the onion acreage
amounted to more than 22,000 dunams. About 17,500 tons were marketed, enough to satisfy domestic demands.

2. **Legumes.** Legumes are grown in the Central district, especially
in Sharon, and in Haifa, Yizre'el, and Acre in the north. Beans, lubia,

and horse beans are popular, as are chick peas and lentils. A total of 8,250 tons of legumes were produced in 1957–1958, but of this amount only 3,230 tons were available for human use and an additional 3,680 tons had to be imported to satisfy domestic demands.

3. Fruits. The acreage and production totals of the most important varieties of fruits are shown in Tables 2 and 3. A large number of tropical, subtropical, and temperate climate fruits thrive in different regions, and fruit culture is the most important contributor to the economy of the country.

The soil and climate of Israel are especially well suited to citrus cultivation,[5] and the production of citrus fruits is the country's staple industry and most important source of foreign exchange. The first citrus plantations were established in the 1840's, and by 1909 one half million cases of Jaffa oranges were being exported annually to Great Britain. During the period between World Wars I and II, when citrus fruits were in great demand, acreage increased from 67,000 dunams in 1928 to 300,000 in 1936. The blockade of the war years and the Arab–Jewish hostilities, which followed the establishment of the state of Israel, adversely affected citrus plantings. Many groves were destroyed and many more fell into neglect. As a result, the fruit-bearing area was reduced to less than one half of the prewar acreage. Rehabilitation of the groves was undertaken soon after establishment of the state and in the past few years the industry has regained its preeminence in the economy. Productive area at present amounts to nearly 150,000 dunams, largely in the so-called citrus belt, which extends from Ashkelon in the south along the Mediterranean coast to Binyanune in the north. Groves already planted will come into production between 1962 and 1969, and by the end of the latter year acreage in production again will total 300,000 dunams.

Production of citrus fruit is controlled by a semiautonomous Citrus Marketing Board, which was the first of many such Boards and served as a model for similar Boards regulating vegetable production, poultry raising, and other agricultural endeavors. The Board supervises and regulates the extent, location, and variety of plantings, supervises the rehabilitation of groves, and regulates picking, packaging, and marketing of fruit. It has instituted centralized packing and planned marketing and regulates both export of citrus and the sale of supplies on the domestic market. The Board also finances research and supervises pest control methods.

Total production of citrus fruits in 1957–1958 amounted to 435,000 tons, of which 333,950 were oranges, 62,900 grapefruits, 15,500 lemons, and 22,650 were other varieties. The largest part of this production was exported and only 101,000 tons were used locally.

As mentioned below, the production of wine is a well-established industry; a large area is devoted to the cultivation of grapes. The total in 1958 was about 110,000 dunams, of which 72,000 were devoted to table grapes and 38,000 to wine grapes. Most of the crops are grown on unirrigated land, but the unusually severe and prolonged drought of 1957-1960 forced many vineyeards to adopt provisional arrangements for watering.

The largest grape wine area is in Hadera, where 45% of the total area under cultivation is located, followed by Ramle (17%) and Rehovoth (15.5%). Red varieties of grapes constitute about 60% of the total crop. Estimated production of grapes in 1957-1958 included 125,600 tons of table grapes and 22,300 tons of wine grapes, which were expected to produce 20 million liters of wine.

4. Peanuts. Peanuts were introduced recently as a summer crop on irrigated land and have become an important crop in domestic consumption and for export. They are now second only to citrus fruits as a source of foreign exchange. The area planted to peanuts in 1957-1958 amounted to 38,017 dunams and total production was 8,250 tons. A total of 5,986 tons were available for use as food.

5. Sugar crops. Until recently Israel depended on imports for all of its sugar supply. However, studies showed that climatic conditions were particularly favorable to the cultivation of sugar beets as a winter crop in the crop-rotation schedule then in use. Accordingly, cultivation of sugar beets was initiated in 1952, and by 1957-1958 there were 23,141 dunams planted to this crop on Jewish farms. Production in that year amounted to 94,000 tons, which yielded 11,778 tons of sugar, approximately one fifth of total consumption. The 1959 harvest was expected to produce 18,000 tons of sugar. Sugar beets can be grown almost anywhere in the country, but are particularly well adapted to the hotter areas where irrigation is available, such as lower Galilee and parts of the Negev.

There are about 45,000 beehives with an annual yield that fluctuates between 600 and 1,000 tons of honey, depending on temperature and rainfall. Two thirds of the hives are in the citrus belt, and each farm may have from 10 to 800 hives. Production of honey in 1957-1958 amounted to 620 tons.

D. CASH CROPS

The cultivation of several varieties of long-staple cotton has proved economically feasible, and attempts are being made to meet the country's requirements, which in 1957 amounted to twice the total production. Production in 1957-1958 included 4,860 tons of cotton lint and 8,100 tons of seed, grown on 57,974 dunams on irrigated farms in Jewish settlements and 2,717 tons grown on unirrigated lands in Arab farms.

Tobacco is primarily grown by Arab and Druze farmers in Galilee, Nazareth, the Carmel foothills, and Wadi Arah. Tobacco in Israel must be grown on nonirrigated lands because the water contains large amounts of chlorine, which is deposited in the leaf and affects its combustibility. Production in 1957–1958 amounted to 1,475 tons grown on 31,863 dunams in Arab farms and on 4,539 dunams in Jewish settlements.

A limited amount of flax is grown, and since its introduction in 1952 has shown itself well adapted to unirrigated cultivation in areas with an annual minimum of 350 mm. of rainfall. A small flax mill has been set up in the south to process the flax and approximately 400 tons are produced annually.

With the increasing importance of livestock raising large areas are being planted to hay and fodder crops, as shown in Table 2. Without irrigation, however, fodder produced is low in quality and the cost of production is high; in addition, excessive amounts of water are required for cultivation. The acreage and yield of alfalfa have increased, and the crop is a useful fodder with a high protein and caloric content. Approximately one fifth of the crop is dehydrated for use as poultry meal. Clover (**berseem**) is another fodder crop with high yields that serves as fresh fodder for livestock in winter and spring. Mangolds (fodder beets) are increasing in area sown and yield, and serve as summer feed for livestock. Other fodder crops include Sudan grass, **Setaria,** white millet, and winter crops, such as oats, field grass, rye grass, and others.

E. ANIMAL PRODUCT RESOURCES

Recent large increases in supplies of animal products have considerably improved Israeli diets. Animal proteins, formerly supplied in small quantities by limited imports, are now abundantly available from local production of milk and poultry, and there has been a considerable increase in animal protein consumption. Local agriculture supplied 70% of animal protein supplies in 1955–1956 and 81% in 1957–1958. The number and kind of livestock in Israel in 1948 and in 1950 to 1958 are presented in Table 5. There were an estimated 192,000 cattle, of which 152,000 were on Jewish and 40,000 on Arab farms. Cattle are kept both for meat and for milk, but of the two, dairy cattle are more important; cattle are kept in the southern district, Jizre'el, Sharon, Samaria, Upper Galilee, and elsewhere.

Beef cattle are of two kinds, calves born in dairy herds and sold immediately, or those reared on the farm for meat and beef cattle herds, numbering 39,000 head in 1957–1958. Beef cattle herds are maintained mainly on natural pastures. Experts estimate that natural grazing lands can maintain a cattle population of 80,000 head if pastures are improved and feeding is supplemented with the waste products of industrial crops, such as sugar beets.

Sheep are important on both Jewish and Arab farms; the number in 1957-1958 included 74,000 sheep on Arab farms and 117,000 on Jewish farms, the latter in approximately 400 flocks. The introduction of mechanical milkers in the collective settlements has made it possible to increase sheep holdings without increasing manpower. Sheep raising is based on locally produced feed.

Attempts have been made to limit goats on Jewish farms to thorough-bred varieties, and these animals are not allowed to pasture freely and destroy the ground cover, as goats do elsewhere in the Middle East. An estimated 40,000 goats are kept on Jewish farms. The Arab farmers own about 129,000 goats, of local origin and kept in traditional fashion.

A certain number of work animals are kept for draft purposes on both Jewish and Arab farms, as detailed in Table 5. Totals include 4,000 oxen and 11,000 camels on Arab farms, and 22,000 horses and mules and 20,500 asses on both Jewish and Arab cultivations.

A steep rise in the production of poultry and eggs has been noticeable in recent years to such an extent that there was an over production and a consequent drop in prices, which was so sharp that it impelled many poultry breeders to reduce or liquidate their holdings. As a result there was a shortage of poultry and eggs that lasted for several months. To prevent the recurrence of such a shortage, an agreement has been signed between the Poultry Breeders Association and the Government, assuring breeders of minimum prices for their products.

There are an estimated 5,700,000 laying hens in Israel (1957-1958), of which all but 200,000 were in Jewish settlements. Geese, ducks, and turkeys on Jewish farms numbered an additional 400,000. Most of the laying hens are in large commercial poultry-raising establishments, but almost all farms raise some chickens and keep a few to supply domestic needs.

The production of eggs in 1957-1958 totalled 886 million, and production of poultry meat was 34,200 tons, from some 13 million birds. This was equivalent to a 250% rise in egg production and a 520% rise in poultry meat production in comparison with 1948. Poultry provides about 65% of the total meat supply and is becoming an important export item, either canned or frozen. Eggs and one-day-old chicks are also export items of increasing importance, so that the poultry industry not only provides domestic food supplies but also foreign exchange credits.

Milk production has increased so much in recent years that it is now available in surplus quantities, and milk and milk products constitute the largest single source of mixed farming income in Israel, Dairying is generally carried out in large communal settlements, and it is estimated that these communities own about 40% of the milch cattle, concentrated in herds of 600 to 700 cows each.

Total milk production in 1957-1958 was estimated at 258,000 kilo-
liters, of which 216,500 was cow's milk and the rest sheep and goat
milk. About 170,000 kl. of the total was marketed to dairies, as compared with 60,000 kl. in 1949. The production of pasteurized and bot-
led milk was begun in 1955 with the aid of equipment supplied by
UNICEF, and these plants process most of the milk sold. During the
years when milk was in short supply, dairies supplemented fluid milk
with milk powder, but this practice is no longer necessary. Increased
production of milk has encouraged the manufacture of soft and processed cheese, cream, and butter.

Goats and sheep have been introduced only recently into Jewish
dairy farming although they have always been the chief source of milk
products on Arab farms. Swiss goats have been imported and milk
yields of native sheep and Damascus goats have been improved by
selective breeding. Sheep and goat milk contributed about 12% of the
milk supply in 1957-1958.

Production of meat is subsidiary to dairying, sheep breeding, and
poultry raising, and consumption of meat is low. Meat supplies in
1957-1958 amounted to 52,700 tons, of which cattle, sheep, and goats
provided about 30% and poultry the remainder. Of the total of 10,200
tons, live weight, of beef produced, some 8,800 tons were derived from
dairy herds and 1,200 tons were from beef cattle herds. Total slaughter in abbatoirs during 1957-1958 included 27,559 head of cattle,
41,148 of sheep and goats, and 21,534 head of other livestock. The
number of heads slaughtered by kind and district is shown in Table 6.

Supplies of all kinds of local and imported fish average about 20,000
to 25,000 tons a year, of which local fishing produces more than one
half. Fresh fish supplies are derived from three sources: marine
fishing, fresh water, (mostly lake) fishing, and fish bred in artificial
ponds. Table 7 lists the total catch of fish and gives details of the
amounts caught in marine fishing, in lakes, and harvested from fish
ponds, as well as the number of boats and men engaged in the industry.
During 1958-1959 the total catch rose to 13,000 tons of which 2,000
tons were caught in trawl fishing, 1,000 from shore, 1,500 in upper
waters, 1,000 from lake fishing, and 7,500 tons in fish ponds.

Marine fishing during the British mandate was confined to coastal
waters and was virtually a monopoly of Arab fishermen. After the
establishment of the Israeli State, several fishing fleets were established, based on Achzib, Naharia, Acre and Tirah, Athlit, Gesher,
Zaika, Tel Aviv, and Nebi Rubin. Some Arab fishermen are again operating from Acre, Gesher, Zaika, and Haifa, and there are some
mixed Arab-Jewish fishing fleets. Israeli fishing is mainly based on
trawlers, some of them fitted with ring nets. Several of the fishing
boats are owned by the factories that process the catch. The possibility of expanding deep-sea fishing in the Red Sea area is under study.
A fishing port recently was completed at the mouth of the Kishon River.

Lake fishing is carried out mainly in Kinneret and Hulah. Some 260 men were engaged in this type of fishing.

Fish-breeding ponds were first established in 1939 in the Beth Shean Valley, where water is abundant but saline, and where conditions are generally unfavorable to agriculture. The area devoted to fish culture has steadily increased and attempts have been made recently to limit this expansion, first, because fish ponds require excessive amounts of water, (more than ten times as much as summer crops) and, second, because sometimes land used for this purpose could have been more productively put to agricultural uses. Plans are now under way to stock reservoirs, such as Beth Netupha, with fish so as to put reservoirs to double use.

A substantial proportion of the fish catch is now processed in domestic factories and exports of fish are increasing.

F. EXPORTS AND IMPORTS

Trade in agricultural products is of vital importance to the economy of Israel. The country is not as yet self-sufficient in food supplies and probably can never be, with regard to certain specific items such as wheat, tea, and coffee. Large quantities of these and other items in short supply therefore must be imported yearly. On the other hand, the export of certain agricultural items, primarily citrus fruits and by-products, provide Israel with a major portion of her foreign exchange. Thus, in 1958 agricultural raw exports accounted for 40.3% of the total value of exports, and an additional 4.1% of total exports consisted of manufactured goods of the citrus industry.

The balance of this trade in agricultural produce is still unfavorable to Israel—that is, Israel imports more agricultural produce than she exports—but the gap between the two is steadily closing and the Government hopes to achieve a favorable balance of trade in the near future. Imports of agricultural products in 1958, including fodder for livestock and grains for brewing, amounted to $90,110,000, of which slightly more than two thirds was food for human consumption. On the other hand, exports of agricultural items amounted to $57,121,000 of a total export value of $142,351,000. The total quantities and values of the most important agricultural imports and exports are presented in Table 8.

One of the main advantages enjoyed by Israeli agriculture is that local climatic conditions enable Israel to supply European markets during the off-season, when these products are in greatest demand.

The most important export items in Israeli foreign trade are citrus fruits; during the 1958-1959 season exports of oranges, grapefruits, lemons, and various other citrus fruits amounted to a total of 9,514,939 cases.

The export of eggs has increased from 18 million in 1957 to 190 million in 1958. Day-old chicks, hatching eggs, dressed fowl, and goose liver also are increasing in importance as export items.

Vegetable product exports are in general limited to those of very high quality, including especially honeydew melons and other melon varieties. Plans are under way to increase the number of refrigerated ships available for the transportation of fresh fruit. Peanuts, only recently introduced, are becoming an important export crop, and 5,619 tons were exported in 1957-1958. Fruits other than citrus fruits that are successfully exported include grapes, bananas, avocados, olives, and pomegranates. A large variety of other fruit and vegetables are being tested for possible export potential.

With the expansion of the food-processing industry, processed foods are accounting for an increasing share of the foreign markets. Among processed foods that are finding increased markets are citrus products, goose liver paste, and frozen poultry.

Imports of food products accounted for 20% of all imports in 1958. Principal products imported include cereals, especially soft and hard wheat, grain sorghums, and millet. The total import value of this category amounted to nearly $35 million and constituted 9.2% of total imports and 41.6% of agricultural imports. Edible oil seeds (2.6% of the total) and sugar (1.5%) were next in importance among imported food items. Raw cotton was the most important agricultural import not destined for use as food. The United States was the main supplier of imported goods, except for special items such as sugar, coffee, tea, and cocoa.

G. INTERNATIONAL TECHNICAL AID

The Food and Agriculture Organization of the United Nations has carried out technical aid programs and studies in Israel since 1951. Experts have been sent to Israel to advise on agriculture and nutrition, financial support has been given to experimental projects, and fellowships have been granted to Israelis for work and study abroad. As of 1959, the FAO supported projects in improvement of land use and farm machinery, agricultural production and protection, animal disease control, agricultural economics, fisheries development, and nutrition. Israel is a participant in the Mediterranean Development Project sponsored by FAO.

The United States Operation Mission carries out a Point Four Program in Israel, and its agricultural section has been in operation since 1952. Work has been carried out in improvement of natural pastures, control of animal diseases, sanitary milk processing, poultry breeding, and improved use of water resources. Agricultural education, instruction, and research have been fostered both within Israel itself and through fellowships for study of Israelis abroad.

UNICEF supplied equipment for the establishment of the first pasteurized milk processing plants in 1955 and has cooperated in other
projects in the field of nutrition and child welfare.

H. FOOD INDUSTRIES, STORAGE AND TECHNOLOGY

1. Food processing. Food-processing industries have been in operation in Israel since the early stages of Jewish settlement in Palestine, but major expansion in the size and scope of operations has taken
place primarily in the years between 1950 and 1955. During this period, 1,000 new factories were set up, varying in size from small in-
dividually operated establishments to large modern factories. At the
end of 1958, a total of 2,000 food processing factories were in operation, employing some 21,000 persons, or approximately 15% of the
industrial labor force. The various categories of food enterprises in
operation at the end of 1958 are listed in Table 9.

A large variety of foods are produced by these establishments and
the amount of each category of processed food manufactured between
1940 and 1958 is presented in Table 10. The quality of manufactured
goods is under the control and supervision of the Food Division of the
Ministry of Commerce and Industry.

The marketing and production of flour has been a state monopoly
since the establishment of the Government of Israel. The government
imports the grain or purchases it from local producers and has it
milled to government specification by privately owned mills. There
are 23 flour mills, which work only at about 60 to 70% of their monthly
capacity of 37,000 tons. During 1958 an estimated 300,000 tons of
grain were processed, producing 240,000 tons of flour and 60,000 tons
of bran. A trend toward the production of white flour has been marked;
in 1949 only 25% of bread flour produced was white, while in 1958
more than 60% of flour marketed was white instead of "standard,"
showing an increased popular preference for bread made with white
flour. A special flour is milled for the Bedouin population of the Negev.

There are 849 establishments engaged in the production of bread,
pastries, and other flour products, including 364 that manufacture
European breads, 119 that make Oriental-style bread, 356 that bake
cakes and pastries, and 10 that bake matzohs. The present capacity of
these bakeries is about double the requirement, so that few of them
work more than eight hours a day.

The production of bottled, pasteurized, and sterilized milk was begun in 1955; by 1958 about 80 million liters of bottled milk were sold,
amounting to 90% of all fluid milk marketed. The dairy industry has
undergone considerable development and expansion and provides increasing quantities of locally produced milk, and soft and processed
cheese, cream, and butter.

Milk marketed in 1958-1959 amounted to 182.3 million liters. Formerly skim milk powder was added to milk in months when milk was in short supply, but this practice was discontinued in 1959 with the increase in local supplies. Slightly more than half (95 million liters of 182 million) of the milk marketed is consumed in the fluid state, the rest is converted to soft and processed cheese, cream and butter, and other dairy products.

Expansion of the oil-extraction industry has been rapid, and there are now 64 presses and 7 extraction plants. The yearly output capacity of local presses amounts to 200,000 tons and their refining capacity is about 85,000 tons. Some 145,000 tons of raw material were actually processed, yielding 25,000 tons of edible oils and 116 tons of oil cakes for use as animal feed. The industry still depends on imports of oilseeds for raw material. Capacity of the three margarine plants in operation has been increased by 50%, and the production of such items as mayonnaise and other spreads and of hydrolyates derived from oilseed meal proteins has been expanded. The olive oil industry also has been modernized, and two continuous crushing plants have been erected. Three modern Arab plants of the semicontinuous type have been built with government assistance and many existing village presses have been modernized.

The canning and other processing of fruit and vegetables comprise an important segment of the food-processing industry. Here production is seasonal, with most of the factories processing more than one type of crop during the year; several of the largest operating departments manufacture other types of food products, such as dehydrated soups and fish pastes. In general, citrus fruits are processed primarily for export, while other fruits and vegetables are produced for local markets. In 1957, for example, 85% of all citrus products were exported, but only 35% of the tomato products and 11% of the canned or pickled vegetables were shipped out of the country.

Citrus fruits are processed in 24 factories capable of processing 170,000 to 180,000 tons of fruit. These factories prepare marmalade, peel, canned pulp, essential oils, and squashes. The location of the plants does not necessarily correspond to that of the citrus-producing areas. Fourteen of the factories make concentrated and pasteurized juices, while two make frozen citrus concentrate. Some 21 factories extract tomatoe juice and 18 of these are equipped to produce tomato concentrates. During the 1957 season these factories only operated at 25% of capacity since they could not compete with market prices for the fresh produce. Nine factories process garden peas, which are produced principally for the local market although appreciable quantities are exported, particularly to England. These factories worked at only 23% of capacity in 1957. In general, the production facilities of the canning and vegetable processing industries are only partially utilized.

Some of the leading factories manufacturing fruit and vegetable products belong to the Citrus Canned Products Association, which markets 70 to 80% of total citrus-product exports. The Association supervises independent factories in various parts of Israel, including the south and the Sharon, Samaria, and Jordan valleys; some of these factories are among the largest and most modern in operation. A control laboratory is maintained at Rehovoth; this laboratory also gives advice on technical problems to members and conducts research on the development of new products.

Two plants for the processing of beet sugar are in operation at Affuleh and at Ramat Gan. During 1958 these two units processed 11,450 tons of white refined sugar, twice the amount of previous years. A third plant, with a proposed capacity of 16,000 tons is being built.

The largest factory in the Middle East for the manufacture of chocolate and cocoa, candy, chewing gum, and similar products is located in Tel Aviv. This is one of eight chocolate candy factories in the country. In addition, 120 small factories are engaged in the manufacture of **halvah** and other oriental candy products.

The wine-making industry of Israel was established in the 1880's by Baron Rothschild. There are two main types of local wines produced—table wines and sweet dessert wines. The great wineries of Rishon le Zion and Zichron Yaacov, which produce over 80% of the country's wines, have been equipped recently with modern plants and machinery for the fermentation of wine and the distillation of alcohol. The marketing and export of wine is carried out by the Israel Wine Institute, an association to which most of the large grape growers belong.

Meat preserves, sausages, canned meat and poultry, day-old chicks, and frozen poultry are some of the products of the expanding meat and poultry industry. Tinned meat, which only a few years ago was comparatively rare, now is abundantly available. Israel's climatic conditions are particularly favorable to the maintenance, breeding, and fattening of geese on a year-round basis, instead of only during a few months of the year as is the case in Europe, and the production of goose liver has increased to the point at which it is becoming an important export item.

The processing of fish is another food industry that is rapidly expanding. During 1958-1959 the industry used 1,500 tons of a total catch of 13,000 tons, and produced 8 million tins of fish. A method of salting sardines has been developed that will help reduce imports of salted fish. In addition, lobsters and filleted fish are now frozen and are being exported in substantial quantities.

2. Storage and refrigeration. Until recently, food was so scarce that all available supplies were sold immediately without regard to quality or price; hence, marketing and storage of produce was not a major problem. However, in the last few years surpluses of some

goods, such as vegetables, milk, and eggs, have been produced, and
the efficient marketing, handling, and storage of these surpluses has
become a necessity.

The need for building reserve grain stocks and the influence of
climate have made imperative the provision of adequate storage for
large quantities of grain. Storage capacity had increased to 50,000
tons by 1955 and by 1958 it totaled 170,000 tons, including storage for
40,000 tons of feed grains. The largest installation is that of the
Dagon Transit Silo at Haifa, where grain is pumped directly from the
ships' holds to storage silos. The capacity of these silos is now
20,000 tons, and it is being increased to 40,000. Storage silos have
also been built at flour mills, and in 1958 a total of 107,000 tons could
be stored in bulk at the mills at one time. Planned construction calls
for an increase of 80,000 tons of grain storage facilities in various
agricultural settlements.

The daily over-all capacity of ice-making plants now amounts to
3,500 tons, while maximum summer consumption is only about 2,000
tons. The low consumption is ascribed to the increased use of electric
refrigerators in homes and to the scanty use of ice in the display and
marketing of fruits, vegetables, fish, and poultry.[21]

Household refrigeration equipment is in much more common use
in Israel than elsewhere in the Middle East. A survey of wage-earning
and salaried families conducted in 1956-1957 indicated that approximately 37% of households were equipped with electric refrigerators
and 57% with nonelectric refrigerators. The communal agricultural
settlements also are reportedly equipped with food preservation facilities.

Several factories are engaged in the production of frozen foods, including one that processes frozen chickens for export, and there are
two frozen citrus juice plants. Details on the location and capacity of
these factories were not obtainable.

Rising agricultural production has led to the expansion of cold-
storage facilities. As of 1958-1959, there were 95 such installations,
of which most had modern refrigerating machinery. The total cold-
storage capacity was 65,000 tons, and more than 80% of this was devoted to foods such as carrots, beets, lettuce, and cabbages, as well
as to poultry, meat, and eggs. Large quantities of eggs, reportedly
as much as 30 million at a time, also are stored. Surplus amounts
of frozen meats, filleted fish, butter, and cheese, all of which require
a high degree of refrigeration, are stored in refrigerated storage
space of 10,000 tons capacity rented by the Ministry of Commerce and
Industry.

Plans are under way to construct an additional 12,000 tons of cold-
storage facilities, one third of which will be located in agricultural
areas.[21]

The capacity of storage facilities at present includes storage for

35,000 tons of oilseeds that are processed in the vegetable oil extraction plants.

According to government sources, total food-storage facilities, excluding cold storage, amounted to 500,000 tons in 1959.

III. DIET TYPES

A. GENERAL

The enormous variation in the background and cultural characteristics of the multiple components of the Israeli population render it difficult to make any generalizations on the national diet. Each cultural group, as outlined below, in large measure retains its dietary pattern, although each is influenced by other groups and by the relative availability of different foods. As a matter of fact, the relation of food habits to the nutrition, health, and social adaptation of immigrants is considered one of the more serious problems in their absorption into the national life. This problem was particularly acute in the early years of Israel, when almost all foods were in short supply and under severe rationing, and when many of the foods to which immigrants were accustomed were not available.

The consumption of food in Israel between the years 1949-1950 and 1957-1958 is shown in a series of tables (Tables 11 to 14) giving the consumption of the principal foodstuffs in kg. per capita per year (Table 11), the number of calories that each category of food contributed to the diet (Table 12), the intake of proteins (Table 13), and the intake of fats (Table 14). For purposes of comparison, available data on food consumption in prewar Palestine are included in Table 11, and similar data for United States and Great Britain are found in Tables 11 to 13.

Despite the enormous increase in population and the difficulties besetting the formation of the state and the establishment of agriculture, present-day food consumption compares favorably with prewar diets. Per capita consumption of cereals, potatoes,vegetables, vegetable oils, eggs, fish, meat, and sugar have increased—in some cases more than doubled—and only milk and fruits are consumed in lower amounts.

The present day Israeli diet includes large amounts of cereals, although less in relation to total diet than is customary in other Middle Eastern countries. The consumption of vegetables and potatoes is high, and fruits, especially citrus fruits, are abundant. Meat consumption is low, but the proportion of animal proteins to total proteins is satisfactory because of the high consumption of milk, poultry, and eggs.

The general pattern of food consumption in Israel is more like that in Western European countries and the United States than in other

Middle Eastern countries. This may be due in part to the predominantly Western European origin of Israel's Jewish population and in
part to the more advanced state of food production. Consumption of
cereals, vegetables, and fruits was higher than in either of the two
countries contrasted, whereas intake of meat and sugar was considerably lower.

A complete food balance sheet for Israel for the year 1957-1958 is
given in Table 15, showing details of production, exports and imports,
net food supply, and per capita consumption of each of a wide variety
of food stuffs within the categories summarized in Table 11 to 14.

The per capita consumption of cereals amounts to 123.6 kg. per
year. Cereals and cereal products provide 1,187 of a total daily consumption of 2,755 calories per capita and 40.9 gm. of the total protein
intake of 86.7 gm. They also provide about one third of the calcium
and riboflavin, one half of the iron and nicotinic acid, and two thirds
of the thiamine intake.

Wheat is the principal cereal, constituting 118.3 kg. per year, or
15% of the total cereal intake, and it is eaten primarily as wheat flour
in breads. Two types of bread are eaten: white bread, made from
low-extraction flour (0 to 52%), and dark bread, made from standard
flour (52 to 87%). The remaining portion of the extracted grain contains the major portion of nutrients and is used for feeding animals.
To offset the loss of nutrients in milling, white flour is now being enriched with thiamine, riboflavin, and calcium, as well as with small
amounts of soybean flour.

A variety of bread is baked, among which are the flat Oriental-
style **pitta,** the European light and dark breads, and the flat Jewish
matzohs. In recent years white bread has been increasing in popularity, and today about two thirds of all flour milled is for the preparation of this type of bread. Wheat also is used in **burghul,** parboiled
wheat, mostly by oriental Jews. Smaller quantities of rye, oats, and
corn meal also are consumed. Rice is preferred to potatoes by Jews
of Oriental extraction; among these groups consumption is higher than
the national average, which amounts to 4.8 kg. per capita per year.

Meat always has been in short supply and consumption is low in
almost all groups. The total annual consumption per capita amounted
to 25.9 kg. per year, and meats contribute only 114 calories daily to
the diet and only 10% of the total intake of proteins.

Most of the meat, as much as 65% of the total, is derived from
poultry, primarily chickens, although geese are becoming relatively
numerous and smaller quantities of other fowl are available. Poultry
is prepared according to the style of diet, being roasted, stewed, fried,
or baked. Meats are eaten roasted or in stews by European groups,
whereas in Oriental families they are stewed with vegetables or rice,
grilled in chunks (**shashlik**), or chopped and grilled with vegetables.

Eggs are important staples, the average consumption being 19.4 kg.

per capita per year. As the poultry-raising industry has expanded, consumption has risen steadily from the low point of 12 kg. recorded in 1952-1953.

During the worst of the food shortage, when imported fish—smoked, preserved, or frozen—was about the only type of meat available, consumption of fish was higher than at present, reaching a maximum of 18.6 kg. per capita during 1950-1951. With increases in the supplies of milk, eggs, poultry, and other foods, the total consumption of fish has decreased to the present 11.4 kg. per capita (1957-1958), but the proportion of fresh fish, as compared to imported, has increased. Fresh fish is a favorite in the diet and is increasingly available with the expansion of the fishing industry. It is served in a multitude of ways: grilled and flavored with sesame oil, chopped in **gefulte** fish, or stewed in tomato sauce.

Milk and milk products are both popular and in abundant supply, so that total consumption is high. Per capita intake has increased from 93.3 kg. in 1951-1952 to 106.6 kg. in 1957-1958, which is still lower than prewar consumption and lower than consumption in the United States and in Great Britain, but higher than Near East averages. Consumption is not uniform in the population: in addition to variations in use of milk due to cultural differences in diet, recent surveys found that consumption of milk in large families was only about one half that in small families because of lower per capita purchasing power.[12]

Milk is used mostly as fluid milk, with small quantities of cheese, cream, and yoghurt or other processed milk products. In this respect, Israeli diet patterns differ from those in other Middle East countries where milk is consumed primarily in processed or fermented form, such as cheese, **leben, yoghurt, ghee,** and others. Thus, although the Israeli diet included 72.9 kg. of cow's milk and 14.5 of sheep's milk, per capita consumption of cheese of all kinds was only 9.0 kg. and of **leben, lebenia,** and **yoghurt** only 4.8 kg.

As may be seen from the above discussion of consumption of meat, eggs, milk, and fish, the proportion of animal proteins in the diet has been steadily increasing. For example, in 1952-1953, animal proteins provided only 26.0 gm. (30%) of a total protein consumption of 87.8 g., whereas in 1957-1958 animal proteins provided 33.6 g. (39%) of a total intake of 86.7 g. per day.

Fruits, including watermelons and sugar melons, are important in the diets of all groups, and consumption amounts to 118.3 kg. per capita per year. As is to be expected in an important citrus-producing country, citrus fruits are the ones most commonly eaten and consumption totals about 50 kg. per capita per year. Watermelons and other melons are next in popularity, with an annual consumption of 28.3 kg. per capita. Per capita consumption of bananas amounted to 12.5 kg. and of grapes to 11.0 kg. per year.

The consumption of vegetables and potatoes is high and is steadily increasing. Potatoes, tomatoes, and onions are used in the diets of almost all population groups, and these and other vegetables are cooked in combination with legumes, meat, or fish or are served fresh in salads. Total annual consumption per capita is now 122.8 kg. of vegetables and 41.3 of potatoes and starches, for a total of 164.1 kg. Although they are not important in the diet as sources of calories or proteins, vegetables provide many of the protective elements essential to good nutrition.

Legumes are popular with all dietary groups, although the type of legumes preferred varies. Consumption amounts to 3.1 kg. per capita per year. Chick peas (**houmous**), primarily in use in Oriental commun- ities, are becoming universally popular, especially in a dish called **felafel**, which consists of a seasoned paste of chick peas, fried in little cakes and served in a flat roll (**pitta**) with a dressing of sesame oil. Houmous salad also is popular.

Soup is common in the diets of all national origins, and a large pro- portion of vegetables consumed are eaten in soups or stews.

Large quantities of oil-bearing seeds are produced and additional quantities are imported and processed in oil-extraction mills to pro- vide the vegetable oils that are the main sources of oil and fat for the Israeli diet. Average consumption includes 8.4 kg. of vegetable oil, most of which is olive oil and the rest mainly sesame, 7.6 kg. of mar- garine, and only 1.3 kg. of butter, for a total consumption of fats and oils of 17.3 kg. per capita per year.

Vegetable oils and butter provide more than one half of the intake of fat in the diet, 43.2 m. of a total of 83.5 m. per capita per day. Milk (12.3 g.), meat (8.2 gm.), and eggs (5.5 gm.) provide almost all the remaining fats. Sesame seed oil, **tachina**, primarily of Oriental origin, is becoming popular with all population groups. It is used as a season- ing for salads, especially those that include chick peas, as well as for baking and frying.

B. VARIATIONS IN DIETS

1. **Ethnic and national variations.** Differences in diets among pop- ulation groups in Israel are primarily on a cultural basis rather than on a regional basis, as is the case in other areas of the Middle East. The small size of the country and the relatively advanced state of transportation allows adequate distribution of produce; hence, produc- tion regions are not isolated from each other and have not developed divergent dietary patterns.[5] The same hold true for distinctions be- tween rural and urban diets. From the beginnings of Jewish settle- ments on the collective farms, which are so characteristic of Israeli agriculture, emphasis has been placed on growing a diversity of crops to allow the settlements to become self-sufficient. The Government

control of cereal crops, the only one of the major staples of diet in
short supply, and the stabilizing influence of the various growers associations also tend to equalize distribution of available food supplies.
Such differences as exist, therefore, are either economic differences,
cultural differences traceable to the varied origins of the Jewish population, or occupational differences among the Arab minority (either
nomadic herders in the Negev or settled agriculturists).

The Jews now in Israel may be divided into two large categories,
those of European origin and those migrating to Israel from Oriental,
mostly Middle Eastern countries. Oriental Jews, in general, prefer
rice, vegetables, salads, and oily fried foods, while European Jews
are meat and potato eaters and dislike vegetables. Both groups eat
large quantities of bread and increasingly prefer white bread, which
is of lower nutritional value, to the darker breads of their native
countries.[15]

The above statement is a broad generalization. In actual fact, each
of these broad categories includes a large number of variant groups,
and local diets are as heterogenous as national origins. A few examples will illustrate the variety of dietary customs to be found.[15]

Within the European group of Jews there are Hungarians who eat
goulashes and prefer paprika as seasoning; Czechs, with their dump-
lings and **knoedl**; Americans and English, with their preference for
roast beef, steak, and chops; and Poles, who like a diet primarily of
meat and potatoes. South African Jews are generally of Lithuanian
origin and retain the **gefulte** fish, **latkes**, chicken, and **kugel** dishes
characteristic of that latter area. Jews from Balkan states prefer
olives, tomato paste, dried fish, goat cheese, and eggplant, while
Bulgarians prepare rissoles of leeks or spinach cooked in lemon
sauce, and they eat beans and yogurt as staples.[15]

One of the largest of the Oriental groups is that of the North Afri-
cans, such as migrants from Tunisia and Morocco. These eat **tagine**,
a mixed stew of pulses, rice, or potatoes with vegetables and oil.
This stew may or may not contain meat or fish. Desserts are made
with semolina and pastes boiled in syrup or honey. Iraqi Jews combine vegetables with meat, fish, or rice, and eat a large variety of
foods including cheese and **leben**. Vegetables, including grape leaves,
peppers, or **lazi** (sugar beet leaves), are commonly stuffed with rice,
burghul, or meat. Curry is the preferred seasoning and oil and
samneh are used as fats. **Rubbeh** is a national dish of **burghul** paste,
filled with meat and nuts and fried or cooked. Egyptian Jews fry fish
and then cook it with rice. Meat is seldom eaten alone, but in a dish
with vegetables or potatoes (**gvetch**). **Bamia** (okra) is fried and then
boiled in tomato sauce, while **moussaka** is a popular dish consisting
of layers of fried egg plant, rice, and sometimes chopped meat.
Yemeni Jews have a rather monotonous diet characterized by the fact
that very little cooking is done. The caloric content is low and the in-

take of fats is lower than the Israeli average, possibly because Yem-
enis do not drink milk or eat cheese or use any spreads on bread.

Many of the Oriental dishes are becoming popular with the European
groups, principally chick peas (**houmous**), oriental types of cheese,
and fermented milk products such as **leben**. Also becoming popular
is the Oriental way of preparing vegetables as appetizers, parboiling
them slightly and then marinating them in vinegar highly spiced with
fresh green pepper and cayenne. Vegetables prepared in this way include beets, turnips, green beans, peppers, and egg plants.

Whether or not a national diet will evolve from all these variant
groups is impossible to predict. The limited availability of certain
foods, such as meat, and the fact that other foods cannot be grown or
that import restrictions are still placed on certain items, tends to
make uniform the type of food available. Studies show that such adap-
tive changes have occurred in some groups. However, dietary differences may tend to be perpetuated by the present agricultural policy of
settling new immigrants in villages (**moshavim**), that each contain
settlers not only from the same country, but also from the same background within that country.

The Arab population of Israel, which in 1959 numbered 225,000 in
a total population of slightly over 2 million, to a great extent preserve
the traditional habits of diet. Thus, the nomadic Bedouins of the
Negev depend to a great extent on their flocks for food supplies, subsisting on a diet of milk products supplemented by barley and other
cereals and some dried fruit. Arab farming is still based on production for domestic consumption, i.e., it is carried out on a subsistence
basis and the diet of the Arab rural population depends on the crops
grown in that particular region. The fact that Arab farming is all
without irrigation places harvests at the mercy of weather conditions
and has a direct effect on diets consumed. Arab crops include primarily wheat and barley, maize and millet, cucumbers, potatoes, and
vegetables, and these are supplemented by livestock products, particularly of sheep and goats.

2. Variations in diet among different income groups. Diets also
vary according to economic status. During the first few years of the
existence of Israel, a system of strict food rationing and price control
was in operation, balanced by subsidies to producers of principal
foodstuffs, including bread, milk, eggs, and fish, and supplemented by
a monopoly of imports and exports of foods. This system lasted until
about 1952. Rations supplied the basic nutritional requirements; although the diet was well below the standards of quantity and variety
customary in Western Europe, it was still above the level to which
Middle Eastern immigrants were accustomed.[6]

After 1952, there was a gradual liquidation of this austerity regime
and of government control of markets, rationing of foods and price
subsidies were abolished, and free markets for most foods came into

effect. As a result, although supplies of food were generally abundant, prices of nearly all commodities rose sharply. Average incomes compared favorably with those of other countries, but in Israel, as elsewhere, there is a fairly large group of low-income families. Paradoxically, although more food was available, the diet of a large proportion of the population deteriorated sharply; poorer sections of the population could not afford to pay the higher prices for food. The distribution of foodstuffs between the various economic classes of the population was now for the first time unbalanced, and diets of lower income groups became inadequate from a nutritional standpoint. In these groups, white wheat flour supplied 55 to 60% of the total caloric intake, fats and sugar 20%, and protective foods and animal products only 20%. The lower income groups had to devote the larger portion of their income to food purchases and the limited means were spent on bulky high calorie foods to prevent actual undernourishment.

In order to restore an adequate level of nutrition in the poorer classes, milk and bread continued to be subsidized for a time, although on a limited scale. Whole milk powder was supplied at reduced prices in community settlements and cheap school meals were provided. Lastly, flour and margarine have been enriched, the former with defatted soybean flour, calcium carbonate, and riboflavin, and the latter with vitamins A and D.

IV. ADEQUACY OF FOOD RESOURCES

The production of food supplies in normal times is ample with regard to vegetables (including potatoes), fruits, milk, meat products, eggs and poultry, groundnuts, and some industrial crops. Supplementary imports of the cheaper agricultural commodities, such as wheat and other bread grains and sugar, probably always will be necessary, and smaller imports of oilseeds, beef and lamb, fish, tea, coffee, and spices will probably continue at least for some years, although the country hopes to become self-sufficient in most of these foods. However, the high-quality, high-value exports, such as citrus fruits, eggs and poultry, peanuts, and processed agricultural products will, under ordinary market conditions, provide sufficient exchange credits to finance necessary imports.

There are two types of stress situation, however, which can and have adversely affected the adequacy of Israeli food resources: these are climatic and man made. The most important of the climatic factors is drought. The worst drought in 11 years of record ended in March, 1960. This record drought lasted for three years and cost the Government millions of pounds in reimbursements to farmers for out-of-pocket losses, food subsidies, and other expenses. Too much rainfall on occasion can also adversely affect the supplies of food. For example, excessive rainfall at fruit-picking time in 1957-1958 interfered with the harvesting of the citrus crops and was responsible for a sharp drop in production, while hail storms in 1958-1959 caused serious damage to citrus trees. This latter year also was marked by severe damage caused by storms, cold waves that damaged bananas and early vegetables, and a locust invasion that exceeded any of recent decades. Damage due to all these causes was estimated to amount to 3% of total agricultural production.

The second category of events affecting the adequac. of food supplies may be categorized as man-made, such as wars and depressions, including those in which Israel may not be directly involved. Any economic depression affecting countries that are the usual markets for Israeli exports will adversely affect the nation's food supplies by cutting off sources of foreign exchange which the country needs in order to purchase cereals and other staples in short supply. Any outbreak of hostilities involving Jewish markets has the same effect; thus the citrus industry, one of the mainstays of the economy, suffered severely from blockades and curtailment of markets in both World Wars I and II. The direct effect of hostilities also affect productive capacity. During the Arab-Jewish fighting many citrus groves were destroyed or damaged by lack of necessary cultivation and water, and enormous numbers of livestock were killed.

V. NUTRITIONAL DISEASE PATTERNS

It is extremely difficult to make any generalizations on the present status of nutrition in Israel because of the variation in the composition of the population resulting from the tremendous influx of immigrants from widely divergent countries and cultures. The dietary differences among these groups have been touched upon in the discussion of diets, but data concerning the exact incidence of nutritional diseases in the various groups is not available.

No country-wide surveys of all population groups has yet been carried out, but some good studies exist on limited groups, and these allow the drawing of some conclusions with regard to the prevalence of deficiency disease.[8]

The lower income urban population consumes the poorest diet from a nutritional point of view, and some evidence is available on the occurrence of severe malnutrition in this group. Examination of more than 200 children and infants up to the age of 12 in Tel Aviv and its suburbs disclosed signs of malnutrition in almost all; the children were below normal in height and weight.[9] Although there were no signs of clinical avitaminosis, blood levels of vitamin A were almost zero.

Occasional cases of kwashiorkor, a severe protein deficiency in infants, occur, but the incidence is unknown.[12] These cases are ascribed to the use by some mothers of corn starch in infant feeding. Although corn flour thus used is supposed to be added to milk as a dietary supplement, in which case it is of some value, most mothers using it could not afford to buy milk and mixed the starch with water or at best with diluted milk. During 1957 a total of 17 cases of kwashiorkor were reported from Rehovoth alone.

Rickets is relatively common but is rarely severe.[10] During 1957 a study of 817 children aged 1 month to 1 year, admitted to a government hospital at Srifin, disclosed that 9.1% had clinical and radiological signs of rickets.

Widespread riboflavin deficiency was reported among poorer sections of the population.[8] A study of pregnant women attending a clinic showed that 20% were suffering from this deficiency. This avitaminosis is expected to disappear with the recently introduced use of flour enriched with riboflavin.

Scurvy is rare, but it is seen occasionally in infants and children fed on a cereal diet for long periods of time without added fruit or vegetable juices.

Nutritional anemia is observable in both adults and children, particularly in low income groups.[12] Among 2,500 pregnant women examined, 11% showed hemoglobin levels below 10 mg. So common are levels of 11 to 13 gm. that these are accepted as normal. A survey of 3,000 adults showed hemoglobin levels lower by 1.0 to 1.5 gm. than those considered normal in Northern Europe and America. In general, hemoglobin levels appear to be lower among the coastal population and higher in Jerusalem.[10]

VI. CONCLUSIONS

Agriculture has been, until recently, the chief contributor to the Israeli economy, although it appears that industrial production has now surpassed agriculture in this respect.

The scarcity of water is the main limiting factor in agriculture, and planning of cultivation is determined by yield per cubic meter of water rather than by other factors.

The food supply pattern has changed in the past few years from one of scarcity to one of relative abundance, especially with regard to milk and milk products, vegetables, and fruits. Citrus fruits are the country's staple crop and its greatest foreign exchange earner.

Food-processing industries are highly developed and processed foodstuffs are becoming important export items.

A great variety of diet types is found, reflecting the various national origins of the inhabitants. In general, however, the pattern of food consumption is more European than Middle Eastern. Consumption of milk, fruit, and vegetables is high in comparison with those of some neighboring countries. Consumption of cereals is higher and of meat is lower than is typical in a Western European diet.

Food production is adequate with regard to milk, fruit, eggs, poultry, and vegetables, but cereal production is insufficient to meet demand, and certain other foods also must be imported to offset production deficits.

Malnutrition appears to be a problem primarily among lower income urban groups. Rickets is reportedly common but rarely severe, nutritional anemia is observable, and occasional cases of other deficiency diseases are reported.

SELECTED REFERENCES

1. Halperin, C. Changing Patterns in Israeli Agriculture. London, Routledge and Kegan Paul, 1957.
2. Linking Agriculture with Industry. *Israel Economic Forum,* Vol. 9, No. 1-2, December, 1958; *ibid.,* No. 3-4, July, 1959.
3. Israel, Ministry of Commerce and Industry. Israel Export Catalogue, Part I, Foodstuffs. (2nd edit.) 1959.
4. United States Department of Agriculture, Foreign Agricultural Service. Principal Agriculture Commodities Export and Import by Country of Destination, 1958. February, 1960.
5. Israel, Ministry of Agriculture. Agriculture in Israel. Jerusalem, April, 1959.
6. Black, A. G. Report to the Government of Israel on National Plans and Programs in Agricultural Policy. *F. A. O. ETAP No. 1032.* Rome, 1959.
7. Israel, Central Bureau of Statistics. *Statistical Abstract of Israel,* No. 10, 1958-59.
8. Israel, Ministry of Health. Health Services in Israel, A Ten Year Survey. Jerusalem, 1959.
9. Hirsch, W., and Fisher, I. Observations on Malnutrition in Children. Harefuah, February, 1956.
10. Winter, S., and Griffel, B. Rickets in Israel. Harefuah, August, 1955.
11. Ergash, M. The Problem of Rickets in Israel. Harefuah, September, 1955.
12. Lepkovsky, S. Report on Food and Nutrition Policy in Israel. *F. A. O. ETAP No. 891.* Rome, 1958.
13. Fellows, L. Record Drought Ends in Israel. *New York Times,* March 26, 1960.
14. Muhsam, H. V., and Zaslany, A. Effect of Siege of Jerusalem on School Children. *Statistical Bulletin of Israel,* Vol. 1, No. 8, [no date]. p. 16.
15. Cornfeld, L. How Israel Eats. New York, Israeli Information Office, [no date].
16. Strauss, W. Continuation and Expansion of a Nutritional Survey within Various Groups of the Population of Israel. Hebrew University, 1955.
17. Brunner, D., and Lobl, K. Survey of Diets of Yemenites in Israel. *Annual Internal Medicine,* October, 1958, pp. 732-750.
18. United States Department of Agriculture. The Pattern of World Milk Production. *Foreign Agriculture Report No. 83,* 1955.
19. Russell, Sir E. J. World Population and World Food Supplies. London, Allen & Unwin, 1954.
20. Food and Agriculture Organization. Mediterranean Development Project. Rome, 1959.
21. Republic of Israel. Israel Government Yearbook, 5720 (1959-1960). Jerusalem, 1960.

Table 1

Cultivated Area in Israel
(in 1000 dunams)[a]
1948/49, 1950/51—1958/59[b]

	1958/59	1957/58	1956/57	1955/56	1954/55	1953/54	1952/53	1951/52	1950/51	1948/49
All Farming										
Total[c]	4,040	3,940	3,820	3,685	3,590	3,560	3,550	3,475	3,350	1,650
thereof: irrigated	1,290	1,185	1,100	965	890	760	650	540	470	300
Field crops (unirrigated)	2,365	2,376	2,359	2,365	2,335	2,354	2,449	2,299	2,111	1,066
Area in preparation[d]	50	50	30	30	25	100	100	300	439	—
Field crops, (irrigated)	465	414	368	305	265	191	165	127	118	64
Vegetables, potatoes, and groundnuts	285	262	275	262	270	270	244	198	157	70
Fruit plantations	680	645	598	536	515	475	433	410	892	355
Fish ponds	42	42	41	40	37	35	35	30	27	15
Miscellaneous (auxiliary farms, nurseries, flowers, etc.)	153	151	149	147	143	135	124	111	106	80
Jewish Farming										
Total[c]	3,345	3,240	3,145	3,030	2,965	2,940	2,960	2,895	2,705	1,310
thereof: irrigated	1,264	1,161	1,079	946	873	745	638	539	460	292
Field crops (unirrigated)	1,845	1,848	1,851	1,870	1,852	1,873	1,987	1,840	1,588	828
Area in preparation[d]	50	50	30	30	25	100	100	300	439	—
Field crops (irrigated)	465	414	368	305	265	191	165	127	118	64
Vegetables, potatoes, and groundnuts	250	228	240	227	241	236	212	165	120	51
Fruit plantations	557	525	481	424	413	381	347	330	312	275
Fish ponds	42	42	41	40	37	35	35	30	27	15
Miscellaneous (auxiliary farms, nurseries, flowers, etc.)	136	133	134	134	132	124	114	103	101	77
Other Farming										
Total[c]	695	700	675	655	625	620	590	580	645	340
thereof: irrigated	26	24	21	19	17	15	12	11	10	8
Field crops (unirrigated)	520	528	508	495	483	481	462	459	523	238
Vegetables, potatoes, and groundnuts	35	34	35	35	29	34	32	33	37	19
Fruit plantations	123	120	117	112	102	94	86	80	80	80
Miscellaneous (auxiliary farms, nurseries, flowers, etc.)	17	18	15	13	11	11	10	8	5	3

(a) dunam equals 1/4 acre.　　(b) Relating to crop area and not to physical area, i.e., an area is included as many times as it is sown. Generally, the physical area of irrigated field crops, vegetables and potatoes constitutes about 80% of the crop area.　　(c) Excluding forests and natural pasture.　　(d) New cultivated areas which were ploughed and prepared for sowing winter grains the following year.　　Source: Statistical Abstract, 1958/59.

Table 2

Cultivated Area of Principal Crops

Area Planted to Field Crops, Vegetables and Legumes and Fruit Trees
1948/49—1952/53—1956/57—1957/58

(in dunams) [a]

	1957/58 Other Farming	1957/58 Jewish Farming	1957/58 All Farming	1956/57 All Farming	1952/53 All Farming	1948/49 All Farming
FIELD CROPS Unirrigated Crops						
ALL CROPS	527,773	1,848,520	2,376,293	2,358,741	2,448,848	1,065,503
Winter Crops						
Hay	1,510	347,122	348,632	341,435	376,868	120,925
Green fodder	60	2,879	2,939	4,337	7,305 }	5,789
Pasture, sown	—	6,987	6,987	6,484	10,355 }	
Silage	—	35,569	35,569	35,126	22,473	2,358
Green manure	—	119,143	119,143	104,267	82,446	12,856
Pulses for grain	23,581	63,256	86,837	106,196	125,470	38,556
Barley	203,887	378,860	582,747	519,136	827,488	155,421
Wheat	171,774	420,937	592,711	572,885	346,912	302,491
Oats	—	8,569	8,569	8,698	19,599	9,069
Rye	—	—	—	10	140	11,126
Flax for fibre	—	3,495	3,495	5,178	6,980	—
Linseed	—	—	—	45	710	—
Sugar beet	—	—	—	—	2,338	—
Peas for canning	600	4,827	5,427	10,915	10,915	—
Safflower, winter	—	11,034	11,034	20,944	—	—
Miscellaneous	—	557	557	573	247	—
Summer Crops						
Hay	—	1,540	1,540	1,939	5,992	5,616
Green fodder	—	8,489	8,489	17,054	35,414	17,585
Silage	—	3,813	3,813	9,108	32,090	7,965
Pulses for grain	14,439	17,309	31,748	16,493	6,354	4,882
Maize for grain	1,510	9,435	10,945	13,895	51,439	66,145
Sorghum for grain	7,544	153,285	160,829	218,429	174,126	43,896
Sunflowers	2,012	15,684	17,696	25,138	12,590	4,206
Sesame	24,082	944	25,026	29,243	7,902	32,184
Safflower, summer	—	876	876	3,478	14,160	4,177
Tobacco	31,863	4,539	36,402	31,329	35,127	8,700
Cotton	2,717	—	2,717	—	—	—
Watermelons	22,682	13,270	35,952	40,251	70,119	33,383
Sugar melons	7,200	11,452	18,652	18,005	14,344	3,898
Pumpkins	—	332	332	269	578	—
Sorghum for brooms	—	—	—	—	2,055	—
Cultivated fallow	12,312	203,562	215,874	197,777	145,767	174,115
Miscellaneous	—	755	755	104	545	160
Irrigated Crops						
ALL CROPS	145	413,871	414,016	367,582	164,676	64,848
Winter Crops						
Sugar beet	—	23,141	23,141	13,379	4,427	—
Green fodder	45	87,550	87,595	78,666	45,088	27,707
Green manure	—	17,243	17,243	7,208	5,098	911
Miscellaneous	—	—	—	—	—	—

(a) dunam equals 1/4 acre.

Table 2 (Continued)

	Other Farming	1957/58 Jewish Farming	All Farming	1956/57	1952/53	1948/49
				All Farming		

FIELD CROPS (continued)
Irrigated Crops (continued)

Summer Crops

Hay	—	9,647	9,647	6,191	—	—
Pulses for grain	—	619	619	725	—	—
Maize for grain	35	48,916	48,951	70,032	16,761	296
Sorghum for grain	—	12,866	12,866	12,324	4,352	60
Rice	—	4,475	4,475	621	—	—
Cotton	—	57,974	57,974	48,253	—	—
Green fodder	65	123,893	123,958	102,442	65,045	30,186
Pasture, sown	—	14,913	14,913	17,252	14,397	3,436
Silage	—	8,693	8,693	6,484	5,382	—
Green manure	—	840	840	670	2,314	1,294
Miscellaneous	—	3,101	3,101	3,335	1,812	958

VEGETABLES AND LEGUMES

	Other Farming	Jewish Farming	All Farming	1956/57	1952/53	1948/49
TOTAL (b)	32,406	191,514	223,920	220,759	222,563	130,765
Potatoes	1,085	49,010	50,095	51,379	37,956	23,058
Tomatoes	8,539	30,138	38,677	35,633	38,942	32,268
Cabbage	660	6,033	6,693	8,156	8,108	4,752
Cauliflower	607	5,000	5,607	7,926	8,689	4,317
Carrots	—	10,248	10,248	12,155	12,015	6,077
Beet	—	3,156	3,156	4,555	5,639	2,467
Cucumbers	4,541	14,535	19,076	18,318	18,945	11,458
Radishes	243	3,061	3,304	3,993	4,876	2,012
Marrows	1,265	5,070	6,335	5,910	6,485	4,391
Peppers	656	6,083	6,739	7,074	5,666	3,694
Eggplants	1,126	3,817	4,943	4,959	5,283	2,781
Beans	1,367	5,123	6,490	6,725	4,311	4,547
Lubia	722	—	722	765	1,054	
Horse beans	41	3,194	3,235	1,940	2,044	798
Lettuce	—	824	824	869	735	791
Spinach	7	403	410	217	82	271
Kohlrabi	—	451	451	602	945	488
Radishes, red	21	684	705	589	830	507
Green peas (c)	1,353	1,284	2,637	4,047	4,169	3,910
Sweet potatoes	—	472	472	436	1,100	198
Okra	2,513	3	2,516	2,650	4,481	4,743
Spring onions	2	4,026	4,028	2,461	5,012	2,224
Dry onions	5,251	13,144	18,395	16,108	16,885	4,886
Garlic	2,115	168	2,283	2,008	3,428	1,396
Pumpkins, irrigated	—	960	960	826	1,248	502
Sugar melons, irrigated	—	10,194	10,194	6,870	4,716	1,318
Watermelons, irrigated	—	7,111	7,111	4,252	. .	. .
Strawberries	—	1,130	1,130	758	202	83
Other vegetables	292	6,192	6,484	8,578	18,717	6,828
GROUNDNUTS	1,340	36,677	38,017	54,605	21,488	2,316

(b) Excluding groundnuts.   (c) Excluding peas for canning.

Table 2 (Continued)

FRUIT ORCHARDS[(d)]

| | Area Classified As To: | | | | | | |
| | Productivity | | Cultivation | | Farming | | |
	Of Non-Productive Age	Of Productive Age	Irrigated	Unirrigated	Other	Jewish	Total
TOTAL	166,308	369,412	311,187	224,533	112,207	423,513	535,720
Citrus	90,027	122,907	212,934	—	2,310	210,624	212,934
Oranges, Shamouti	38,064	86,553	124,617	—	1,656	122,961	124,617
Oranges, Valencia	14,297	15,225	29,522	—	273	29,249	29,522
Grapefruit	2,213	11,256	13,469	—	68	13,401	13,469
Lemons	2,887	3,449	6,336	—	151	6,185	6,336
Clementines	2,817	3,808	6,625	—	—	6,625	6,625
Mandarines	322	817	1,139	—	103	1,036	1,139
Washington navel	2,200	398	2,598	—	—	2,598	2,598
Citrons	12	69	81	—	—	81	81
Other citrus	830	1,332	2,162	—	59	2,103	2,162
Rootstocks	26,385	—	26,385	—	—	26,385	26,385
Grapes	25,089	77,108	31,405	70,792	12,612	89,585	102,197
Table grapes	17,838	48,179	23,544	42,473	12,612	53,405	66,017
Wine grapes	6,675	28,029	7,285	28,319	—	35,604	35,604
Rootstock production vineyard	576	—	576	—	—	576	576
Pome fruit	12,500	5,695	17,715	480	446	17,749	18,195
Apples	10,487	5,060	15,141	406	411	15,136	15,547
Pears	1,129	297	1,387	39	8	1,418	1,426
Quinces	884	338	1,187	35	27	1,195	1,222
Stone fruit	11,738	12,705	12,756	11,687	7,025	17,418	24,443
Plums and prunes	7,276	8,346	9,195	6,427	3,624	11,998	15,622
Peaches	2,102	466	2,447	121	141	2,427	2,568
Apricots	846	1,686	296	2,236	1,312	1,220	2,532
Almonds	1,422	2,199	718	2,903	1,948	1,673	3,621
Cherries	92	8	100	—	—	100	100
Subtropical fruit	2,688	2,087	4,775	—	340	4,435	4,775
Avocados	1,001	313	1,314	—	—	1,314	1,314
Mangoes	216	82	298	—	—	298	298
Guavas	1,054	1,514	2,568	—	340	2,228	2,568
Loquats	301	109	410	—	—	410	410
Annonas	55	33	88	—	—	88	88
Persimmons	61	36	97	—	—	97	97
Other fruit plantations							
Olives	6,540	122,501	7,497	121,544	82,732	46,309	129,041
Bananas	—	15,123	15,123	—	53	15,070	15,123
Carobs	14,218	868	3,292	11,794	676	14,410	15,086
Figs	630	6,656	522	6,764	4,734	2,552	7,286
Pomegranates	1,029	2,138	2,217	950	678	2,489	3,167
Dates	564	587	1,151	—	81	1,070	1,151
Pecans	1,067	9	1,076	—	—	1,076	1,076
Miscellaneous	218	1,028	724	522	520	726	1,246

(d) According to 1956 Census.
Source: Statistical Abstract, 1958/59.

Table 3

Production of Principal Crops

Total Production; Production of Jewish Farms and Other Farms

(1948/1949—1957/1958)

(Tons, unless otherwise stated)

	1957/58	1956/57	1955/56	1954/55	1953/54
All Farming					
Field Crops					
Cereals and Pulses					
Wheat	62,500	83,000	74,000	36,000	34,000
Barley	53,300	74,200	85,000	42,100	89,900
Oats	800	1,050	1,200	800	1,400
Maize	28,300	38,000	23,000	26,000	22,900
Sorghum	34,400	37,700	25,500	11,100	19,500
Rice (paddy)	2,100	250	—	—	—
Other cereals	500	600	350	200	150
Pulses	8,250	§ 9,800	§ 8,280	§ 5,625	§ 7,950
Fodder					
Hay	110,800	123,000	109,250	91,070	126,100
Greenfodder and silage	1,301,300	1,217,600	940,300	866,500	672,000
Industrial Crops					
Groundnuts	12,700	17,900	14,200	19,200	15,100
Sunflower	1,500	2,750	950	500	1,620
Safflower	700	1,050	1,450	1,100	500
Flax	1,020	2,300	660	160	480
Cotton lint	4,860	4,100	3,200	2,200	250
Cottonseed	8,100	6,700	5,250	4,000	500
Sesame	950	1,520	1,450	420	700
Tobacco	1,475	1,760	1,375	2,335	3,050
Sugar beet	94,000	56,000	28,000	21,000	6,750
Other industrial crops	1,750	4,350	3,400	2,165	2,725
Miscellaneous					
Water melons, sugar melons and pumpkins	61,200	69,000	58,000	38,000	41,600
Straw	114,500	148,500	122,000	55,800	83,000
Vegetables and Potatoes	363,000	335,000	323,500	291,000	284,000
Potatoes	98,000	93,000	92,500	82,000	79,000
Vegetables	265,000	242,000	231,000	209,000	205,000
Citrus Fruit	435,500	439,000	452,000	392,000	470,500
Other Fruit	125,500	97,400	101,900	57,800	79,300
Table grapes	22,300	20,100	18,500	14,000	17,500
Wine grapes	25,600	23,400	14,200	11,000	12,600
Olives	17,900	7,000	25,000	2,800	21,500
Bananas	29,000	20,300	23,500	17,000	11,300
Deciduous fruits	18,800	16,600	11,800	6,700	11,000
Other fruits	11,900	10,000	8,900	6,300	5,400
Milk (kilolitre)	258,000	224,800	209,600	192,100	176,800
Cow milk	216,500	184,000	171,500	159,000	146,600
Sheep and goat milk	41,500	40,800	38,100	33,100	30,200
Eggs (1,000 units)	886,000	630,000	510,000	503,500	414,000
Honey	620	620	1,030	520	470
Meat (live weight)	52,700	37,900	36,600	26,900	14,900
Cattle	10,200	9,400	7,900	6,150	4,000
Sheep and goats	4,500	3,500	3,100	2,700	1,600
Poultry	34,200	22,200	23,200	16,300	9,300
Other meat	3,800	2,800	2,400	1,750	—
Fish	12,350	11,400	10,900	11,000	9,000

Table 3 (Continued)

	1957/58	1956/57	1955/56	1954/55	1953/54
Jewish Farming					
Field Crops					
Cereals and Pulses					
Wheat	56,000	70,000	62,000	28,800	23,800
Barley	48,000	56,500	68,500	36,200	77,600
Oats	800	1,050	1,200	800	1,400
Maize	28,100	37,700	22,800	25,900	22,700
Sorghum	33,800	36,900	24,500	10,400	17,800
Rice (paddy)	2,100	250	—	—	—
Other cereals	500	600	250	200	150
Pulses	6,800	§ 7,400	§ 6,355	§ 4,125	§ 5,650
Fodder					
Hay	110,500	122,600	109,000	91,000	126,000
Green Fodder and Silage	1,300,800	1,217,400	939,300	865,500	671,000
Industrial Crops					
Groundnuts	12,500	17,500	14,000	19,000	15,000
Sunflower	1,400	2,550	800	450	1,500
Safflower	700	1,050	1,450	1,100	500
Flax	1,020	2,300	575	105	480
Cotton lint	4,820	4,100	3,200	2,200	250
Cottonseed	8,020	6,700	5,250	4,000	500
Sesame	50	70	100	20	—
Tobacco	225	260	225	185	150
Sugar beet	94,000	56,000	28,000	21,000	6,750
Other industrial crops	1,600	4,200	3,050	1,815	2,725
Miscellaneous					
Watermelons, sugar melons and pumpkins	42,900	42,000	36,500	25,400	21,500
Straw	103,500	128,000	103,000	46,600	66,000
Vegetables and Potatoes	334,500	306,500	294,000	266,000	258,000
Potatoes	96,500	91,500	91,000	81,000	78,000
Vegetables	238,000	215,000	203,000	185,000	180,000
Citrus Fruit	435,500	439,000	452,000	392,000	470,500
Other Fruit	106,500	85,300	76,600	51,600	55,300
Table grapes	20,600	17,700	16,000	12,600	14,400
Wine grapes	25,600	23,400	14,200	11,000	12,600
Olives	4,900	2,500	7,000	1,000	5,200
Bananas	29,000	20,300	23,500	17,000	11,300
Deciduous fruits	17,800	15,100	10,500	6,200	9,300
Other fruits	8,600	6,300	5,400	3,800	2,500
Milk (kilolitre)	239,300	207,000	193,000	178,000	163,000
Cow milk	208,000	176,000	164,000	152,000	140,000
Sheep and goat milk	31,300	31,000	29,000	26,000	23,000
Eggs (1,000 units)	875,000	620,000	501,000	495,000	406,000
Honey	600	600	1,000	500	450
Meat (live weight)	47,650	34,000	33,300	24,400	13,650
Cattle	8,800	8,100	6,900	5,500	3,600
Sheep and goats	2,450	2,000	1,800	1,650	850
Poultry	34,000	22,000	23,000	16,200	9,200
Other meat	2,400	1,900	1,600	1,050	—
Fish	11,950	11,000	10,600	10,750	8,750

Table 3 (Continued)

	1957/58	1956/57	1955/56	1954/55	1953/54
Other Farming					
Field Crops					
Cereals and Pulses					
Wheat	6,500	13,000	12,000	7,200	10,200
Barley	5,300	17,700	16,500	5,900	12,300
Oats	—	—	—	—	—
Maize	200	300	200	100	200
Sorghum	600	800	1,000	700	1,700
Pulses	1,450	2,400	1,925	1,500	2,300
Fodder					
Hay	300	400	250	70	100
Green Fodder and					
Silage	500	200	1,000	1,000	1,000
Industrial crops					
Groundnuts	200	400	200	200	100
Sunflower	100	200	150	50	120
Safflower	—	—	—	—	—
Flax	—	—	—	—	—
Cotton lint	40	—	—	—	—
Cottonseed	80	—	—	—	—
Sesame	900	1,450	1,350	400	700
Tobacco	1,250	1,500	1,150	2,150	2,900
Sugar beet	—	—	—	—	—
Other industrial crops	150	150	250	350	—
Miscellaneous					
Water melons, sugar					
melons and pumpkins	18,300	27,000	21,500	12,600	20,600
Straw	11,000	20,500	19,000	9,200	17,000
Vegetables and Potatoes	28,500	28,500	29,500	25,000	26,000
Potatoes	1,500	1,500	1,500	1,000	1,000
Vegetables	27,000	27,000	28,000	24,000	25,000
Citrus Fruit	0	0	0	0	0
Other Fruit	19,000	12,100	25,300	6,200	24,000
Table grapes	1,700	2,400	2,500	1,400	3,100
Wine grapes	—	—	—	—	—
Olives	13,000	4,500	18,000	1,800	16,300
Bananas	0	0	0	0	0
Deciduous fruits	1,000	1,500	1,300	500	1,700
Other fruits	3,300	3,700	3,500	2,500	2,900
Milk (kilolitre)	18,700	17,800	16,600	14,100	13,800
Cow milk	8,500	8,000	7,500	7,000	6,600
Sheep and goat milk	10,200	9,800	9,100	7,100	7,200
Eggs (1,000 units)	11,000	10,000	9,000	8,500	8,000
Honey	20	20	30	20	20
Meat (live weight)	5,050	3,900	—	2,500	1,250
Cattle	1,400	1,300	1,000	650	400
Sheep and goats	2,050	1,500	1,300	1,050	750
Poultry	200	200	200	100	100
Other meat	1,400	900	800	700	—
Fish	400	400	300	250	250

Source: Statistical Abstract, 1958/59.

Table 4

Harvest Calendar

Crop	Harvest Period	Bulk of Harvest
Wheat	May–June	May
Barley	Apr.–June	May
Oats	May–June	May
Maize	Aug.–Sept.	. . .
Sorghum	July–Aug.	Aug.
Sugar beets	May–July	. . .
Sugar	Campaign starting in May	. . .
Potatoes	{ Nov.–Dec.	Dec. }
	Mar.–July	May–June }
Beets, fodder	May–Aug.	. . .
Onions	Jan.–Dec.	June–Aug.
Tomatoes	Jan.–Dec.	June–July
Cucumbers	May–Dec.	May–June
Melons, sweet	June–Oct.	Aug.
Watermelons	June–Oct.	Aug.
Cabbage	Sept.–May	Jan.–Mar.
Cauliflower	Sept.–May	Nov.–Mar.
Green peas	Feb.–May	Mar.–Apr.
Green beans	May–Dec.	June–Sept.
Carrots	Oct.–July	Dec.–Apr.
Dry peas	May	. . .
Broad beans	May	. . .
Chick peas	May–June	June
Lentils	May–June	May
Vetch	May–June	June
Apples	June–Sept.	July–Sept.
Grapes, table	May–Nov.	July–Aug.
Grapes, for wine	Aug.–Sept.	. . .
Oranges	Nov.–Apr.	Dec.–Mar.
Mandarins and tangerines	Oct.–Mar.	Nov.–Dec.
Grapefruit	Oct.–Mar.	Nov.–Mar.
Lemons	Jan.–Dec.	Nov.–Mar.
Figs	June–Dec.	Sept.–Oct.
Bananas	Jan.–Dec.	Dec.–May
Olives	Aug.–Jan.	Oct.–Nov.
Groundnuts	Sept.–Oct.	Oct.
Cottonseed	Aug.–Nov.	Sept.
Linseed	May–July	June
Sesame	July–Sept.	Aug.
Sunflower seed	July–Sept.	Aug.
Safflower	June–July	July
Tobacco	July–Oct.	Aug.
Cotton	Aug.–Nov.	Sept.
Flax	May–July	June

Source: F. A. O. World Crop Harvest Calendar, Rome, 1959.

Table 5

Livestock Holdings

Number and Type of Livestock on Jewish Farms—1948 to 1958
And on Other Farms, 1958

	Other Farming 1958	Jewish Farming									
		1958	§1957	1956	1955	1954	1953	1952	1951	1950	1948
Cattle											
TOTAL	(a)40,000	152,400	115,700	91,600	84,100	79,010	72,465	65,750	61,005	47,735	33,580
Cows	19,500 {	55,000	44,000	40,000	36,500	38,370	37,240	35,105	31,690	25,645	19,065
Heifers		15,000	12,000	8,000	8,000	8,450	8,050	8,470	9,980	6,200	4,540
Calves	16,500 {	43,000	32,400	28,500	28,200	26,840	23,710	20,215	18,000	15,100	9,615
Beef cattle		39,000	27,000	14,800	11,100	5,005	3,025	1,530	775	410	—
Bulls	4,000 {	400	300	300	300	345	440	430	460	380	360
Working oxen		—	—	—	—	—	—	—	—	—	—
Poultry											
Laying hens	200,000	5,500,000	4,000,000	3,500,000	3,100,000	3,300,000	2,800,000	2,470,000	2,643,000	2,912,000	1,426,000
Geese, ducks and turkeys	...	400,000	250,000	120,000	170,000	133,000	62,000	12,000	12,600	14,500	21,000
Sheep and Goats											
Sheep	74,000	117,000	112,000	102,000	90,000	75,000	61,000	49,000	43,500	37,000	22,000
Goats, thoroughbred	—	40,000	45,000	45,000	45,000	45,000	40,000	25,000	20,000	15,000	4,900
Goats, local	129,000	—	—	—	—	—	—	—	—	—	—
Work Animals											
Horses and mules	6,300	15,700	15,000	14,000	13,500	12,500	12,000	10,900	10,200	8,900	5,000
Asses	15,500	5,000	5,000	5,000	5,000	5,300	5,500	5,600	5,900	5,600	2,300
Camels	11,000	—	—	—	—	—	—	—	—	—	—
Beehives	(b)1,000	43,000	42,000	40,000	38,000	37,000	35,000	33,000	31,000	29,000	23,000

(a) Non-thoroughbred cattle.   (b) Except primitive hives.

Source: Statistical Abstract, 1958/59.

Table 6

Slaughterings in Slaughterhouses by District, 1957/58

(head—number; estimated live weight—tons)

	Southern District		Jerusalem District		Tel-Aviv District		Central District		Haifa District		Northern District		Total	
	Estimated Live Weight	Head	Estimated Live Weight	Head	Estimated Live Weight	Head	Estimated Live Weight	Head	Estimated Live Weight	Head	Estimated Live Weight	Head	Estimated Live Weight	Head
ALL LIVESTOCK	385	7,694	1,146	6,954	4,047	18,212	1,942	15,687	2,476	14,265	3,135	27,429	13,131	90,241
Cattle	156	592	996	2,870	3,887	12,182	1,005	4,067	1,885	5,090	755	2,758	8,684	27,559
Thoroughbred and mixed	100	306	747	2,044	3,403	10,146	792	2,898	1,534	3,874	545	1,675	7,121	20,943
Cows and Heifers	56	133	190	492	491	1,160	96	247	486	1,022	136	317	1,455	3,371
Bulls and Oxen	14	36	523	1,402	1,975	4,820	215	556	940	2,336	263	657	3,930	9,807
Young stock, male	20	83	31	135	772	3,281	449	1,910	78	344	122	560	1,472	6,313
Young stock, female	10	54	3	15	165	885	32	185	30	172	24	141	264	1,452
Local	46	256	121	485	261	1,314	184	1,107	171	777	192	1,022	975	4,961
male	36	193	95	364	231	1,116	170	1,036	140	613	140	677	812	3,999
female	10	63	26	121	30	198	14	71	31	164	52	345	163	962
Imports	10	30	128	341	223	722	29	62	180	439	18	61	588	1,655
male	4	12	114	305	212	682	29	62	125	297	7	23	491	1,381
female	6	18	14	36	11	40	—	—	55	142	11	38	97	274
Sheep and Goats	229	7,102	150	4,084	160	6,030	92	3,184	119	4,454	571	16,294	1,321	41,148
Sheep	108	3,112	102	2,947	156	5,934	77	2,732	102	3,925	425	12,639	970	31,289
matured, male	60	1,093	49	895	51	919	25	450	25	452	149	2,722	359	6,531
matured, female	15	368	24	600	10	247	13	333	16	404	155	3,846	233	5,798
lambs	33	1,651	29	1,452	95	4,768	39	1,949	61	3,069	121	6,071	378	18,960
Goats	121	3,990	48	1,137	4	96	15	452	17	529	146	3,655	351	9,859
matured, male	62	1,235	32	640	2	34	6	124	10	207	102	2,029	214	4,269
matured, female	33	923	15	438	1	25	8	230	4	115	34	935	95	2,666
kids	26	1,832	1	59	1	37	1	98	3	207	10	691	42	2,924
Other Livestock	—	—	—	—	—	—	845	8,436	472	4,721	1,809	8,377	3,126	21,534

Source: Statistical Abstract, 1958/59.

Table 7

Fishing Industry

Annual Catch: Quantity and Value: 1948/49 to 1957/58

	1957/58	1956/57	1955/56	1954/55	1952/53	1948/49
Quantity (Tons)						
TOTAL	12,350	11,400	10,900	11,000	7,600	3,500
Lake fishing	1,005	1,300	944	878	761	358
Inshore fishing	755	535	686	682	507	188
Pelagic fishing	1,125	615	500	319	319	
Deep sea fishing	1,615	1,640	1,383	1,826	1,302	445
Fish ponds	7,850	7,310	7,387	7,295	4,711	2,509
Value (IL. 1,000)						
TOTAL	17,471	14,494	11,995	11,566	7,861	1,584
Lake fishing	1,384	1,518	795	596	731	141
Inshore fishing	1,306	849	760	821	732	97
Pelagic fishing	956	445	285	161	158	
Deep sea fishing	1,685	1,264	960	1,135	952	139
Fish ponds	12,140	10,418	9,195	8,853	5,288	1,207

Source: Statistical Abstract, 1958/59.

Table 8

Foreign Trade in Agricultural Products: 1957 and 1958
Exports and Imports; Quantities and Values of Principal Commodities

Exports[a], by Class and Principal Commodities (IL. 1,000)

Commodity	Unit	1958		1957	
		Value	Quantity	Value	Quantity
TOTAL	—	252,747	—	§ 254,255	—
Class 1.—Food, Drink & Tobacco	—	115,273	—	§ 109,287	—
All citrus fruits in cases	Case	86,740	7,998,420	87,164	8,353,025
Oranges, Shamouti	"	57,732	5,196,654	59,682	5,611,533
Oranges, Valencia	"	15,308	1,375,224	12,156	1,144,929
Grapefruit	"	10,450	1,057,255	§ 12,831	§ 1,322,250
Lemons	"	2,045	204,285	1,622	170,263
Citrus fruits, other	"	1,205	166,002	873	104,050
Citrus fruits in gift parcels	Ton	195	398	206	541
Citrons	No.	239	39,498	194	36,587
Bananas	Ton	529	1,938	247	965
Melons and watermelons	"	207	1,444	63	326
Fruit juices	"	4,612	8,334	4,892	7,587
Concentrated, unsweetened	"	1,798	1,559	2,704	2,173
Natural, unsweetened	"	1,884	4,904	1,588	4,228
Sweetened	"	930	1,871	600	1,186
Vegetables, fresh	"	239	1,684	37	136
Wheat	"	1	1	4,548	26,799
Tomato juice and other tomato products	"	332	923	305	831
Groundnuts in shell	"	3,257	5,619	2,389	3,870
Fruits, preserved (incl. citrus by-products)	"	5,331	8,580	1,750	3,190
Olive oil & other oil, edible	"	1,498	2,387	2,772	3,303
Cauliflowers and Cucumbers, pickled	"	155	464	266	872
Eggs in shell	1,000	8,719	179,450	§ 1,130	§ 17,144
Meat and meat products	Ton	534	110	231	38
Cocoa powder	"	500	452	1,321	1,179
Chocolates and sweets	"	755	596	641	517
Chocolates	"	292	191	224	130
Chewing gum	"	191	123	159	87
Various sweets	"	272	282	258	300
Spirits	Litre	798	757,913	701	744,004
Other commodities of Class 1.	—	632	—	430	—

Table 8 (Continued)

Imports, by Class and Principal Commodities (IL. 1,000)

Commodity	Unit	1958		§ 1957	
		Value	Quantity	Value	Quantity
TOTAL	—	773,670	—	783,911	—
Class 1.—Food, Drink and Tobacco	—	155,478		139,204	—
Barley	Ton	2,556	23,732	4,695	41,628
Haricot beans	"	502	2,062	741	3,468
Maize	"	4,734	41,299	5,748	42,339
Millet, unhusked	"	24,058	243,710	10,885	98,380
Rice	"	1,523	6,823	3,016	11,747
Wheat	"	38,293	278,778	45,067	319,622
Cake and meal of fish & meat	"	6,013	22,565	4,875	17,694
Cake and meal of rape, soya, nuts, seeds and oil seeds	"	2,214	14,808	2,109	11,160
Meat, frozen and chilled	"	8,419	10,722	11,815	7,216
Corned beef, tinned	"	133	76	527	588
Cattle and buffaloes	No.	164	1,006	847	4,804
Butter	Ton	13,366	8,003	233	13
Cheese	"	3,872	3,671	2,024	2,107
Milk powder	"	6,421	12,899	2,255	8,603
Cocoa beans	"	942	572	743	662
Cocoa butter	"	1,320	430	1,002	453
Cocoa block, unsweetened	"	1,008	1,175	1,407	1,682
Coffee beans, raw	"	3,293	2,204	2,770	1,930
Nescafé	"	190	14	307	23
Herring in brine	"	1,624	6,632	1,073	4,307
Fish, frozen	"	907	1,611	242	728
Fish fillet, frozen	"	2,151	3,116	2,527	3,709
Cottonseed oil, edible	"	1,539	1,989	188	220
Edible fats	"	1,049	1,474	1,560	2,090
Sugar	"	11,765	66,324	14,261	51,637
Tea	"	1,715	764	2,102	891
Cotton, raw	Ton	9,074	6,501	4,190	3,117

Source: Statistical Abstract, 1958/59.

Table 9

Food Enterprises in Operation at the End of 1958

Product or Branch	Number of Enterprises
Noodles and other Pastry products	23
Citrus Packing Houses	137
Biscuits, etc.	17
Ice cream	138
Soda water	80
Fish Preserves	40
Sausages and Meat Products	58
Fruit Juices and Syrups	64
Sugar	2
Sweets	127
Jams and Marmalades	42
Fruit and Vegetable Preserves	47
Chocolate and Cocoa Powder	9
Flour Mills (including seasonal)	43
Coffee Roasting Establishments	133
Cold Stores	86
Oil Refining	11
Soap and Detergents	34
Milk Collection Centers	65
Dairies	48
Bakeries	849

Source: Israel Economic Forum, Vol. IX, 1958–1959.

Table 10

Food Processing Industries

Principal Categories of Processed Food Products: Quantities; 1949–1958

Food	Unit	1958	1957	1956	1955	1954	1953	1952	1951	1950	1949
Flour											
Standard	Ton	90,343	94,229	94,574	103,391	129,366	153,301	128,703	105,424	86,496	72,602
Other (2)	"	145,439	148,970	147,502	130,409	122,613	85,692	67,959	51,939	71,610	24,212
Groats	"	148	322	150	1,137	703	662	801	663	635	··
Burghul	"	276	376	560	648	736	799	909	994	153	··
Oats (Quaker)	"	216	307	403	409	461	796	··	··	··	··
Starch (Cornflour)	"	2,514	2,967	1,907	1,026	892	827	469	532	387	··
Starch (except cornflour)	"	990	1,066	1,035	669	492	66	150	132	214	··
Pudding	"	306	238	232	121	136	67	43	156	337	··
Biscuits	"	5,206	4,684	5,190	4,586	3,855	4,634	3,707	2,289	3,845	··
Waffles	"	1,453	1,226	§1,130	941	851	598	674	799	1,047	··
Noodles	"	8,415	8,621	§9,470	9,819	10,884	11,746	10,791	8,421	7,510	··
Matzot and matzot flour	"	6,337	6,092	5,839	5,464	5,346	4,367	4,952	4,478	3,550	··
Preserves and Juices											
Preserved fruit	"	12,046	5,043	§3,112	2,781	2,994	1,814	1,391	3,447	1,028	1,345
Jams and marmalades	"	5,003	6,519	5,925	7,222	7,403	8,044	5,085	4,495	3,729	2,427
Citrus concentrates (1:4—1:6)	1,000 litre	2,207	2,224	2,560	2,040	3,601	2,749	3,932	4,444	1,099	2,533
Pasteurized juice	"	3,332	3,388	4,834	1,906	1,639	7,462	13,888	··	··	··
Citrus fruit drinks	"	10,557	7,514	9,523	13,153	9,632	··	··	··	··	··
Grape juice	"	164	375	131	361	··	155	··	··	··	··
Citrus syrup	"	3,933	2,689	2,332	3,912	3,821	1,382	319	··	··	··
Syrup of other fruits	"	3,323	3,020	1,845	2,848	2,674	2,135	1,539	··	··	··
Synthetic syrup	"	308	356	287	168	137	122	691	··	··	··
Glucose	Ton	1,827	1,635	1,174	538	155	8	106	1,258	650	··
Fruit pulp	"	516	408	108	277	527	708	332	431	128	··

Table 10 (Continued)

	Unit	1949	1950	1951	1952	1953	1954	1955	1956	1957	1958
Food (continued)											
Preserved Vegetables	Ton	2,432	4,436	3,549	7,230	5,727	4,732	5,079	7,825	5,744	7,146
Tomatoes	"	705	778	548	3,039	2,264	2,144	1,777	3,166	2,028	3,794
Peas	"	415	127	322	718	1,132	1,286	1,667	1,729	1,409	1,812
Other vegetables	"	1,312	3,531	2,679	3,473	2,331	1,302	1,635	2,930	2,307	1,540
Pickled Vegetables	"	2,682	2,826	3,593	4,450	5,258	2,256	3,295	4,266	2,062	2,640
Cucumbers	"	1,335	2,235	2,065	3,190	3,524	2,130	2,470	3,254	1,261	2,109
Cabbage	"	674	528	937	664	1,516	56	631	413	700	386
Other vegetables	"	673	63	591	596	218	70	194	599	101	145
Pickled Olives	"	..	1,688	1,062	3,070	1,938	2,008	1,722	1,962	2,282	2,428
Milk and Milk Products											
Pasteurized milk	1,000 litre	—	—	—	—	—	—	4,144	37,322	55,789	76,949
Sterilized milk	"	—	—	—	—	—	—	783	3,239	2,587	2,709
Local butter	Ton	..	..	..	..	..	327	523	850	1,096	1,996
Sour cream	"	..	..	..	..	..	4,662	5,263	5,904	7,174	7,386
Sweet cream	"	..	..	..	..	..	351	314	427	396	430
Soft cheese	"	..	..	..	..	..	9,536	8,986	10,904	11,860	13,264
Salt cheese	"	..	..	..	..	..	1,485	1,488	1,415	1,572	1,523
Hard cheese	"	..	..	..	..	..	..	..	1,035	1,099	1,225
Boiled cheese	"	..	..	..	..	..	334	319	396	557	506
Leben	"	..	..	..	..	..	498	816	1,145	2,025	3,515
Lebenia	"	..	..	..	..	..	6,398	6,232	5,687	5,894	5,354
Yoghurt	"	..	..	..	..	..	..	..	602	916	740
Sugar											
Refined sugar	"	—	—	—	—	—	—	—	1,927	14,903	17,369
Molasses	"	—	—	—	—	—	—	—	2,222	3,589	5,276
Dry pulp	"	—	—	—	—	—	—	—	1,896	3,405	10,459
Chocolate and Sweets											
Chocolate	"	2,818	2,592	1,637	1,589	1,829	1,500	1,777	1,739	2,038	2,246
Chocolate spread	"	..	..	..	3	3	4	20	57	98	101
Sweets	"	3,530	4,381	2,919	2,640	3,301	3,651	4,822	5,909	6,347	7,610

	Unit										
Cocoa	Ton	356	796	669	687	612	784	..	..	..	..
Coffee	"	343	352	323	295	307	314	..	..	..	..
Coffee substitutes	"										
Oils											
Margarine	"	15,108	15,630	9,667	10,011	7,784	13,768	12,158	5,748	7,807	7,278
Refined Oils	"	26,332	23,861	21,809	17,688	14,219	16,346	17,152	11,749	12,546	10,617
Groundnut	"	199	371	2,473	1,058	6,554	—	443	1,569	313	618
Coconut	"	5,550	7,372	4,344	4,162	2,602	8,162	11,930	4,993	4,695	3,501
Cotton seed	"	1,338	1,868	4,232	818	339	601	828	1,168	3,289	2,642
Sesame seed	"	—	—	—	—	48	431	314	13	1,990	1,583
Sunflower seed	"	96	3,210	2,239	2,337	2,560	4,233	426	799	281	2,273
Safflower seed	"	—	205	264	190	90	81	95	1	54	—
Soya	"	17,026	10,810	8,243	8,746	1,648	2,836	3,116	3,206	1,924	—
Maize	"	109	13	14	4	22	2	—	—	—	—
Palm oil	"	41	12	—	373	356	—	—	—	—	—
Niger	"	1,973	—	—	—	—	—	—	—	—	—
Linseed oil, cooked	"	548	343	278	274	285	41	272	56	69	..
Essential oils	"	17	43	46	41	75	43	478	20	18	..
Tehina	"	1,220	913	580	395	321	327	159	190	527	1,479
Mayonnaise	"	519	561	480	426	480	581	706	365	616	444
Oil cake	"	107,731	79,257	59,458	57,012	29,182	29,352	38,227	23,744	14,886	15,423
Intoxicating Liquors											
Wine	1,000 litre	15,599	12,620	9,098	7,352	3,064	2,506	3,793	..	..	..
Beer	"	16,865	13,773	12,986	14,550	14,253	14,019	15,399	14,528	12,288	8,936
Arrack (marketing)	"	937	891	771	695	583	631	..	..	..	..
	1,000 lit. Alc.	415	399	358	317	269	295	..	..	..	..
Brandy (marketing)	1,000 litre	1,101	907	656	585	468	625	..	..	..	..
	1,000 lit. Alc.	438	380	262	231	189	250	..	..	..	..
Other spirits (marketing)	1,000 litre	1,270	1,037	882	926	1,008	952	..	..	..	..
	1,000 lit. Alc.	678	535	434	420	438	442	..	..	..	..

Source: <u>Statistical Abstract, 1958/59.</u>

Table 11

Consumption of Food Per Capita Per Year as Compared to Pre-war
Averages and Consumption in the United States and the United Kingdom

Consumption of Food Per Capita Per Year (Kg.)

	1957/58	1956/57	1955/56	1954/55	1953/54	1952/53	1951/52	1950/51	1949/50	1934–1938	U. S. (d)	U. K. (e)
Cereals and Cereal Products	123.6	138.7	141.0	140.8	152.5	151.0	146.7	133.1	131.2	115	69.0	88.4
Potatoes and Starches	41.3	46.1	43.8	43.5	38.6	31.3	46.6	41.8	46.3	12.6	48.9	98.5
Sugar and Honey	27.5	25.7	26.1	24.2	21.9	21.1	19.7	19.2	17.5	16.0	47.7	49.9
Pulses, Nuts and Oil Seeds	8.2	9.0	7.8	9.9	6.2	6.9	6.8	8.5	5.6	3.4(a)	7.2	6.3
Vegetables	122.8	117.1	117.2	114.4	113.7	121.0	112.5	103.1	111.1	55.0	98.0	58.5
Fruits (including watermelons and sugar melons)	118.3	115.6	115.3	100.3	116.4	118.3	124.8	103.9	107.9	138.0	81.5	45.7
Meat	25.9	22.0	21.6	18.3	11.2	10.5	10.7	14.9	18.6	12.5	81.5	63.7
Eggs	19.4	16.8	14.2	15.0	13.0	12.0	12.8	15.6	14.8	9.0	21.2	12.6
Fish	11.4	10.9	11.4	12.8	13.2	13.8	15.6	18.6	17.4	3.8	4.8	9.8
Milk and Milk Products	106.6	106.5	106.0	104.6	103.7	97.7	93.3	96.7	96.4	128.2(b)	194.7	157.7
Oils and Fats	17.3	16.2	18.0	18.2	17.5	16.0	16.0	17.0	15.5	3.0(c)	22.0	22.1
Miscellaneous	6.8	7.8	7.1	8.2	8.7	7.7	6.7	7.7	8.2			

Notes: (a) Pulses Only.   (b) Including Butter.   (c) Excluding Butter.   (d) Average, 1954–56.   (e) Average, 1954/55 to 1956/57.

Sources: Statistical Abstract, Israel, 1958/59.   F. A. O. Food Balance Sheets, 1954–56 Averages.

Table 12

Consumption of Calories Per Capita Per Day as Compared to
Consumption in the United States and in the United Kingdom

	Calories Per Capita Per Day (Number)										U. S. (a)	U. K. (b)
	1957/58	1956/57	1955/56	1954/55	1953/54	1952/53	1951/52	1950/51	1949/50		
TOTAL	2,755	2,846	2,876	2,860	2,849	2,736	2,706	2,677	2,610	3,150	3,250
Cereals and Cereal Products	1,187	1,331	1,353	1,351	1,463	1,450	1,408	1,277	1,260	689	862
Potatoes and Starches	95	101	93	90	78	66	93	91	98	95	182
Sugar and Honey	290	268	275	255	231	223	208	202	184	489	523
Pulses and Oil Seeds	97	108	96	114	73	73	70	86	62	75	67
Vegetables	72	66	69	69	69	70	66	62	65	72	40
Fruits (including watermelons and sugar melons)	124	118	116	102	117	101	116	107	105	115	81
Meat	114	105	99	87	50	49	54	75	95	574	519
Eggs	77	66	56	59	51	47	57	75	61	84	53
Fish	23	23	23	27	25	27	36	49	58	20	28
Milk and Milk Products	231	230	234	229	236	210	184	212	197	434	346
Oils and Fats	379	354	394	400	377	352	354	369	343	502	537
Miscellaneous	66	76	68	77	79	68	60	72	82		

Notes: (a) Average, 1954-56.   (b) Average, 1954/55 to 1956/57.
Sources: Statistical Abstract, Israel, 1958/59.   F. A. O. Food Balance Sheets, Averages 1954-56.

Table 13

Consumption of Protein Per Capita Per Day as Compared to
Consumption in the United States and the United Kingdom

Grams Per Capita Per Day

	1949/50	1950/51	1951/52	1952/53	1953/54	1954/55	1955/56	1956/57	1957/58	U.S. (a)	U.K. (b)
TOTAL	83.9	88.2	84.9	87.8	86.7	88.8	89.2	90.1	86.7	94.1	85.0
Thereof: from animals	32.2	33.7	26.2	26.0	27.6	29.9	30.5	31.5	33.6	66.0	48.9
Cereals & Cereal Products	41.4	42.9	47.3	51.4	48.5	45.5	46.4	45.8	40.9	16.2	25.2
Potatoes and Starches	2.2	2.0	2.2	1.4	1.8	2.1	2.0	2.1	1.8	2.3	4.6
Sugar and Honey	—	—	—	—	—	—	—	—	—	—	—
Pulses and Oil Seeds	3.2	4.9	4.2	4.1	3.8	6.1	5.0	5.6	4.8	4.6	3.4
Vegetables	2.9	2.8	3.0	3.1	3.1	3.1	3.2	3.3	3.5	3.6	2.1
Fruits (including watermelons and sugar melons)	1.8	1.6	1.8	1.6	1.7	1.8	1.9	1.6	1.9	1.3	0.8
Meat	7.4	6.0	4.2	3.9	4.3	7.0	7.9	8.4	9.4	31.9	21.3
Eggs	4.6	5.8	4.4	3.6	3.9	4.5	4.3	5.1	5.9	6.4	4.0
Fish	7.1	7.4	5.9	4.5	4.1	4.0	3.5	3.5	3.7	2.5	4.4
Milk and Milk Products	13.1	14.4	11.7	14.0	15.2	14.3	14.7	14.5	14.6	25.1	19.1
Oils and Fats	—	0.1	—	—	0.1	0.1	0.1	—	—	0.2	0.1
Miscellaneous	0.2	0.3	0.2	0.2	0.2	0.3	0.2	0.2	0.2	0.2	—

Notes: (a) Average, 1954–56.   (b) Average, 1954/55 to 1956/57.
Sources: Statistical Abstract, Israel, 1958/59.   F. A. O. Food Balance Sheets, Averages, 1954–56.

Table 14

Consumption of Fats

Fat per Capita per Day (Gm.)

(1949/50—1957/58)

	1949/50	1950/51	1951/52	1952/53	1953/54	1954/55	1955/56	1956/57	1957/58
TOTAL	73.9	74.4	68.2	68.3	75.3	82.2	82.9	80.0	83.5
Cereals & Cereal Products	5.4	5.5	6.1	6.2	6.3	5.7	5.7	5.6	5.0
Potatoes and Starches	0.1	0.1	0.1	0.1	0.1	0.1	0.1	0.1	0.1
Sugar and Honey	–	–	–	–	–	–	–	–	–
Pulses, Nuts and Oil Seeds	2.9	2.2	1.9	2.6	3.7	5.7	5.5	5.6	5.8
Vegetables	0.2	0.3	0.2	0.3	0.4	0.4	0.4	0.4	0.6
Fruits (including watermelons and sugar melons)	1.1	0.8	1.3	1.0	0.8	1.0	0.9	1.1	1.2
Meat	6.9	5.4	3.7	3.6	3.7	6.2	7.2	7.6	8.2
Eggs	4.4	5.4	4.1	3.4	3.7	4.3	4.0	4.8	5.5
Fish	3.3	2.0	1.1	0.8	0.8	0.9	0.8	0.8	0.8
Milk and Milk Products	9.3	10.0	8.9	9.7	12.0	11.6	12.6	12.6	12.3
Oils and Fats	39.0	41.9	40.3	40.1	43.0	45.4	44.8	40.4	43.2
Miscellaneous	1.3	0.8	0.5	0.5	0.8	0.9	0.9	1.0	0.8

Source: Statistical Abstract of Israel, 1958/59.

Table 15

Food Balance Sheet, 1957/58

Average Population: 1,987,000

(Quantities in metric tons unless otherwise specified)

Commodity	Production	Change In Stocks (a)	Foreign Trade Imports	Foreign Trade Exports	Available Supply	(b) For Industry And Not For Human Consumption	Food (Net)	Per Capita Supplies Kg. Per Year	Grams Per Day	Calories Per Day (No.)	Fat Per Day (gram)	Protein Per Day (grams)
Cereals & Cereal Products (c)												
Wheat	62,500	+16,358	287,880	5,050	328,972	36,225	(d)235,076	118.3	324.1	1,134	4.9	40.0
Rye	—	− 1,352	—	—	1,352	600	(e)489	0.2	0.5	2	—	—
Oats, flakes	260	—	—	—	260	—	260	0.1	0.3	1	—	—
Pearl barley	126	—	—	—	126	—	126	0.1	0.3	1	—	—
Rice, milled	1,350	+ 1,564	9,796	—	9,582	35	9,547	4.8	13.2	48	0.1	0.9
Buckwheat, hulled	—	—	125	—	125	—	125	0.1	0.3	1	—	—
Total Cereals & Cereal Products								123.6	338.7	1,187	5.0	40.9
Potatoes and Starches												
Potatoes	98,000	+ 3,000	8,038	1,327	101,711	23,349	78,362	39.4	107.9	76	0.1	1.8
Potato flour	1,053	+ 451	191	—	793	363	430	0.2	0.5	2	—	—
Cornflour	2,667	− 320	349	—	3,336	—	3,336	1.7	4.7	17	—	—
Total Potatoes and Starches								41.3	113.1	95	0.1	1.8
Sugar and Honey												
Sugar	11,778	+ 2,443	55,796	—	65,131	11,081	54,050	27.2	74.5	288	—	—
Honey	620	—	—	—	620	—	620	0.3	0.8	2	—	—
Total Sugar and Honey								27.5	75.3	290	—	—
Pulses and Oil Seeds												
Pulses edible, dry	3,230	—	3,680	(f) 35	6,910	760	6,150	3.1	8.5	30	0.3	1.8
Sesame seed	950	− 570	16	—	1,501	19	1,482	0.7	1.9	11	1.0	0.3
Groundnuts, shelled	8,250	− 3,450	—	3,650	8,050	2,064	5,986	3.0	8.2	45	3.6	2.1
Sunflower	1,500	− 1,250	—	—	2,750	45	2,705	1.4	3.8	11	0.9	0.6

Vegetables	268,750	—	877	5,800	263,827	19,797	244,030	[illegible]	[illegible]	[illegible]	[illegible]	[illegible]
Fruit												
Bananas	29,000	—	—	1,419	27,581	2,760	24,821	12.5	34.2	23	0.1	0.3
Citrus fruit												
Oranges	333,950	—	—	269,800	64,150	1,600	62,550	31.5	86.3	28	0.1	0.5
Grapefruit	62,900	—	—	51,400	11,500	300	11,200	5.6	15.3	4	—	0.1
Lemons	15,550	—	—	7,800	7,750	200	7,550	3.8	10.4	3	—	0.1
Other citrus fruit	23,100	—	—	3,800	19,300	500	18,800	9.5	26.0	8	0.1	0.2
Watermelons and Sugar Melons	59,200	—	—	1,450	57,750	1,600	56,150	28.3	77.5	10	—	0.2
Other Fruit												
Olives, edible	4,050	—	—	12	4,038	—	4,038	2.0	5.5	6	0.6	0.1
Grapes	47,900	- 547	—	165	48,282	26,350	21,932	11.0	30.1	19	0.1	0.2
Deciduous fruit	18,800	+ 2,644	—	—	16,156	—	16,156	8.1	22.2	12	0.1	0.1
Miscellaneous fruit	11,900	+ 1,058	—	50	10,792	—	10,792	5.4	14.8	7	0.1	0.1
Raisins, edible	165	+ 133	333	—	365	—	365	0.2	0.5	1	—	—
Other dried and preserved fruits	—	—	800	—	800	—	800	0.4	1.1	3	—	—
Total Fruit								118.3	323.9	124	1.2	1.9
Meat												
Beef, fresh and frozen	5,100	+ 2,163	9,550	—	12,487	—	12,487	6.3	17.3	38	2.9	2.6
Sheep and goats } Carcass Weight	820	—	—	—	820	—	820	0.4	1.1	3	0.2	0.1
Lambs and kids } Carcass Weight	1,175	—	—	—	1,175	—	1,175	0.6	1.6	2	0.1	0.2
Other meat } Carcass Weight	2,650	—	260	—	2,910	—	2,910	1.5	4.1	13	1.3	0.4
Offal and other edible parts of above mentioned animals	1,180	—	(g) 50	—	1,230	—	1,230	0.6	1.6	2	0.1	0.3
Poultry (dressed, not drawn)	31,800	—	—	20	31,780	—	31,780	16.0	43.8	53	3.4	5.4
Preserved	—	22	908	—	930	—	930	0.5	1.4	3	0.2	0.4
Total Meat								25.9	70.9	114	8.2	9.4
Eggs	48,950	+ 1,900	315	6,250	41,115	(h) 2,640	38,475	19.4	53.2	77	5.5	5.9
Fish												
Fresh (round weight)	12,350	—	—	10	12,340	—	12,340	6.2	17.0	8	0.2	1.5
Frozen and chilled (round weight)	—	—	542	—	542	—	542	0.3	0.8	—	—	0.1
Frozen and chilled (fillet)	—	+ 533	4,317	—	3,784	—	3,784	1.9	5.2	4	—	0.9
Salted and Miscellaneous	—	- 64	5,814	—	5,878	—	5,878	3.0	8.2	11	0.6	1.2
Total Fish								11.4	31.2	23	0.8	3.7
Milk and Milk Products												
Cow milk (thousand tons)	223,428	—	—	—	223,428	78,640	144,788	72.9	199.7	116	5.8	6.6
Sheep and goat milk (thousand tons)	42,920	—	—	—	42,920	14,162	28,758	14.5	39.7	30	1.9	1.6
Milk, whole, dried	—	- 60	215	—	275	55	220	0.1	0.3	1	0.1	0.1

Table 15 (Continued)

Commodity	Production	Change In Stocks (a)	Foreign Trade Imports	Foreign Trade Exports	Available Supply	(b) For Industry And Not For Human Consumption	Food (Net)	Per Capita Supplies Kg. Per Year	Grams Per Day	Calories Per Day (No.)	Fat Per Day (gram)	Protein Per Day (grams)
Milk, skim, dried	—	+ 2,026	12,416	—	10,390	7,781	2,609	1.3	3.6	13	—	1.3
Cheese, soft, skim milk	6,434	—	—	—	6,434	—	6,434	3.2	8.8	7	—	1.2
Cheese, soft, whole milk	6,574	—	—	—	6,574	—	6,574	3.3	9.0	14	0.8	1.2
Cheese, salted	1,585	+ 160	—	—	1,425	—	1,425	0.7	1.9	5	0.3	0.4
Cheese, processed	500	—	—	—	500	—	500	0.3	0.8	2	0.1	0.2
Cheese, other	1,212	+ 1,097	2,978	9	3,084	100	2,984	1.5	4.1	14	1.0	1.1
Cream	7,853	—	—	—	7,853	—	7,853	4.0	11.0	20	1.8	0.3
Leben	3,162	—	—	—	3,162	—	3,162	1.6	4.4	2	0.1	0.2
Lebenia and yogurt	6,331	—	—	—	6,331	—	6,331	3.2	8.8	7	0.4	0.4
Total Milk & Milk Products								106.2	292.1	231	12.3	14.6
Oils and Fats												
Vegetable oils, refined, edible	27,900	+ 388	3,400	800	30,112	13,448	16,664	8.4	23.0	203	23.0	—
Margarine	15,531	—	—	—	15,531	507	15,204	7.6	20.8	150	17.3	—
Butter	1,730	+ 7,250	8,078	—	2,558	24	2,534	1.3	3.6	26	2.9	—
Total Oils and Fats								17.3	47.4	379	43.2	—
Miscellaneous												
Chocolate and cocoa powder	2,989	—	—	971	2,018	—	2,018	1.0	2.7	13	0.8	0.2
Sweets	6,457	—	—	353	6,104	—	6,104	3.1	8.5	32	—	—
Jam	5,480	—	—	65	5,415	—	5,415	2.7	7.4	21	—	—
Total Miscellaneous								6.8	18.6	66	0.8	0.2
Grand Total										2,755	83.5	86.7
From Animals												33.6
From Vegetables												53.1

Notes: (a) A plus sign (+) indicates the increase in stocks at the end of the year over those at the beginning of the year, a minus sign (−) represents the decrease in stocks. (b) Including waste and quantities used for animal feed and seeds. (c) Maize, sorghum and oats do not appear in the balance sheet, since these were used chiefly for feeding animals, the products of the above commodities which were used for human consumption, such as cornflour, pearl barley and oats, appear as special items. (d) Wheat flour, extraction rate—80.3%. (e) Rye flour, extraction rate—65.0%. (f) Quantity used for the production of Halva for export. (g) Including offal from imported live animals slaughtered in local slaughterhouses. (h) Eggs for hatching.
Source: Statistical Abstract for Israel, 1958/59.

TURKEY

I. GENERAL REMARKS

A. AGRICULTURE IN TURKEY

Turkey occupies the large peninsula of Asia Minor, or Anatolia, and a small region in Europe, known as Thrace. The country is 1,500 km. long and 480 km. wide, and has a total area 776,980 sq. km. (300,000 square miles), about one tenth that of the United States. Roughly rectangular in shape, Turkey is bounded on three sides by the Black Sea, the Aegean, and the Mediterranean, and is bordered by Russia, Iran, Iraq, and Syria.

The Anatolian Peninsula, which comprises 97% of the total land surface, consists of a series of plateaus varying in altitude from 600 meters in the west to 1,800 meters in the east, surrounded by a chain of mountains. The climate of these plateaus varies but is generally continental in type with severe wet winters and hot summers. The climate of coastal areas generally is Mediterranean with milder temperature ranges.

Approximately 30% of the total land area is arable and probably 20% is under cultivation at any one time. The amount of land under cultivation has increased steadily from 12.9 million hectares in 1944 to 22.5 million in 1956, as shown in Table 1. The typical agricultural pattern is one of extensive cultivation on dry-farming lands, with cereals as the principal crops, but a variety of other agricultural products are grown in different regions. Agricultural techniques in general are still primitive with much hand labor. Mechanization is increasing but thus far is mostly limited to the new areas of cereal cultivation on the central plateau, where the terrain is adapted to such processes. An estimated 10 to 12% of the total cultivated area is farmed by mechanized means.

Animal husbandry is second only to cereal production as a source of farm income and is most extensively practiced on the Anatolian plateau. However, techniques are primitive, pastures are seriously overgrazed, and almost no forage crops are produced, so that livestock nutrition is at a low level.

Agriculture is the basis of Turkey's economy, and about three fourths of the population derive their livelihood from agricultural and pastoral pursuits, while many more persons are engaged in processing and marketing agricultural commodities. The farming population is scattered among 40,000 villages that are more or less isolated, especially at certain seasons of the year, by inadequate transportation. In contrast to the situation in most other Middle East countries, farms are owned by the cultivators so that the majority of the land is in the hands of small owners. The average area of these farms is small, 70% being less than 5 hectares in extent. These small farms are uneconomical to run, and attempts are being made to consolidate scattered holdings by redistribution of lands and the establishment of farmers' cooperatives to supply more efficient means of cultivation.

A major problem facing agriculture in Turkey, as elsewhere in the Middle East, is the scarcity and undependability of present water supplies. This problem is especially acute in Turkey since the major part of agriculture, as previously mentioned, is on a dry-farming basis. The extensive central plateaus, where a major portion of the cereal cultivation is carried out, has scanty rainfall and droughts are frequent, occurring on an average of once every five years. Extension of irrigation from the present limited acreage would end dependence on irregular rainfall, and would permit the growing of high-value cash crops that would provide the farmer with a higher income than the grain now farmed. Table 2 lists the irrigation programs completed or under construction as of 1957.

Extensive work in agricultural development is planned under the ten year agricultural development program announced in 1959. Major projects to be financed include irrigation and drainage projects, pest control, improvement in agricultural techniques, and the manufacture of fertilizer. Details of the plan are not available, nor is it known what effect if any the recent (1960) change in regime will have on the execution of these projects.

B. AGRICULTURAL REGIONS [4,8]

The large extent of Turkish territory, the wide range of climatic conditions, and the great variety of topographical features result in a number of well-defined geographical regions exhibiting great variations in their agricultural characteristics. Map 1 outlines these areas, which are discussed below.

One of the most important of the agricultural areas (Zone 7 on the map), is the Black Sea region that extends from the Russian border to Zanguldak on the Black Sea. Climate here is primarily maritime and the rainfall is heavy, decreasing from east to west. The cultivated coastal strip of this area produces hazel nuts, one of the most important export crops; citrus fruits also are grown, although climatic conditions are not too satisfactory. The Scharschamba plain is one of the

most important areas for the cultivation of maize. The maize grown
here feeds the population of both the hazel nut-growing and the tea-
growing district, where virtually no grain is produced. Tobacco is
grown on a large scale in the dryer and less fertile sites, especially
in the district of Bafra.

Another agricultural area is that around the Sea of Marmara (Zone
3), where the maritime climate of the Black Sea area gradually changes
into etesian. Rainfall here is extraordinarily low in summer. Wheat,
maize, sugar, beets, tobacco, sunflowers, olives, and livestock are the
main agricultural products. Large-scale fruit, vegetable, and, especially, grape-growing also are carried out here, chiefly for the Istanbul markets.

The region of the Aegean (Zone 2) has a moderate climate and almost completely dry summers. Both the coastal plains and the river
valleys reaching far inland are extraordinarily fertile. Green olives,
figs, and grapes grow on unirrigated land, and cotton, maize, and vegetables grow with irrigation. Smyrna figs, world famous, are grown
on a strip 100 by 10 km. in extent in the eastern section of the Great
Meander valley, while Sultanina grapes, which are dried into raisins
for export, grow in Gediz.

The southern region of Turkey (Zone 4) covers all of the southern
coast as far as the Gulf of Iskanderun. The most important areas
here, agriculturally, are the coastal plains of the Antlaya in the west
and the Cilician plains in the east. The Antlaya plain has a marked
subtropical climate. Rainfall is inadequate for intensive cultivation
but abundant rivers favor the development of irrigation. Citrus and
bananas and early vegetables are among the most important crops.
On the Cilician plains, conditions are less favorable for the production of fruits and vegetables, except in some sheltered coastal strips,
so the cultivation of wheat and cotton is predominant. This is also a
good region for the cultivation of fodder crops and maize and is therefore suited for the expansion of livestock production.

The central plateau of Anatolia includes five different economic
and geographic regions that may be considered jointly, since their
agricultural production is similar although there is considerable variation in climate. The most extreme climatic conditions prevail in
the center of the plateau, with very scanty rainfall. Rainfall is greater
in the peripheral areas of the plateau, making possible a crop rotation
system through which a grain crop can be followed by fodder crops
instead of by fallow, as is the case in the central plateau. In both
areas, grain is produced by dry-farming.

The cultivated area of the central plateau has been extended in
recent years, encroaching, in the process, upon grazing lands and
causing erosion problems. The rainfall of the plateau not only is
scanty, but also variable: it is estimated that there is drought one
year in five, relatively high precipitation another year, and scanty but

adequate rainfall the remaining three years of the five. The relation between yields per hectare and rainfall are clearly demonstrated in Graph 1, which correlates rainfall and wheat production in the Ankara experimental farm from 1941 to 1956. On this farm, where production techniques, soil cultivation, plant protection, and quality of seeds used were all optimal, yields ranged between 400 kg. per hectare in drought years and 1,700 kg. per hectare in years with particularly good rainfall; i. e., rainy years gave four times the yield of drought years.

II. FOOD RESOURCES

A. GENERAL

Both agriculture and animal husbandry contribute to food supplies although the amount and type of food stuff produced varies with the year and with the regions of the country. The latest available data on area planted and production of the principal crops are presented in Table 3, while data on livestock products are discussed below.

A typical farm in Turkey on the Anatolian plateau would comprise approximately 8 to 10 hectares. The owner might have had a couple of years in school, his wife would have had none, and they would work the farm together with their children. They might have a team of horses doing most of the work of plowing and they might get help for a short time from a hired tractor. In addition to the land, they would own 20 sheep and two cows that would graze the village communal lands or the fields that are left fallow. The grass never gets high enough for the animals to be satisfactorily fed, because these pastures are heavily over-grazed, due to the system providing that the first owner that comes is the first served. In addition, the family might own 12 to 15 chickens, supplying 550 eggs and 35 chicks. Such a family would have an annual income of between $280 to $300, and would be permanently in debt for about $175.[6]

Most crops are harvested in June, July, and August, although some fruits and a few other crops are harvested in late fall. Table 4 lists the harvest seasons for each of the principal crops grown.

B. CEREALS

The production of cereals is the mainstay of the national food supply and of the agricultural economy. Almost 90% of the total cultivated area is devoted to grain products; of this amount, 59% is in wheat and 21% in barley.[11] Besides wheat and barley, rye, oats, rice, maize, millet, and sorghum also are grown.[1] Acreage and production of ce-

reals are shown in Table 3, while a brief discussion of the most important cereals grown is presented below.

Production and marketing of cereals is carried out by **Toprak**, an
autonomous agency reporting to the Minister of Economy. This office
has been responsible for administering support prices for grain, for
purchase of grain from farmers to supply urban centers, and for ex-
ternal trade in cereals.

Wheat is the major cereal and the most important crop in the economy of Turkey.[1] During 1958 there were 7,681,000 hectares planted
to wheat, and total production reached 7,998,000 tons. Durum wheat,
which constitutes 60% of wheat marketed, is produced in coastal areas,
the interior of Thrace, southeastern Anatolia, and along the periphery
of the central plateau. The interior of the central plateau is the principal soft-wheat producing region and this is the type of wheat principally consumed in rural areas. This central region is the one in
which the greatest expansion of crop land occurred up to 1953, an expansion which amounted to 43% of the period prior to 1948. Most of
the new area was grazing land and it was farmed by mechanized means.
The increase in acreage was concomitant with and spurred by an unusual cycle of good weather, and resulted in an extremely high production of wheat that allowed Turkey to export large quantities of this
grain. A drought on the Anatolian plateau in 1954, however, completely
reversed this favorable picture, and within the period of one year
Turkey shifted from a major exporter of grain to a sizable importer
and has had to import wheat every year since 1954 in order to fulfill
domestic demands.[15] The fluctuations in the imports and exports of
wheat are of interest, reflecting the variation in crop yields during
those years:

Trade in Wheat: 1953-1958

Year	Imports			Exports		
	Hard	Soft	Total	Hard	Soft	Total
1953	0	0	0	240.4	360.1	600.5
1955	3.6	218.9	222.5	83.8	75.1	158.9
1956	35.5	150.0	185.5	136.7	38.8	175.5
1957	37.6	397.5	435.1	0	0	0
1958	10.0	49.7	59.7	22.3	7.9	30.2

As seen above, exports dropped from 600,500 metric tons in 1953
to zero in 1957, while imports, which were zero in 1953, amounted to
435,100 tons in 1957.

The area planted to barley is about one third as extensive as wheat
plantings; during 1958 a total of 2,700,000 hectares were planted,
principally in the central plateau, and production reached 3,600,000

metric tons. Barley is used principally for livestock feed and often is preferred to wheat by the farmer because it is less susceptible to failure in years of low rainfall and grows well on alkaline or saline land.

Planting of rice is limited to coastal regions and other areas where irrigation is abundantly available. It is a very popular food but, outside of cities or of districts in which it is grown, it is more or less of a luxury.[9] Production in 1958-1959 was estimated at 75,000 tons and for 1959-1960 at 90,000 tons.

Millet is grown in the eastern section of the country where the climate is severe and the growing season short. A total of 50,000 hectares were planted to millet in 1958 with a yield of 65,000 metric tons. Negligible amounts were used for food, the crop being grown primarily for feed.

Maize is planted along the Black Sea coast and in the western and Mediterranean regions. During 1958 some 690,000 hectares were sown, producing about 900,000 metric tons of corn.[3] Approximately one half of the crop is used for animal feed and the remainder for food.

C. OTHER EDIBLE CROPS

1. **Vegetables and legumes.** Many vegetables are grown in all parts of the country and average production in 1954-1957 was estimated at 2,690,000 metric tons per year. In addition there were approximately 100,000 acres planted to potatoes,[8] and production was estimated at 1,069,000 tons in 1954-1957 and 1,200,000 in 1958-1959. The most important vegetables in terms of acreage planted and production include onions, tomatoes, peppers, and squash.[8]

Distribution and availability of vegetables follows a seasonal pattern: tomatoes, egg plants, green beans, cucumbers, green peppers, and okra are the most popular summer vegetables, while leeks, spinach, potatoes, cabbages, carrots, and celery are available in winter.[11]

The most popular and commonly grown legumes used as food include haricot beans (dry beans), chick peas, lentils, broad beans, and peas. Total production in 1954-1957 was estimated at 305,000 tons a year. Production in 1958 had risen to about 400,000 tons, so it is possible that there has been a slight increase in consumption in the past two years as compared with the 1954-1957 estimates.

2. **Fruits.**[1] The extremely wide range of climatic and topographic conditions allows the cultivation of a variety of fruits. Pome fruits, such as apples, are grown primarily in the Black Sea mountain areas and in central Anatolia.[7] Stone fruits, including peaches and cherries, are grown throughout Turkey, especially around Duzce in the Black Sea mountains and in the Sakarya Valley.[7] Among the nut fruits, hazel nuts are grown extensively along the Black Sea coast and pistachios in

southeastern Turkey around Gaziantep. Hazel nuts are important both
in domestic consumption and as export items. Production is apt to
fluctuate considerably from year to year;[7] for example, yields between
1946 and 1955 varied from 26,057 tons in 1950 to 123,141 in 1954 with
a yearly average of 71,622 tons.[4] Production in 1958-1959 was 55,000
tons and in 1959-1960 was estimated at only 30,000 tons.[13] Walnuts
are grown almost throughout the country and, together with other nuts
of various kinds, are important export crops.

Grapes are common in most parts of the country and raisins are an
important export item. Grapes are eaten fresh, as raisins, or are
used in making wine or grape juice (**pezmez** or **pegmeg**). In general,
wine and table grapes are grown in Marmara, Thrace, central Anatolia,
and the southeast.[8] The seedless varieties used in making raisins are
particularly common along the Aegean.

Citrus fruits, mostly oranges, grow along the Mediterranean and
Black Sea coasts.[8] Citrus production is increasing in the southern
regions, especially in Merzin and Antlaya, and declining in the Black
Sea area, where climatic and soil conditions are not as favorable.
The number of trees in the Black Sea area declined from 350,000 in
1946-1947 to 159,000 in 1953, while in the south they increased from
3,230,000 to 6,000,000 in the same period. Production of oranges,
mandarins, and clementines amounted to 249,000 tons in 1957 while
2,000 tons of grapefruit and 63,000 tons of lemons, limes, and other
citrus fruits were grown.

Figs are cultivated along the Aegean coast in Izmir and Aydin and
olives in both the Aegean and Mediterranean, with lesser groves in
the southeast. Some 482,000 tons of olives were harvested and 9,000
tons of olive oil were produced in 1958. Bananas are cultivated on a
very small scale on the Mediterranean coast, primarily in the regions
of Antlaya and Anamur.

The total annual production of fruits for the years 1954 to 1957 is
contrasted below with production in 1958-1959 and estimated production in 1959-1960:

	average 1954-1957	1958-1959	1959-1960 estimate
	(in 1,000 metric tons)		
Fresh fruits	1,355	3,081	2,746
Dried fruits	185	89	112
Citrus fruits	134	245	228
Nuts	187	130	108

3. **Oil-bearing seeds.** Oil-bearing crops grown include cottonseed,
sesame, sunflower, and soybean seeds, and peanuts.[1] The area and
production of each type of seed during 1958 is listed in Table 3 and
amounted to 491,000 metric tons, of which 319,000 were cottonseed.

Some 58,000 tons of edible vegetable oils were produced yearly between 1954 and 1957.

4. **Sugar crops.** Sugar beets are the most important sugar crop and their cultivation is undergoing rapid expansion.[8] The production of sugar beets is largely controlled by a company that enjoys some government subsidies.[8] The corporation owns ten factories in central Anatolia, with the main plant located at Eskisehir. Some sugar cane is grown near the Mediterranean coast, but cultivation is not extensive.[8] Production of beet sugar in 1959 amounted to 507,000 metric tons, as compared with 161,000 tons averaged during the period 1948-1952.

5. **Tea.** Tea is grown in the high rainfall areas of the Black Sea coast around Rize.[8] Production has increased from 30 kg. in 1938, when the first cultivation trials were carried out, to 10,976 metric tons of green leaf in 1957, which produced 2,414.7 tons of tea. Plantings are subsidized by the government.

D. CASH CROPS

1. **Cotton.** Cotton is the most important fiber crop although lesser quantities of flax and hemp also are grown.[8] Cotton is cultivated primarily in the Izmir, Aegean, and Adana regions, although there are four smaller producing areas, Sakarya, Malabya, Igdir, and Antlaya. The area planted to cotton in 1959 amounted to 617,000 hectares (unofficial figures) and production totaled 180,000 tons of cotton lint. Yields per acre are relatively low, more so in the Adana area.

2. **Tobacco.** The Oriental type of tobacco (Turkish tobacco) grown in Turkey has always been an important crop and one of the chief sources of foreign credit, since large quantities are exported. The United States is the biggest buyer of Turkish tobacco and normally takes about three fourths of the export crop.

Acreage planted to tobacco has increased from an average of 56,000 hectares between 1934 and 1938 to an average of 124,000 hectares in 1946 to 1950, while production increased from 72,000 to 95,000 metric tons. During 1958 the cultivated area amounted to 168,000 hectares and production reached 106,100 tons.

E. ANIMAL PRODUCT RESOURCES

Animal husbandry is second only to cereal production in the agricultural economy of Turkey but it is still carried out, for the most part, at a very primitive level.[8] Pastures are poor, rainfall scanty, and the climate severe, so that the numbers of livestock of all types are limited by the low levels of nutrition. Animals feed in summer on the weeds growing on fallow lands near villages and on available pas-

tures. When the cereal crops are harvested, livestock is fed on the
stubble, while winter feeding is supplemented with straw, hay, and
barley. The use of beet sugar residue as fodder for livestock recently
has been introduced with the cooperation of the USOM in Turkey, and
may improve livestock nutrition.

Another factor that damages the livestock industry has been the
extension of cereal cultivation onto grazing lands, which decreased
pastures from 32 million hectares in 1944 to 23.1 million in 1956.
Despite the decreased pasturage the total number of animals has increased, existing at an even lower level of nutrition than heretofore.

Livestock raising is carried out throughout Turkey, but the largest
livestock-producing areas are in central and eastern Anatolia. Species kept include cattle, sheep, goats, and buffaloes, while work animals include horses, mules, asses, and camels. There are very few
pigs since the Moslem religion interdicts their use as food. Poultry
raising is common, with chickens and turkeys the prevailing varieties.
Below are the latest available estimates of the kind and number of
livestock.[3]

Animal	Date	Number
Cattle	1958–1959	12,484,000
Sheep	"	30,823,000
Goats	"	24,233,000
Buffaloes	1957–1958	107,500
Horses	"	1,291,000
Mules	"	138,000
Asses	"	1,778,000
Camels	"	66,000
Chickens	1958–1959	26,320,000
Turkeys	"	1,602,000

Cattle are used primarily as draft animals but also for milk and
meat.[4] Cattle strains that have been developed are those which can
endure the often harsh climate and poor feeding conditions, at times
deteriorating into near famine. As a result, Anatolian steppe cattle
are of small build, with a short lactation period and low milk yields.

Only fat-tailed sheep can be successfully raised under feeding conditions prevailing in the central plateau,[4] which is the principal sheep-
raising area. During the months when pastures are green these sheep
are able to accumulate a food reserve by means of which they can survive the months of fodder shortage. This layer of fat weighs an average of 4 to 12 kg. and may even reach 20 kg. This type of sheep constitutes approximately 70% of the total sheep population; the remaining
30% are of the long-tailed variety.

Goats are kept by villagers as a supplementary source of meat and milk, but they cause great damage to pastures and, as elsewhere in the Middle East, are one of the chief causes of the extensive erosion and deforestation so common in the area.[8]

Water buffaloes are raised chiefly along the Black Sea coast, in the northern region of central Anatolia, and in Thrace.[8]

Large numbers of chickens are kept by farmers but rarely on a commercial scale. Production of eggs in 1958 was estimated at 1238 million, equivalent to 61,900 tons.

The poor level of nutrition of livestock results in extremely poor meat yield per head.[7] Available figures for meat production refer only to inspected meat at slaughterhouses, and amount to 136,000 metric tons in 1958, of which 66,000 were beef and veal and 70,000 were mutton and lamb.[3] The actual production of meat, taking into account animals slaughtered on farms, probably is much higher and more predominantly mutton and goat. Total meat production between 1954 and 1957, including the above kinds of meat, as well as poultry, rabbit, and game, was estimated at 389,000 tons.

The poor quality of native herds of cows, sheep, goats, and buffaloes, and the accompanying characteristic low milk yields, make it impossible for the majority of villagers to obtain a year-round supply of milk. Except for a few dairy herds in the vicinity of large cities, cattle are not kept primarily for milk but are general purpose animals supplying draft power for the farms, some milk for domestic use, and a calf to sell for meat or to keep for work. Under these circumstances milk yields generally are low. The same applies to sheep and goats, which furnish milk, wool, meat, and hides. Lambs are sold as soon as possible after birth so that the ewes may be milked.

The production and processing of milk still is carried out largely along primitive lines. Most of the milk produced is sold and consumed locally, and there are few facilities for storing, transporting, handling, and processing milk. Much of the milk consumed on farms is converted to fermented milk products, cheese, or butter, all of which have better keeping powers than fluid milk.[12] Total production of milk in 1954-1957 was estimated at 1,866,000 metric tons of whole milk, 1,249,000 of skim milk, and 78,000 tons of cheese. Production in 1958 was estimated at 1,814,000 tons, and it rose to 2,349,000 in 1959.

Turkey has a coast line 7,126 km. in length and includes some 25,760 hectares of lakes, so that fisheries are one of the most important natural resources of Turkey and could be developed to supply adequate amounts of animal proteins, which the diet sorely lacks. The average yearly catch is about 115,000 metric tons, of which about 20% is caught in inland waters, but production may vary widely from year to year. The bulk of the catch consists of migratory pelagic species and the fishing is divided into distinctly separate seasons. Fishing as an industry is more highly developed in the Black Sea and the Sea of Marmara, which supply about 90% of the fish caught. An estimated 25,000 men are engaged in the fishing industry and some 6,000 boats are in use, of which 1,230 were motorized as of 1959. About 15% of the fish catch is exported and 10% converted to fish meal and oil. The remainder is sold in domestic markets, principally in Istanbul.

A great variety of fish are caught in Turkish waters, the most abundant being anchovies (**hamsi**) and horse mackerel (**istavrit**), which together make up about one half of the total catch in a normal year. Anchovies are very delicate and perishable because of their small size and their high oil content; they therefore are a very difficult fish to process and must be marketed and consumed without delay. Horse mackerel is the second largest catch, most of it landed in Trabzon. It is a good fish for fresh consumption but it spoils quickly and must be marketed without delay. However, since it is not as delicate as are anchovies, it can be refrigerated, stored, and even frozen. This species also is used for making fish meal and oil.[1] Mackerel and bonito are caught during their annual migrations in and around the Bosphorus. The small bonito, up to 0.5 kg. called **pelamut** or **palamut**, is not processed and is often very cheap and difficult to dispose of; the larger bonito, called **torik**, is a popular variety and keeps well when frozen. The annual catch is apt to vary widely, in some seasons as much as 30,000 to 40,000 tons may be caught while in others the catch is nil. Mackerel (**uskumru**) is very popular and one of the cheapest fishes, about 2,000 tons being caught per year. Spanish mackerel, **kolyos**, is caught in the Sea of Marmara during the summer, when other fish are in short supply. At present, most of the Spanish mackerel is exported to Greece, where is it salt cured. Tuna is available, but only in small quantities, and most of the supplies are canned. Turbot (**kalkan**) is a valued fish caught in many places at almost any time of year, so that supplies are relatively steady in contrast with those of migratory fishes. Swordfish is caught mostly in the Sea of Marmara at different times of year. The sardine catch is probably about 200 tons per year, of which a small portion is canned for domestic consumption.[1]

The Fish and Meat Office of the Government (**Et ve Balik Kurumu**) is in charge of developing fisheries and operating cold storage plants, fish canneries, and freezing plants. It also carries out research on fishing operations. Fish is consumed fresh or canned, and a relatively large amount is salted locally or exported fresh for salting in Greece.

F. EXPORTS AND IMPORTS

The export of agricultural products constitutes a major portion, 82 to 90%, of the value of Turkey's export trade, as may be seen from Table 5, which lists trade by principal commodity groups between 1946 and 1958. Export items include tobacco, raisins, figs, filberts and other nuts, mohair, and carpet wool.

Tobacco is the most important export item and its value amounted to 34.1% of the total value of exports in 1958. The recent increase in sugar production has meant an increase in exportable surpluses. Thus, although only 15,100 tons of sugar were exported in 1958, some 101,500 tons of a total production of 507,000 tons were exported in 1959. Filberts (hazel nuts) amounted to 12.0% in value of total exports, while raisin and dried fig exports totaled 7.6 and 1.5% of export value, respectively. Most of the exports were to Western Europe and the United States, although trade with Communist countries was increasing in volume and importance. During 1956 this trade accounted for 20% of total exports and had risen to 23% in 1958.

Under normal conditions and in a reasonably good crop year Turkey imports very few food items and exports a great many. Agricultural products imported include fine wool, jute, tea, coffee, cocoa, and small amounts of other foods. In recent years there have also been substantial imports of fats and oils. Wheat, barley, and other food grains are exported during years of good cereal harvests and imported in poor crop years. The variation in the cereal trade can be considerable, as was shown above.

Approximately 30% of Turkey's limited agricultural imports come from the United States, and include all the soybean oil, cottonseed oil, wool, wheat, corn, and dairy products imported to satisfy domestic requirements. Agricultural products accounted for only 12% of total import trade in 1958.

A large part of Turkey's agricultural trade is now covered by various types of bilateral agreements, which may take the form of a rather general agreement listing the products to be bought and sold, with some measure of quantities.

Exports were encouraged until recently by export subsidies that, until 1957, were allowed on cotton, raisins, olive oil, fruits, vegetables, meat, and other items. These subsidies had all been discontinued by 1960. Imports are discouraged and an import tax is imposed on a variety of items. Table 6 presents the principal agricultural imports and exports of Turkey as of 1958.

G. INTERNATIONAL TECHNICAL AID PROGRAMS

The agricultural development of Turkey has been helped by economic and technical aid received from American and international agencies, including especially those belonging to the United Nations.

The Food and Agriculture Organization of the U. N., for example, has carried out projects on plant production and protection, animal disease control, rural welfare, fisheries development, and development of forest resources. One of the pilot project areas established by the Mediterranean Development Project of the FAO is located in the Antlaya area of southern Anatolia. The project area includes 3.6% of the total area of Turkey and 2.3% of its population. The development work to be done by this pilot project is financed through a United Nations Special Fund.

The United States program offering economic and technical aid to Turkey has been in operation since 1948; by 1957 a total of $113 million of $526 million in economic aid funds and $2.6 million of a total of $14.9 million in technical cooperation funds had been expended in agricultural development. Projects financed with these funds include agricultural extension programs, construction of grain storage and marketing facilities, and mechanization of agricultural techniques.

H. FOOD INDUSTRIES, STORAGE AND TECHNOLOGY

1. Food processing. Several large food-processing establishments and many smaller ones are in operation in Turkey, some privately owned and others that are government institutions. A great range exists in the size of factories, the quality and extent of modernization of equipment, and the hygienic conditions under which operations are carried out. One of the factors that most influences the variable quality of the finished product is the poor handling of raw materials used in the factories. Perishable foods sold in markets often are of low quality, owing to wasteful methods of handling and lack of preservation and sanitation facilities.[5] In Istanbul, for example, the fish catch normally is sold at auction at a central market and then is transported over considerable distances to processing plants. Fish are inspected at markets but are not graded and, in general, only fish that are completely spoiled are rejected. Transportation to canning factories often is carried out under such unfavorable conditions that fish of good quality, when purchased, may spoil before processing.

The main types of food-processing activities in Turkey and the annual production capacity as of 1957 were:

Type	Production capacity
Fruit and vegetable canning	2,927,000 tins
Flour mills	951,560 tons flour
Vegetable oil milling (edible)	34,010 tons oil
Citrus fruits	1,500,000 cases citrus fruits
Flour products	3,528 tons macaroni
	300 tons biscuits
Confectionery	1,152 tons **taheen**
	2,100 tons **halvah**
	1,440 tons Turkish Delight
	600 tons jam

Forty-three canning factories,[4] as listed in Table 7, are in operation, most of them in the Istanbul area where there is a supply of raw
materials and a good market for the finished product. A secondary
center for processing fruits and vegetables is in the Bursa area.
Other important factories are located in Ismir, in Gelibolu, and in
some towns on the Black Sea coast; in eastern Turkey there are only
two or three factories. The distribution of these factories is shown
on the map.

Canneries in Istanbul generally are located in old and unsuitable
buildings not primarily designed for use as factory buildings. The
same holds true for Bursa, Canakkale, and Gelibolu, although factories in these centers usually are better located than in Istanbul. Most
of the canneries are poorly equipped and some of the machinery is old
and obsolete.

Except for one new canning factory devoted to fish canning on the
Isla of Marmara, all canneries handle a variety of products. In the
summer they process peas, beans, tomatoes, green peppers, cucumbers, okra, artichokes, egg plants, pumpkins, green vine leaves,
mushrooms, and rice, as well as peaches, apricots, apples, plums,
oranges, strawberries, and cherries. Fish are canned in the autumn
and winter in canneries located near the coast. In most canneries,
fruits and vegetables are the main products and fish is canned only
when there is an abundant supply both of fish and tinplate, which often
is in short supply. The most commonly canned fish are sardines,
mackerel, bonito, and tuna. Total production is estimated at 15 million cans per year.[14]

A large proportion of the fish catch is frozen. Facilities for freezing foods are discussed under cold storage and refrigeration below.

There are in operation at least 11 large flour mills, of which seven
are reported to be entirely modern. However, much of the wheat is
still ground in numerous small mills throughout the country. These
small mills produce a high-extraction flour of excellent nutritive
value.

The drying of fruits and other agricultural products as a method
of preserving them for storage or export has been traditional for
centuries, but modern facilities are practically nonexistent. This is
especially true of the drying of vegetables. Dried fruits, such as raisins, apricots, and others are an important item of export and a constituent of the diet in winter months. Some dehydrated soup mixtures
are produced and marketed, but they are expensive, of poor quality,
and improperly packaged.

The first sugar beet factories were constructed in 1926. Since
then 13 new factories have been built, including 11 constructed in connection with Turkey's agricultural expansion program. Sugar production amounted to 380,000 tons in 1958 and rose to 507,000 in 1959,
enough to satisfy domestic demands and leave an exportable surplus.

Dispatching slaughterhouses have been built in Erzurun and Konya, and from here the carcasses are transported in refrigerated cars to Istanbul (see map).[4] The capacity of the slaughterhouse at Erzurun is 500 head of cattle and 3,000 sheep.[15] These installations are two of the four ultramodern plants that have been built and were in operation as of 1958.[8] All were working below capacity since these plants were designed for a livestock industry much more highly developed than Turkey's is at present.

Four modern milk pasteurizing plants have been built in recent years in the largest cities. There are also two modern milk-processing plants, plus recombining plants operated by the United States Military Mission to Turkey. Most of these plants are not operating to capacity. As in the case of the meat-processing plants described above, they are designed for a dairying industry more highly developed than Turkey's is at present.[15]

The preservation of food for use in the home is traditional and, in some sectors, essential, because of the difficulties in transporting and distributing food and the scarcity of supplies in the unusually long winters. Many methods are in use, in most cases carried out in accordance with long-established usage, often following family recipes handed down for generations.

Meat is preserved either as **kavourma** or **pastourma**; the former is made by browning meat in fat and storing it covered with fat; the latter is a smoked meat preparation flavored with tomato, paprika, and garlic. Vegetables may be dried, salted, or, especially in the eastern part of Turkey, pickled. Cabbages, turnips, peppers, spinach, and parsley often are dried. Tomato paste is prepared and dried in the sun. Fruits are preserved by being sun dried (e.g., figs and grapes), compoted in thick syrups, or made into dried fruit pastes. Bunches of grapes also are hung to dry on rafters. Fats are preserved by clarifying or rendering, which enhances their keeping qualities. Milk is converted to a variety of dairy products with increased keeping qualities, including cheese, yoghurt, and many others.[5,10]

2. **Storage and refrigeration.**[4] With the establishment of **Toprak** the Turkish Government assumed control over the marketing, storage, and transportation of grain in an attempt to accumulate grain stocks sufficient to offset the effects of fluctuations in harvest yields. The total capacity of grain storage facilities was increased from 45,000 tons in 1938 to 986,000 tons in 1955. During the last decade a commercial grain storage program has increased available storage to an estimated 2 million tons. Low crop yields in recent years and large domestic demands have delayed the accumulation of a grain reserve and, as of April, 1957, there were in storage only an estimated 45,000 tons, practically all of which was imported wheat. Delays and difficulties in handling imported wheat have been caused by the fact that port facilities, such as the terminal grain silo of 34,000 ton capacity

in Istanbul, were designed during the pre-1954 period of large grain
harvests and export surpluses and were therefore equipped for exporting grains but did not possess facilities for handling incoming
grain from ships.[15] Graph 2 shows the increase in grain storage
capacity between 1952 and 1958.

The expansion of grain storage facilities has been accompanied by
the construction of silos, of facilities for aerating, fumigating, and
cleaning grain, and by a conversion to handling of grain in bulk instead of by bag or sack. Map 2 shows the distribution of mechanized
grain silos in Turkey.

Most of the cold-storage facilities are owned and operated by the
government corporation that controls the production and marketing of
fish. Plants are of two types, those for making ice and providing cold
storage only and those that, in addition, have freezing plants and facilities for frozen storage. The former type faciltitates the distribution
of catches by supplying ice and refrigerated storage, while the latter,
in addition, preserves the peak supplies of the fishing seasons that
cannot be marketed fresh. Most of the frozen fish is exported and no
attempts have been made to distribute frozen products in the country,
primarily because there are no facilities for distributing retail supplies and shops are rarely equipped for dealing in frozen foods. The
location, ice-making capacity, cold-storage capacity, and freezing
facilities of plants in Turkey are shown in Table 8, and the location of
these plants is marked on Map 1. The most frequently used species
for freezing include bonito, tuna, horse mackerel, swordfish, and carp.
Storage temperatures of freezing plants seldom is below − 15° C., a
temperature too high to allow fish to be kept frozen for long periods.[14,1]

III. DIET TYPES

A. GENERAL

Cooking habits play an important part in the selection of the diet
and, in turn, cooking methods in use are dictated primarily by the
shortage of and high cost of fuel. This shortage probably is responsible for the almost universal practice of cooking enough at one time to
cover the needs of an entire day. The custom of serving cooked vegetables in a cold salad and of eating many other foods cold is probably
related to this shortage. One-dish meals, in which all the ingredients
are cooked in the same pot, are popular. Breakfast usually consists
of coffee, bread, and perhaps olives with cheese; lunch is a light meal
and often consists of reheated left-overs from the previous evening's
meal. The evening meal generally is the most important of the day.

The latest available information on diets in Turkey is presented

in Table 9, which contains a food balance sheet for the years 1954 to
1957. The production, imports, exports, and net food consumption of
a large variety of food stuffs is detailed, as well as the per capita
consumption in kilograms per year and the daily intake of proteins
and calories. Although these tables are now three years old, they
still present a more or less accurate picture of food consumption
levels in Turkey, since the diet patterns and amounts consumed have
not altered radically within this short space of time.

As has been repeatedly mentioned, cereals, especially in the form
of bread, are the staple article of diet in Turkey and provide a major
portion of the caloric and protein intake. During the years 1954-1957
Turks consumed an average of 197.4 kg. per capita per year of cereals. Cereals provided more than one half, or 1,893, of the estimated
2,660 calories consumed daily, as well as 71% of the total protein and
23.5% of the total fats.

Wheat consumption in Turkey is high and is increasing steadily.
About one half of the total caloric intake is supplied by wheat, and the
average per capita consumption between 1954 and 1957 amounted to
162.8 kg. per year, as compared to United States consumption of 57.3
kg. in the same year. This increase in consumption is ascribed to the
improvement in the standard of living, changes in the composition of
bread, which is increasingly being made of wheat flour, and shifts in
consumption patterns in such areas as the Black Sea region, where
corn meal is being replaced by wheat as the chief staple of diet.

Bread is made largely from wheat flour, although corn, barley, and
rye also are used in combination with wheat in different areas. Leavened bread is used in the center and west, while unleavened bread
is popular in the southeast. Wheat is prepared in a variety of ways in
addition to its use in bread-making. One of the most popular is **bulgur**,
which is wheat that has been parboiled and then sun-dried before being
cracked and sifted. Large-sized **bulgur** often is used as a substitute
for rice in **pilafs**, while the finer grade is used in soups or for stuffing
vegetables.

Tarhana or **tarana** can be made in a variety of ways. Basically, it
is a paste of wheat flour with yoghurt or milk, which is kneaded, broken into pieces the size of a quarter lentil, and dried in the sun. Many
variants are common, including some made with red or green peppers
and onions. One popular **tarana** is prepared with tomato paste and has
a pink color when dried. **Tarana** is important as a way of preserving
milk proteins and it is generally made in the season when milk is in
abundant supply. The product may be used as a breakfast porridge
with milk, in soups, with cheese, or in many other dishes. It is an
important item of diet and the average per capita consumption is estimated at 8 kg. per year. Both **bulgur** and **tarana** are reportedly more
extensively used in rural areas than by townspeople.

Other forms in which wheat is used include **irmik**, which is the aleurone layer of wheat endosperm, made into a dessert, kantaif, which looks like shredded wheat.

Rice is a popular ingredient in the diet. It is used in pilaf, as an accompaniment to meals, for stuffing vegetables, such as grape leaves, and in soups or desserts. The annual consumption of rice was estimated at 3.0 kg. per capita.

Consumption of barley for food was estimated at only 0.3 kg. per capita, while human consumption of maize was estimated at about 15.7 kg. per capita per year.

The total annual production of milk in 1957 was estimated at 2,881,000 metric tons, of which 1,369,000 tons were from cows, 678,000 from goats, 635,000 from sheep, and 199,000 from buffaloes. The average per capita consumption of milk was estimated at 31.3 kg. per year. Total calories provided by milk amounted to 71 per capita per day of a total of 2,660 calories, a very low intake.

Milk rarely is drunk fresh, except as an ingredient of soups, porridges, beverages, or desserts. Most of the milk consumed is converted into a variety of milk products of which the most popular is yoghurt. Yoghurt is prepared by boiling whole or skimmed milk to reduce the volume, cooling it, and fermenting it with the addition of a starter culture, called mayer. Milk converted to yoghurt keeps well without refrigeration, although poor storage methods or the use of dirty containers may contaminate the finished product. One recent survey showed that 20% of samples tested were contaminated with Escherichia coli. Sheep's milk is preferred for the making of yoghurt, but any other kind may be used. Yoghurt may be eaten alone or in combination with many foods, including vegetables and fruits. A favorite beverage called iran is made from defatted buttermilk or from yoghurt diluted with water and beaten. This beverage is a popular summer drink, especially in the central, eastern, and southern parts of the country.

Cheese is an important and popular item of diet. The most common varieties include beyas, a soft white cheese made from whole or partly skimmed milk, touloum, a traditional cheese prepared in the skin of an animal, kasseri, a hard cheese and graviera. Beyas and kasseri are the two most commonly used. Other varieties of cheese also are prepared in various localities, including some made from whey and several roquefort-type cheeses.

Butter is used primarily as clarified butter. Consumption is low and amounts only to 1.8 kg. per capita per year.

A variety of vegetables are grown, including potatoes, tomatoes, cabbages, egg plants, okra, cucumbers, and many others; average consumption is moderate, amounting to about 110 kg. per capita per year. Typical meals are based on cereals and can be made without the addition of any substantial amount of vegetables. The consumption of green leafy vegetables reportedly is small.

Tomatoes probably are the most important vegetables in the diet and are ingredients of many dishes, either fresh when in season or as tomato paste. There are two varieties of tomato paste, or **salca**: the traditional form is made of dried tomato juice and the more modern one is a purée of double strength. Fresh salads are popular, but the season for fresh vegetables is in most places very short, which may explain why the amount of green leafy vegetables eaten is small. Vegetables are prepared either raw or parboiled in salads (squash, egg plant), stuffed with rice, cereals, or meat (grape leaves, squash, peppers), or pickled (tomatoes, egg plants, cabbage, peppers), as well as occasionally in soups and stews.

Legumes of all types are popular although the net consumption only amounts to 9.7 kg. per year.

Cherries, peaches, pears, fresh figs, grapes, and melons are abundant in the summer and autumn months, but the average consumption is low since they are rarely available during the winter and spring months. The estimated supply for human consumption, according to food balance sheets for 1954 to 1957, was 87.0 kg. per year and included 38.3 kg. of melons, 4.3 kg. of citrus fruits, 4.5 kg. of dried fruits, and 37.5 kg. of other fresh fruits. Where olives are grown, both fruits and oil are important articles of diet and consumption is estimated at 2.4 kg. per year. Consumption of nuts, including chestnuts and peanuts, amounted to about 2.7 kg. per capita per year. Nuts contributed an average of 34 calories daily to the diet and fruits an additional 122 calories.

As may be seen from the above figures, dried fruits do not appear to be important items of diet in Turkey, as they are in other Middle East countries. Supplies of plums, apricots, figs, oranges, and grapes have increased substantially in the past few years so that consumption of fresh fruit today probably is higher than 1954-1957 levels.

The most commonly used fats are olive oil, other vegetable oils, clarified butter, and rendered animal fats. The fat-tailed sheep, the predominant species, is a minor source of fat. About 1.8 kg. of butter and 0.6 kg. of animal fats are used per capita yearly. Total fat consumption amounted to 5.5 kg. per capita; only about 5% of the daily caloric intake was derived from fats.

Production and consumption of meat is low and in most families meat rarely is eaten more than once a week, while in some rural areas meat may be almost completely absent from the diet of the peasant families for long periods of time.[9]

Lamb, beef, and goats are the most common meats, in that order. Meats are eaten skewered and roasted as **kebabs**, or ground and mixed with rice or **burghul** and used as stuffing for vegetables. The per capita consumption of meat is low, only about 15.6 kg. per capita per year, and includes roughly equal quantities of beef, mutton, and goat meats with negligible quantities of buffalo meat, poultry, rabbits, and game in addition. The 1954-1957 consumption was estimated at 6.3 kg. of beef and veal, 3.3 kg. of mutton and lamb, 2.6 of goat meat, 1.8 of offal, 1.1 of poultry, rabbits, and game, and 0.5 of buffalo.

Fish is available in abundance only in coastal areas, where it improves the animal protein content of the diet which elsewhere is much too low. Approximately 2.1 kg. per capita per year of fresh fish and 0.5 kg. of canned and preserved fish are consumed in the average diet.

Meat and fish together account for only 6.8 kg. of a total protein intake estimated at 85.3 kg. per capita. Even with the addition of eggs, milk, and milk products, the total animal protein content of the diet is only one seventh of total protein intake.

The estimated consumption of sugar is low, only 12.1 kg. per capita, but sugar and sweets are greatly relished and there is no doubt consumption would be much higher if supplies were available. Among the most popular of the confections made is **loukoum**, or Turkish Delight, and fruits preserved in thick syrup. **Halve** or **halvah** is a type of sweet of which **tahine helve** is the most common. This is made of finely milled sesame cooked into a paste with sucrose and soapwort. **Baklava** and **kantail** are pastries stuffed with nuts and covered with sugar syrup; these are usually served on holidays. Honey and **pekmez** or **petmez** are eaten in rather large amounts and make up one fourth of the total sugar content of the diet. Pekmez is made by concentrating grape juice to a syrup of about 60 to 70% moisture content. Current production is approximately 150,000 tons a year. Marmalades and dried fruit pastes are popular but in short supply.

Raki, vodka, wine, and, recently, beer are the main alcoholic drinks. Turkish coffee and tea are frequently served, with tea more popular in mountain areas. Sour **petmez** is diluted with water to make a refreshing summer drink, as is yoghurt, which is diluted with water to make **iran**.

B. VARIATIONS IN DIETS

1. Regional variations. Considerable variations in the diet are dictated by local conditions, which in turn are influenced by climatic and topographical factors. The diets of various regions differ considerably in quality largely due to the inadequate transportation and distribution of food from surplus areas to areas where there is a shortage. As a result, in any one region there may be an abundance of one kind of food and an inadequate supply of others.

In the northeast, for example, there is plenty of meat, dairy products, and cereals but only a limited supply of fruits and vegetables, especially during the long cold season, which may list as long as seven months. Fish is readily available in coastal areas and rarely in inland ones because of lack of transportation and preservation facilities, so that consumption of fish is largely limited to cities and coastal regions. Fresh fruits and vegetables are abundantly available in the Mediterranean coastal belt of the south and west, but they cannot be distributed to other areas where there is a shortage of these items.

A further factor in the regional variation of diets, in addition to topography and climate, is the influence of the dietary patterns of neighboring countries. Thus, in the west of Turkey, the area nearest to Europe, diet is very similar to that of the neighboring Greeks, while in the northeast it has many of the characteristics of the Russian diet.

The following diet regions may be delineated. In the Anatolian plateau wheat is the main food, in combination with cheese and yoghurt or other dairy products. Consumption of fats and oils probably is at its lowest in this area. Diet in the Black Sea region is characterized by the use of corn and corn bread, which are staples. However, the Government is encouraging a shift to the use of wheat and other cereals, so consumption of wheat is increasing. Fruits and vegetables are available in large quantities in this region. Wheat bread also is the staple of diet in European Turkey and in the Aegean region, but here there is abundant consumption of fresh vegetables and fish.

IV. ADEQUACY OF RESOURCES

The adequacy of food supplies in Turkey depends on variable climatic and agricultural factors. In a normal crop year with relatively good harvests, the supply of food produced may be enough to satisfy the high cereal diet of the people and even leave exportable surpluses. Even in such a good year, however, the consumption of meat, milk, and dairy products is close to the essential minimum levels of nutrition and the intake of all protective foods is low.

During a poor crop year production of the cereals, which are the mainstay of the diet, is adequate and additional supplies must be imported. Expert opinion agrees that Turkey will continue to be a wheat-importing country as long as present production techniques are not radically altered. Production of food supplies cannot keep pace with the increase in population and increased demand, as shown by the fact that although the food production index rose in 1957 to 1960, as compared with 1952-1954 averages, the per capita level of production was lower:

	1952-1954 av.	1957-1958	1958-1959	1959-1960
Food production index	100	111	110	103
Per capita food production index	100	99	96	87
Population index (1953 population = 22,791,000)	100	112	115	118

Some of the problems that influence the adequacy of food supplies include the lack of rainfall, overgrazing of pastures and overextension of areas under cultivation, encroachment on forest lands, and unbalanced irrigation.

Two thirds of the territory is subarid and there are wide yearly variations in the amount of rainfall, with drought a constant threat. Cereal production is carried out without irrigation, and yields in bad years may fall as low as 400 to 700 kg. per hectare. For example, rains during 1959 were below average in quantity and untimely and uneven in occurrence, so production of most crops was markedly below 1958 levels.

There is no surplus land available and large areas are cultivated that are fundamentally unsuited to crop growing. The area that could be cultivated without threat of erosion was estimated at 16.4 million hectares, and yet a total of 22.4 million hectares is now in use. The cultivation of unsuitable land and the subsequent erosion that follows upsets the levels of groundwaters and streams, contributes to the flood hazard, reduces the productivity of the land, and chokes up streams and reservoirs.

Expansion of arable land has been at the expense of steppe pastures, which decreased from 32 million to 23 million hectares. At the same time the number of animals kept on this decreased pasturage was greater by about 20%, so that the average feeding acreage per animal was reduced by 50%. This aggravated the already acute problem of animal undernutrition and aggravated existing erosion.

There has been a serious imbalance between the construction of major irrigation works and the actual irrigation of the land. In 1943 it was estimated that the lag amounted to 37,000 hectares and in 1957 to 57,000. This has been due in great measure to the fact that investments in levelling, drainage, and other work required for full utilization facilities have been inadequate.

Political and economic factors also affect the adequacy of food supplies. Loss of world markets for agricultural exports, for example, would seriously disrupt the agricultural economy.

V. NUTRITIONAL DISEASE PATTERNS

The nutritional status of the population varies in different parts of the country and among various population groups. The physical condition of the inhabitants in the south and west is reportedly better than in other areas, while the nutritional status of families in the Erzurun reportedly was poor. Frank deficiency diseases are generally not a serious problem but they do occur in certain areas and at certain seasons. Diet appears to be adequate in calories so that outright malnutrition is rare, but there is some evidence that the diet is deficient in vitamins and in animal proteins. The most common nutritional diseases are rickets and osteomalacia, while scurvy has been a problem in some areas, especially in the northeast. The appearance of this disease is largely seasonal, associated with the long winters during which there is a low consumption of fresh fruits; the largest number of cases at Erzurun, for example, were reported from December to February. Rickets and osteomalacia also are common in this area and the lack of sunlight during the long winters may be the determining factor. Pellagra has been reported among the inhabitants of the Black Sea area, whose diet is largely based on corn.

The only available detailed nutritional study of a large group of the population was that carried out on the Armed Forces of Turkey by the United States Interdepartmental Committee on Nutrition for National Defense, at the request of the Turkish Government. This survey, of the group of the population which is presumably best-nourished, i.e., young healthy adult males in the armed forces, included dietary, biochemical, and physical studies. The dietary deficiencies discovered in the survey are discussed in some detail below since they represent conditions in an optimum-nutrition group and are probably much worse in other groups that are less favored.

The dietary, biochemical, and physical examination data were in close agreement and indicated that the diet was adequate in calories, protein, iron, calcium, thiamine, and niacin. The nutrient content of the diets is detailed in Table 10. The major problem discovered by the survey was the poor vitamin C intake. The ascorbic acid content of diets was calculated and was found everywhere to be low and sometimes deficient. Blood serum ascorbic acid values were low or deficient in almost three fourths of those examined. Lesions such as red and swollen gums, bleeding gums, and "scorbutic type" gums, sometimes associated with low vitamin C intake, were of high incidence.

The intake of vitamin A and its precursor, carotene, also was low. By dietary analysis, troops had adequate amounts only in one area, and on chemical analysis the diet of only one area was in the acceptable range. On physical examination 21.1% of those examined had follicular kertosis, a clinical sign often associated with low vitamin A intakes. More serious signs of deficiency, such as Bitot's spots and xerosis were not often observed. Serum determinations showed that 9.2% of the troops had blood levels deficient or low in vitamin A and 24.8% were deficient or low in carotene.

Riboflavin intake appears to be marginal, some units having adequate intake at times and less than optimal amounts at others. Some physical signs associated with riboflavin deficiency were seldom seen while others, such as nasolabial seborrhea (8.9%), angular lesions of the mouth (23.2%), angular scars (16.6%), and cheilosis (26.6%) were frequent.

Table 11 details the physical findings on examination of army, air force, and navy personnel throughout the country, while Table 12 lists the percentage of findings below acceptable levels in biochemical studies, as compared with those of other countries where similar surveys of the armed forces have been carried out.

VI. CONCLUSIONS

The food supply of Turkey generally is adequate to satisfy domestic demands, except in poor crop years when additional supplies must be imported. A great expansion in cultivated area has taken place in the last decade, but this expansion has been, for the most part, on marginal land that is particularly vulnerable to unfavorable weather conditions.

Traditional patterns of agriculture contribute to the slow rate of agricultural development. For the most part, the absentee landlord problem, so common in most other Middle Eastern countries, is not a factor in Turkey; instead, the major part of arable land is in the hands of individual farmers. Unfortunately, many of these holdings are too small to permit efficient cultivation, and attempts are being made to establish cooperatives to finance, on a communal basis, more efficient agricultural methods.

The diet is varied and at a generally good level with regard to caloric intake, although it is low in meat and other animal products and inadequate in the consumption of protective foods. Deficiency diseases are not a particularly serious problem, although some malnutrition exists and certain nutritional deficiencies may occur at certain seasons or in restricted localities.

SELECTED REFERENCES

1. Bergs, H. Report to the Government of Turkey on Fish Handling and Refrigeration. *F. A. O. ETAP No. 282,* 1954.
2. Food and Agriculture Organization, Nutrition Committee for the Middle East. Report of First Session of Joint FAO/WHO Committee, November, 1958. *F. A. O. Nutrition Meeting Report Series No. 24,* 1959.
3. Food and Agriculture Organization. *Monthly Bulletin of Agricultural Statistics,* January to March, 1960.
4. Food and Agriculture Organization, Mediterranean Development Project. Country Studies: Turkey. 1959.
5. United States, Inter-Departmental Committee for Nutrition in National Defense. Nutrition Survey of the Armed Forces of Turkey. April, 1958.
6. International Cooperation Administration. Near East and South East Asia Regional Conference of Food and Agriculture Officers, April 20-25, 1959. Beirut, [1959].
7. Industrial Development Bank. Turkey, 1957.

8. Money-Kyrle, A. F. Agriculture Development and Research in Turkey. *American University of Beirut, Faculty of Agricultural Science, Publ. No. 4,* 1957.

9. Simmons, J. S., *et al.* Global Epidemiology: Vol. 3, The Near and Middle East. Philadelphia, Lippincott, 1954.

10. Tsongas, A. Report on Visit to Turkey. Mimeographed report. Food and Agriculture Organization, 1949.

11. Turkish Information Office. Turkish Cook Book, 1958.

12. The Pattern of World Milk Production. *United States Department of Agriculture, Foreign Agriculture Report No. 83,* 1955.

13. United States Department of Agriculture, Foreign Agriculture Service. Indices of Agricultural Production in 13 Near East Countries. Mimeographed report. November, 1959.

14. Vesterhus, R. Report to the Government of Turkey on the Processing of Fish. *F. A. O. ETAP No. 1088,* 1959.

15. West, Q. M. Agricultural Development in Turkey. *United States Department of Agriculture, Foreign Agriculture Report No. 106,* 1958.

Table 1

Turkey's Soil Cultivation, 1944, 1950 and 1956
(1000 hectares)

Type	1944	1950	1956
Land under crop	8,087	9,868	14,556
Black fallow	4,814	4,674	7,897
Total arable land	12,901	14,542	22,453
Vineyards, fruit and vegetable gardens, olives	1,385	1,466	1,858
Total land under cultivation	14,286	16,008	24,311

Source: Food and Agriculture Organization, Mediterranean Development Project, Country Studies—Turkey, Rome, 1959.

Table 2

Irrigation Projects in Turkey

Name of River Basin	Type of Irrigation	Present Situation	Irrigated Area (ha.)	Important Installations In the Irrigation Areas
Gediz	Gravity	Partly under construction	400 00	Demirkopru Dam Emiralem Weir
Buyuk Menderes	Gravity	Partly under construction	320 00	Kemer Dam Feslek Weir Curuksu Weir Isikh Weir
Konya	Gravity	Construction completed	650 00	Beysehir Weir Sille Dam Ayranci Dam May Dam Altinapa Dam
Sakarya	Gravity	Under construction	560 00	Porsuk Dam Porsuk Weir Sarisu Weir
Yesil-Irmak	Gravity and Pumping	Under construction	300 00	Gomenek Weir Çaykoy Weir Erbaa intake and pumping station
Antakya	Gravity	Under construction	500 00	Aksu Weir
Firat	Gravity and Pumping	Construction completed and under construction	700 00	Altinbasak pumping station
Seyhan, Ceyhan, Berdan, Goksu	Gravity	Under construction	850 00	Seyham Dam Seyham Weir

The irrigated area according to this table totals 427,000 ha.

There are also some private irrigation works which are not included in the above table.

Source: Money-Kyrle, A. F.—Agricultural Development and Research in Turkey. Fac. of Agr. Sci., Am Univ., Beirut, Lebanon, 1957.

Table 3

Area and Production of Principal Crops

Crop	Year	Planted Area (1000 ha.)	Production (1000 m.t.)
Cereals			
Wheat	1959	7,681	7,998
Barley	1958	2,700	3,600
	1959	2,750	3,300
Rice	1957	70	92
Oats	1958	389	480
	1959	283	305
Rye	1958	665	780
	1959	657	665
Millet	1958	50	65
Maize	1958	690	900
	1959	700	1,000
Mixed grain	1957	395	400
Vegetables & Legumes			
Potatoes	1958	137	1,472
Onions	1958	50	405
Dry Beans	1959	124[a]	170[a]
Dry Peas	''	2	2
Broad Beans	''	40	50
Chick Peas	''	85	98
Lentils	''	81	74
Fruits & Nuts			
Peaches	1958/59		75
Apples	1958		193
Pears	''		107
Grapes	1957	74.3	2,010
Figs	''		137.1
Oranges, tangerines	''		249
Grapefruits	''		2
Lemons, limes, et al	''		63
Raisins	''		186
Plums	1958/59		75
Apricots	''		57
Cherries	''		58
Quince	''		31

Table 3 (Continued)

Crop	Year	Planted Area (1000 ha.)	Production (1000 m.t.)
Fruits & Nuts (continued)			
Almonds, unshelled	1958/59		12
Filberts, "	"		55
Pistachios, "	"		9
Walnuts, "	"		54
Olives	1958		48
Olive oil.............	1958		10
Oil Bearing Seeds			
Soybeans	1958	7	5
Groundnuts	1957	8	20
Cottonseed	1958	631	319
Linseed	1958	36	24
Rapeseed	No		
Sesame	1958	82	48
Sunflower seed	1958	138	95
Vegetable oil	1958/59		105
Industrial Crops			
Tobacco	1958	168	106.1
Cotton (lint)	1958 1959	631 617[a]	180 180[a]
Sugar beet	1959	167	3,175
Raw sugar	1959		579[a]
Flax fiber	1958	36	4.4
Hemp fiber	1958	15	14.2

(a) Unofficial figures.

Source: Food and Agriculture Organization Data and Estimates of the United States Department of Agriculture.

F. A. O.—Production Yearbook, 1958.

U. S. Dept. of Agr., For. Agr. Service—Indices of Agr. Prod. in 13 Near East Countries. Washington, 1959.

Table 4

Harvest Calendar for Principal Crops

Crops	Harvest Period	Bulk of Harvest
Wheat	June–Aug.	Aug.
Rye	June–Aug.	July
Barley	June–July	June
Oats	June–July	June
Mixed grains	June–Aug.	July
Maize	Aug.–Sept.	Sept.
Millet	July–Aug.	Aug.
Rice	Sept.–Oct.	Oct.
Sugar beets	Aug.–Oct.	Oct.
Sugar	Campaign from August through December	
Potatoes	July–Sept.	Sept.
Onions	July–Aug.	Aug.
Fresh peas	May–June	June
Broad beans, fresh	Apr.–June	May
Dry beans	Sept.	Sept.
Dry peas	Aug.–Sept.	Aug.
Dry broad beans	June–July	July
Chick peas	July–Aug.	Aug.
Lentils	July–Aug.	Aug.
Apples	Sept.–Oct.	Oct.
Pears	July–Nov.	Aug.
Grapes	July–Nov.	Sept.
Raisins	Aug.–Sept.	Sept.
Apricots	June–July	July
Oranges	Nov.–Mar.	Jan.
Lemons	Nov.–Mar.	Dec.
Figs	July–Sept.	Aug.
Olives	Nov.–Jan.	Dec.
Olive oil	Dec.–Jan.	Jan.
Soybeans	Sept.	Sept.
Groundnuts	Sept.–Oct.	Oct.
Cottonseed	Sept.–Dec.	Oct.
Linseed	July–Aug.	Aug.
Rapeseed	June–July	July
Sesame seed	Aug.–Sept.	Sept.
Sunflower seed	Aug.–Sept.	Sept.
Tea	May–Sept.	May
Tobacco	July–Aug.	July
Cotton	Sept.–Nov.	Oct.
Flax fiber	Aug.–Sept.	Aug.
Hemp fiber	Aug.–Sept.	Aug.

Source: Food and Agriculture Organization. World Crop Harvest Calendar, Rome, 1959.

Table 5

Foreign Trade of Turkey by Commodity Groups, 1938, 1946—1958

(Million £.T.)

Export

Year	Grain and Grain Products	Pulses	Fruit and Vege- tables	Livestock and Animal Products	Forestry Products	Seed	Industrial Raw Material and Plants	Ores	Finished Goods And Half- Finished Goods	Other Export Goods	Total(a)
1938	15,8	2,7	37,4	10,3	1,3	2,1	62,7	9,0	3,2	0,5	144,9
1946	56,6	18,6	110,9	66,5	11,4	7,4	121,2	19,9	16,7	3,0	432,1
1947	134,6	24,8	103,0	65,2	12,6	15,0	214,6	32,4	20,2	2,9	625,2
1948	19,2	18,5	85,4	67,8	5,7	48,2	255,7	31,1	16,4	3,0	551,0
1949	13,3	16,5	114,9	77,3	4,4	28,6	376,7	45,2	14,0	2,8	693,9
1950	5,4	11,4	141,7	61,4	7,1	19,6	427,7	42,5	18,5	2,3	737,6
1951	56,7	16,7	110,0	58,7	10,1	29,2	476,1	88,2	29,6	4,2	879,4
1952	248,5	12,6	109,2	1,2	8,0	24,6	406,2	136,6	24,0	5,3	1 016,2
1953	240,4	7,9	104,3	42,7	5,7	28,1	511,2	136,3	29,2	3,1	1 109,0
1954	214,1	2,3	131,2	31,6	3,2	6,1	430,5	84,4	30,9	3,6	937,8
1955	64,6	1,9	175,8	42,5	5,0	6,2	433,0	109,0	35,4	4,0	877,4
1956	81,7	1,5	159,8	36,6	3,5	4,4	390,0	132,2	39,3	5,2	854,0
1957	6,7	—	201,6	30,5	2,2	6,4	566,1	115,5	34,2	3,4	966,6
1958	31,1	6,5	168,2	19,4	3,2	5,9	391,8	86,2	30,1	4,8	739,3

(a) Differences arise through rounding off of figures.
Source: Republic of Turkey, Prime Ministry, Central Statistical Office, "Monthly Bulletin of Statistics," Ankara, 1958, No. 54, August, p. 82f.

Table 6

Trade In Agricultural Products — 1953-1958

Quantities (1000 metric tons) and Value (1000 dollars)

		1953	1955	1956	1957	1958
		EXPORTS				
Barley	Q	159.9	93.4	163.1	0	156.7
	V amt	12455	5507	8974	0	5420
	% of total	—	—	3.0	0	2.2
Citrus Fruits	Q	9.7	8.8	8.5	4.6	13.3
	V amt	1366	1510	2111	1029	2061
	% of total	—	—	.7	.3	.8
Cotton	Q	100.8	52.7	34.6	60.6	34.5
	V amt	78663	45750	26361	41444	22398
	% of total	—	—	8.8	12.0	9.1
Dried Figs	Q	14.1	17.0	15.7	12.2	17.4
	V amt	2268	4039	3575	4161	3610
	% of total	—	—	1.2	1.2	1.5
Filberts	Q	29.2	44.5	25.4	40.7	31.7
	V amt	21696	43563	29759	44516	29539
	% of total	—	—	10.0	12.9	12.0
Livestock (heads)	No.	122577	134387	101754	67381	83748
	V amt	3791	4515	4028	2191	1252
	% of total	—	—	1.3	.6	.5
Mohair	Q	4.5	3.9	3.8	3.2	3.8
	V amt	9990	8290	9206	14113	7522
	% of total	—	—	3.1	4.1	3.0
Opium	Q	.1	.3	.2	.2	.2
	V amt	2309	3708	84	2700	3121
	% of total	—	—	0.3	.8	1.3
Pistachios	Q	1.0	.4	1.7	1.2	0
	V amt	879	395	1812	1379	0
	% of total	—	—	.6	.4	0
Raisins	Q	32.6	33.3	48.4	59.4	50.2
	V amt	7104	8057	15019	18454	18751
	% of total	—	—	5.0	5.3	7.6
Rice	Q	13.4	6.3	0	0	0
	V amt	3015	1206	0	0	0
	% of total	—	—	0	0	0
Tobacco	Q	71.7	60.0	59.5	86.7	56.1
	V amt	85255	88994	93537	138614	84205
	% of total	—	—	31.3	40.2	34.1

Table 6 (Continued)

		1953	1955	1956	1957	1958
		EXPORTS (continued)				
Walnuts	Q	1.0	1.4	.4	1.2	0
	V amt	296	1093	35	697	0
	% of total	—	—	.1	.2	0
Wheat, hard	Q	240.4	83.8	136.7	0	22.3
	V amt	24800	7286	13920	0	2059
	% of total	—	—	4.7	0	.8
Wheat, soft	Q	360.1	75.1	38.8	0	7.9
	V amt	32704	4919	3356	0	511
	% of total	—	—	1.1	0	.2
Wool	Q	.4	1.1	1	0	0
	V amt	403	1802	9	0	0
	% of total	—	—	.003	0	0
Oilseed cake	Q					113.8
	V amt					5678
	% of total					2.3
Pulses	Q					17.4
	V amt					2410
	% of total					1.0
Hides & Skins	Q					2.4
	V amt					2140
	% of total					.8
Sugar, refined	Q					15.1
	V amt					1641
	% of total					.6
Oats & Millet	Q					17.9
	V amt					1017
	% of total					.4
		IMPORTS				
Cocoa Beans, Powder	Q	2.4	1.0	.2	.3	.2
	V amt	843	555	171	193	209
	% of total	—	—	.04	.05	.1
Coffee	Q	6.7	5.8	3.5	.8	0
	V amt	8264	6534	3365	793	0
	% of total	—	—	.8	.2	0
Corn	Q	71	0	4.5	37.2	9.5
	V amt	11	0	390	2811	581
	% of total	—	—	.1	.7	.2
Fats & Oils (animal)	Q	1.0	12.7	2.7	17.0	0
	V amt	557	4840	529	4133	0
	% of total	—	—	.1	1.0	0

Table 6 (Continued)

		1953	1955	1956	1957	1958
		IMPORTS (continued)				
Hides & Skins	Q	5.7	4.3	4.8	2.5	3.6
	V amt	4042	2711	1995	6074	1560
	% of total	—	—	.5	1.5	.5
Rice	Q	1.0	0	8.9	0	0
	V amt	289	0	1429	0	0
	% of total	—	—	.4	0	0
Seeds	Q	1.1	3.0	.2	0	0
	V amt	518	1919	713	0	0
	% of total	—	—	.2	0	0
Sugar	Q	0	5.5	5.4	0	0
	V amt	0	672	677	0	0
	% of total	—	—	.2	0	0
Tea	Q	2.5	2.1	2.7	3.5	2.8
	V amt	2779	3929	4584	5297	4088
	% of total	—	—	1.1	1.3	1.3
Cottonseed Oil	Q				13.8	19.9
	V amt				5293	9308
	% of total				1.3	3.0
Soybean Oil	Q					26.3
	V amt					10321
	% of total					3.3
Wheat, soft	Q	0	218.9	150.0	397.5	49.7
	V amt	0	16835	12559	33658	3558
	% of total	—	—	3.1	8.5	1.1
Wheat, hard	Q	0	3.6	35.5	37.6	10.0
	V amt	0	276	12324	3290	768
	% of total	—	—	3.0	.8	.2
Wool	Q	6.3	2.4	2.1	1.8	4.1
	V amt	19476	6875	2147	3364	6395
	% of total	—	—	.5	.8	2.0

Source: United States Department of Agriculture. Foreign Agriculture Service, Turkey. — Exports and Imports. Quantity and Value of Principal Agricultural Commodities, 1958. Washington, 1960.

Table 7

List of Canning Factories in Turkey

No.	Name of the Factory	Location	Province
1	Balerin Konserve Fabrikasi		Istanbul
2	Ciftlik '' T. Ltd. Şti.	Sirkeci	''
3	Elmas '' Fabrikasi	Galata	''
4	Ermiş Konservecilik T. A. S.	Yonisehir	''
5	Ceyik Konserve ve Balikcilik Ltd. Ort.	Fener	''
6	Idael Konserve Fabrikasi	Galata	''
7	Istanbul Konserve Fabrikasi	''	''
8	Muteahhit-Ermis-Baniyet-Kartal Konserve Fabrikasi	Ayvansaray	''
9	Pendik Konserve Fabrikasi	Pendik	''
10	Pişkin Konserve Fabrikasi	Fener	''
11	Rekor '' ''	''	''
12	Sirin Konserve Fabrikasi		''
13	Saray '' ''		''
14	Vatan '' ''	Käçäkpazar	''
15	Belkis '' ''	Erdsk	Balikesir
16	Ender '' ''	Marmaraadasi	—
17	Nasli '' ''	''	
18	Basri Gkyar-Yesil Bursa Konserve Fabrikasi		Bursa
19	Celâl Antel '' ''	Hamitler	''
20	Cemâl Alanya '' ''		''
21	Tamek Konserve Fabrikasi		''
22	Antalya Konserve Fabrikasi		Antalya
23	Özen Konserve Fabrikasi	Erdek	—
24	Dogu Konserve Fabrikasi	—	Erzurum
25	Rifat Minare Konserve Fabrikasi	Gemlik	—
26	Balciova Konserve Fabrikasi	Bornova	''
27	Etem Piskin '' ''	Izmir	Izmir
28	Yeçil Tire Konserve Fabrikasi	Tire	''
29	Bima Konserve Fabrikasi	Sapanca	Ismit
30	Özler '' ''	Igdir	Kars
31	Balik Sanayii I. O.	Marmaraadasi	—
32	Ali Koç Konserve Fabrikasi	—	Samsun
33	Devici Konserve ''	—	Samsun
34	Azim Konserve ''	Eregli	Zonguldak
35	Bu. Ba. Bi. Konserve ''	Bartin	Zonguldak
36	Turkili Konserve ''	''	''
37	Akfa Konserve Fabrikasi	Canakkale	Canakkale
38	Alaeddin '' ''	Gelibulu	''
39	Cumhuriyet Konserve Fabrikasi	''	''
40	Cankaya '' ''	''	''
41	Ismaiil '' ''	''	''
42	Yukselen '' ''	''	''
43	Hüseyin Milden	''	''

Source: Vesterhus, R.: Report of the Government of Turkey on the Processing of Fish. F. A. O.   E. T. A. P. No. 1,088, Rome, 1959.

Table 8

Cold Storage, Refrigeration and Freezing Facilities
(Location and Capacity: 1954)

Location	Ice-Making Capacity Tons Per Day	Ice-Storage Capacity Tons Per Day	Fish Cooling Capacity Tons Per Day	Cooled Fish Storage Tons	Fish Freezing Capacity Tons Per Day	Frozen Fish Storage Tons	Other Goods Storage Tons
Cesme	12.5	40	5	20	0	0	0
Canakkale	12.5	40	5	20	0	0	0
Marmara Isl.	25	75	10	15	5	25	0
Besiktas	100	500	60	120	30	900	1620
Haydarpasa	40	200	45	300	0	0	1050
Eregli	12.5	40	5	20	0	0	20
Zonguldak	3	15	5	10	0	0	110
Sinop	25	75	15	25	10	125	0
Samsun	25	75	10	15	5	25	0
Trabzon	25	75	15	25	10	125	100
Iskenderun	40	60	50	100	10	300	120

Source: Bergs, H. Report to the Government of Turkey on Fish Handling and Refrigeration. F. A. O., E. T. A. P. No. 282, Rome, 1954.

Table 9

Food Balance Sheet
(Assembled in collaboration with OEEC)

Population: 24.6 million

3 Years Average: 1954/55—1956/57
(1956/57 provisional)

(thousand metric tons unless otherwise specified)

Commodity	Production	Change in Stocks	Foreign Trade — Gross Exports	Gross Imports	Available Supply	Distribution — Animal Feed	Seed	Manufacture	Waste	Food (Gross)	Extr. Rate %	Food (Net)	Per Capita Consumption — Kg. Per Year	Gm. Per Day	Cal.* Per Day	Protein Per Day Gm.	Fat Per Day Gm.
	(1)	(2)	(3)	(4)	(5)	(6)	(7)	(8)	(9)	(10)	(11)	(12)	(13)	(14)	(15)	(16)	(17)
Cereals																	
Wheat	6099	− 435	222	321	6633	462	1385	130	297	4359	92	4010	162.8	446.1	1562	52.2	6.7
Rye	553	− 55	5		603	168	123		24	288	92	265	10.8	29.5	100	2.6	0.5
Mixed bread grains	428	− 28	91	53	456	222	88		20	126	92	115	4.7	12.7	43	1.3	0.2
Barley	2761	− 3	5	2	2726	2056	522	10	128	10	85	8	0.3	0.9	3	0.1	0.1
Oats	354				351	292	43		16				—	—	—	—	—
Maize	890	− 50	1	16	956	480	34	20	17	405	95	384	15.7	42.8	154	3.9	1.6
Millet	122		1		121	103	10		5	3	85	2	0.1	0.2	1	—	—
Rice (milled)	87	− 1	1	4	91		10		4	77		77	3.0	8.4	30	0.5	—
Total													197.4	540.6	1893	60.6	9.1
Potatoes	1069				1069	35	123	19	106	786		786	31.9	87.4	61	1.4	0.1
Sugar and Syrups																	
Sugar (refined)	241		3	3	241					241		240	9.7	26.6	103	—	—
Pekmez	71				71					71		71	2.9	7.8	25	—	—
Honey	7				7					7		7	0.2	0.6	1	—	—
Total															129		
Pulses and Nuts																	
Pulses	305	− 7	6		306	12	36		18	240	50	240	9.7	26.6	92	5.9	0.5
Nuts (in shell)	187	+ 20	70		97				18	79		39	1.6	4.3	26	0.6	2.5
Chestnuts	26		1		25				1	24	85	20	0.8	2.1	4	0.4	0.1
Groundnuts	16		1		15		1		1	13	60	8	0.3	0.8	4	0.1	0.3
Total															126	7.0	3.4
Vegetables (incl. tomatoes)	2690				2690	134			673	1883		1883	76.6	209.7	46	2.5	0.4

Quantities in columns 1–6 are in 1,000 metric tons.

Commodity	Production	Imports	Gross supply	Exports	Feed, waste & manuf.	Food	Per caput kg/year	g/day	Calories	Protein (g)	Fat (g)
Fruit											
Fresh	1355		1355	376	50	929	37.5	103.2	55	0.9	0.3
Citrus	127	7	134	21		106	4.3	11.7	4	0.1	—
Dried	137	45	185	10		113	4.5	12.4	32	0.3	0.1
Olives	65	1	72	4		61	2.4	6.6	16	0.1	1.6
Melons and water-melons	1912		1912		389	943	38.3	105.0	15	0.4	0.1
Total				580			87.0		122	1.8	2.1
Meat											
Beef and veal	156		156			156	6.3	17.2	23	2.7	1.3
Pork(a)	1		1								—
Buffalo	14		14			14	0.5	1.4	1	0.2	—
Mutton and lamb	81		81			81	3.3	8.9	21	1.0	1.8
Goat	64		64			64	2.6	7.0	9	1.0	0.5
Offal	45		45			45	1.8	4.8	7	0.7	0.3
Poultry, rabbit and game	28		28			28	1.1	3.0	5	0.5	0.3
Total							15.6	42.3	66	6.1	4.2
Eggs	55		54		24	41	1.6	4.3	6	0.4	0.4
Fish											
Fresh and frozen	98	15	113	21		(b)53	2.1	5.7	3	0.5	0.1
Canned	14	1	15	1		13	0.5	1.3	3	0.2	0.1
Total									6	0.7	0.2
Milk and Cheese											
Whole milk	1866		1866		1400	466	18.9	52.0	45	2.3	2.9
Skim milk (Ayran)	1249		1249	187	579	233	9.4	25.7	14	1.1	0.2
Cheese: soft	78		78			78	3.0	8.2	12	1.4	0.6
hard											
skim milk											
Total							31.3		71	4.8	3.7
Oils and Fats (pure fat content)											
Butter	45		45			45	1.8	4.9	44	—	4.9
Olive oil	66			26		36	1.4	3.8	34	—	3.8
Other vegetable oils	58	4			17	43	1.7	4.6	40	—	4.6
Animal fats	16	4				16	0.6	1.8	16	—	1.8
Total							5.5	15.1	134	—	15.1

	Calories	Protein (g)	Fat (g)
Total	2660	85.3	38.7
Animal		12.0	
Vegetable		73.3	

(a) 1954/55 only. (b) Landed weight.
Source: F. A. O.—Food Balance Sheets, 1954–56 av., Rome, 1958.

Table 10

Turkey: Average Nutrient Intake per Man per Day

(Calculated From Mess Survey Data)(a)

Location	Length of Survey (Days)	No. of Men	Type of Unit	Calories	Protein Gm.	Fat Gm.	Cal. mg	Fe mg	Vit. A I.U.	Thiamine mg	Riboflavin mg	Niacin mg	Vit. C mg
Ankara	2	1491	Army Rgt.	3283	111	35	485	25	255	2.84	1.00	24.6	5
Iskenderun	3	2013	Army Rgt.	3662	100	49	459	22	525	2.92	0.97	27.5	18
Izmir	4	1411	Air Force	3219	97	53	510	19	1284	2.60	0.99	26.0	22
Golcuk	4	111	Navy	3903	118	87	432	26	595	3.86	1.07	29.2	10
Trabzon	4	904	Army Rgt.	3468	116	72	268	25	394	2.92	1.09	31.3	7
Erzurum	3	557	Army Bn.	3998	127	65	453	29	6145	3.55	1.42	35.0	18
Diyarbakir	4	1483	Army Rgt.	3293	122	53	384	25	1371	3.16	1.29	34.1	26
Ave. of 7 Messes				3547	113	59	427	24	1510	3.12	1.12	29.7	15
Proposed "Acceptable" Range(b)	–		Range	3200 to 3800	60 to 90		400 to 800	9 to 12	3500 to 5000	1.2 to 1.9	1.2 to 1.5	10.0 to 15.0	30.0 to 50.0

(a) Values corrected for "average cooking losses." Losses probably were greater than "average" in these messes due to extended cooking periods. (Appendix 4)

(b) As consumed, for 25-year-old active males, 67 inches (170 cm) in height and 143 pounds (65 kg) in weight living in a temperate climate and consuming a varied diet.

Source: U. S. Inter–Departmental Committee for Nutrition in National Defense—Nutrition Survey of the Armed Forces of Turkey, Washington, D. C., 1958.

Table 11

Selected Physical Findings, April–June, 1957, By Service and Location

	Army							Air Force	Navy	Total
	Ankara	Iskenderun	Izmir	Istanbul	Trabzon	Erzurum	Diyarbakir	Izmir	Golcuk	
Number of detailed exams	223	233	134	140	178	267	265	135	130	1705
Number of abbreviated exams	899	936	544	560	706	1062	1052	534	521	6814
			PERCENT INCIDENCE							
Skin – Face and Neck										
Nasolabial seborrhea(a)	3.1	12.1	6.2	6.0	11.7	14.6	10.6	3.9	5.2	8.9
Other seborrhea	2.2	3.4	0.0	0.0	2.2	2.6	1.1	0.7	0.0	1.6
Erythema	2.2	0.0	0.0	0.0	0.0	0.0	0.0	0.0	0.0	0.3
Pigmentation	4.0	0.0	0.0	0.0	1.1	0.0	0.4	0.0	0.0	0.7
Eyes										
Thickened conjunctivae	7.6	38.2	0.0	0.0	0.6	3.4	0.0	30.4	0.0	9.2
Pingueculae	0.0	0.4	0.7	0.0	0.0	0.0	0.0	0.0	0.0	0.1
Bitot's spots(a)	0.1	0.3	0.0	0.0	0.2	0.2	0.2	0.0	0.2	0.1
Circumcorneal injection	0.0	1.3	0.0	0.0	1.1	0.0	0.4	0.0	0.8	0.4
Conjunctival injection	12.1	23.6	4.5	5.0	0.6	1.1	15.8	22.2	3.8	10.3
Blepharitis	0.4	0.0	0.0	0.0	0.0	0.0	0.0	0.0	0.0	0.1
Lips										
Angular lesions(a)	5.8	23.1	29.1	36.9	33.6	26.8	26.1	8.8	19.7	23.2
Angular scars only(a)	7.4	23.4	22.9	20.4	19.5	14.4	10.9	15.7	22.9	16.6
Cheilosis(a)	2.4	15.0	19.2	24.6	33.9	58.1	39.0	3.9	22.6	26.6
Tongue										
Filiform pap. atrophy, slight(a)	13.7	17.1	23.5	20.0	26.5	38.6	29.4	18.7	24.4	24.3
Filiform pap. atrophy, moderate, severe(a)	2.6	10.2	6.2	9.7	16.4	9.1	7.1	2.7	18.3	8.9
Fungiform pap. atrophy	0.9	8.2	0.7	0.0	3.4	23.6	7.2	0.7	1.5	6.6
Papillary hypertrophy, slight	4.5	7.3	6.0	9.3	10.1	20.2	4.5	4.4	6.2	8.6
Papillary hypertrophy, moderate, severe	2.2	0.4	1.5	1.4	0.6	3.0	1.1	0.7	0.8	1.4
Furrows	12.1	21.9	22.4	35.7	10.7	10.9	35.1	12.6	23.8	20.4

Table 11 (Continued)

	Army							Air Force	Navy	Total
	Ankara	Iskenderun	Izmir	Istanbul	Trabzon	Erzurum	Diyarbakir	Izmir	Golcuk	
Fissures, erosions or ulcers	0.9	2.6	0.7	0.0	1.7	2.6	1.1	0.7	0.0	1.3
Serrations and swellings	0.9	0.9	2.2	0.7	3.4	1.5	1.9	0.0	2.3	1.5
Red, tip and/or lateral margins	24.7	12.9	6.7	2.1	8.4	19.5	1.1	12.6	13.1	11.8
Glossitis(a)	1.0	2.2	0.1	1.4	1.2	0.5	0.1	0.3	1.4	0.9
Magenta colored tongue(a)	0.0	0.3	0.0	0.0	0.0	0.1	0.0	0.0	0.0	0.0
Geographic tongue	0.4	0.0	0.7	0.0	0.0	0.0	0.0	0.0	0.0	0.1
Gums										
Red or swollen gums	57.8	43.8	29.1	27.1	27.5	26.6	13.2	21.5	43.1	32.1
Atrophy of papillae	0.9	1.3	0.7	0.7	0.0	0.0	2.6	0.0	0.8	0.9
Recession of papillae	12.1	3.0	2.2	0.7	3.9	2.2	3.8	0.0	1.5	3.7
Bleeding gums	16.6	15.9	4.5	6.4	11.8	13.5	3.0	4.4	12.3	10.3
"Scorbutic type" gums(a)	1.4	19.2	6.9	5.0	7.4	1.7	2.2	4.2	4.5	5.8
Teeth										
No caries	55.2	50.6	59.7	49.3	51.7	70.0	58.9	37.8	51.5	55.3
1 – 2 carious teeth	26.9	35.2	32.8	35.0	27.5	20.6	26.0	36.3	29.2	29.0
3+ carious teeth	17.9	14.2	7.5	15.7	20.2	9.4	15.1	25.9	19.2	15.6
3+ unfilled caries	12.1	13.7	6.7	13.6	11.2	7.1	9.8	14.1	18.5	11.4
Worn teeth	15.7	7.7	0.7	1.4	3.9	1.9	0.0	0.0	0.0	4.0
Fluorosis	11.2	4.7	0.7	0.7	16.9	8.2	0.0	1.5	0.0	5.4
Malposition	7.2	4.3	1.5	2.1	5.1	3.0	4.5	3.7	2.3	4.0
Skin – General										
Follicular keratosis(a)	11.9	18.5	23.9	35.7	26.1	30.9	7.1	20.3	25.3	21.1
Xerosis	1.8	0.0	0.0	0.0	0.0	0.7	0.0	0.0	0.0	0.4
Crackled skin	0.4	0.0	0.0	0.7	0.0	0.0	0.0	0.0	0.0	0.1
Acneform eruption	6.3	12.0	9.7	3.6	1.1	0.4	4.5	10.4	8.5	5.9
Scrotal dermatitis(a)	0.0	0.4	0.9	1.6	4.8	2.6	2.0	0.5	0.5	1.5
Thickened pressure points	0.0	0.4	0.0	0.0	0.0	0.0	0.0	0.7	0.0	0.1
Hyperpigmentation	0.9	0.0	0.0	0.0	1.1	0.0	0.0	0.0	0.0	0.2
Pellagrous lesions(a)	0.1	0.0	0.1	0.0	0.0	0.2	0.1	0.0	0.0	0.1

(a) Percentages are based on combined detailed and abbreviated examinations.

Source: U. S. Inter-Departmental Committee for Nutrition in National Defense; Nutrition Survey of the Armed Forces of Turkey, Washington, D. C., April, 1958.

Table 12

Turkey: Biochemical Findings: Comparison Among Countries Surveyed

	Level	Korea	Iran	Pakistan	Philip-pines	Turkey
		Percent of Incidence				
Serum Vitamin C	<0.2 mg/100 ml	1.0	51.3	43.1	17.1	72.8
Serum Carotene	<mcg/100 ml	7.4	58.1	11.2	12.3	24.8
Serum Vitamin A	<20 mcg/100 ml	17.6	23.7	0.7	1.1	9.1
Urinary Riboflavin Excretion	<30 mcg/6 hr	16.3	21.3	2.5	6.4[a]	5.2
Urinary Thiamine Excretion	<25 mcg/6 hr	5.0	8.6	5.8	41.0[a]	4.3
Urinary N'Methyl-nicotinamide Excretion	<0.6 mg/6 hr	0	2.0	4.8	6.0[a]	7.6
Hemoglobin	<12.0 gm/100 ml	25.2	1.5	0.2	1.1	1.5
Total Plasma Protein	<6.6 gm/100 ml	28.9	0.2	0.4	53.3[b]	4.5

(a) Based on percent of samples below 80 mcg. riboflavin, 66 mcg. thiamine and 1.6 mg N'Methylnicotinamide per gram creatinine.

(b) Percent of samples below 6.4 gm/100 ml.

Source: Inter-Departmental Committee for Nutrition in National Defense; Nutrition Survey of the Armed Forces of Turkey, Washington, D. C., 1958.

Graph 1

TURKEY: Wheat yields compared with spring and
fall rainfall, Ankara Experimental Farm, 1941-56

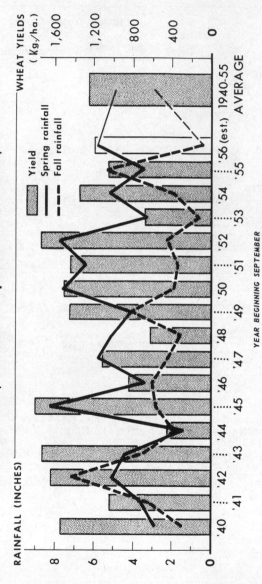

Source: West, Q.M.; Agricultural Development in Turkey. Foreign Agriculture Service, U. S. Dept. of Agr., Washington, D. C., 1958.

Graph 2

TURKEY

GRAIN STORAGE CAPACITY ACQUIRED BY CONSTRUCTION OF SILOS AND RENOVATION OF WAREHOUSES

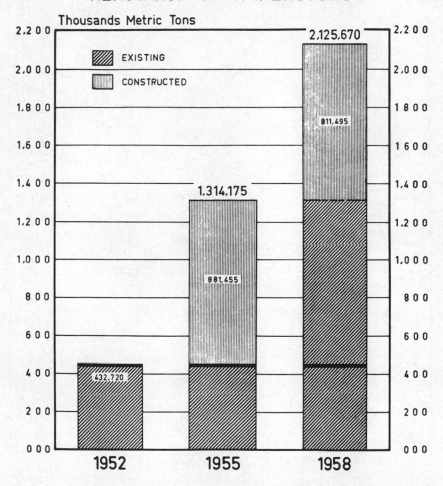

Thousands Metric Tons

EXISTING
CONSTRUCTED

2,125.670

811,495

1.314.175

881,455

432,720

1952   1955   1958

TOTAL INCREASE IN GRAIN STORAGE −1.692.950 Tons

Source: Bross, H. E.; Grain Storage Progress Report on Africa, Near East and South Asia. U. S. Operations Mission, Beirut, Lebanon, 1958.

Map 1

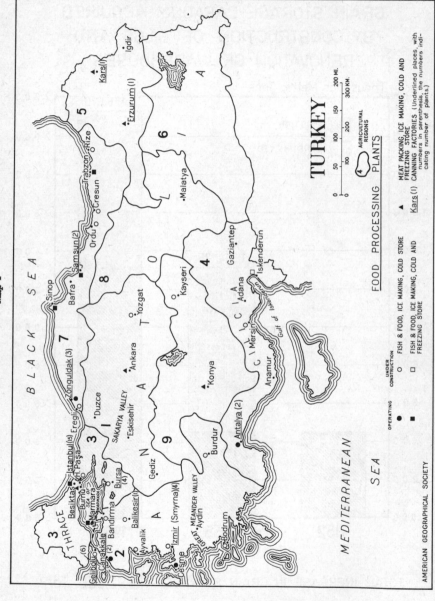

BLACK SEA

Kars(I)
Igdir
Erzurum (I)
5
6
Rize
Trabzon
Oresun
Ordu
Samsun(2)
Sinop
Bafra
7
Zonguldak (3)
Duzce
Ereğli
İstanbul(15)
H.Paşa
Beşiktaş
SEA OF
MARMARA
Bursa (4)
Bandırma
Balıkesir(I)
İzmir (Smyrna)(4)
Aydın
GREAT MEANDER VALLEY
Çeşme
Ayvalık
2
Çanakkale
(2)
THRACE
Gallibolu
(6)
3
SAKARYA VALLEY
Eskişehir
Gediz
8
Yozgat
Ankara
9
Konya
Burdur
Antalya (2)
Bodrum
A
N
A
T
O
L
I
A
Malatya
Kayseri
4
Gaziantep
Adana
Mersin
İskenderun
Gulf of İskenderun
Anamur
Gulf of

MEDITERRANEAN SEA

TURKEY

FOOD PROCESSING PLANTS

AGRICULTURAL REGIONS

4

0   50   100 150 200 MI.
0   100   200   300 KM.

▲ MEAT PACKING, ICE MAKING, COLD AND
   FREEZING STORE

▲ CANNING FACTORIES

Kars (I) (Underlined places, with
          numbers in parenthesis, the numbers indi-
          cating number of plants.)

OPERATING
○ FISH & FOOD, ICE MAKING, COLD STORE
■ FISH & FOOD, ICE MAKING, COLD AND
   FREEZING STORE

UNDER CONSTRUCTION
○ FISH & FOOD, ICE MAKING, COLD STORE
□ FISH & FOOD, ICE MAKING, COLD AND
   FREEZING STORE

AMERICAN GEOGRAPHICAL SOCIETY

Map 2

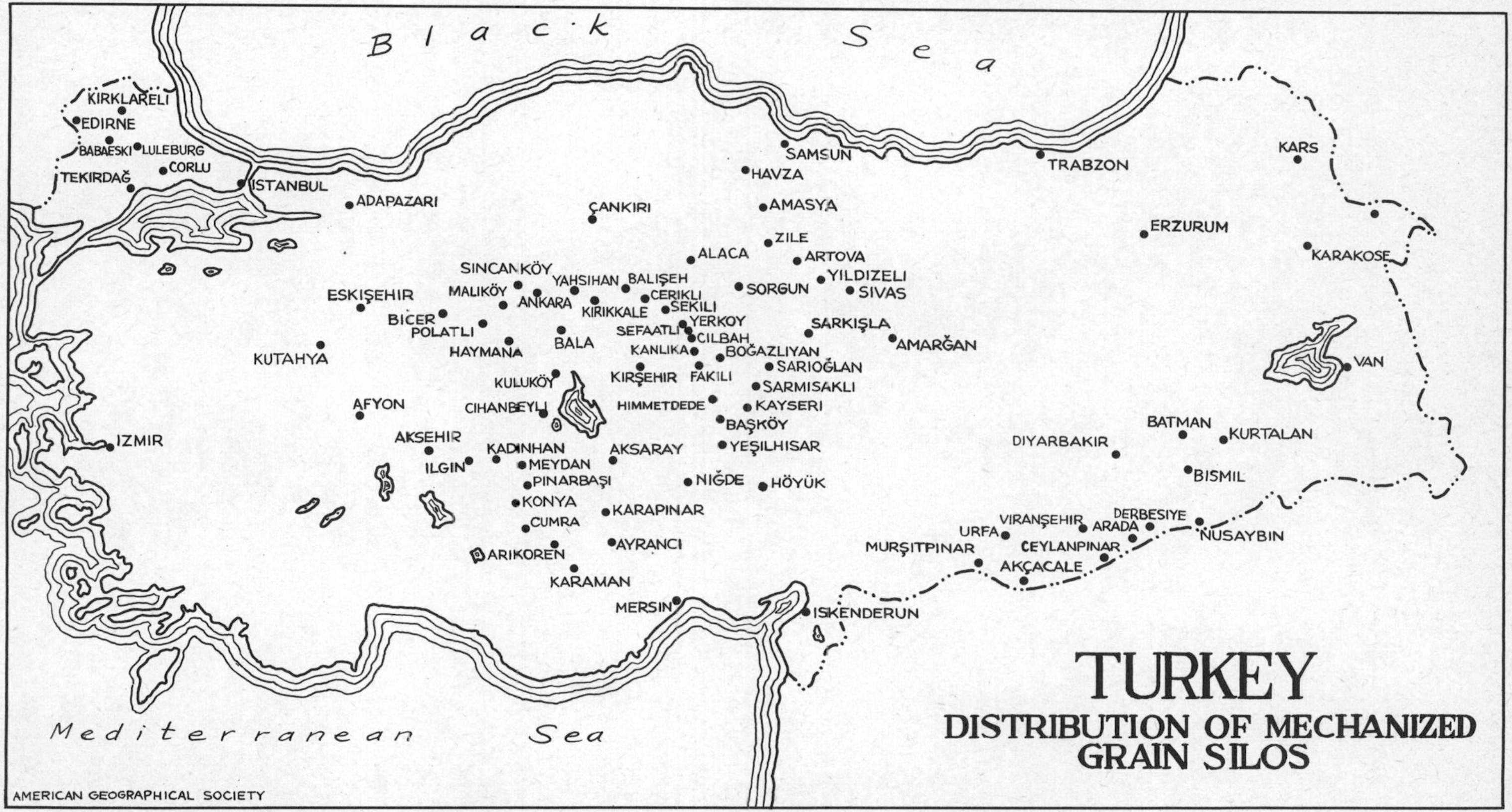

TURKEY
DISTRIBUTION OF MECHANIZED GRAIN SILOS

Black Sea

Mediterranean Sea

KIRKLARELİ
EDIRNE
BABAESKİ • LÜLEBURG
ÇORLU
TEKİRDAĞ

İSTANBUL

ADAPAZARI

ÇANKIRI

İZMİR

KÜTAHYA

AFYON

ESKİŞEHİR
BİÇER
POLATLI

AKSEHİR

HAYMANA

KULUKÖY
CİHANBEYLİ

SİNCANKÖY
MALIKÖY
ANKARA
YAHSİHAN BALIŞEH
KIRIKKALE
ÇERİKLİ
SEFAATLI
KANLIKA
KIRŞEHİR
BALA

KADINHAN
İLGİN
MEYDAN
PINARBAŞI
KONYA
ÇUMRA

ARIKÖREN

KARAMAN

MERSİN

İSKENDERUN

SAMSUN

HAVZA
AMASYA
ZİLE
ALACA
ARTOVA
YILDIZELİ
SORGUN
SİVAS
ŞARKIŞLA

AMARĞAN

YERKÖY
CİLBAH
BOĞAZLIYAN
FAKILI
SARIOĞLAN
SARMISAKLI
KAYSERİ
HİMMETDEDE
BAŞKÖY
AKSARAY
YEŞİLHİSAR
NİĞDE
HÖYÜK
KARAPINAR
AYRANCI

TRABZON

ERZURUM

KARS

KARAKÖSE

VAN

BATMAN
KURTALAN
BİSMİL
NUSAYBİN

DİYARBAKIR

DERBESİYE
ARADA
VİRANŞEHİR
CEYLANPINAR
AKÇACALE
URFA
MÜRŞİTPINAR

AMERICAN GEOGRAPHICAL SOCIETY

EGYPT

I. GENERAL REMARKS

Egypt, which since 1958 constitutes the southern province, or region, of the United Arab Republic, may best be described as a long, narrow, extremely fertile valley surrounded by desert. This is well shown in Map 1, depicting Egypt's agricultural lands. At present, at least 95% of its 100 million hectares are either desert or otherwise uncultivable land and, as a result, almost all the inhabitants, estimated to number about 25 million, live within the confines of the Nile Valley and the Nile Delta. Population density along these areas may be as high as 695 persons per square kilometer, while the population is increasing at a rate of over 2% per annum. The pressure of a large and expanding population on the limited agricultural resources of the country is probably the most serious problem Egypt must face.

Agriculture is the most important constituent of the national economy of Egypt, providing 290 million Egyptian pounds of a total national income of 955 million pounds (1958). Approximately 70% of the inhabitants derive their livelihood from agricultural pursuits, too high a percentage if it is remembered that less than 5% of the total land area is arable. There is therefore an excess of agricultural labor available, and the extremely high yields per hectare are in contrast to the extremely low yields per man hour of labor. An estimated 30% of the total agricultural population is considered surplus and there is no alternate employment. Industrial development plans, such as the Five Year Plan currently in operation, seek to provide additional employment opportunities, while the hydroelectric power to be provided by the Aswan Dam, now under construction, is expected to spur a considerable industrial expansion that may employ some of these surplus workers.

Since the basic problem facing Egyptian agriculture in general and food production in particular is one of lack of cultivable land, many avenues of attack are being explored in attempts to increase acreage. One of the most successful has been conversion of basin irrigated land to perennial irrigation as more water has become available from storage dams. Basin irrigation, the type of irrigation practiced for centuries, permits the sowing of only one crop a year, whereas with perennial irrigation two and sometimes even three crops a year may be grown. Table 1 shows the total area devoted to winter (Chetwi), summer (seifi), and autumn (nili) crops between 1940 and 1957. Land planted with summer crops has increased with the extension of perennial irrigation. The High Dam at Aswan alone is expected to convert 700,000 feddans from basin to perennial irrigation.

Other methods of increasing the cultivated area depend on reclamation schemes of various kinds. The Liberation (Tahir) province is located in the desert west of the delta and south of Alexandria, and consists entirely of reclaimed land that is expected to include eventually over 400,000 hectares. Twelve districts of 11 villages each are planned, to be inhabited by carefully selected families. Agriculture in this province is expected to specialize in fruit and vegetable growing and it already contains the largest orchard in Egypt.[19] Another type of reclamation, such as that carried out in Abis, consists of draining delta marsh lands that are now uncultivable and preparing them for agriculture. The most important reclamation scheme is that connected with the Aswan dam. This dam, started in 1960, is expected to increase the cultivable land of Egypt by 30% (2 million acres), most of it to be reclaimed from what is now desert.

Another reclamation scheme now under way is that of the New Valley land in the vicinity of Kharga, Dakhla, Siwa, and Farafia. This project is under the aegis of the Desert Reclamation Authority.

Appendix 1 discusses the different types of schemes for increasing the cultivable area of Egypt and briefly describes the most important projects in each category, including those touched upon above.

As in other Middle Eastern countries, the traditional type of absentee land ownership in Egypt has been a deterrent to agricultural progress. Only a small proportion of the fellaheen owned the land they farmed. The remainder were either tenant farmers or sharecroppers. A considerable portion of the cultivable land was in the hands of large absentee owners who charged high rentals or received most of the harvest, so that net earnings of peasants were very low. The present regime in Egypt approved a land redistribution scheme that prohibited ownership of more than 80 to 120 hectares of cultivable land. The excess was bought and paid for with 30-year bonds and the land thus purchased was distributed, preferably to cultivators already working the land, at the rate of 1 to 2 hectares per family. Land covered by the act affected only 10% of the total available, a maximum of 325,000 hectares. As of 1958, some 114,360 hectares had been distributed to 68,737 families, totaling 466,495 individuals.[19]

Where the farm was owned by the cultivator, holdings were generally extremely small, the majority less than one acre in extent. This was partly because of inheritance laws that resulted, ultimately, in the division of property in unworkably small plots.

II. FOOD RESOURCES OF THE COUNTRY

A. GENERAL

A major portion of Egypt's arable land is devoted to the growing of food and fodder. The average allocation of cultivated land can be summarized as follows:

Crops grown	% of total land under cultivation
Cereals for human consumption	50
Fodder	21
Cotton	16
Vegetables	2
Fruit	1
Other crops	9

Since food crops occupy a major portion of cultivated land, the cash value of food crops produced far surpasses the value of nonfood crops. This is shown in Table 2, which details the cash value of the most important categories of crops grown between 1954-1955 and 1956-1957. As shown by the table, food crops in 1956-1957 had a cash value of 319 million Egyptian pounds, while nonfood crops had a cash value only of 188 million pounds.

Most crops are gathered in late spring or early summer since, as already shown in Table 1, most crops are planted in winter. The harvest seasons of the principal crops grown are shown in Table 3.

Production of many food crops has increased substantially in recent years, in line with the Government's aim of making the country self-sufficient in foods. Production of vegetables has reportedly doubled since 1952, wheat production increased by 28%, rice by 69%, and sugar rose by 7% between 1952 and 1957.

Table 4 lists the latest available data on area and production of the principal food and cash crops, all of which are discussed in some detail below. The percentage distribution of crops in the different provinces is shown in Map 2. The data on the map refer to 1950 but, although the area of arable land has increased since that date, the proportion of lands planted to various crops has remained substantially as shown.

B. CEREALS

Corn, wheat, barley, rice, and sorghum are the principal cereals grown. Although land planted and yields have increased substantially in recent years, the amounts produced are not sufficient to satisfy demand and additional quantities have to be imported.

About 70% of the total area planted to grains is devoted to corn and wheat, while sorghum and barley, also used as bread grains, occupy less than one fifth of cereal acreage and rice about one tenth. Grain yields are among the highest in the world.[24]

Corn, locally called **thura** or **dura shami**, is the most important grain, occupying about one fifth of the total crop area and 44% of the land devoted to cereals. Production of corn in Egypt in 1958 amounted to 1,758,000 metric tons.[16] This grain constitutes the staple food of the fellaheen, while the dry stalks left on the field after harvesting provide fodder for farm animals.[7] Seed is planted in late summer, from mid-July to early August, and harvesting takes place in October to November. About 70% of the total area planted to corn is in the delta and most of the remainder is planted north of the Asyut Barrage, since to the south, sorghum replaces corn as the important grain crop.

Corn plantings occupy more than one half the total crop area in Sharqiya, Minufiya, Gharbiva, and Beheira, and more than 20% in Qalubiya, Minya, Giza, and Beni Suef.[2]

Large quantities of wheat are harvested and production rivals that of corn, averaging slightly over 1,400,000 tons a year,[8] grown on about 600,000 hectares. The amount produced supplies only slightly more than one half of local demand and additional quantities must be imported.

Two types of wheat are grown, the **baladi**, which is indigenous, and the **lindi**, which was introduced from India. The latter, which has higher yields and better baking qualities, is now the dominant variety. More than 60% of wheat grown is planted in the delta and the remaining acreage is about equally divided between Middle and Upper Egypt. Sarqiya, Gharbiya, and Beheira are the principal wheat-growing areas in the delta and Faiyum is the chief area south of the delta, but in each province wheat occupies at least 10% of total crop land. Sowing is done in October and November and harvesting begins in March.

Rice (**roz** or **orz**) is a popular food, especially in urban areas, but is not as important in the diet as maize or wheat.[12] In years of poor corn harvest, consumption of rice increases. The Nile delta is the main rice-growing area, containing about 96% of the total area planted to this crop. Rice cultivation in any one year depends on the amount of water available in storage fron Nile floods and, in years of water shortage, the government fixes the amount of land that can be planted and assigns to each grower his share of the total. Consequently, there are large yearly variations of from 80,000 to 300,000 hectares in the land devoted to rice. Production of rice varies in proportion; thus, the amount produced in 1957 was 1,709,000 tons, in 1958 only 1,082,000 tons, and in 1959 it rose to 1,545,000.[16] During 1958, rice exports were prohibited by the Ministry of Supply (**Ministère d'Approvisionnement**) in order to conserve supplies for local markets.

Sorghum, (**dura baladi, dura oweiga,** or **dura raffi'a**) is grown only

in the Nile valley, where the drier, hotter climate is more suited to
this crop than the climate of the delta. This is the principal grain
crop south of the Asyut Barrage, and about one half of the total area
planted to sorghum lies in the Asyut and Gharbyia provinces.

Sorghum supplements and, in southern areas to a large extent replaces, corn as the principal cereal in the diet and the entire crop,
which varies between 500,000 and 600,000 tons a year, is consumed on
the farms.

Barley, or **sha'ir,** is the least important of Egypt's food grains and
it is grown chiefly for use in brewing and as fodder in areas too poor
to yield good wheat crops.[19] In addition, it is grown on some 15,000
hectares of irrigated land and on an additional 7,000 of rain-fed
coastal lands cultivated by bedouins. The yield in these coastal areas
is uncertain because of the fluctuations in rainfall.[7] Total acreage
and production of barley has considerably decreased from prewar
totals, which averaged 233,000 tons between 1935 and 1939,[8] to less
than 150,000 tons in recent years. Production in 1959 was estimated
at 142,000 tons grown on 59,000 hectares. Beheira province in the
delta and Qena in Upper Egypt are the principal growing areas, with
Aswan and Sharqiya second in importance.[21]

C. OTHER EDIBLE CROPS

1. Vegetables. Many kinds of vegetables are grown; the yield in
general is high and the quality is good. Except for onions, however,
vegetables have only a very limited place in the rural diet and in urban areas are eaten largely on a seasonal basis and in small quantities. Total area devoted to vegetable cultivation in 1957 was estimated
at about 150,000 hectares, 3% of the total crop area. Most of the crop
is eaten where it is grown and commercial truck farming is carried
out only near large urban centers.

Except for onions and garlic, Egypt is a net importer of almost all
vegetables. Onions are by far the most important vegetable grown,
both as a component of the diet and as a cash crop for export. They
are eaten almost daily by the rural population and consequently are
grown almost everywhere in the valley and the delta. Commercial
growing for export is confined to the Upper Valley, which produces
85% of the export crop, mostly in Girga and Minya. Beheira is the
only important onion-growing area in the delta, but its yield and quality are inferior to valley-grown onions. During 1959 some 58,000
hectares of onions were planted and production was estimated at
462,000 tons.

Tomatoes are plentiful year-round but are used primarily for cooking and are not generally eaten fresh. They were grown on some
43,000 hectares in 1957 and production amounted to 604,000 tons, of

which a small proportion was exported. Potatoes were grown on
15,000 hectares and a total of 240,000 tons was produced. Other vegetables of lesser importance include egg plants, okra, cauliflower,
cabbages, and spinach. The acreage and production of the most important varieties grown in 1957 are shown in Table 4.

   2. Seed legumes.[7] Seed legumes are important crops used almost
exclusively for domestic consumption. They are grown over a wide
area and some, such as lentils, can be found almost anywhere. Chick
peas, a staple of diet, are grown under basin irrigation, chiefly in
Middle and Upper Egypt. The vetchling, or prass pea, sometimes is
planted in Upper Egypt, while the bitter tupin, which must be boiled to
remove the bitter taste before it can be used as food, is adapted to
sandy areas and is grown to the west of the Nile and in the Liberation
province. **Moki,** or lima beans, are well adapted to hot, dry climates
and have the further advantage of being considerably resistant to
drought. Horse beans are one of the most important of the seed
legumes. During 1958, 33,000 hectares of lentils sown yielded 48,000
tons, 149,000 hectares of broad beans produced 210,000 tons, and
4,000 hectares of chick peas produced 6,000 tons.

   Fenugreek, **Trigonella foenumgreekum,** is used in varying proportions in the baking of the corn bread that is the main component of the
rural diet. The aromatic seeds are popular both in cooked and in un-
cooked dishes so that the annual crop, which is estimated at some
30,000 tons, is all consumed locally. Although it is grown throughout
Egypt, about 70% of production is in the Upper Valley, mainly in Girga
and Qena provinces.

   Table 4 includes the acreage and production of some of the more
important pulses grown.

   3. Fruits. A large variety of fruits are grown, including tropical
and subtropical types as well as a few characteristic of temperate
climates.[7] Many are of high quality and their early ripening would
insure a good market for them in Europe if they could be produced in
exportable amounts. However, the total area devoted to orchards is
still extremely small and production is low. Reasons for this include
lack of agricultural capital, the long wait required before there are
returns from investment in comparison with immediate returns from
annual crops, lack of trained personnel, and the high cost of marketing
the fruit.[21]

   Despite these disadvantages, land devoted to fruit growing is increasing and has more than tripled in comparison with prewar cultivation. A large part of the increased area is devoted to citrus fruits.
The total area and production of the most important fruits grown between 1954 and 1957 are shown in Table 4.[21]

   Despite increases in production, amounts of fruits available are
still so low as to place the price of fruits beyond the reach of all except the well-to-do.

The principal orchard area is the southeastern part of the delta, where the markets of Cairo and the Suez Canal are within reach. The privinces of Qalubiya and Sharqiya in this area contain 30% of all orchards. A second important fruit-growing zone is in Beheira province near Alexandria, where 20% of the fruit growing is undertaken.

Some temperate zone fruits are grown, but the total number of trees is small and the fruit, except for apricots, are of poor quality. Apples do not grow well and only a few hundred **feddans** are devoted to apple orchards. Pears are the major pome fruit grown, although some quinces and loquats also are produced. Among the stone fruits, peaches, apricots, plums, nectarines, and cherries are grown in limited amounts. The first three mentioned are the most important.

Nuts, including almonds, pecans, and pistachios, all are grown, but their cultivation is of relatively little importance to the agricultural economy. The almond grows especially well in cultivated areas of the western desert and is a good potential crop for that region.

The most important of the subtropical and tropical fruits grown include citrus fruits, dates, bananas, grapes, guavas, mangoes, and olives.

Citrus fruits are grown on some 60,000 **feddans** and include mainly oranges (**bortoqal**) and limes (**leimoon**). Planted land increases yearly but total annual production of about 350,000 tons (1958) is barely sufficient for local demand; at times additional quantities are imported.

Egypt ranks sixth among the date-producing countries of the world. Date palms are found all along the Nile from the Mediterranean coast to Khartoum and in the large oases, including Siwa, Bahariya, Farafia, Dekhla, Kharga, and Faiyum. There are probably more than 6 million trees, of which 44% are in the delta, 40% in Middle Egypt, and the remaining 16% in the four southernmost provinces. Many types of dates are grown, some through seedlings and others, known as varietals, are propagated from trunk shoots.[21] Production in 1957 amounted to 364,000 tons and most of the crop is consumed locally.

Grapes have been increasing in importance as a crop and production has about trebled from a prewar average of 30,000 tons a year.[8] At first only table grapes were grown, but today many of the vineyards supply grapes to wineries, which have been recently established, for example in Alexandria. Beheira province is the chief growing region and contains nearly one half of the vineyard area.[21] Guavas are not extensively marketed and are not important as a commercial crop, but they are one of the principal fruits eaten by the rural inhabitants and for that reason are important in the diet. They are grown everywhere and it is estimated that there are more than 750,000 trees.[21]

Mangoes, which rank in importance after citrus and grapes as market fruits, also are extensively used. Principal growing areas are in Giza, Sharqiya, and Beheira provinces and the cultivated area has increased from 1,674 hectares in 1945 to 6,967 in 1957.

There are nearly 400,000 pomegranate trees, chiefly in the Nile valley; the Manfalut district in Asyut is particularly noted for its fine pomegranates.[21] Bananas are rather intensively grown and are a cash crop of some importance. Plantings, mostly located in Beheira, Minufiya, and Qalubiya have increased greatly from 1,458 hectares in 1945 to 3,273 in 1957. Watermelons are extremely popular and are an important crop, cultivated on some 22,500 hectares. Figs are grown to a limited extent in coastal areas, with the principal producing districts in Qalubiya province in the delta. Figs are all consumed in the producing area since the varieties grown are extremely perishable and cannot be transported without damage.

4. Oil crops. The amount of oil crops produced is insufficient to supply the oil-extraction industry, and small additional quantities of oil-bearing seeds are imported from the Sudan.

Peanuts (**fool sudani**) and sesame (**simsim**) are important as food crops both when eaten directly and as sources of the cooking oils extracted from them. Total area grown in 1958 included 16,000 hectares of peanuts and 17,000 of sesame, and production amounted to 33,000 tons of peanuts and 14,600 tons of sesame.

Both peanuts and sesame are grown throughout the Nile valley, but areas of concentrated production are limited. About 60% of the peanuts are grown in the eatern part of Sharqiya province, while 85% of the sesame crop comes from only three provinces: 35% from Sharqiya, 30% from Asyut, and 20% from Girga.[21]

Another important source of edible vegetable oil is cotton, the seeds of which, a by-product of ginning the fibers, are an important source of cooking oil. Some 852,000 tons of seeds were produced in 1958. Cottonseeds are the source for most of the vegetable oil consumed.

5. Sugar crop. Climate and soil conditions of the Upper Nile valley are particularly suited to the planting of sugar cane and this has become the principal industrial crop of the four southernmost provinces. Land planted in Qena, where sugar is the leading summer crop, contributes about 60% of total production. Some 54,875 hectares were planted to sugar cane in 1957 and production was estimated at over 4 million tons. Three fourths of the cane planted was used for the manufacture of sugar and the remainder was eaten fresh or used for making molasses. Growing of sugar cane is largely concentrated in the vicinity of the larger mills, including the ones at Kom Ombo in Aswan and at Armaut and Nag Hammadi in Qena. These mills produce three fourths of the raw sugar milled, which amounts to 300,000 tons a year.

D. CASH CROPS

Cotton is the most important cash crop of Egypt and the main source of foreign exchange. The production, distribution, and marketing of cotton are very efficiently organized, and a large amount of excellent agricultural research has been devoted to improving the crop.[7] Approximately 800,000 hectares are planted to cotton and the average production is more than 400,000 tons per year.[8] Acreage planted to cotton may be limited at times by the government in order to ensure the planting of food crops, or when foreign sources of food staples are cut off, as happened during the last war. Restrictions on cultivation also are imposed when floods have been low and the water levels in storage reservoirs drop. The land planted to cotton therefore may vary from year to year.

Foreign exchange provided by cotton enables Egypt to import food stuffs required to supplement domestic supplies. In addition, as mentioned above, cottonseeds constitute the main source of vegetable oils in the diet.

E. ANIMAL PRODUCT RESOURCES

Livestock raised in Egypt include cattle, water buffalo, sheep, goats, horses, donkeys, mules, camels, rabbits, and poultry. Horses, donkeys, and mules are used primarily as beasts of burden; cattle, water buffaloes, and camels are used both as work animals and as sources of meat and milk, and sheep and goats provide meat, milk, and wool. The limited amount of land available for agricultural purposes restricts the development of animal husbandry and the number and type of animals that can be raised economically.[7] Animal husbandry is integrated with the farming economy to a much greater extent in Egypt than elsewhere in the Middle East, principally because of the planting of **berseem**, Egyptian clover, as a rotation crop on most farms.[9] This is the main fodder crop grown.

Meat, poultry, eggs, and milk are not much used by the fellaheen producing them. Most of the milk produced is sold for cash either in the fluid state or as butter and cheese. The same is true for eggs, which are rarely eaten by the peasants. The only source of animal proteins in regular use in rural communities is skim milk cheese.[15]

Dairy cattle are more common in the lowlands of the delta since they are the source of supply of milk and dairy products for the large city markets.[7] Beef cattle, on the other hand, are more common in other parts of Egypt.

The water buffalo or **gamoosa** is hardy, more resistant to disease, well adapted to the climate, and of gentle disposition.[17] The buffalo is favored as a farm animal, especially on smaller farms, where it may live with the family and serves in winter as a heating unit. The number of cattle and water buffaloes are about equal, with the buffalo the more important as a milk producer since it contributes about 65% of the milk supply; cattle are valued more for meat than for milk. The number of cattle in 1958 was 1.4 million and the number of buffalo probably the same or slightly higher.

Sheep are kept primarily for meat and wool and goats for hair, milk, and meat. They provide farmers with a second cash income while supplementing the domestic milk supply. Approximately 1.26 million sheep and 723,000 goats were owned in 1958; about 10% of the animals are herded by bedouins and most of the remainder are kept by small farmers although there are a few large flocks. Larger numbers are raised along the valley than in the delta, which contains only about 35% of the sheep and 20% of the total number of goats.

Pigs are raised in small numbers by the Copt population in Qena, Asyut, and Minya, and pork meat is consumed by Copts and European residents only, since Moslems are forbidden the use of pork by their religion. Amounts produced are not sufficient to supply domestic demand and additional quantities are imported.

The donkey is the principal beast of burden and slightly less than one million were owned in 1958. Camels are not well adapted to the climate of the valley and delta but are still used in some numbers as beasts of burden; about 200,000 were owned in 1958. Horses and mules seldom are seen outside of urban areas, and there were only 45,000 horses and 11,000 mules in 1958.

Before World War II, Egypt was an exporter of shell eggs at the rate of 100 to 200 million per year. Although production has increased in recent years, demand has increased in such proportion that all supplies are now sold in local markets.[11]

Poultry are raised everywhere in the countryside. Chickens, geese, turkeys, pigeons, and ducks have the run of houses and yards and live on what they can forage. As a result, animals are ill-nourished, their meat is tough and stringy, and they produce eggs small in size and few in quantity.[17]

Eggs are sold or bartered for sugar, tea, soap, and vegetables. They are occasionally eaten by the men and older boys in the rural families but are considered bad for the liver and are generally avoided. Egg production amounted to 35,300 tons in 1957, equivalent to more than 750 million eggs. The number of eggs produced and incubated and the number of chickens hatched between 1941 and 1957 is shown in Table 5.

Turkey breeding is at an early stage in Egypt, but is has great possibilities for development in desert regions. Egyptian turkeys are a mixture of different types, colors, and sizes, but generally they are smaller, less productive, and less palatable than foreign types. Ducks and geese are the most popular water birds and are often seen in flocks on swamps and canals near farms and villages.

The total number of poultry in 1957-1958 was estimated at slightly over 62 million, a rise of 2 million in one year.

Fish is an article of diet only in producing areas, i.e. near coasts or lakes, since facilities for transporting fish long distances to markets are nonexistent.[12] Marine fishing produces about 10,000 tons of fish per year, while inland waters yield about 25,000 tons of fish. Areas of inland water amount to about one fifth of the area of arable land. The chief areas of inland fishing include the four large delta lakes, Menzaleh, Brullos, Idku, and Mariut, together with Lake Qarun in the Faiyum basin. The fisheries of Lake Qarum alone employ 2,000 men.[13] The species of fish eaten varies with the region and the season. One of the most popular fishes eaten is the mullet or **bouri**, which is used fresh or salted, when it is known as **fessikh**.

Meat is obtained from animals that are either slaughtered by farmers at local abbatois—with the meat then sold in the market—or from animals sold to butchers on the hoof. Total animal slaughter in 1957 included 75,000 cattle, 421,000 calves, 62,000 buffaloes, 26,000 pigs, 457,000 sheeps and 21,000 goats. Total production of meat in that year was estimated at 234,000 tons, including 192,000 tons of beef and veal, 41,000 tons of mutton and lamb, and 1,000 tons of pork. Production is not enough to satisfy local demands and must be supplemented by imports. Cattle, sheep, camels, and goats are imported for slaughter in addition to canned meat and meat preparations.

Most of the milk produced comes from animals kept primarily for draft purposes; although there are some herds of dairy cattle, few of these have high-quality dairy stock. Over one million tons of milk are produced yearly, of which more than 70% is buffalo milk, about 35% cow's milk, and the remainder sheep and goat milk. Approximately 50% of the total milk supply is converted into butter, 40% into cheese, and only about 10% is consumed as fresh milk. The division into by-products for the years 1954-1956 was as follows:[4]

Amounts of fluid milk used in manufacturing dairy products

Year	Butter	White cheese	Dry cheese	Milk
1954	665,054	493,690	17,280	123,052
1955	693,014	514,445	18,007	138,643
1956	712,080	549,696	19,968	142,416

Fluid milk rarely is used in Egypt, except for cooking, and less than 4 kg. per capita are used in this form. Milk is sold from door to door in cities and generally is boiled before using. Adequate transportation and refrigeration facilities are lacking at present. Pasteurized milk is available in small amounts in some of the larger cities and production in 1957 amounted to 4,624 tons of fluid milk in addition to small amounts of pasteurized milk products, including 893,469 cartons of yoghurt, 2 tons of condensed milk, 216 tons of butter, and 47 tons of cheese.

Most of the butter and cheese is processed on a family basis in rural households or as a cottage industry in villages and towns. Butter, in both urban and rural households, is converted into clarified butter or **ghee**, which is called **samna** or **masli** in Egypt. This is a coarsely granular rather rancid fat which keeps well without refrigeration and is a common article of diet.

Cheese making is also primarily a household industry. The most common type is a moist white skim milk cheese; it is stored by both urban and rural families in large earthenware jars that can keep one year's supply at a time to ripen. Some 109,939 tons of this cheese were made in 1957.

F. EXPORTS AND IMPORTS

Exports of agricultural products constitute the main source of foreign exchange and amount in value to more than 80% of the value of all exports:

	1954	1956	1957	1958
Percentage of total value of exports	87.8	84.1	85.2	82.4

Cotton is by far the most important export product, ranging in value from 65% to 75% of the value of all exports. The tonnage exported and the value fluctuates from year to year in accordance with the acreage planted and the yield, but in any given year cotton is the paramount export.

The second most important agricultural product exported is rice, which accounted for more than 8% of all export sales in 1958. Other agricultural products exported included fresh and dehydrated onions, which made up 2.4% of total exports, and a variety of other items including white cheese, garlic, tomato sauce, peanuts, and potatoes. The amount and value of the principal agricultural exports of Egypt in 1958 are detailed in Table 6.

Egypt must supplement domestic production with imports of certain food stuffs that are in short supply. The most important food item imported is wheat, which constitutes 10.2% of total imports in value and 40% of the value of all agricultural imports.

Tea is second to wheat in importance among food items imported and accounts for 3.2% of total import value, while coffee amounts to only 0.9% of the total value of imports. Other items imported in smaller amounts include powdered, condensed, and evaporated milk, processed cheese, vegetables, legumes, and preserved and frozen meat preparations, as well as edible oils. Severe import restrictions designed to foster the development of Egyptian industries and to reduce the unfavorable trade balance are in effect and have served to reduce imports of food stuffs. Table 6 lists the kind, amounts, and value of the principal imports as well as the percentage of total trade that each category represents.

G. INTERNATIONAL TECHNICAL AID

Several international and national agencies have helped to finance cooperative technical aid programs in agriculture and nutrition. Most important among these are the various United Nations technical agencies, including the Food and Agriculture Organization, the World Health Organization, and UNICEF.

As of 1959, the FAO financed projects in land and water use, plant production and protection, control of animal diseases, rural welfare, agricultural economics, fisheries development, and nutrition. Excellent studies in nutritional problems in Egypt have been prepared by experts of both the FAO and the WHO, usually working together. The WHO cooperates in the development of the Nutrition Institute of Egypt and works with the FAO in regional nutrition programs and committees.

The United States Operations Mission in Egypt of the International Cooperation Administration has carried out numerous studies and projects in such fields as soil salinity, drainage, underground water supplies, and livestock improvement.

H. FOOD INDUSTRIES, STORAGE AND TECHNOLOGY

1. Food processing. Egypt is not a highly industrialized country and food-processing industries are not too highly developed. Agricultural products provide the raw material for nearly three fifths of all factories, employing 64% of industrial workers, but more than one half of these are cotton gins, textile mills, and other factories processing nonfood crops.[3]

Except for the milling of cereals, only a small percentage of food is processed before use; must of this processing, including especially the preparation of dairy products and the baking of bread, is carried out on a small household or communal scale in villages.

Later estimates are not available, but for the period 1947-1951 the proportion of processed crops to total production of principal crops was as follows:

onions	4%	millet	94%
citrus fruits	5%	corn	88%
peanuts	12%	rice	89%
barley	20%	wheat	191% (incl. imports)
	sugar 70%		

Large modern food processing factories are of rather recent introduction, a development that has been given impetus by the industrial development plan now in operation. Factories built under this plan include a cannery, a date-drying plant, a factory for processing cheese, and one for the preparation and packaging of frozen shrimps. The cost, capacity, and number of employees of new factories already in operation as of 1959 was as follows:[2]

Project	Cost, £E	Capacity, tons	Employees, No.
Edfina canned foods	200,000	4,000	100
Date-drying factory	300,000	3,500	120
Processed cheese factory	22,000	300	16
Frozen prawn plant	75,000	600	60

Other factories that were to have been in operation by December 1959, included the following:[2]

Project	Cost, £E	Capacity, tons	Employees, No.
Sardines and shrimp plant	170,000	2,500	100
Milk plant	700,000	10,500	120
Oil extraction plant	210,000	1,200	80

New plants for dehydrating foods and for processing dairy and other products are planned but details on location and type are not available.

Total amounts of the different food stuffs processed between 1949 and 1957 are listed in Table 7, which details the amounts of rice, canned food products, confectionery, dairy products, and alcoholic beverages produced throughout those years.[4]

The imposition in 1932 of a high tariff on imports of flour and meal stimulated the development of the milling industry, and there are several thousand mills in operation, constituting more than 40% of food-processing establishments. Although numerous small village mills are in operation, most of the flour used is produced in large mills distributed along the Nile Valley and easily accessible to producing farms. More than one half of the flour milled is processed in the 226 flour mills operated by the **Ministérè d'Approvisionnement.** Two kinds of flour are milled: ordinary flour of 82% extraction rate, which is used in making the **baladi** type of bread, and a **de luxe** flour of 72% extraction rate, which is used to make European-style breads, **chami** bread, and pastries. This type of flour is milled exclusively from imported wheat.

The husking and bleaching of rice is a special branch of the milling industry, and numerous **rizeries** are scattered throughout the producing areas of the northern delta, principally in Alexandria Rosetta, Damietta, El Mansura, Faraskur, Dikirnis El Manzulla, and El Mahalla el Kubra. During 1957-1958 some 1.8 million tons of paddy rice were processed, yielding 1.1 million tons of milled rice.

More than 2,000 bakeries are in operation, most of them small establishments in cities and towns, since urban dwellers are the main consumers of baked goods. Baking in rural communities is done in the home or by each housewife in a communal bakery. Most of the bread baked is the flat, Oriental style made of unbleached white flour, although European-style breads and pastries are available in larger towns.[21]

Local demand for macaroni products is almost fully supplied by local producers. During 1957, some 20,000 tons were manufactured and only four tons were imported, while 300 tons were exported.

Although the dairy industry has received great impetus in the past few years, production of milk is not enough to supply the low domestic demands.[6] The main factor limiting consumption is the high price of dairy goods to the consumer while the main factor limiting production is the lack of an assured market.

Only a small proportion of the milk produced, probably less than 10%, is consumed in fluid form. The remainder is converted into butter, cheese, and other dairy products. Over 200 plants operating around Cairo, Alexandria, and in the larger towns of the northern delta process dairy foods, but most of these factories are small and antiquated.[3]

About 50 to 60% of the total amount of milk available is converted into butter, most of it in rural households, and the product is then packed and marketed with little if any reworking. Almost all butter produced is converted by both rural and urban families into clarified butter, called in Egypt **samna** or **masli**. Some **samna** is made by larger dairies and is packed in tins for marketing.

Cheese making also is generally carried out in rural areas, and the fresh white cheese produced is a part of the diet of most farm families and is also sold in towns and cities.

During 1956 a total of 549,696 tons of milk were used to produce 109,939 tons of white cheese. Small amounts of processed cheese, less than 700 tons a year, also are produced.

Small amounts of pasteurized milk are produced in a few of the larger cities and production amounted only to 4,624 tons in 1957. Plans for the expansion of the pasteurized milk industry are included in development plans now in operation. As of 1957 there were 12 collection and refrigeration centers, each with a daily capacity of 5,000 kg. of milk, and plans call for the ultimate establishment of a network of such centers to bring milk from the farms to the cities.

A milk-processing plant has been set up at Sakha with the aid of

UNICEF funds. This plant can convert 20,000 liters of fluid milk into powdered milk daily and can pasteurize an additional 2,000 liters of milk a day. Part of the powdered milk produced is to be distributed free of cost to poor families.[1]

Numerous slaughterhouses are in operation but for the most part hygienic standards are low and slaughtering practices are wasteful. All abbatoirs must be licensed and inspected by the municipality, but it is estimated that at least one third of meats marketed come from animals slaughtered illegally in an effort to forestall condemnation of diseased animals.[3]

Meat preserving is carried out on a small scale, largely by Italian and Greek butchers who prepare ham, bologna, and sausages for foreign residents in the larger cities. These products do not have a wide demand since Moslems eat only fresh meat. During 1957, some 247 tons of sausages, 158 tons of bologna, and 37 tons of hams were prepared.[5]

Frozen shrimp are becoming an important food processing and export item. As of 1958-1959, five factories were in operation and production in 1958 amounted to 488 tons.

The vegetable canning industry is limited by the small local demand and the lack of surplus vegetables suitable for processing, so that dehydrating onions and garlic for export may be regarded as the only important vegetable-processing industry. This is a rapidly expanding field, as is shown by the fact that production increased from 601 tons in 1950 to 4,866 in 1957. Five factories were in operation in 1953, four of them in or near Alexandria and one in Upper Egypt.[3] Employment in this industry is seasonal during the onion harvest, which usually lasts from April to August.

Small amounts of dried tomatoes, tomato paste, and other tomato products are prepared, including 10 tons of dried tomatoes and 836 tons of tomato sauce in 1957. Canned vegetables processed in that year included 250 tons of canned peas and 341 tons of okra. Beans, lentils, and other seed legumes also are canned on a small scale. Production of canned vegetables was to be substantially increased with the opening of the Edfina Canning Co. factory in 1959.

The cultivation of oil-bearing seeds and the extraction of their oil is one of Egypt's most important agricultural processing industries and there are a number of large, modern, and efficient extraction plants. Most of the plants are devoted to the extraction of cottonseed oil, since cottonseeds provide by far the largest proportion, about 95%, of vegetable oil consumed. Annual output of cottonseed oil is around 100,000 tons of which about one fourth is used for soap making. Consumption of sesame seed oil amounts to about 7,000 tons a year, of which local production supplies about one fourth and the rest is extracted from imported seed. A small amount of olive oil is extracted from home-grown olives, but the varieties used are poor oil producers and total output is only a few hundred tons. During 1957 some 85,742 tons of edible vegetable oils from locally-grown seed were consumed and an additional 20,000 tons were imported to satisfy domestic demand.

Margarine is produced in several factories; the five largest of these produced 10,931 tons of margarine in 1957 or 70 to 80% of an annual production of 13,000 to 14,000 tons.[4]

Production of sugar[1,2] used to be a monopoly of the General Company of Sugar Mills and Refineries, but the management of this corporation has now been taken over by the Government. The industry is rapidly expanding, but as of 1958 it still did not produce enough sugar to satisfy domestic needs, although it is possible that production is now sufficient for domestic purposes.[3] During 1957 production amounted to 299,130 tons, of which 17,360 tons were exported and an additional 39,000 tons were imported, leaving a net use of 320,770 tons; in 1958 production amounted to 308,000 tons.

There are more than 100 mills in Upper and Middle Egypt including those at Kom Ombo in Aswan and in Nag'Hammadi; one refinery is in operation at El Hawamdriga. Mills work on a seasonal basis but the refinery operates all year round.

Molasses is an important secondary product and supplies amount to about 90,000 tons a year. About one fourth of the total is exported and most of the remainder is used as a sweetener by rural inhabitants, except for small amounts utilized in the manufacture of alcoholic beverages and the flavoring of soft drinks.[4]

Halawa, a popular confection made with sesame paste, is prepared in numerous small factories. Production has decreased in recent years because a large proportion of the domestic sesame was exported. During 1958 such exports were prohibited unless they were matched by imports. Production of **halawa** in 1957 amounted to 23,884 tons, compared with 26,914 in 1956.

Recent restrictions on imports of cacao and the rise in the price of sugar have resulted in a decrease in production of chocolate candies. During 1957 only 1,750 tons were produced, as compared with 1,935 tons in 1956.

Soft drinks, carbonated beverages, and beer are the most important beverages produced in Egypt. Large quantities of alcohol are distilled from domestic molasses but this is used primarily for vinegar or in the chemical industries, while about one fifth is exported.

More than 100 plants produce soft drinks and carbonated beverages of various kinds. Flavorings and other basic ingredients usually are imported. These beverages are popular primarily among urban dwellers, and consequently the soft drink industry is concentrated in Cairo, Port Said, Ismailia, and Suez, but there are small plants in most of the provincial capitals. Coca Cola and Pepsi Cola have been manufactured for the past few years near Giza and have become universally

popular. Some 368 million bottles of carbonated drinks were produced
in 1957; this amounts to about 40% of the total capacity of the bottling
plants.

Numerous small breweries, usually Greek-owned, make beer, using
both domestic and imported barley. Some 9.7 million liters were produced in 1957 as compared with 9.98 in 1956. About 50,000 liters are
exported annually, while severe import restrictions have reduced imports of beer from 200,000 to 50,000 liters.

Only about 1.5 million liters of alcoholic beverages are made,
mostly rum (38%), brandy (21%), and liqueurs (20%).

2. Storage and refrigeration. Cotton has long been the only crop
efficiently marketed, but the government is now taking steps to organ-
ize and improve the marketing of food stuffs. Four new markets for
the wholesale distribution of cereals and two wholesale markets for
perishable foods have been established. Two new wheat silos are under construction, one at Cairo with a capacity of 40,000 tons, and one
in Alexandria, with 30,000 tons' capacity.[2]

Food-processing industries are being encouraged to utilize perishable foods in their seasons. Model factories for processing both
agricultural and dairy products are operated by the Ministry of Agriculture.

Large packing houses, especially at entry ports such as Alexandria,
Port Said, and Cairo, which is the principal distribution center, are
engaged in repacking food imports for the retail market. Coffee, tea
cocoa, and spices are the principal commodities involved.

There were a total of 45 ice-manufacturing plants as of 1957 with
a total production of 11 million blocks of ice.[4] The seven factories in
Cairo produced 6.5 million blocks, the 11 factories in Alexandria produced 2.2 million blocks, while the remaining 27 factories, scattered
throughout the country, manufactured the balance. Present production
represents only one fifth of the potential capacity of the plants, estimated at 35 million blocks a year.

Present cold-storage facilities were for the most part established
during World War II in connection with food production and distribution
and in order to preserve supplies. Plants were established in Cairo
and at the seaports of Alexandria, Port Said, Suez, and Ismailia. There
are, at present, approximately 30 cold-storage plants with a 1957
capacity of 99,450 cubic meters. Reports state that these plants are
not utilized to capacity. One large plant in Alexandria stores goods
in transit as well as the produce of local markets.

Refrigeration facilities for the storage of food products in farms or
for the safe transportation of perishable goods are almost nonexistent.

III. DIET TYPES

A. GENERAL REMARKS

The diet of the various population groups in Egypt varies in accordance with their geographical distribution, rural-urban composition, and economic status. These variations in diets will be discussed below. Nevertheless, although there is no set pattern that might represent a uniform national diet,[28] there are certain characteristics of food consumption that are common to almost all groups, and the average consumption of available food resources indicates diet patterns in common use.

The major portion of the calories in all population groups is supplied by cereals, which may constitute as much as 75% of the total calories consumed. Legumes are almost universally popular and vegetables, especially onions, are represented on the diet, but fruits are consumed in limited quantities and vegetables and fruits together contribute less than 10% of caloric intake.[17] Cereals also provide a major portion of the proteins of the diet and animal proteins from all sources only account for about 16% of total proteins consumed. Animal foods in the diet are primarily skimmed milk, cheese and clarified butter, with fish available on a regional basis and all meats in very limited amounts.

Food balance sheets prepared for 1947-1948 to 1954-1955 show a gradually increasing consumption of certain foods such as cereals, sugar, and vegetables, but unchanged or diminishing intake of most other diet staples. A summary of the findings of food balance sheets for this interval, presented as Table 8, shows a gradual increase in consumption of cereals, sugar, vegetables, fruits, and meat and a lower consumption of legumes, milk, cheese, and vegetable oils.

The nutrient composition of the diet on a per capita basis, as calculated on data provided by food balance sheets for 1954-1955, is presented in Table 9. This table does not make allowances for waste of nutrients in the preparation and cooking of the meal. The average diet, while adequate in calories and in low-quality proteins, is poor in calcium, vitamin A, riboflavin, and ascorbic acid. The following comparison of actual consumption (deducting cooking allowances for waste) with recommended allowances show these differences clearly:

Nutrient Consumption Level and Recommended Daily Allowances

Nutrient	Consumption level	Recommended allowances
Calories	2200	2200
Protein	69	63
Calcium	0.45	0.98

Nutrient	Consumption level	Recommended allowances
Iron	14.6 mg.	11.6 mg.
Vitamin A	2660 I.U.	4425 I.U.
Thiamine	1.86 mg.	1.19 mg.
Riboflavin	0.94 mg.	1.47 mg.
Niacin	12.8 mg.	11.9 mg.
Ascorbic acid	52 mg.	71 mg.

The total amount of food available, including imports would provide an adequate caloric intake with somewhat low levels of protein consumption, especially of animal proteins, and a low intake of protective foods. These figures for average consumption, however, conceal the very great inequalities in the distribution of available food resources. There is a disproportionately high level of intake among certain economic groups and a correspondingly low consumption in others. In addition, the regional distribution of certain food patterns, as will be discussed below, results in the appearance of specific nutritional diseases in one population groups that are absent in others. For example, pellagra appears in the delta and rickets is observed in Upper Egypt.

The scarcity and high cost of fuel limits cooking to one hot meal a day, usually served in the evenings; sometimes, among very poor families, a hot meal is prepared only every two to three days.[10] Three meals a day are the general rule, with the most important meal of the day the evening one.

Among all but the well-to-do the purchase of food is the most important expense in the family budget. This is true even among the rural population, which expends a major portion of its cash earnings in the purchase of foods it does not produce or produces in insufficient quantities.

Because of the lack of modern storage and canning methods and deficiencies in means of transportation, perishable foods tend to be consumed only at the season and in localities where they are produced.[29] Similarly, poor crop years in a certain area may result in severe local shortages.

B. COMPOSITION OF THE AVERAGE DIET

A detailed food balance sheet that presents the production, trade, supply, distribution and net food supply per capita per year for the years 1954-1956 is included as Table 10. The total caloric intake in those years averaged 2,580 calories, while the protein intake amounted to 75.2 g. of which only 12.9 g. were animal proteins and 62.3 g. were proteins of vegetable origin.

Cereals are the most important components of the Egyptian diet, contributing slightly more than 70% of the total caloric intake, 68% of the proteins, and 33% of the fats.

Total average consumption of wheat between 1954 and 1956 was estimated at 72.2 kg. per capita, but actual consumption is probably much higher in towns and lower in rural areas, since wheat replaces maize as a cereal among the urban population.[12]

Estimated consumption of maize during 1954-1956, based on an annual production of 1,733,000 tons, was 68.3 kg. per capita. Since the population has increased between 1956 and 1958, per capita consumption probably was lower in the latter year. At the 1954-1956 average rates, corn provided about one quarter of the calories consumed, while rice consumption during the same period amounted to 55 lb. of paddy rice per capita.

Average consumption of millet was estimated at 20.8 kg. per capita per year but this is unevenly distributed, being much higher among the rural inhabitants of the southern provinces.

Bread is the invariable staple of diet in all population groups, the daily per capita intake ranging between 480 and 890 g., the amount depending on the economic level of the family—the poorer the family the greater the consumption of bread in relation to other foods. Bread is the main source of calories and in some rural communities may contribute an estimated 75% of the caloric and protein intake.[26] This results in an unbalanced diet with a low consumption of certain vitamins and minerals.

The type of bread eaten will differ in composition and way of preparation in different regions.[26] In the rural communities of the delta, bread is composed mainly of corn meal with varying proportions of wheat flour and about 3% of fenugreek added to enhance the flavor and baking qualities. This type of bread, known as **bettai** or **bettawa**, is baked in thin, flat loaves about 14 inches in diameter. The flour and grain are ground locally, and the bread is baked by the housewives about every 7 to 10 days.[10] Wealthier families use wheat daily, while others mix varying amounts with their corn meal only on feast days to make a special bread.

Wheat flour largely replaces corn meal as an ingredient of bread and is used in most urban communities, although here again proportions vary with local custom and economic status. Commercially baked bread is available in towns and cities. In the south of the country sorghum replaces maize as an ingredient of the staple bread baked.

Cereals also may be eaten in a variety of other ways. A popular dish consists of soured milk mixed with flour and then dried. The composition of this paste (called **kishk**) varies in different communities and may include vegetables, such as red peppers, or other ingredients. Rice is a popular dish but is not as important in the diet as wheat, maize, or sorghum; average consumption of rice amounts to only about one seventh of total cereal consumption.

The diet of Egypt is largely vegetarian, and consumption of meat is

very low, except among the wealthier classes, averaging about 12.7
kg. per capita per year, including 4.3 kg. of beef and veal, 3.7 kg. of
buffalo meat, 1.2 kg. of mutton and lamb, and 2.1 kg. of poultry, as
well as negligible amounts of pork and of goat and camel meat. Meat
is eaten once or twice a week by the well-to-do, once or twice a month
by poorer families, and sometimes only on a half a dozen or so feast
days in the year. The poorest peasants eat meat only once a year on
the occasion of some celebration, and then the meat may only be that
of a very old camel—so tough it must be stewed for three or four days
before it can be eaten.[30] Camel and buffalo are the most commonly
used meats, with sheep and goats reserved for feasts.[10]

Poultry is kept both by rural inhabitants and by town dwellers, who
keep their small flocks on the roofs of their houses.[32] Consumption
of eggs amounted to 1.1 kg. per capita per year, and that of poultry
was estimated at less than 2 kg. per capita for the period 1954 to 1956.
Rabbits and ducks also are raised, but are kept for sale in the markets
and are eaten only on special occasions. Eggs are more commonly
sold than eaten,[32] or they may be bartered for sugar, tea, soap, or
vegetables. Folk superstition considers them bad for the liver and
they are generally avoided in the diet.[10]

Average annual consumption of milk was estimated at 23.3 kg. of
cow's milk and 27.9 kg. of buffalo milk. Milk production generally is
seasonal. During the summer the animals are fed on dry stuff and, in
addition, most of them are pregnant, so that the milk supply is diminished.[31] Many fellaheen own cattle but, as a general rule, milk obtained is sold either in fluid form or as butter or skimmed milk cheese.
This is especially true in the vicinity of cities, where there is a better
market for milk supplies; milk consumption of the rural population
around urban centers may be even lower than the average.[32]

Milk rarely is used in fluid form, except as an ingredient of dishes
such as the flour paste (**kishk**).[32] Skimmed or sometimes whole milk
is soured, then mixed with salt and wheat flour and formed into a
dough, which is dried in the sun and stored for later use. This **kishk**
usually is cooked with water and is eaten at the evening meal. Cream
is made into butter and the skim milk is clotted and made into soft
white cheese, which is a staple of diet. Another popular milk product
is **mish,** which consists of cheese that is aged with a mixture of buttermilk, salt, fenugreek, and red pepper.[10] This product is stored in
earthenware pots.

Fish is not available to the general population but is in common use
along the coast and the Suez Canal area, as well as in fishing villages
on lakes between Alexandria and Port Said.[32] Total consumption of
fish was estimated to average 4.6 kg. per capita per year, including
3.8 kg. of fresh fish, 0.4 kg. of salted, and 0.4 kg. of canned.

Legumes are a favorite dish and an important part of the diet, providing the main source of good quality vegetable protein. Consumption

of legumes for the period 1954 to 1956 amounted to 10.3 kg. per capita
per year and included 5.4 kg. of broad beans and 2.3 kg. of lentils.
The boiled legumes are served flavored with oil or **samna** and onions.
Chick peas, lubia, lupins, and fenugreek are served in this way. Beans
are universally eaten; the dry beans are either boiled and served with
oil, in which case they are known as **ful medanis,** or they are covered
with water and allowed to sprout before boiling, in which case they are
known as **ful nabit.** Another popular bean dish is **tamia,** made by
pounding boiled beans into a paste with leek or parsley, shaping the
paste into cakes, and frying in oil, usually sesame oil.[32]

One of the most detrimental changes in the average diet has been a
reduction in the consumption of legumes, which in 1954-1956 was less
than 50% of prewar consumption and only about 40% of consumption in
1947-1948. Dry legumes are an excellent source of high-quality protein and are especially important in a country with such a low intake
of animal proteins.

During the cooler months leafy vegetables, both wild and cultivated,
are eaten by all groups. In the spring the leaves and tender seeds of
broad beans and chick peas are special delicacies.[10] A large variety
of other vegetables are enjoyed in season, including potatoes, sweet
potatoes, cabbages, egg plants, okra, and many others. The following
list details the methods of serving vegetables in most frequent use.
All the vegetables on the list, except radishes, are eaten boiled; in
addition, those marked with an R are eaten raw, those marked with a
P are pickled, either in brine or vinegar, while those marked D are
dried and stored for future use:

Root and fruit vegetables[32]		Green leafy vegetables	
Turnips	P	Meluchia mallow	D
Carrots	P; R	Cabbage	
Radishes	P; R	Spinach	
Potatoes		Lettuce	R
Taro		Purslane	R
Sweet potatoes			
Onions			
Egg plants			
Okra	D		
Cucumbers	P; R		
Tomatoes	P; R		
Marrows			
Sweet peppers	P		

Watermelons, other types of melons, dates, and other fruits generally are available from July to September, but fruits still rank as an
occasional luxury for all but the well-to-do.[32] Total annual consumption of all fruits was estimated at only 65.7 kg. per capita, and they

contribute less than 5% of calories to the diet. Consumption is higher
among the urban population. In rural communities mulberries, guavas,
and mangoes are grown and consumed locally, and oranges and other
citrus fruits are purchased in small quantities. The total fruit intake,
both in rural and urban areas, is low.

Excessive use of tea and sugar, where families earn regular cash
incomes, proves to be a serious drain on family finances and one that
diverts into relatively nonnutritive purchases money that could be
spent on improving the nutritive value of the diet. The same is true
of the use of carbonated beverages, which enjoy growing popularity in
all areas in which they have been introduced.[10]

1. Urban and rural diets. Urban diets are more varied than rural
ones, since a much wider range and variety of foods is available in
the markets. There are several differences between diets of urban
and rural workers, of which perhaps the most outstanding is the pre-
ponderance of wheat in urban areas, replacing corn as the staple of
diet and the main ingredient of bread. Bread eaten in towns is often
leavened bread made from wheat, and it rarely contains more than
one fourth maize.[32] The diet of urban workers is less dependent on
milk products, but instead they consume larger amounts of meat, fish,
and legumes. Meat is eaten in large quantities by those who can afford
it; among the poorer classes legumes are used as a substitute source
of protein. Another characteristic of urban diets in contrast to rural
is that in towns coffee is the main beverage, while in the country tea
is more generally consumed.

The diet of the fellaheen is more motononous and in general of
lower nutritive value. Unleavened corn bread, the major food item, is
supplemented by vegetables, primarily onions, and by skim milk
cheese, virtually the only source of animal proteins.

The relative importance of these items in the rural diet can be estimated from the results of a survey of the Sindibis area, which showed
that 12% of the families subsist on bread and cheese alone, 56% of the
families add milk products and vegetables occasionally to these two
staples, 25% eat all the above plus meat occasionally, and only 6% eat
vegetables and meat regularly.

Detailed dietary surveys have been carried out by the staff of the
Nutrition Institute of Egypt on two villages in the Toukh district, Kafr
el Hassafa and Mansuriet Namoul. The average food consumption per
adult of certain commodities, in grams per capita per day, is shown
in Table II. Although these figures are not comparable to the national
averages of the food balance sheets, which refer to total population, it
is interesting to note that corn occupies a much more prominent position in these rural diets than it does in the national averages.

The major portion of the cash income of the fellaheen is expended
in the purchase of food. A survey of rural families in three villages
in Ghiza showed that more than 65% of the total income was spent on

food, including approximately 27% on the purchase of cereals and
starches, 7% on sugar, 13% on meat, fish, and eggs, 4% on milk, excluding butter, 1.5% on fats and oils, including butter, and 10% on beverages.

2. **Regional differences in diets.** Important differences in the diet
occur among inhabitants of the delta as contrasted with those of the
Middle and Upper Nile valley, and these differences determine the
type of nutritional deficiency disease most prevalent, as discussed
below.

The diet of the rural inhabitant of the delta, as described above,
consists primarily of corn, some wheat, and rice, and legumes as
staples, supplemented by varying quantities of milk and milk products
and also vegetables and fruit. Fish is eaten in the northern delta but
other types of meat are rarely consumed. Families with a water buffalo make butter, which they sell for cash, and also convert the
skimmed milk to cheese, some of which they also sell. Families without a water buffalo purchase small amounts of cheese and mish or do
without.[10] Vegetables are eaten in season when available, but fruit is
not a regular part of the diet.[10]

Diet patterns change as one progresses South along the Nile. In
Upper Egypt bread is made from millet and wheat flour. Consumption
of corn is almost nil since the climate is more suitable for the cultivation of sorghum and millet. In Middle and Upper Egypt lentils are
grown and consumed in relatively large amounts, and the diet also includes less milk than in the delta, but it does contain plenty of dates.
Other fruits and vegetables are consumed in minimal amounts. Fish
from Aswan Dam is important in the surrounding area.[27]

Diet of the inhabitants of the numerous oases includes cereal, which
is either locally grown or imported from producing areas. Milk and
fish are not part of the diet and olive oil is virtually the only fat.
Dates and other fruits and vegetables are generally abundant, and lentils are an important item in the winter diet of the bedouins.

3. **Variations in diets of different economic classes.** The influence of income level on the selection of the diet is most apparent with
regard to the amount of meat consumed and the availability of milk
products, other than skimmed milk and of fruits, which are, in general,
a luxury item. Some reports state that the very wealthy classes are
badly nourished because they eat too much of too many rich foods,
while the poorer agricultural families, as repeatedly mentioned above,
subsist at a low level of consumption, especially of protective foods
and animal proteins.

A detailed survey was carried out in a rural village in 1951 of the
differences in the diets of industrial workers, landowners, and agriculturists.[26] The village contained a total of 1,005 families of industrial workers, 450 agricultural workers' families, and 661 land-owning
households, and the diets of a selected sample of each group were

compared. It should be noted that more than 80% of the land-owning families owned less than 5 acres. The study showed that industrial laborers, enjoying a higher income, ate more meat, fish, milk and milk products, green vegetables, and fruits than their agricultural neighbors. The average daily caloric intake per adult was highest in the agricultural worker groups, since a larger portion of their diet consisted of cereals. If the three groups were divided as to caloric intake, 72.7% of industrial families, 33.3% of agricultural families, and 60.0% of land-owning families lived on a caloric level below 2,400 calories daily. Table 12 gives details of the average daily food consumption of the most common food items for each of the three groups.

IV. ADEQUACY OF FOOD RESOURCES

The present food resources of Egypt are not enough to satisfy domestic demand, and additional quantities of certain foods, principally wheat, must be imported. This is true in spite of the fact that most of the arable land is devoted to food crops and that food crops contribute by far the greatest share of the value of agricultural products.

The principal reason for this lies in the fact that there is very little arable land, relative to total area, and the expansion of cultivated acreage has not kept pace with the exceedingly rapid rise in population. Thus, in the first 50 years of this century the cultivated area increased by 10% while the population doubled. As a result, larger quantities of food were available before the war on a per capita basis, although total production now is much higher than it was in 1935–1939. This is shown by the following figures, which compare recent agricultural production and food production indices with prewar figures on a total and per capita basis:

Agricultural Production Prewar and 1952 to 1960

	Average 1935–1939	Average 1952–1954	1957– 1958	1958– 1959	1959– 1960
Agricultural production					
Total	90	100	115	116	116
Per capita	123	100	106	104	101
Food production					
Total	83	100	117	114	118
Per capita	114	100	107	102	103
Population index (1953 population = 22,003,000)	73	100	109	112	115

The present land development and reclamation schemes, as outlined in APPENDIX 1, may result in a considerable increase in the acreage of cultivated land, but even this increase may not be able to match the very high rate of population growth, which is about 2% a year.[37]

Other factors that affect the adequacy of food resources include, among others, the prevalence of insect and other crop pests, which cause losses estimated at £40 million Egyptian each year. Animal diseases are prevalent and reduce livestock yields.

Both climatic and human stress factors may further reduce the levels of food production or availability. Droughts may reduce the amount of water available for irrigation—on which all agriculture depend. When the Nile flood is not sufficiently high, less water is available in storage reservoirs and the acreage planted the succeeding year must be reduced accordingly. An economic depression affects the foreign markets for Egypt's cotton, which in turn reduces the amount of foreign exchange needed to purchase food crops not produced in adequate amounts. Equally disruptive are the effects of war and of political disturbances, either of which may seriously reduce the productive capacities of the country.

V. NUTRITIONAL DISEASE PATTERNS

An analysis of the prevalence of deficiency diseases is difficult since information on the occurence and incidence of nutritional diseases is meager; the picture is complicated by the wide occurrence of parasitic infestations that aggravate the effects of poor diets. As has been repeatedly pointed out above, the average diet of the majority of the Egyptian population is not a balanced one nutritionally, and perhaps as many as 75 to 80% of the inhabitants do not receive an adequate diet. Although the caloric intake and total protein consumption is at or above recommended levels, most of the proteins consumed are of vegetable origin and the total consumption of animal products is at an extremely low level. The intake of vegetables and fruits and other food stuffs in the category of protective foods also is extremely low, and available evidence indicates that this is especially true with regard to calcium intake and consumption levels of vitamins A, B_2, and C.

One of the most important characteristics of deficiency diseases in Egypt is the regional nature of their occurence. Thus, pellagra is important in the delta areas and in other areas where maize is the principal cereal, whereas rickets and osteomalacia are more commonly seen in those areas of the Middle and Upper Valley where calcium intake is particularly low.

Although, in general, the presence or absence of nutritional disease

depends on the composition of the regional diet, sometimes factors
other than diet induce secondary or conditioned deficiencies, and it is
probable that a fair number of the nutritional disorders found in Egypt
may be of secondary origin.[28] Examples of this are to be found in the
association of anemia with both low intake of iron and the presence of
hookworm disease, and also in the apparent interaction between
schistosomiasis and pellagra.

In general it would seem safe to state that a variable, but rather
important, proportion of the total population is undernourished, and
that this evident pattern of undernourishment is general throughout
Egypt. Manifestations of this low level of nutrition include the high
infant mortality rate, the high mortality among preschool children,
and the retarded growth rates of infants and young children. There is
a marked difference between the average heights and weights of the
children of rich families and poor children, at least up to the age of
puberty, after which these differences tend to level out. This is due
in part to poverty and in part to ignorance, as is shown in traditional
feeding patterns for children. Parents do not seem to recognize the
special nutritional needs of infants and children and in most families
the growing child receives relatively little attention from a dietary
point of view.[28]

The most important deficiency diseases include pellagra and rickets,
with iron deficiency anemia and others of minor importance. Pellagra
is endemic in Egypt, being associated with the high consumption of
maize and with poverty, which restricts the type of food stuffs available in the diet. There are seasonal peaks of incidence correlated
with periods of maximum exposure to sunlight. The main rise is in
March, with a secondary rise in incidence in October and November.
The disease is most common in villages of the delta but is uncommon
along the coast and in southern Egypt, where millet, wheat, and dates
replace maize as a staple of diet. Pellagra also is rare in cities,
since here wheat replaces corn, to a large extent, as the main cereal
of the diet. Incidence ranges from 0 to 2% with an estimated over-all
incidence of 0.5%.

Numerous pellagra surveys have been carried out and they all bear
out the distribution of the disease outlined above. Thus, an examination of 440 school children in Cairo and in different provinces of
Lower and Upper Egypt disclosed only one case of pellagra, yet at the
same time sporadic cases were reported in the villages around Cairo.
Persons suffering from pellagra may congregate at endemic disease
hospitals, attracted by the free lunches offered to patients attending
clinics, and around Cairo persons suffering from pellagra may constitute as much as 20% of new admissions.

There is a high incidence of pellagra in Qualuba province, north of
Cairo. At Sindibis Hospital, which serves a population of 31,000 at
least 1.6% of all new clinic admissions were for pellagra, and it is

estimated that at least 0.2% of the population shows signs and symptoms of pellagra during February and March, the months of highest
incidence. In this same Sindibis area the incidence of pellagra in
1948, as measured by the presence of gross skin lesions, was tabulated as follows:[30]

| | Males | | Females | |
	No.	%	No.	%
Under 5 years	382	1.0	353	1.0
5 to 9 years	278	9.0	226	12.0
10 to 19 years	358	21.8	275	10.2
over 20 years	976	7.3	1,239	4.1
Total	1,994	9.0	2,093	5.0

At the Kafr el Dawar Hospital, situated in an inland area of the
northern delta, 215 of 10,000 new admissions to the hospital were for
pellagra.

Rickets is prevalent in large towns. In one survey in Cairo 45% of
children under two years of age and 80% of children under 10 years of
age showed definite signs of rickets. Rickets also is common in Upper
Egypt and, to a lesser extent, in Middle Egypt. During 1955 an examination of 3,000 children in a rural area showed that 53% had signs of
rickets.[15] Fifteen per cent of young children reporting at maternal
and child health centers and/or admitted to hospitals in Cairo showed
frank signs of rickets. Aside from these studies definite information
is lacking, but the general impression is that rickets is common, especially in young children. This seems strange in a land of such
strong sunshine, but it should be remembered that when infants are
taken in the street they are swaddled in heavy garments.[33]

Little information is available on the incidence of deficiency diseases due to low intake of riboflavin, vitamin A, and other vitamins,
but such conditions are by no means uncommon.[27]

The incidence of hypochromic anemia due to iron deficiency is high
and it is increased by the high rate of infection with parasites, especially hookworm,[15] and severe cases of anemia often occur. In consequence, anemias of pregnancy are very prevalent; in one study 56%
of the women had low hemoglobin levels.[34]

Kwashiorkor is reportedly common in poorer social groups. Infantile wasting secondary to undernutrition accounted for 16.5% of total
admissions of sick children to the Alexandria University Hospital.[37]
Poverty and ignorance are the underlying causes, since very often
poor mothers will feed infants who are no longer lactating on rice
water or other poor milk substitutes.[28]

VI. CONCLUSIONS

Agriculture is the most important constituent of the economy, providing a substantial portion of the national income while affording a livelihood to about 70% of the working population. There is a large surplus of agricultural labor since arable land amounts to about 5% of total area and the possibilities for expansion are limited. The population is large and increasing rapidly, and the pressure of this expanding population on the limited agricultural resources probably is the most serious problem Egypt must face.

More than one half of the arable land is devoted to the production of food and the total production of most crops has increased substantially in recent years. However food production still is insufficient to supply domestic demand, and additional quantities of certain food stuffs, particularly wheat, must be imported.

The average diet contains enough calories and proteins of vegetable origin, since 70% of total calories and 69% of proteins are supplied by grains. Consumption of animal products, especially of meat, is low, as is the intake of protective foods.

A substantial proportion of the inhabitants exist at a rather low level of nutrition, as manifested by the high infant mortality rate, the high mortality rate among preschool children, and the retarded growth rates of infants and young children. Specific deficiency diseases may be of some importance, especially pellagra in the delta area and rickets in Upper Egypt.

SELECTED REFERENCES

1. UNICEF. Extension of Milk Conservation Program in Egypt. E/ICEF/L952. 1956.
2. United Arab Republic, Information Department. The Year Book, 1959.
3. Little, A. D. Opportunities for Industrial Development in Egypt. Republic of Egypt, Ministry of Commerce and Industry, 1955.
4. Federation Egyptienne de l'Industrie. Annuaire, 1957/58. Cairo, 1959.
5. L'Egypte Industrielle, Vol. 34, No. 7, November, 1958.
6. Food and Agriculture Organization, Commission on Commodity Problems. Report on Milk Mission to Egypt. September 20, 1954.
7. Money-Kyrle, A. F. Agricultural Development and Research in Egypt. American University of Beirut, Faculty of Agricultural Science, Publ. No. 3, 1957.
8. United States Department of Agriculture, Foreign Agriculture Service. Indices of Agricultural Production in 13 Near East Countries. Mimeographed report. November, 1959.
9. Keen, B. A. The Agricultural Development of the Middle East. Middle East Supply Center, 1946.
10. Ross, M. A. Nutrition and Home Economics Programme in Egyptian Villages. Proceedings of the Nutrition Society of London, 1956, pp. 30-40.
11. Food and Agriculture Organization. Meeting on Poultry Production in the Near East. 1957.

12. Fouad, A. H. Parallelle entre l'alimentation normale et cette de l'ouvrier agricole egyptien. Paris, Theses, 1943.
13. Fisher, W. B. The Middle East. (3rd edit.) London, Methuen, 1956.
14. Sidki, A. R. The Milk Situation in Egypt. Egypt, Ministry of Agriculture, 1951.
15. Omram, A. R. Major Health Problems in Egypt. New York, Columbia University School of Public Health and Administrative Medicine, Community Health Project. Mimeographed report. *P. H. 214,* 1956.
16. Food and Agriculture Organization. Yearbook of Production, Vol. 12, 1958.
17. Yale University, Human Relations Area File. Country Survey Series: Egypt. (G. L. Harris, edit.) 1957.
18. Abdal Raheem, A. A. The Bouri or Mullet. *Journal of the Egyptian Medical Association,* 1958, p. 174.
19. United Arab Republic (Southern Region). Agriculture, 1959.
20. Republic of Egypt, Ministry of Agriculture. Animal Breeding Improvement in Egypt. 1955.
21. Platt, R. R., and Hefny, M. B. Egypt: A Compendium. New York, American Geographical Society Handbook Series, 1958.
22. Abdou, I. A Study of the Patterns and Trends of Egyptian Diets and Their Relations to Health. *Journal of the Egyptian Public Health Association,* Vol. 33, No. 1-2, 1958.
23. Issawi, C. Egypt at Mid-Century: An Economic Survey. London, Oxford University Press, 1954.
24. Bureau des Documentations Syriennes et Arabes. Étude mensuelle sur la vie économique et financière de la République Arabe Unie et des pays arabes.
25. Permanent Nutrition Committee of Egypt. Report for 1939-1946.
26. Barakat, M. R., and Mohamed, G. A Comparison of Food Consumption of Industrial and Agricultural Laborers in Rural Egypt. *Journal of the Royal Egyptian Medical Association,* 1951, p. 462.
27. United States National Food Administration. A Brief Review of Food and Nutrition in Five Countries. 1943.
28. Hassan, A. Problems of Nutrition in Egypt. *Journal of the Egyptian Public Health Association,* Vol. 33, No. 6, 1958.
29. Abassy, M. A. Nutrition Problems in the Middle East. *Journal of the Royal Egyptian Medical Association,* Vol. 30, 1947, p. 502.
30. Russell, Sir E. J. World Population and World Food Supplies. London, Allen & Unwin, 1954.
31. Wishaby, A. G. El Labatt: An Egyptian Vegetable Milk. *Journal of the Egyptian Medical Association,* Vol. 41, No. 9-10, 1958.
32. Wilson, W. H. The Food Problem in Egypt. *Journal of the Egyptian Medical Association,* 1939, p. 283.
33. Food and Agriculture Organization, Egyptian National Commission. Report to the Food and Agriculture Organization on the State of Nutrition in Egypt. 1951.
34. Yousef, A. F., and Ali, A. M. Anemia in Pregnancy. *Journal of the Egyptian Medical Association,* 1954, pp. 319-322.
35. Trowell, H. C. The World Distribution of Kwashiorkor. *Acta Union Internatl. Contra Cancrum 13,* No. 4-5, 1957.
36. Weir, J. M. An Evaluation of Health and Sanitation in Egyptian Villages. *Journal of the Egyptian Public Health Association,* 1952.
37. West, Q. M. Agriculture as the Key to the Egyptian Situation. *Foreign Agriculture,* Vol. 21, No. 4, April, 1957, pp. 10-12.
38. Food and Agriculture Organization, Nutrition Committee for the Middle East. Report of First Session of Joint FAO/WHO Committee, November, 1958. *F. A. O. Nutrition Meeting Report Series No. 24,* 1959.
39. Badr el Din. Management of Food Intolerance in the Infant. *Journal of the Egyptian Medical Association,* 1955, pp. 93-101.

APPENDIX 1

PROJECTED METHODS OF INCREASING ACREAGE
OF ARABLE LAND

(Details of Schemes Proposed and in Operation)

1. **Increase in water storage capacity.**
   a. The High Dam. This will be situated south of Aswan. Its capacity will be 135 milliard cubic meters. It will hold all the annual supply of water and will be capable of providing 6000 million kilowatts hours of electricity. It is estimated that it will take about 15 years to build but that it should be in use as a reservoir after 5 years.
   b. The Wadi Ryan. This is a depression to the south of Faiyoum of about 700 km^2. In some places it is about 42 meters below sea level with surrounding rock up to 22 meters above sea level. The scheme is to divert flood waters of the Nile into the Wadi Ryan, and either pump the water back into the Nile or use it to irrigate the land South of Faiyoum.
   c. The Salheia Reservoir. This is an area of land east of the Delta which might be used as a reservoir. It is about 100 km^2 with a capacity of 623 milliards. It is very shallow, evaporation losses would be very high and it is unlikely that this project would be carried out.
   d. Qattara depression. This is 200 km west of the Delta. Two possible development schemes have been considered. The first is to use this as a reservoir for the Nile water. This is unlikely to be practical as a very wide area is salty.

   The second possibility is to cut a canal or tunnel from the sea and allow the sea water to run in through turbines. The evaporation should maintain a difference in level and allow the generation of considerable electrical power. The evaporation from the inland sea should improve the climate. The Qattara depression is some 70 km from the sea with intervening rocks some 128 meters above sea level. Its average depth is perhaps 50 meters below sea level. The difficulty is that of making a canal tunnel through very deep rocks.

2. Increase in crop area and change from basin to perennial irrigation.

The increase in water made available by storage dams and irrigation canals has provided an increase of land under cultivation and conversion from basin to perennial irrigation, permitting the growth of summer crops, as can be seen from the following figures taken from Hurst (2) and Selim (3).

AREA UNDER CULTIVATION IN (1,000,000) FEDDANS

TYPE OF IRRIGATION

	Basin	Perennial
1886	2	2.9
1919	1.2	4.0
1946	1	5.0

The cultivated area now stands at 5,900,000 feddans with less than a million feddans of basin land. It is estimated that if extra water were available from the high dam, at least another 2.4 million feddans could be irrigated, bringing the total cultivated land to 8.4 million feddans, an increase of 40 percent over the present cultivated area. If the lift were greater than 10 meters, the area that might be cultivated has been estimated to be up to 10 million feddans (Issawi p. 102) on the assumption that the water used per feddan can be reduced. However, Hurst states "Our conservative estimate of $7\frac{1}{2}$ million feddans may after careful investigation be extended a little, but 10 million feddans of perennial irrigation, together with the development of the Sudan, would take more water than any scheme of projects could get from the river"

The stages in reclamation planned, according to Issawi (1), are reclamation of 1.5 million feddans in Lower Egypt, conversion of 676,000 feddans from basin irrigation in Upper Egypt to perennial irrigation, and reclamation of a further 1.5 million feddans. The possible areas which could be reclaimed are said to be 1 million feddans along the Nile from Cairo to Aswan, 1.5 million feddans in the western Desert and from 0,5 to 1.5 million feddans in the eastern Delta.

3. The reclamation of saline & alkaline land in the Delta.

Reclamation of low lying lands in the Delta has been proceeding steadily during the last 25 years. According to Issawi (1) the government has reclaimed 300,000 feddans of state domains and the Société du Behera and Aboukir company have reclaimed 75,000 and 26,000 feddans respectively. Reclamation of 20,000 feddans in the ABIS area by the Egyptian-American Rural Improvement Society will be discussed later.

Reclamation is a slow and costly business, open drains are dug and the soil is washed free of salt. The stages in reclamation after

the establishment of a drainage system, are to flood the area during the time of the Nile flood and grow barley, rice, berseem, and
wheat in that order. Sometimes a grass (Dineba) **Panicum crus-
galli** is grown before cropping starts. It usually takes at least 3
years before profitable crops can be grown. The Société Anonyme
du Béhéra has introduced a system of selling land to cultivators
under far better conditions of rural employment than are usually
found in Egypt according to Warriner (4). The chief point of this
system is that the ownership is transferred to the cultivator when
the land is partially reclaimed.

4. Development of desert lands.

The chief projects for development of desert lands are, (a) irrigation of Liberation Province, (b) the land west of Liberation Province, (c) land adjacent to cultivated land along the Nile, and (d) Sinai
Peninsula.

a. Irrigation of Liberation Province. This province lies to the
west of a line drawn from Cairo to Alexandria. The first part
of the project is to reclaim 25,000 feddans by means of water
brought from the Nile. This may one day be extended to a million feddans. Six thousand feddans have so far been reclaimed.

The stages in reclamation are as follows. Areas of 200 feddans are marked out with a ditcher. Then roads are built by
bulldozers. Silt brought by barge is mechanically mixed with
the sand to stabilize the road surface. The fields are roughly
levelled into 5 feddan areas by means of a scraper and finely
levelled by a land leveller. The canals are then made and lined
with cement blocks. The land is flooded with Nile water to a
depth of 2 or 3 feet in order to deposit silt, and then organic
manure, at the rate of 10 cubic meters per feddan, is spread
over the land. Legumes such as alfalfa, berseem or lupines are
first grown and then the land may be sown to cereals or planted
with mangoes and citrus. The Nile water is supplemented by
water from underground wells which keep the water table at a
depth of 7 to 8 meters. Each well supplies water for about 250
reddans.

Animal husbandry is being developed and Friesian cattle do
well on the alfalfa. There are chickens, turkeys, ducks and
geese kept under the most modern conditions. Field trials are
used to test the quantity and frequency of irrigation and the
amount and kind of fertilizer to be used.

Each village has 230 houses, about 1500 feddans of land, a
mosque and public health centre. The settlers come from the
crowded province of Munafir. They take a 6 months' training
course, work for a year and are then given a share in the profits
equivalent to 5 feddans of land. The farming operations are

highly mechanized and are now carried out by experts. However,
it is suggested that in the future they will be planned by a village
council.

b. Irrigation of land west of Liberation Province. It is suggested
that this land could be irrigated.

c. Irrigation of land adjacent to the cultivated area. If flood water
is stored by the high dam, some of the water could be used to
irrigate the areas adjacent to the Nile which are not too high
above the Nile level.

d. Sinai Peninsula. Some of this peninsula could be irrigated from
the Nile by a canal passing under the Suez canal. UNRWA has a
project for a scheme to settle Palestine refugees in this area
and a detailed report including soil surveys has been drawn up.

5. Development of Mediterranean Coast.

This area extends for over 600 km along the Mediterranean
coast between Alexandria and the Libyan frontier. It comprises an
area of 3,000,000 feddans. Up to 15 km from the Mediterranean
coast there is some rainfall and the Bedouin grow crops of barley
and keep sheep. It is probable that better use could be made of the
land and two projects at Bourg-el-Arab and Ras-el-Hekma have
been initiated.

Bourg-el-Arab is situated about 60 km to the west of Alexandria,
where the Ministry of Agriculture has established an experimental
farm. The average annual rainfall is 4 inches with a maximum of
10 inches. Well water containing 5000 to 8000 parts per million of
sodium chloride has been used to irrigate olives, almonds and
carob trees. It has been found that these trees can withstand a high
degree of salinity, provided that the rainfall can prevent salts from
accumulating. There are records of trees being watered from this
well plus 4 inches of rainfall for 25 years. The successfull planting
of rainfed olive trees in this region is described under horticulture.

An area has been enclosed to prevent the grazing by the Bedouin
sheep and if the grazing is prevented the local plants such as
Agropyron, Atriplex, Cynodon dactylon and some wild strains of
alfalfa grow well.

At Ras-el-Hekma there is a desert range project carried out by
the Egyptian Government in cooperation with the United States Operations Mission. Colonel Omar Draz is in charge of the project
and the American advisors are Mr. Bradford Knapp and Mr Pierce.
Ras-el-Hekma is situated in the coastal strip half way between
Alexandria and the Tripoli frontier near Sodium. This area has a
rainfall of between 70 and 150 mm with most of the rain falling in
winter. The general relief is one of big slopes and wide valleys.
There is a vegetation of bushes and some ground flora.

In this project 25,000 feddans have been fenced to make a dem-

onstration and experimental range. The three main objectives of
the project are, protection from daily grazing, reseeding, and
water spreading. Protection from daily grazing is one of the most
important parts of the project. Controlling the grazing allows the
palatable herbs to multiply. Reseeding is being carried out on
areas where there is no cover and on not more than 10 percent of
the total area.

Water spreading is being used on 800 to a 1000 feddans. Dykes
are built across gullies and the water led off on to slopes of less
than 1 percent. These areas are reseeded.

Native sheep are being used at the moment but some Rambouillet
(French Merino) will be tried. It is hoped that the range will be
able to keep at least twice the number of sheep under the condition
of the demonstration, perhaps 8 feddans to a sheep as opposed to
16. Moreover the sheep kept will be of a more valuable type. Two
botanists have reported unfavourably on this project.

6. Development of Wadi Natron.

Wadi Natron is a depression 100 km from Cairo and a few kilometers from the Cairo-Alexandria road. The government has
initiated a small land reclamation scheme which is under the administration of the army. By June 1955, 850 feddans of land had
been reclaimed.

The land has been divided into fields of varying size, surrounded
by windbreaks made of bundles of rush, and planted with **Casuarina**
trees. The water table is from 40 cm to 2 m deep and the water
rises by capillarity 30 to 50 cm above the water table so that the
main problem is to get the plants started until their roots reach
the water table. This has been done by flood or sprinkler irrigation. The flood irrigation requires 400 m^3 per feddan, the sprinkler
irrigation 80 m^3 and irrigation m^3 and irrigation is at roughly 10
day intervals. Good crops of wheat and barley are obtained. Other
crops are onions, tomato, castor bean, and water melons. Citrus
and olive trees are doing well.

7. Development of Oases.

The five oases are Dakhla, Bahria, Farafra, Silwa and Kharga.
A well drilling programme at the Dakhla and Kharga oases has
been started by the Egyptian Government in cooperation with the
United States Operations Mission. Until recently there were only
shallow wells and the work consists of drilling deep wells into the
Nubian sandstone to provide supplementary irrigation water. At
Dakhla these wells are at 300 meters but at Kharga they are up to
600 meters deep. Each well supplies from 4000 to 8000 m^3 of
water per day.

Source: Money-Kyrle, 1957.

Table 1

Acreage Planted to Seasonal Crops

Type of Planting		1940-1944 (average)	1945-1949 (average)	1952	1957
		(in hectares)			
"Chetwi"	(Winter)	2,266,799	2,265,675	2,202,763	2,376,327
"Seifi"	(Summer)	1,242,357	1,406,573	1,530,259	1,701,547
"Nili"	(Autumn)	568,554	907,900	922,442	949,325

Source: Federation Egyptienne de l'Industrie Annuaire, 1957/58.

Table 2

Value of Agricultural Products
1954/55 to 1956/57

(in 1000 Egyptian £.)

Crops	1954/55	1955/56	1956/57
Grains	125,909	120,984	173,050
Legumes	12,388	12,905	13,546
Vegetables	14,151	15,824	17,785
Fruits	13,803	16,016	17,410
Other Food Crops	14,487	16,888	17,057
Total Food Crops	180,738	182,617	238,848
Edible Animal Products	92,045	92,362	80,411
Total Food Products	272,783	274,979	319,259
Total Non-Food Products[a]	158,525	153,294	187,766

(a) Cotton, Flax, Clover, Wool.

Source: Annuaire de la Federation Egyptienne de l'Industrie.

Table 3

Harvest Calendar of Principal Crops

Crops	Harvest Period
Wheat	Mid Apr.-June
Barley	Apr.-May
Beans	Mar.-Apr.
Maize:	
Seifi	Mid Aug.-Mid Sept.
Nili	Mid Oct.-Mid Dec.
Sorghum:	
Seifi	Mid Aug.-Mid Sept.
Nili	Mid Oct.-Mid Nov.
Rice:	
Seifi	Mid Sept.-Mid Nov.
Nili	Mid Oct.-Mid Dec.
Sugar cane	Dec.-Mar.
Sugar	Campaign starting in January
Potatoes:	
Autum	Jan.-Mar.
Spring	May-July
Sweet potatoes and yams	Dec.
Taro	Nov.-Jan.
Onions:	
Winter	Mid Feb.-Apr.
Summer }	Apr.
Autumn	
Tomatoes	Jan.-Dec.
Cucumbers	Apr.-Sept. and Oct.-Nov.
Pumpkins	Mid July-Sept.
Melons, sweet	Mid May-Aug.
Watermelons	June-Sept.
Cabbage	Mid Oct.-Feb.
Cauliflowers	Oct.-Feb.
Green peas	Dec.-Mar.
Green beans	Oct.-Jan. and May-June
Carrots	Nov.-Mar.
Dry beans:	
Spring	Mid May-Mid June
Winter	Dec.-Jan.
Broad beans	Jan.-Feb.
Chick peas	Apr.-Mid May
Lentils	Mar.-Mid Apr.
Dry peas	Apr.-May
Cowpeas	May-July
Lupins	Apr.-May
Fenugreek	Mar.-Apr.
Apples	June-Aug.
Pears	Mid July-Aug.
Apricots	Mid Apr.-May
Peaches	July-Aug.
Plums	June-July

Source: F.A.O. World Crop Harvest Calendar, Rome, 1959.

Table 4

Acreage and Production of Principal Crops

Cereals	Year	Area (1000 ha.)	Production (1000 m.t.)
Maize	1958	821	1758
	1959	821(a)	....
Wheat	1958	599	1412
	1959	620	1443
Rice	1958	218	1082
	1959	306	1545
Sorghum	1957	189	566
	1958	178	543
Barley	1958	57	135
	1959	59	142
Vegetables			
Onions	1958	56	481
	1959	58	462
Garlic	1957	4.8	40
Tomatoes	1957	43	604
Potatoes	1957	15	240
Sweet Potatoes & Yams	1958	4	64
Eggplants	1957	5.2	89
Cabbage	"	8.9	174
Cauliflower	"	2.2	40
String Beans	"	1.7	9
Radishes	"	2.2	24
Parsley	"	.3	9
Artichokes	"	.7	5
Spinach	"	1.0	11
Lettuce	"	1.2	17

Legumes	Year	Area (1000 ha.)	Production (1000 m.t.)
Broad Beans	1957	149	254
	1958	149	210
Lentils	1958	33	48
Chick Peas	1958	4	6
Dry Beans	1959	5	7
Lubia	1957	.7	.8
	"	1.7	2
Fruits			
Orange	1957	16.5	192
Mandarines	"	4.5	74
Citron	"	4.2	39
Sweet Citron	"	.7	1.9
Grape	"	9.5	90
Fig	"	.8	5.4
Guava	"	3.1	36
Olive	"	1.1	7.1
Mango	"	6.9	73
Apricot	"	1.0	6.6
Banana	"	3.3	44
Other Crops			
Peanuts	1958	16	33
Sesame	1958	17	14.6
Cotton	1958	800	446
Sugar (raw)	1959	739	452
Sugar Cane	1958	55	308(a)
	1957		4000

(a) Unofficial figures.

Sources: Food and Agriculture Organization Data in Production Yearbook, 1958, Federation Egyptienne de l'Industrie, 1957/58.

Table 5

Production of Eggs, Numbers Incubated and Chicks Hatched 1941/42 to 1952/57

Year	Eggs Produced in Millions	Incubators Used	Eggs Incubated in Millions	Eggs Hatched	Proportion of Eggs Hatched
1941/1942	753	632	108,727	74,395	68
1942/1943	797	640	122,007	82,846	68
1943/1944	887	631	147,920	98,310	66
1944/1945	1053	568	111,347	74,097	67
1945/1946	794	544	98,251	64,768	66
1946/1947	694	483	75,760	48,792	64
1947/1948	523	410	68,208	43,520	64
1948/1949	518	410	61,385	38,266	62
1949/1950	455	392	57,664	35,202	61
1950/1951	419	400	62,600	38,200	61
1951/1952	455	464	74,982	44,953	60
1952/1953	535	501	83,963	49,406	59
1953/1954	588	489	84,494	49,698	59
1954/1955	591	542	101,299	59,294	59
1955/1956	706	605	110,616	63,538	57
1956/1957	756	561	104,131	60,785	58

Source: Federation Egyptienne de l'Industrie. Annuaire 1957/58.

Table 6

Trade in Agricultural Products—Egypt 1958

Commodity	Quantity (1000 tons)	Value (1000 dollars)	Share of Total Value of Exports (%)
	EXPORTS		
Cotton	282.7	315,299	67.5
Rice	360.1	38,866	8.3
Onions	161.5	11,379	2.4
Sugar, refined	27.6	3,475	.7
Peanuts	9.9	2,923	.6
Potatoes	45.1	2,557	.5
Edible fruits	14.0	1,493	.3
Rice bran	25.1	1,117	.2
Wheat bran	20.8	957	.2
Cottonseed oil	1.6	540	.1
Sesame	1.5	356	.1
Cottonseed oil cake	50.3	2,203	.5
Other Agricultural Exports	—	3,622	.8
Total Agricultural Exports	—	384,787	82.4
	IMPORTS		
Wheat	774.0	50,506	7.4
Wheat flour	278.6	18,880	2.8
Tea	22.9	22,027	3.2
Coffee	5.8	6,312	.9
Live Animals (1000 head)	113	5,784	.8
Meat & meat prep.	10.5	3,809	.6
Cottonseed oil	11.5	3,652	.5
Corn	58.8	3,390	.5
Other oils	9.6	3,286	.5
Edible fruits & nuts	22.8	2,272	.3
Dairy products	2.8	2,144	.3
Sugar, raw	21.6	2,107	.3
Cocoa	.4	566	.1
Cottonseed	4.8	351	.05
Other Agricultural Imports	—	47,819	6.9
Total Agricultural Imports	—	172,905	25.2

Source: United States Department of Agriculture, Foreign Agriculture Service. Exports and Imports Agricultural Commodities by Principal Country of Destination, 1958. Washington D.C., 1960.

Table 7

Output of Food Processing Industries—1949–1957

Article	Unit	1949	1950	1951	1952	1953	1954	1955	1956	1957
Ice	Blocks	—	—	—	—	—	9349497	10519468	11085466	—
Rice:										
Paddy	Dariba	1235865	1314314	656471	546829	690090	1183047	1385604	1665000	1808013
White	"	803000	842000	430000	350000	433550	770000	872000	900900	1175208
Processed Foods:										
Tomato Sauce	Tons	—	135	159	315	475	474	431	391	837
Other Tomato Prod.	"	—	1	1	24	15	20	88	51	11
Canned Greens	"	—	50	95	107	273	233	706	902	997
Canned Vegetables	"	—	37	163	459	683	458	928	1005	1067
Dehydrated Onions	"	—	601	1274	1137	2555	2964	3214	2816	4866
Garlic Powder	"	—	30	6	25	88	82	88	12	21
Garlic Essence	"	—	49	20	63	220	36	141	—	21
Frozen Shrimps	Kgs.	—	—	—	—	—	273	440	246	246
Confectionery:										
Raw Sugar	Tons	190803	174707	195042	184477	228000	270881	318505	312017	299130
Carbonated Water	Million Bottles	—	—	—	—	303	304	334	324	368
Halawa Tehinia	Tons	—	20718	30900	31068	24432	20078	23003	27584	23884
Chocolate	"	—	—	1550	970	1191	1109	1796	1935	1751
Marmalades	"	—	21	20	89	124	265	399	498	595
Syrups	"	—	217	333	327	277	235	563	626	821

Dairy Products:										
White Cheese	Tons	–	–	–	–	–	98738	103889	103600	109939
Processed Cheese	"	–	–	–	–	–	1920	2000	2500	–
Pasteurized Milk	"	–	–	–	–	–	–	3578	4516	4625
Canned Meats:	"	–	–	–	–	140	260	162	360	373
Mortadella	"	273	275	–	229	220	214	249	260	240
Salami	"	46	54	–	64	96	48	91	159	158
Ham	"	39	37	–	64	55	63	68	25	37
Alcoholic Beverages	Million Litters									
Beer		11	13	13	12	8	9	12	10	10
Wine	"	845655	1125554	1620819	1618646	1999875	1690767	2278862	1897005	1836638
Brandy	"	–	–	–	57285	61920	59586	66824	82145	115866
Rum	"	–	–	–	110688	134980	128547	139740	139945	214198
Date Arak	"	–	–	–	17747	15185	14444	12729	11387	12303
Zibib	"	–	–	–	30901	31451	30003	34131	29573	38683
Tafia	"	–	–	–	418081	373466	319640	352836	283087	33334
Tafia 30% Brandy	"	–	–	–	14998	11323	7785	6307	7563	1171
Fermented Molasses	"	–	–	–	53	20	92	66	51	40
Fernet	"	–	–	–	8587	8846	2434	2444	2535	3023
Vermouth	Million Litters	–	–	–	905	2078	942	1584	1089	1026
China	"	–	–	–	56030	90254	62830	75013	67926	39130
Liqueurs	"	–	–	–	15105	18681	23028	29770	29123	144471

Source: Federation Egyptienne de l'Industrie: Annuaire 1957/58.

Table 8

Comparison of Food Consumption Levels—1947/48 to 1954/55

(in grams per capita per day)

Commodity	Year							
	47-48	48-49	49-50	50-51	51-52	52-53	53-54	54-55
Cereals	487.1	508.5	449.9	468.9	464.4	456.4	516.7	519.4
Starchy foods (others)	22.5	26.8	23.9	18.9	21.0	20.2	21.3	23.6
Sugar & sugar syrups	35.8	43.3	38.9	40.0	43.9	46.0	44.4	47.9
Pulses, nuts & seeds	47.4	32.9	34.0	26.7	29.4	27.9	27.7	28.8
Vegetables fresh	88.0	132.6	93.5	93.7	120.2	139.7	161.1	165.2
Fruits(a)	94.2	88.2	80.7	91.3	138.6	167.7	172.8	178.9
Meats	23.2	20.2	22.3	25.4	24.9	31.7	30.7	32.6
Eggs	3.2	2.2	1.6	1.6	1.9	2.5	2.7	2.7
Fish	8.2	8.1	8.2	9.5	6.2	7.4	7.4	8.0
Milk (& Cheese)	29.3	143.7	179.6	164.7	133.9	120.3	116.2	124.5
Vegetables oils	15.6	9.8	9.8	9.5	8.1	10.1	10.1	9.8
Vegetable protein	59.0	60.3	54.8	55.4	57.2	56.7	62.8	62.8
Animal protein	9.4	11.4	14.0	13.0	11.5	10.8	10.4	11.0
Protein & Total	68.4	71.7	67.8	68.4	68.7	67.5	72.2	73.8
Calories	2364	2466	2296	2336	2319	2315	2524	2572

(a) Beginning 1951-52, the figures for vegetables and fruits exclude the nonedible portion.

Source: Abdou, I. A Study of the Patterns and Trends of Egyptian Diets and their Relation to Health. J. Egy. Pub. Health Assn., 1958.

Table 9

The Daily Available Per Capita Supply of Nutrients in Egypt (1954-1955)

Commodity	Grams	Calories	Protein	Fat	Ca.	Fe.	Vit. A	Vit. B$_1$	Vit. B$_2$	Niacin	Vit. C
	Gm.	Cals.	Gm.	Gm.	mg.	mg.	I.U.	mg.	mg.	mg.	mg.
Cereals(a)	519.4	1840	51.8	12.9	167.1	12.89	377	2.15	0.49	12.79	—
Starchy Foods (Others)	23.6	20	0.4	—	3.0	0.16	27	0.02	0.01	0.24	4.0
Sugar & sugar syrups	47.9	174	—	—	0.02	0.003	—	—	0.00	0.001	0.01
Pulses, nuts & seeds	28.8	105	6.5	1.5	25.7	1.47	52	0.52	0.07	0.85	1.0
Vegetables, Fresh	165.2	39	2.3	0.3	53.7	1.09	1674	0.08	0.09	0.75	38.1
Fruits	178.9	129	1.8	0.9	38.9	1.13	648	0.12	0.10	2.30	30.1
Meats	32.6	50	4.3	3.2	2.6	0.59	—	0.02	0.04	1.01	—
Eggs	2.7	4	0.3	0.3	1.2	0.07	31	0.003	0.01	0.003	—
Fish	8.0	14	1.7	0.7	7.5	0.07	2	0.004	0.01	0.23	—
Milk (& Cheese)	124.5	110	4.7	7.7	180.4	0.20	176	0.05	0.17	0.13	1.2
Vegetable oils	0.8	87	—	9.8	—	—	—	—	—	—	—
Total	1411	2572	73.8	37.3	480	17.66	3000	2.98	1.01	18.12	74.4

(a) Extraction rate of wheat flour was 93.3.
Source: Abdou, I. See Table 8.

Table 10

Food Balance Sheet

(thousand metric tons unless otherwise specified)

Population: 22.2 million   2 Years Average: 1954/55—1955/56

Commodity	Production	Change in Stocks	Foreign Trade: Gross Exports	Foreign Trade: Gross Imports	Available Supply	Distribution: Animal Feed	Seed	Manufacture	Waste	Food (Gross)	Extr. Rate %	Food (Net)	Per Capita: Kg. Per Year	Gm. Per Day	Cal. Per Day	Protein Gm. Per Day	Fat Gm. Per Day
	(1)	(2)	(3)	(4)	(5)	(6)	(7)	(8)	(9)	(10)	(11)	(12)	(13)	(14)	(15)	(16)	(17)
Cereals																	
Wheat	1590	− 131		270	1991		116		80	1795	87.7	1568	70.8	194.0	679	22.7	3.0
Wheat flour (imported)			6	37	31					31		31	1.4	3.9	14	0.4	—
Barley	122				122	86	8		7	21	75.0	16	0.7	1.9	7	0.2	—
Maize	1733			24	1757		63	24	72	1598	94.6	1512	68.3	187.0	674	17.3	7.5
Millet	543			2	545		4		38	503	92.0	462	20.8	57.1	196	5.8	1.8
Rice (paddy)	1214	+ 34	275		905		38	10	18	839	68.8	577	26.0	71.3	256	4.8	0.5
Total													188.0	515.2	1826	51.2	12.8
Roots and Tubers																	
Potatoes	204	+ 9	52	6	149		24		15	110		110	5.0	13.7	10	0.3	—
Sweet potatoes	45				45				5	40		40	1.8	5.0	5	—	—
Taros	15				15		2		1	12		12	0.5	1.5	1	—	—
Starch	7				7			2		5		5	0.3	0.6	2	—	—
Total															18	0.3	—
Sugar and Syrups																	
Sugar (cane)	4172				4172		192	3189	42	749	9.0	67	3.1	8.3	22	—	—
Sugar (raw)	316	− 7	14		317			292		25		25	1.1	3.1	11	—	—
Sugar (refined)	289	− 3	13	8	279					279		279	12.6	34.5	133	—	—
Glucose	14				14					14		14	0.7	1.7	7	—	—
Honey	2				2					2		2	0.1	0.2	1	—	—
Total															174	—	—
Pulses, Nuts and Seeds																	
Broad beans	251			22	273	118	22		14	119		119	5.4	14.7	50	3.3	0.3
Lentils	55		1	4	58		5		2	51		51	2.3	6.3	22	1.4	0.1
Other pulses	50			14	64		4		2	58		58	2.6	7.2	25	1.6	0.2
Peanuts, in shell(a)	27		10	3	20		1			19	74.0	14	0.6	1.7	9	0.4	0.7
Coconuts, in shell(a)				1	1					1		1	negl.	negl.		—	—
Treenuts, in shell				2	2					2		2	0.1	0.2	1	—	0.1
Sesame	16		2	7	21			18		3		3	0.1	0.3	1	0.1	0.2
Total															109	6.7	1.6

(a) 1955/56 only.

Vegetables																	
Onions	397	+ 29	231	1	138				6	132		132	6.0	16.3	6	0.2	—
Other vegetables	1408		11		1397				140	1257		1257	56.8	155.4	34	2.2	0.3
Total															40	2.4	0.3
Fruits																	
Bananas, fresh	44		2		42				4	38		38	1.7	4.7	4	—	—
Citrus, fresh	348		1	2	349				35	314		314	14.2	38.9	12	0.2	0.1
Dates, fresh	202				202				10	192		192	8.7	23.8	27	0.5	0.1
Melons	575		2	2	575				58	517		517	23.4	63.9	9	0.2	0.1
Grapes	89				89				9	80		80	3.6	9.9	6	0.1	—
Other fruits, fresh	130		4	5	131				13	118		118	5.3	14.5	7	0.1	0.1
Dates, dried and paste	159			26	185				9	176		176	8.0	21.8	54	0.6	0.2
Olives, processed	4			4	8					8		8	0.4	1.0	2	—	0.2
Other fruits, dried				8	8					8		8	0.4	0.9	2	—	—
Total															123	1.7	0.8
Meat																	
Beef	40			12	52					52		52	2.4	6.3	15	0.9	1.1
Veal	42			1	43					43		43	1.9	5.3	8	0.8	0.6
Buffalo meat	84				84					84		84	3.7	10.4	9	1.4	0.3
Mutton and lamb	23			4	27					27		27	1.2	3.3	8	0.4	0.7
Goat	13				13					13		13	0.6	1.5	2	0.2	0.1
Pork	1				1					1		1	—	0.1	—	—	—
Camel	18				18					18		18	0.8	2.2	4	0.3	0.2
Poultry and rabbit	47				47					47		47	2.1	5.8	7	0.7	0.5
Total													12.7	34.9	53	4.7	3.5
Eggs	26				26			2		24		24	1.1	2.9	4	0.3	0.3
Fish																	
Fresh	92				92				9	83		83	3.8	10.2	13	2.0	0.5
Salted				8	8					8		8	0.4	1.0	3	0.4	0.1
Canned				8	8					8		8	0.4	1.0	3	0.2	0.2
Total															19	2.6	0.8
Milk(a)																	
Cow	316		3	204(b)	517					517		517	23.3	63.8	43	2.3	2.5
Buffalo	617				617					617		617	27.9	76.3	77	3.0	5.7
Sheep	1				1					1		1	—	0.1	—	—	—
Goat	2				2					2		2	0.1	0.2	—	—	—
Total													513		120	5.3	8.2
Vegetable Oils (Pure fat content)																	
Cotton seed oil	80	- 6	5	2	83			11		72		72	3.3	8.9	79	—	8.9
Sesame seed oil	10				10					10		10	0.5	1.3	11	—	1.3
Shortening(c)				3	3					3		3	0.1	0.4	3	—	0.4
Total													3.9	10.6	93	–	10.6
											Total				2580	75.2	38.9
											Animal					12.9	
											Vegetable					62.3	

(a) Including milk for making butter and cheese.
(b) Imports 1954/55 48000 MT, Imports 1955/56 360000 MT, including the United States Grants. (c) 1955/56 only.
Source: F.A.O. Food Balance Sheets, 1954-56 av., Rome, 1958.

Table 11

Average Food Consumption Level in Kafr El Hasafa & Mansuriet Namoul

(Gm/day/Adult)

Commodity	Gm.	Commodity	Gm.
Wheat	118	Fruits	23
Maize	504	Meat	43
Rice......................	21	Fish....................	2
Potatoes	26	Eggs	5
Sugars...................	8	Milk....................	31
Legumes.................	12	Cottage Cheese..........	68
Onions...................	25	Mish	8
Other vegetables...........	148	Fats....................	18

Nutritive value[a]:

Nutrient	Quantity	Nutrient	Quantity
Calories	3074 Cals.	Vit. A.	4770 I.U.
Animal Protein	23 gm.	Thiamine	2.63 mg.
Vegt. Protein	75 "	Riboflavin............	1.23 "
Calcium	0.35 "	Niacin...............	17.19 "
Iron....................	17.8 mg.	Vit. C.	61 "

(a) No deductions for waste or destruction were made.
Source: Abdou, I. See Table 8.

Table 12

Comparison of Diets in a Rural Village

Average Daily Food Consumption Among Industrial Workers, Landowners and Cultivators

Food		Daily consumption in grams		
		Industrial	Owners	Agricultural
Meat:	Beef	22.2	22.1	20.9
	Offals	20.9	21.1	25.6
	Mutton	6.4	35.5	1.3
	Liver	—	4.8	—
	Rabbit	15.0	22.3	1.8
	Chicken	14.8	—	—
	Total	76.3	60.3	28.4
Cereals:	Wheat bread	46.4	29.3	21.6
	Millet bread	435.4	521.2	668.6
	Rice	12.4	38.5	9.1
	Kishk	8.9	20.5	38.1
	Ferik	—	16.6	41.8
	Macaroni	20.7	29.2	—
	Total	523.8	759.3	829.8
Fish & salted fish		37.0	60.3	28.4
Legumes:	Lentils	20.6	—	—
	Stewed beans	73.0	58.7	87.9
	Green beans	40.1	93.1	257.9
	Bean-cakes	18.3	—	—
	Total	152.0	151.8	345.8
Milk & milk products:	Skim cheese	95.6	66.1	110.1
	Full cream cheese	—	38.1	—
	Milk	131.0	46.8	—
	Clarified butter	8.4	6.0	—
	Butter	6.2	5.7	—
	Salted whey (Mish)	4.8	—	—
	Total	246.0	162.7	110.1
Cooking oil		5.0	2.5	3.3
Eggs		8.5	6.0	—

Food		Daily consumption in grams		
		Industrial	Owners	Agricultural
Tubers:	Potatoes	56.5	56.6	—
	Colcasia	—	37.1	—
	Turnip	62.6	8.2	17.1
	Radish	15.8	—	—
	Onions–dry	6.0	6.5	—
	" green	14.8	23.0	18.1
	Total	104.9	131.4	35.2
Green Vegetables:	Tomatoes	24.6	19.5	31.4
	Mallais	24.9	—	—
	Chicory	33.3	11.7	9.6
	Spinach	—	44.6	—
	Green pepper	—	3.9	—
	Total	82.8	79.7	41.0
Sweets:	Sugar	14.0	8.3	7.1
	Treacle	—	2.5	4.6
	Jam	—	26.0	—
	Halawa	—	—	1.8
	Total	14.0	37.8	13.5
Fruits:	Oranges	20.9	13.2	—
	Bananas	—	85.7	—
	Dates dried	16.0	35.0	29.7
	Total	36.9	133.9	29.7

Source: Barakat and Mohamed, A Comparison of Food Consumption of Industrial and Agricultural Laborers in Rural Egypt, J. Roy. Egy. Med. Assn. 1951.

INDEX

675